S0-BFL-813

Enter

into His Gates with

Thanksgiving

and into His Courts with

Praise

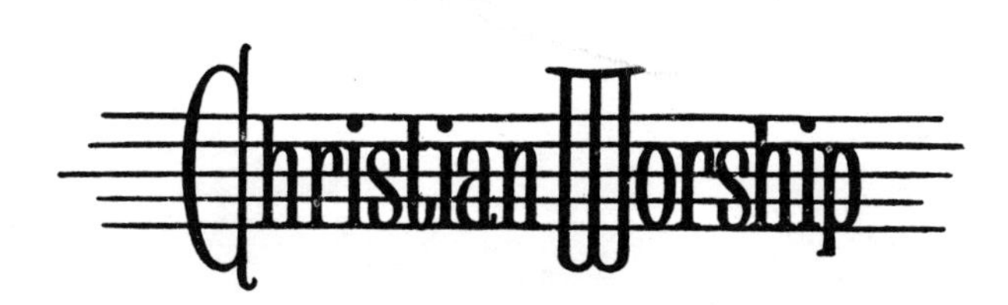
Christian Worship

Enter His Gates with Thanksgiving,
And His Courts with Praise!
Give Thanks to Him, Bless His Name!

This hymn book is a part of the furnishings of this church consecrated to the worship of God. Respect it as such.

Let it open to you the gates of thanksgiving and praise. Let it bear to your heart messages of faith and courage and hope.

As you join with others in the responses and in singing, may the sense of unity with the people of God everywhere be strengthened and the discords of life be subdued in love and adoration for Christ.

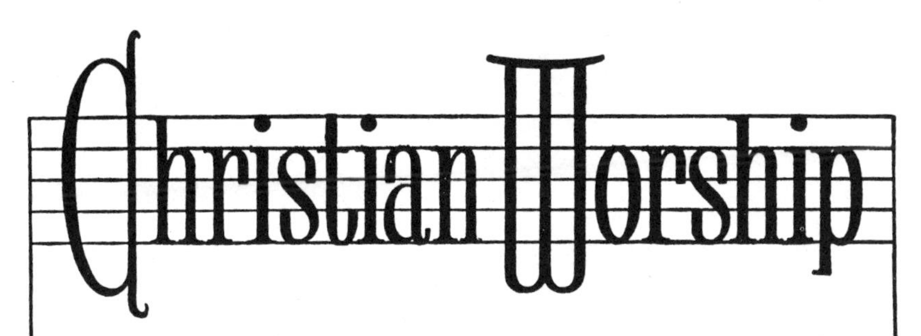
Christian Worship

A HYMNAL

JP

SPECIAL EDITION

Using Text of the
Revised Standard Version of the Bible

The Judson Press
VALLEY FORGE, PENNSYLVANIA
CHICAGO KANSAS CITY LOS ANGELES SEATTLE

Special Edition

Tenth printing, 1966

Printed in the United States of America

Preface

It is an event of special significance that Baptists and Disciples of Christ jointly offer our churches this new hymnbook. For years many of our people have sensed an imperative need for a hymnal particularly suited to our form of worship—a book that would combine a choice selection of the best hymns with other desirable aids to Christian worship. Then the idea of producing the book jointly by these two communions strongly appealed to all those with whom it was discussed.

In order that the work might be prepared as a mutual responsibility, the publishing houses of the American Baptist Convention and of the Disciples of Christ each appointed representatives to serve as a joint committee. On this committee were those who gave expert counsel in the selection of the great hymns and others whose experience in worship fully qualified them to guide the committee in the choice of worship materials.

The committee met under the influence of the epochal changes in thought and life caused by world-engulfing war and social revolution. Necessity was laid upon us to take heed of the demands of the hour, in and of the churches, and to conserve the timeless values out of the past, and anticipate the requirements of Christian faith in a new world, emerging out of mankind's agony.

We believe it most fitting that this hymnal be named *Christian Worship*. It offers not only the great historic hymns of the church, but also a larger number of the best modern hymns. In addition to these, a careful selection of widely used and inspiring gospel hymns has been included. In every particular the book has been planned and arranged so as to guide and enrich the worship service. Responsive readings, musical responses, and other special features provide adequate and appropriate materials for the well ordered service of worship.

PREFACE

Here are hymns of comfort and courage, of cheer and assurance, of salvation and new life. In the selections there is no straining to interpret either the social or individual gospel. Both are here because both are in the teachings of Christianity, and in the experience of the church across the ages. It will be adaptable to the more dignified and formal worship of the stately church and to the simple service of the less pretentious. We believe it will be found to be the best all-service hymnal yet prepared.

The joint committee is confident that the new hymnal will prove a source of help and inspiration in the worship of both the city and the rural church. It is in the use of such hymns as here offered that Christians may express their common experience and triumphant faith. Therefore, it is our earnest hope that for many years to come this book will meet the universal need of our churches.

The fellowship and unity of thought and purpose shared by the members of this committee leads us to voice the hope that by the use of a common hymnal these two great Christian bodies may feel the bond of unity drawing them still closer together.

MEMBERS OF THE JOINT COMMITTEE

American Baptist Convention	*Disciples of Christ*
William S. Abernethy, Chairman	Raphael H. Miller, Chairman
Stanley A. Gillet	George A. Campbell
Richard Hoiland	Lin D. Cartwright
James D. Morrison	William E. Moore
Luther Wesley Smith	Oreon E. Scott
Wiley J. Smith	W. P. Shelton
Hillyer H. Straton	William A. Shullenberger
Norris L. Tibbetts	B. Fred Wise

Under the direction of the Joint Committee, B. Fred Wise gave invaluable leadership as the editor for the committee. Acknowledgment also is made of the aid given by Dr. Edwin McNeill Poteat and Mrs. R. H. Milligan, who, though not members of the committee, have rendered helpful assistance in the compilation of this book.

Acknowledgments

The Committee desires to express its gratitude for the generous cooperation which has been given by many authors, composers and publishers, who have extended us the use of copyrighted materials. Special acknowledgment is due Dr. William Robinson of Birmingham, England, for his courtesy in allowing the use of hymns from the Christian Hymnary and the Christian Hymnary Tune Book and also for his tireless efforts in securing for us the present addresses of British owners of copyrights under existing disturbed conditions. We are also indebted to the Rev. Thomas Tiplady of the Lambeth Mission, London, for a similar service and the unrestricted use of his many compositions.

We have made every effort to trace the ownership of all hymns. If we have neglected to give proper credit for any material used, we shall make proper acknowledgment in future editions of the hymnal. We are deeply grateful for permissions to the following persons and publishing houses:

Mrs. Ernest Bourner Allen
Mrs. Horace E. Allen
American Peace Society
American Tract Society
American Unitarian Association
Cyril E. Barker
Mrs. Dorothy M. W. Bean
Clifford Booth
George Wallace Briggs
Miss Evelyn Brooke
Mrs. George Sargent Burgess
Mrs. Guernsey Camp
Chautauqua Institution
Church Hymnal Corporation
Mrs. Bascom Copenhaver
Purd E. Deitz
Doubleday Doran Company
Canon Winfred Douglas
The Abbott of Downside
W. Gwenlyn Evans and Sons
Mrs. Harry Webb Farrington
Harry Emerson Fosdick
E. J. Fullwood, Trustee Fellowship Hymn Book
Funk and Wagnalls Company
Winfred E. Garrison
F. J. Gillman
Mrs. John H. Gower
Marion Franklin Ham
S. Ralph Harlow
Earl Enyeart Harper
Basil Harwood
John Haynes Holmes
Houghton Mifflin Company
W. H. Walsham How
L. S. Hunter, Bishop of Sheffield
Mrs. Robert F. Jefferys
Miss E. R. Johnson
Shepherd Knapp
Howard Elvet Lewis
H. V. Lowry
Mrs. Mary Runyon Lowry
Mrs. Peter C. Lutkin
The Macmillan Company
Bishop Howard E. Mather
Charles E. Merrill Company
William Pierson Merrill
Methodist Publishing House
Thomas Moss
Robert H. Murray
Novello & Co.
Oxford University Press
Parker C. Palmer
Emily S. Perkins
Pilgrim Press
Edwin McNeill Poteat
Presbyterian Tribune
Theodore Presser Company
Henry B. Robins
William Robinson
The Christian Hymnary
Margaret E. Sangster
Rolland W. Schloerb
Jay Holmes Smith
Miss Dorothy Tarrant
Thomas Tiplady
Miss Julia L. Turner
Henry H. Tweedy
Wesleyan Methodist Publishing Ass'n
Westminster Press
P. K. Whelpton
The Woman's Press

Contents

Comment on Responsive Readings xi
Alphabetical Index of Responsive Readings xii
Responsive Readings .... Numbers 1-52
Calls to Worship .... Numbers 53-63
Invocations .... Numbers 64-72
Scriptures for Baptism .... Numbers 73-78
Scriptures for the Lord's Supper .... Numbers 79-84
Benedictions .... Numbers 85-93
General Classification of Hymns .... Page 72
Hymns .... Numbers 94-610
Doxologies, Responses and Amens .... Numbers 611-650

Indexes

Topical Index .... Pages 515-523
Index of Authors, Translators and Arrangers .... Pages 524-526
Index of Composers, Arrangers and Sources of Tunes ... Pages 527-529
Metrical Index of Tunes .... Pages 530-532
Alphabetical Index of Tunes .... Pages 533-534
Index of First Line of Responses .... Page 535
Index of Hymns for Use With Children .... Page 536
Index of First Line of Hymns .... Pages 537-542

Responsive Readings

Calls to Worship ✠ Invocations

Scriptures for Baptism and the Lord's Supper

Benedictions

✠

Comment on Responsive Readings

There are fifty-two topics with one hundred and four Responsive Readings, an Old Testament Reading (in the left column) and a New Testament Reading (in the right column) for each Sunday of the year. All Readings are taken from the Bible, using Revised Standard Version.

The Readings from both the Old and the New Testaments have been provided for each Sunday to meet the need of pastors who desire to use two Scripture lessons in the same service. The pastor may desire, however, to use only one Reading responsively and use the other for his own Scripture reading. Or he may wish to use one Reading in the morning and the other in the evening service. The method of using the Responsive Readings is left to the pastor and the church leaders.

The Responsive Readings have been arranged with significant periods, church days, seasons, and religious activities in mind. Many of the Readings have been prepared for the special days that are usually observed by our churches. The Readings for these impressive occasions are spaced in the numbers from one to fifty-two, so as to appear in the month the church gives particular emphasis to them. Other Readings have been selected to emphasize the elemental and vital truths of our undying faith.

Some of the Readings, especially from the New Testament, are not solely devotional, but narrative and didactical; they have been included intentionally so that the congregation may become familiar with some of the recorded teachings of Jesus and the early church which it might not otherwise receive.

We have also included many of the best and most readable *Invocations* and a large number of *Calls to Worship,* selected from both the Old and the New Testaments. Believing that the observance of the *Lord's Supper* and *Baptism* calls for deeper enrichment than is usually given these sacred ordinances, we have included many scriptural passages which may be used to interpret within the mood of worship the spiritual significance of these vital Christian experiences.

Index of Responsive Readings

Advent of Jesus ---- Reading 49
All Saints ---- Reading 44

Bible, The ---- Reading 48
Blessed Life, The ---- Reading 52
Bread of Life, The ---- Reading 12
Brotherhood ---- Reading 5

Children's Day ---- Reading 22
Christian Unity ---- Reading 24
Christmas ---- Reading 50
Church ---- Reading 4
Church Universal ---- Reading 29
Confidence ---- Reading 13
Courage ---- Reading 18

Discipleship ---- Reading 17
Discipleship ---- Reading 25
Discipleship ---- Reading 38

Easter ---- Reading 15

Fellowship with Christ ---- Reading 16
Forefather's Day (Independence) ---- Reading 27
Friendship ---- Reading 34

God
1. God's House ---- Reading 4
2. God's Presence ---- Reading 2
3. God's Word ---- Reading 48
4. Longing for God ---- Reading 33
5. Trust in God ---- Reading 31

Gratitude ---- Reading 43
Gratitude ---- Reading 46

Heaven ---- Reading 44
Heaven ---- Reading 32
Home ---- Reading 19

Immortality ---- Reading 15
Immortality ---- Reading 32

Jesus
1. Advent of Jesus ---- Reading 49
2. Birth ---- Reading 50
3. Resurrection ---- Reading 15
4. Savior of the World ---- Reading 51

Kingdom of God ---- Reading 11

Labor Day ---- Reading 35
Life
1. The Blessed Life ---- Reading 52
2. The Bread of Life ---- Reading 12
3. The Enduring Life ---- Reading 32
4. Eternal Life ---- Reading 18

Love ---- Reading 20
Love for One Another ---- Reading 42
Lord's Day ---- Reading 36

Memorial Day ---- Reading 21
Ministry, The Christian ---- Reading 40
Missions
1. Home Missions ---- Reading 47
2. World Missions ---- Reading 9

Mother's Day (Festival of the Christian Home) ---- Reading 19

New Life ---- Reading 25
New Life ---- Reading 52
New Year ---- Reading 1

Palm Sunday ---- Reading 14
Patriotism ---- Reading 7
Peace ---- Reading 45
Pentecost (Whitsunday) ---- Reading 23
Prayer ---- Reading 6
Purity, Inner ---- Reading 30

Race Relations ---- Reading 5

Security ---- Reading 39
Social Justice ---- Reading 28
Stewardship ---- Reading 41

Temperance ---- Reading 26
Temptation ---- Reading 10
Thanksgiving ---- Reading 46
Thanksgiving ---- Reading 43
True Riches ---- Reading 38
Trust in God ---- Reading 31

Unity, Christian ---- Reading 24

Wisdom ---- Reading 37
Worshipers, Contrite ---- Reading 3

Youth ---- Reading 8

Responsive Readings

NEW YEAR 1

OLD TESTAMENT

Make a joyful noise to the LORD, all the lands!
Serve the LORD with gladness!

Come into his presence with singing!

Know that the LORD is God!
It is he that made us, and we are his;

We are his people, and the sheep of his pasture.

Enter his gates with thanksgiving, and his courts with praise!

Give thanks to him, bless his name!

For the LORD is good;
his steadfast love endures for ever,

And his faithfulness to all generations

Upon those who fear him,

And his righteousness to children's children,

to those who keep his covenant and remember to do his commandments.

Bless the LORD, O you his angels,

You mighty ones who do his word. hearkening to the voice of his word!

Bless the LORD, all his hosts,
his ministers that do his will!

Unison

**Bless the LORD, O my soul;
and all that is within me, bless his holy name!**

Psalm 100
Psalm 103

NEW TESTAMENT

Therefore, my brethren, whom I love and long for, my joy and crown, stand firm thus in the Lord, my beloved.

I have learned the secret of facing plenty and hunger, abundance and want.

I can do all things in him who strengthens me.

Rejoice in the Lord always; again I will say, Rejoice.

In everything by prayer and supplication with thanksgiving let your requests be made known to God.

And the peace of God, which passes all understanding, will keep your hearts and your minds in Christ Jesus.

One thing I do, forgetting what lies behind and straining forward to what lies ahead,

I press on toward the goal for the prize of the upward call of God in Christ Jesus.

Finally, brethren, whatever is true, whatever is honorable, whatever is just,

Whatever is pure, whatever is lovely, whatever is gracious,

If there is any excellence, if there is anything worthy of praise, think about these things.

What you have learned and received and heard and seen in me, do; and the God of peace will be with you.

Philippians 3
Philippians 4

2 GOD'S PRESENCE

OLD TESTAMENT

O Lord, thou hast searched me and known me!

Thou knowest when I sit down and when I rise up;

Thou discernest my thoughts from afar.

Thou . . . art acquainted with all my ways.

Even before a word is on my tongue,

lo, O Lord, thou knowest it altogether.

Thou dost beset me behind and before,

and layest thy hand upon me.

Such knowledge is too wonderful for me;

It is high, I cannot attain it.

Whither shall I go from thy Spirit?

Or whither shall I flee from thy presence?

If I ascend to heaven, thou art there!

If I make my bed in Sheol, thou art there!

How precious to me are thy thoughts, O God!

Search me, O God, and know my heart!

Try me and know my thoughts!

And see if there be any wicked way in me,

and lead me in the way everlasting!

Psalm 139

NEW TESTAMENT

"The Counselor, the Holy Spirit, whom the Father will send in my name,

He will teach you all things, and bring to your remembrance all that I have said to you.

Peace I leave with you; my peace I give to you; not as the world gives do I give to you.

Let not your hearts be troubled, neither let them be afraid.

You heard me say to you, 'I go away, and I will come to you.'

And now I have told you before it takes place, so that when it does take place, you may believe."

"Go therefore and make disciples of all nations, baptizing them in the name of the Father and of the Son and of the Holy Spirit, teaching them to observe all that I have commanded you;

And lo, I am with you always, to the close of the age."

"If you keep my commandments, you will abide in my love, just as I have kept my Father's commandments and abide in his love.

These things have I spoken to you, that my joy may be in you, and that your joy may be full.

I chose you and appointed you that you should go and bear fruit and that your fruit should abide;

So that whatever you ask the Father in my name, he may give it to you."

John 14
Matthew 28
John 15

CONTRITE WORSHIPERS 3

OLD TESTAMENT

The earth is the LORD's and the fulness thereof,

The world and those who dwell therein;

For he has founded it upon the seas,

And established it upon the rivers.

Who shall ascend the hill of the LORD?

And who shall stand in his holy place?

He who has clean hands and a pure heart,

Who does not lift up his soul to what is false,
and does not swear deceitfully.

He will receive blessing from the LORD,

And vindication from the God of his salvation.

Lift up your heads, O gates!
and be lifted up, O ancient doors!

That the King of glory may come in.

Who is the King of glory?

The LORD, strong and mighty,
the LORD, mighty in battle!

Lift up your heads, O gates!
and be lifted up, O ancient doors!

That the King of glory may come in!

Who is this King of glory?

The LORD of hosts,
he is the King of glory!

Psalm 24

NEW TESTAMENT

He also told this parable to some who trusted in themselves that they were righteous and despised others:

"Two men went up into the temple to pray, one a Pharisee and the other a tax collector.

The Pharisee stood and prayed thus with himself, 'God, I thank thee that I am not like other men, extortioners, unjust, adulterers, or even like this tax collector. I fast twice a week, I give tithes of all that I get.'

But the tax collector, standing far off, would not even lift up his eyes to heaven, but beat his breast, saying, 'God, be merciful to me a sinner!'

I tell you, this man went down to his house justified rather than the other;

For every one who exalts himself will be humbled, but he who humbles himself will be exalted."

"But the hour is coming, and now is, when the true worshipers will worship the Father in spirit and truth, for such the Father seeks to worship him.

God is spirit, and those who worship him must worship in spirit and truth."

"Ask, and it will be given you; seek and you will find; knock, and it will be opened to you.

For every one who asks receives, and he who seeks finds, and to him who knocks it will be opened."

Luke 18
John 4
Matthew 7

4 GOD'S HOUSE

OLD TESTAMENT

I was glad when they said to me,
"Let us go to the house of the LORD!"

Our feet have been standing

within your gates, O Jerusalem!

One thing have I asked of the LORD,

That will I seek after;

That I may dwell in the house of the LORD

all the days of my life,

To behold the beauty of the LORD, and to inquire in his temple.

For he will hide me in his shelter in the day of trouble;

He will conceal me under the cover of his tent,

he will set me high upon a rock.

How lovely is thy dwelling place,

O LORD of hosts!

My soul longs, yea, faints
For the courts of the LORD;

My heart and flesh sing for joy to the living God.

Even the sparrow finds a home,

and the swallow a nest for herself,

where she may lay her young,

At thy altars, O LORD of hosts,
my king and my God.

Blessed are those who dwell in thy house,

ever singing thy praise!

Psalm 122
Psalm 27
Psalm 84

NEW TESTAMENT

And Jesus entered the temple of God and drove out all who sold and bought in the temple, and he overturned the tables of the money-changers and the seats of those who sold pigeons.

He said to them, "It is written, 'My house shall be called a house of prayer'; but you make it a den of robbers."

And he came to Nazareth, where he had been brought up; and he went to the synagogue, as his custom was, on the sabbath day.

And he stood up to read; and there was given to him the book of the prophet Isaiah.

He opened the book and found the place where it was written,

Unison

"The Spirit of the Lord is upon me,

because he has anointed me to preach good news to the poor.

He has sent me to proclaim release to the captives

and recovering of sight to the blind,

to set at liberty those who are oppressed,

to proclaim the acceptable year of the Lord."

And he began to say to them, "Today this scripture has been fulfilled in your hearing."

And all spoke well of him, and wondered at the gracious words which proceeded out of his mouth.

Matthew 21
Luke 4

BROTHERHOOD—RACE RELATIONS 5

OLD TESTAMENT

O sing to the LORD a new song;
sing to the LORD, all the earth!

Sing to the LORD, bless his name;
tell of his salvation from day to day.

Declare his glory among the nations,
his marvelous works among all the peoples!

Worship the LORD in holy array;

Let the heavens be glad, and let the earth rejoice;
before the LORD, for he comes,
for he comes to judge the earth.

He will judge the world with righteousness,
and the peoples with his truth.

Let the peoples praise thee, O God;
Let all the peoples praise thee!

Let the nations be glad and sing for joy,
For thou dost judge the peoples with equity
and guide the nations upon earth.

Let the peoples praise thee, O God;
Let all the peoples praise thee!

The earth has yielded its increase;
God, our God, has blessed us.

God has blessed us;
let all the ends of the earth fear him!

Psalm 96
Psalm 67

NEW TESTAMENT

So Paul, standing . . . said, "Men of Athens, I perceive that in every way you are very religious. For as I passed along, and observed the objects of your worship, I found also an altar with this inscription, 'TO AN UNKNOWN GOD.'

What therefore you worship as unknown, this I proclaim to you.

The God who made the world and everything in it, being Lord of heaven and earth, does not live in shrines made by man,

Nor is he served by human hands, as though he needed anything, since he himself gives to all men life and breath and everything.

And he made from one every nation of men to live on all the face of the earth.

'In him we live and move and have our being;'

As even some of your poets have said."

There is neither Jew nor Greek, there is neither slave nor free, there is neither male nor female;

For you are all one in Christ Jesus.

If any one says, "I love God," and hates his brother, he is a liar;

For he who does not love his brother whom he has seen, cannot love God whom he has not seen.

And this commandment we have from him, that he who loves God should love his brother also.

Acts 17
Galatians 3
1 John 4

6 PRAYER

OLD TESTAMENT

Have mercy on me, O God,
according to thy steadfast love;

According to thy abundant mercy blot out my transgressions.

Wash me thoroughly from my iniquity,

And cleanse me from my sin!

In thee, O LORD, do I take refuge;
let me never be put to shame!

In thy righteousness deliver me and rescue me;
incline thy ear to me, and save me!

For thou art my rock and my fortress.

Rescue me, O my God, from the hand of the wicked,
For thou, O Lord, art my hope,

For he delivers the needy when he calls,
the poor and him who has no helper.

He has pity on the weak and the needy,
and saves the lives of the needy.

From oppression and violence he redeems their life.

Unison

Blessed be the LORD, the God of Israel,
who alone does wondrous things.
Blessed be his glorious name for ever;
may his glory fill the whole earth!
Amen and Amen!

Psalm 51
Psalm 71
Psalm 72

NEW TESTAMENT

"But when you pray, go into your room and shut the door and pray to your Father who is in secret;

And your Father who sees in secret will reward you.

And in praying do not heap up empty phrases as the Gentiles do;

For they think that they will be heard for their many words.

Pray then like this:

Unison

Our Father who art in heaven,
Hallowed be thy name.
Thy kingdom come,
Thy will be done,
On earth as it is in heaven.
Give us this day our daily bread;
And forgive us our debts,
As we also have forgiven our debtors;
And lead us not into temptation,
But deliver us from evil.
For thine is the kingdom and the power and the glory, forever. Amen."

When Jesus had spoken these words, he lifted up his eyes to heaven and said,

Unison

"Father, the hour has come; glorify thy Son that the Son may glorify thee, since thou hast given him power over all flesh, to give eternal life to all whom thou hast given him. And this is eternal life, that they know thee the only true God, and Jesus Christ whom thou hast sent."

Matthew 6
John 17

PATRIOTISM 7

OLD TESTAMENT

And God spoke all these words, saying,

Unison

"I am the LORD your God
"You shall have no other gods before me.
"You shall not make yourself a graven image.
"You shall not take the name of the LORD your God in vain;
"Remember the sabbath day, to keep it holy.
"Honor your father and your mother.
"You shall not kill.
"You shall not commit adultery.
"You shall not steal.
"You shall not bear false witness.
"You shall not covet."

"You shall be careful to do therefore as the LORD your God has commanded you.

"You shall walk in all the way which the LORD your God has commanded you, that you may live, and that it may go well with you.

"Now this is the commandment, the statutes and the ordinances which the LORD your God commanded me to teach you, that you may do them in the land to which you are going over, to possess it;

that you may fear the LORD your God, you and your son and your son's son, by keeping all his statutes and his commandments, which I command you, all the days of your life."

Exodus 20
Deuteronomy 5, 6

NEW TESTAMENT

Do not be deceived; God is not mocked, for whatever a man sows, that he will also reap.

For he who sows to his own flesh will from the flesh reap corruption; but he who sows to the Spirit will from the Spirit reap eternal life.

And let us not grow weary in well-doing, for in due season we shall reap, if we do not lose heart.

So then, as we have opportunity, let us do good to all men.

Finally, be strong in the Lord and in the strength of his might.

Put on the whole armor of God, that you may be able to stand against the wiles of the devil.

Therefore take the whole armor of God, that you may be able to withstand in the evil day, and having done all, to stand.

Stand therefore, having girded your loins with truth, and having put on the breastplate of righteousness, and having shod your feet with the equipment of the gospel of peace; above all taking the shield of faith, with which you can quench all the flaming darts of the evil one.

And take the helmet of salvation, and the sword of the Spirit, which is the word of God.

Pray at all times in the Spirit, with all prayer and supplication. To that end keep alert with all perseverance, making supplication for all the saints.

Galatians 6
Ephesians 6

8 YOUTH

OLD TESTAMENT

"And it shall come to pass afterward,
that I will pour out my spirit on all flesh;

Your sons and your daughters shall prophesy,
your old men shall dream dreams, and your young men shall see visions.

Rejoice, O young man, in your youth, and let your heart cheer you in the days of your youth;

Walk in the ways of your heart and the sight of your eyes.

But know that for all these things God will bring you into judgment.

Remember also your Creator in the days of your youth,

Before the evil days come, and the years draw nigh, when you will say, "I have no pleasure in them";

Before the sun and the light, and the moon, and the stars are darkened

Before the silver cord is snapped, or the golden bowl is broken, or the pitcher is broken at the fountain, or the wheel broken at the cistern,

And the dust returns to the earth as it was, and the spirit returns to God who gave it.

The end of the matter; all has been heard. Fear God, and keep his commandments; for this is the whole duty of man.

For God wil bring every deed into judgment, with every secret thing, whether good or evil.

Joel 2
Ecclesiastes 11
Ecclesiastes 12

NEW TESTAMENT

You then, my son, be strong in the grace that is in Christ Jesus,

And what you have heard from me before many witnesses entrust to faithful men who will be able to teach others also.

Let no one despise your youth, but set the believers an example in speech and conduct, in love, in faith, in purity.

Do your best to present yourself to God as one approved, a workman who has no need to be ashamed, rightly handling the word of truth.

And as he was setting out on his journey, a man ran up and knelt before him, and asked him, "Good Teacher, what must I do to inherit eternal life?"

And Jesus said to him, "Why do you call me good? No one is good but God alone.

You know the commandments: 'Do not kill, Do not commit adultery, Do not steal, Do not bear false witness, Do not defraud, Honor your father and mother.' "

And he said to him, "Teacher, all these I have observed from my youth."

And Jesus looking upon him loved him, and said to him,

"You lack one thing; go, sell what you have, and give to the poor, and you will have treasure in heaven; and come, follow me."

1 Timothy 4
2 Timothy 2
Mark 10

WORLD MISSIONS 9

OLD TESTAMENT

Comfort, comfort my people,
says your God.
Speak tenderly to Jerusalem,
and cry to her

**That her warfare is ended,
that her iniquity is pardoned,
that she has received from the LORD'S hand
double for all her sins.**

Every valley shall be lifted up,

And every mountain and hill be made low;

The uneven ground shall become level,

And the rough places a plain.

And the glory of the LORD shall be revealed,

And all flesh shall see it together, for the mouth of the LORD has spoken.

Get you up to a high mountain,
O Zion, herald of good tidings;

**Lift up your voice with strength,
O Jerusalem, herald of good tidings,**

Behold, the Lord GOD comes with might,
and his arm rules for him;

**Behold, his reward is with him,
and his recompense before him.**

And a highway shall be there,
and it shall be called the Holy Way;

**The unclean shall not pass over it,
and fools shall not err therein.**

Isaiah 40
Isaiah 35

NEW TESTAMENT

And Jesus came and said to them, "All authority in heaven and on earth has been given to me.

Go therefore and make disciples of all nations, baptizing them in the name of the Father and of the Son and of the Holy Spirit,

Teaching them to observe all that I have commanded you; and lo, I am with you always, to the close of the age."

"And I have other sheep, that are not of this fold; I must bring them also.

So there shall be one flock, one shepherd."

"It is written, that the Christ should suffer and on the third day rise from the dead, and that repentance and forgiveness of sins should be preached in his name to all nations,

Beginning from Jerusalem. You are witnesses of these things."

"But you shall receive power when the Holy Spirit has come upon you; and you shall be my witnesses in Jerusalem and in all Judea and Samaria and to the end of the earth."

Then they returned to Jerusalem; and they went up to the upper room. All these with one accord devoted themselves to prayer.

And they worshiped him, and were continually in the temple blessing God.

John 10
Matthew 28
Luke 24
Acts 1

10 TEMPTATION

OLD TESTAMENT

To thee, O LORD, I lift up my soul.

O my God, in thee I trust,

Let me not be put to shame;

Let not my enemies exult over me.

Make me to know thy ways, O LORD;

Teach me thy paths.

Lead me in thy truth, and teach me, for thou art the God of my salvation;

For thee I wait all the day long.

Remember not the sins of my youth, or my transgressions;

According to thy steadfast love remember me,
for thy goodness' sake, O LORD!

For thy name's sake, O LORD,
Relieve the troubles of my heart, and bring me out of my distresses.

Oh guard my life, and deliver me; let me not be put to shame, for I take refuge in thee.

Commit your way to the LORD; trust in him, and he will act.

Good and upright is the LORD; therefore he instructs sinners in the way.

He leads the humble in what is right,

And teaches the humble his way.

All the paths of the LORD are steadfast love and faithfulness,

For those who keep his covenant and his testimonies.

Psalm 25

NEW TESTAMENT

Then Jesus was led up by the Spirit into the wilderness to be tempted by the devil.

And he fasted forty days and forty nights, and afterward he was hungry.

And the tempter came and said to him, "If you are the Son of God, command these stones to become loaves of bread."

But he answered, "It is written, 'Man shall not live by bread alone,
but by every word that proceeds from the mouth of God.'"

Then the devil took him to the holy city, and set him on the pinnacle of the temple,

And said to him, "If you are the Son of God, throw yourself down; for it is written,
'He will give his angels charge of you,'"

Jesus said to him, "Again it is written, 'You shall not tempt the Lord your God.'"

Again, the devil took him to a very high mountain, and showed him all the kingdoms of the world and the glory of them;

And he said to him, "All these I will give you, if you will fall down and worship me."

Then Jesus said to him, "Begone, Satan! for it is written,
'You shall worship the Lord your God
and him only shall you serve.'"

Matthew 4

THE KINGDOM OF GOD 11

OLD TESTAMENT

For to us a child is born,
to us a son is given;

And the government will be upon his shoulder,

And his name will be called
"Wonderful Counselor, Mighty God,

Everlasting Father, Prince of Peace."

Of the increase of his government and of peace
there will be no end,

Upon the throne of David, and over his kingdom,
to establish it, . . .

. . . And to uphold it
with justice and with righteousness
from this time forth and for evermore.

"And it shall come to pass afterward, that I will pour out my spirit on all flesh;

Your sons and your daughters shall prophesy,

Your old men shall dream dreams, and your young men shall see visions.

Even upon the menservants and maidservants
in those days, I will pour out my spirit.

And it shall come to pass that all who call upon the name of the LORD shall be delivered."

Isaiah 9
Joel 2

NEW TESTAMENT

Jesus came into Galilee, preaching the gospel of God, and saying, "The time is fulfilled, and the kingdom of God is at hand;

Repent, and believe in the gospel."

And he told them many things in parables, saying:

"The kingdom of heaven is like a grain of mustard seed which a man took and sowed in his field;

It is the smallest of all seeds,

But when it has grown it is the greatest of shrubs and becomes a tree, so that the birds of the air come and make nests in its branches."

He told them another parable.

"The kingdom of heaven is like leaven which a woman took and hid in three measures of meal, till it was all leavened."

Jesus answered, "My kingship is not of this world;

If my kingship were of this world, my servants would fight, that I might no be handed over to the Jews;

But my kingship is not from the world."

Pilate said to him, "So you are a king?"

Jesus answered, "You say that I am a king.

For this I was born, and for this I have come into the world, to bear witness to the truth."

Mark 1
Matthew 13
John 18

12 BREAD OF LIFE

OLD TESTAMENT

"Ho, every one who thirsts,
come to the waters;

and he who has no money,
come, buy and eat!

**Come, buy wine and milk
without money and without price.**

Why do you spend your money for
that which is not bread,

**And your labor for that which
does not satisfy?**

Hearken diligently to me, and eat
what is good,

and delight yourselves in fatness.

**Incline your ear, and come to me;
hear, that your soul may live;**

and I will make with you an everlasting covenant,

my steadfast, sure love for David.

"For as the rain and the snow
come down from heaven,

and return not thither but water
the earth,

**Making it bring forth and sprout,
giving seed to the sower and
bread to the eater,**

So shall my word be that goes forth
from my mouth;

It shall not return to me empty,

But it shall accomplish that which
I purpose,

**And prosper in the thing for
which I sent it."**

Isaiah 55

NEW TESTAMENT

Jesus then said to them, "Truly, truly, I say to you, it was not Moses who gave you the bread from heaven; my Father gives you the true bread from heaven.

For the bread of God is that which comes down from heaven, and gives life to the world."

They said to him, "Lord, give us this bread always."

Jesus said to them, "I am the bread of life;

He who comes to me shall not hunger, and he who believes in me shall never thirst.

And this is the will of him who sent me, that I should lose nothing of all that he has given me, but raise it up at the last day.

For this is the will of my Father, that every one who sees the Son and believes in him should have eternal life;

And I will raise him up at the last day."

"I am the living bread which came down from heaven;

If any one eats of this bread, he will live for ever; and the bread which I shall give for the life of the world is my flesh."

"I came that they may have life, and have it abundantly."

"Blessed are those who hunger and thirst for righteousness, for they shall be satisfied."

John 6
John 10
Matthew 5

CONFIDENCE 13

OLD TESTAMENT

For God alone my soul waits in silence;

From him comes my salvation.

He only is my rock and my salvation,

My fortress; I shall not be greatly moved.

On God rests my deliverance and my honor;

My mighty rock, my refuge is God.

Trust in him at all times, O people; pour out your heart before him;

Unison

The LORD is my shepherd, I shall not want;
he makes me lie down in green pastures.
He leads me beside still waters;
he restores my soul.
He leads me in paths of righteousness
for his name's sake.
Even though I walk through the valley of the shadow of death,
I fear no evil;
for thou art with me;
thy rod and thy staff,
they comfort me.
Thou preparest a table before me
in the presence of my enemies;
thou anointest my head with oil,
my cup overflows.
Surely goodness and mercy shall follow me
all the days of my life;
and I shall dwell in the house of the LORD
for ever.

Psalm 62
Psalm 23

NEW TESTAMENT

I rejoice in the Lord greatly that now at length you have revived your concern for me;

Not that I complain of want; for I have learned, in whatever state I am, to be content.

I know how to be abased, and I know how to abound; in any and all circumstances I have learned the secret of facing plenty and hunger, abundance and want.

I can do all things in him who strengthens me.

"Do not lay up for yourselves treasures on earth, where moth and rust consume and where thieves break in and steal,

But lay up for yourselves treasures in heaven,

Where neither moth nor rust consumes and where thieves do not break in and steal.

For where your treasure is, there will your heart be also.

"Therefore do not be anxious, saying, 'What shall we eat?' or 'What shall we drink?' or 'What shall we wear?'

But seek first his kingdom and his righteousness, and all these things shall be yours as well.

"Therefore do not be anxious about tomorrow, for tomorrow will be anxious for itself.

Let the day's own trouble be sufficient for the day."

Philippians 4
Matthew 6

14 PALM SUNDAY

OLD TESTAMENT

Awake, awake,
put on your strength, O Zion;

**Put on your beautiful garments,
O Jerusalem, the holy city;**

How beautiful upon the mountains
are the feet of him who brings
good tidings,

**Who publishes peace, who brings
good tidings of good,**

Who publishes salvation,
who says to Zion, "Your God
reigns."

**Break forth together into singing,
you waste places of Jerusalem;**

For the LORD has comforted his
people,

He has redeemed Jerusalem.

Behold, my servant shall prosper,
he shall be exalted and lifted up,
and shall be very high.

**I will greatly rejoice in the LORD,
my soul shall exult in my God;**

For he has clothed me with the garments of salvation,

**He has covered me with the robe
of righteousness,**

For as the earth brings forth its
shoots,
and as a garden causes what is
sown in it to spring up,

**So the Lord GOD will cause righteousness and praise
to spring forth before all the nations.**

Isaiah 52
Isaiah 61

NEW TESTAMENT

The next day a great crowd who had come to the feast heard that Jesus was coming to Jerusalem. So they took branches of palm trees and went out to meet him,

Crying, "Hosanna! Blessed be he who comes in the name of the Lord, even the King of Israel!"

And when he entered Jerusalem, all the city was stirred, saying, "Who is this?"

And the crowds said, "This is the prophet Jesus from Nazareth of Galilee."

And Jesus entered the temple of God and drove out all who sold and bought in the temple,

And he overturned the tables of the moneychangers and the seats of those who sold pigeons.

He said to them, "It is written, 'My house shall be called a house of prayer;' but you make it a den of robbers."

Now among those who went up to worship at the feast were some Greeks. So these came to Philip, who was from Bethsaida in Galilee, and said to him, "Sir, we wish to see Jesus."

And Jesus answered them, "The hour has come for the Son of man to be glorified.

Truly, truly, I say to you, unless a grain of wheat falls into the earth and dies, it remains alone; but if it dies, it bears much fruit."

John 12
Matthew 21

EASTER 15

OLD TESTAMENT

Who has believed what we have heard?

And to whom has the arm of the LORD been revealed?

For he grew up before him like a young plant,

And like a root out of dry ground;

He had no form or comeliness that we should look at him,

And no beauty that we should desire him.

He was despised and rejected by men;
a man of sorrows and acquainted with grief;

And as one from whom men hide their faces
he was despised, and we esteemed him not.

He was oppressed, and he was afflicted,
yet he opened not his mouth;

Like a lamb that is led to the slaughter,

And like a sheep that before its shearers is dumb,
so he opened not his mouth.

"For I know that my Redeemer lives, and at last he will stand upon the earth;
and . . . then . . . I shall see God."

Isaiah 53
Job 19

NEW TESTAMENT

Now after the sabbath, toward the dawn of the first day of the week, Mary Magdalene and the other Mary went to see the sepulchre.

And behold, there was a great earthquake; for an angel of the Lord descended from heaven and came and rolled back the stone, and sat upon it.

But the angel said to the women, "Do not be afraid; for I know that you seek Jesus who was crucified.

He is not here; for he has risen, as he said. Come, see the place where the Lord lay.

Then go quickly and tell his disciples that he has risen from the dead, and behold, he is going before you to Galilee; there you will see him. Lo, I have told you."

So they departed quickly from the tomb with fear and great joy, and ran to tell his disciples.

But in fact Christ has been raised from the dead, the first fruits of those who have fallen asleep.

For as by a man came death, by a man has come also the resurrection of the dead.

For as in Adam all die, so also in Christ shall all be made alive.

"I am the resurrection and the life; he who believes in me, though he die, yet shall he live, and whoever lives and believes in me shall never die."

Matthew 28
John 11
1 Corinthians 15

16 FELLOWSHIP WITH CHRIST

OLD TESTAMENT

I lift up my eyes to the hills.
From whence does my help come?

**My help comes from the LORD,
who made heaven and earth.**

He will not let your foot be moved,
he who keeps you will not slumber.

**Behold, he who keeps Israel
will neither slumber nor sleep.**

The LORD is your keeper;
the LORD is your shade
on your right hand.

**The sun shall not smite you by day,
nor the moon by night.**

The LORD will keep you from all evil;
he will keep your life.

**The LORD will keep
your going out and your coming in
from this time forth and for evermore.**

He who dwells in the shelter of the Most High,
who abides in the shadow of the Almighty,

**Will say to the LORD, "My refuge and my fortress;
my God, in whom I trust."**

Of old thou didst speak . . .
Because he cleaves to me in love, I will deliver him;
I will protect him, because he knows my name.

**When he calls to me, I will answer him;
I will rescue him and honor him.**

Psalm 121
Psalm 91
Psalm 89

NEW TESTAMENT

If then you have been raised with Christ, seek the things that are above, where Christ is, seated at the right hand of God.

Set your minds on things that are above, not on things that are on earth.

For you have died, and your life is hid with Christ in God.

Therefore, if any one is in Christ, he is a new creation; the old has passed away, behold, the new has come.

Seeing that you have put off the old nature with its practices and have put on the new nature, which is being renewed in knowledge after the image of its creator.

Here there cannot be Greek and Jew, circumcised and uncircumcised, barbarian, Scythian, slave, free man, but Christ is all, and in all.

Put on then, as God's chosen ones, holy and beloved, compassion, kindness, lowliness, meekness, and patience,

Forbearing one another and if one has a complaint against another, forgiving each other; as the Lord has forgiven you, so you also must forgive.

And above all these put on love, which binds everything together in perfect harmony.

And let the peace of Christ rule in your hearts, to which indeed you were called in the one body. And be thankful.

Colossians 3
2 Corinthians 5

DISCIPLESHIP 17

OLD TESTAMENT

O God, thou art my God, I seek thee,
my soul thirsts for thee;

My flesh faints for thee,
as in a dry and weary land where no water is.

So I have looked upon thee in the sanctuary,
beholding thy power and glory.

Because thy steadfast love is better than life,
my lips will praise thee.

So I will bless thee a long as I live;

In peace I will both lie down and sleep;
for thou alone, O LORD, makest me dwell in safety.

O LORD, in the morning thou dost hear my voice;

In the morning I prepare a sacrifice for thee, and watch.

Give ear to my voice, when I call to thee!

Let my prayer be counted as incense before thee,
and the lifting up of my hands as an evening sacrifice!

Set a guard over my mouth, O LORD,

For thou dost bless the righteous, O LORD;
thou dost cover him with favor as with a shield.

Psalm 63
Psalm 4
Psalm 5
Psalm 141

NEW TESTAMENT

As they were going along the road, a man said to him, "I will follow you wherever you go."

And Jesus said to him, "Foxes have holes, and birds of the air have nests; but the Son of man has nowhere to lay his head."

To another he said, "Follow me."

But he said, "Lord, let me first go and bury my father."

But he said to him, "Leave the dead to bury their own dead;

But as for you, go and proclaim the kingdom of God."

Another said, "I will follow you, Lord; but let me first say farewell to those at my home."

Jesus said to him, "No one who puts his hand to the plow and looks back is fit for the kingdom of God."

"He who loves father or mother more than me is not worthy of me;

And he who loves son or daughter more than me is not worthy of me;

And he who does not take his cross and follow me is not worthy of me.

He who finds his life will lose it, and he who loses his life for my sake will find it."

Luke 9
Matthew 10

18 COURAGE

OLD TESTAMENT

"No man shall be able to stand before you all the days of your life;

As I was with Moses, so I will be with you; I will not fail you or forsake you.

Be strong and of good courage; for you shall cause this people to inherit the land which I swore to their fathers to give them.

Only be strong and very courageous, being careful to do according to all the law which Moses my servant commanded you;

Turn not from it to the right hand or to the left, that you may have good success wherever you go.

Have I not commanded you? Be strong and of good courage; be not frightened neither be dismayed;

For the LORD your God is with you wherever you go."

Teach me thy way, O LORD;
and lead me on a level path
because of my enemies.
for false witnesses have risen against me,

Be strong, and let your heart take courage;
year, wait for the Lord!

Cast me not off, forsake me not,
O God of my salvation!

I believe that I shall see the goodness of the LORD
in the land of the living!

Joshua 1
Psalm 27

NEW TESTAMENT

Who shall separate us from the love of Christ? Shall tribulation, or distress, or persecution, or famine or nakedness, or peril, or sword?

No, in all these things we are more than conquerors through him who loved us.

For I am sure that neither death, nor life, nor angels,

Nor principalities, nor things present, nor things to come,

Nor powers, nor height, nor depth,

Nor anything else in all creation, will be able to separate us from the love of God in Christ Jesus our Lord.

Have this mind among yourselves, which you have in Christ Jesus,

Who, though he was in the form of God, did not count equality with God a thing to be grasped,

But emptied himself, taking the form of a servant, being born in the likeness of men.

And being found in human form he humbled himself and became obedient unto death, even death on a cross.

Therefore God has highly exalted him and bestowed on him the name which is above every name,

That at the name of Jesus every knee should bow, and every tongue confess that Jesus Christ is Lord, to the glory of God the Father.

Romans 8
Philippians 2

FESTIVAL OF THE CHRISTIAN HOME
(Mother's Day)
19

OLD TESTAMENT

The fear of the LORD is the beginning of knowledge;
fools despise wisdom and instruction.

Hear, my son, your father's instruction,
and reject not your mother's teaching.

Let not loyalty and faithfulness forsake you;

Bind them about your neck,
write them on the tablet of your heart.

So you will find favor and good repute
in the sight of God and man.

Trust in the LORD with all your heart,
and do not rely on your own insight.

In all your ways acknowledge him,
and he will make straight your paths.

A good wife who can find?
She is far more precious than jewels.

The heart of her husband trusts in her,
and he will have no lack of gain.

Her children rise up and call her blessed;
her husband also, and he praises her.

Unison

Charm is deceitful, and beauty is vain,
but a woman who fears the LORD is to be praised.

Proverbs 1
Proverbs 3
Proverbs 31

NEW TESTAMENT

After three days they found him in the temple, sitting among the teachers, listening to them and asking them questions;

And all who heard him were amazed at his understanding and his answers.

And when they saw him they were astonished; and his mother said to him, "Son, why have you treated us so?"

And he said to them, "How is it that you sought me? Did you not know that I must be in my Father's house?"

And he went down with them and came to Nazareth, and was obedient to them; and his mother kept all these things in her heart.

And Jesus increased in wisdom and in stature, and in favor with God and man.

But standing by the cross of Jesus were his mother, and his mother's sister, Mary the wife of Clopas, and Mary Magdalene.

When Jesus saw his mother, and the disciple whom he loved standing near, he said to his mother, "Woman, behold your son!"

Then he said to the disciple, "Behold your mother!"

And from that hour the disciple took her to his own home.

Luke 2
John 19

20 LOVE

OLD TESTAMENT

"Hear, O Israel: The LORD our God is one LORD; and you shall love the LORD your God with all your heart, and with all your soul, and with all your might.

And these words which I command you this day shall be upon your heart;

And you shall teach them diligently to your children, and shall talk of them when you sit in your house, and when you walk by the way, and when you lie down, and when you rise."

"You shall not hate your brother in your heart, but you shall reason with your neighbor.

You shall not take vengeance or bear any grudge against the sons of your own people,

But you shall love your neighbor as yourself: I am the LORD.

But let all who take refuge in thee rejoice,

For thou dost bless the righteous, O LORD;
thou dost cover him with favor as with a shield.

"Take good care to observe the commandment and the law which Moses the servant of the LORD commanded you,

To love the LORD your God, and to walk in all his ways, and to keep his commandments, and to cleave to him, and to serve him with all your heart and with all your soul."

Deuteronomy 6
Leviticus 19
Psalm 5
Joshua 22

NEW TESTAMENT

And I will show you a still more excellent way.

If I speak in the tongues of men and of angels, but have not love,

I am a noisy gong or a clanging cymbal.

And if I have prophetic powers, and understand all mysteries and all knowledge, and if I have all faith, so as to remove mountains, but have not love,

I am nothing.

If I give away all I have, and if I deliver my body to be burned, but have not love,

I gain nothing.

Love is patient and kind; love is not jealous or boastful; it is not arrogant or rude.

Love does not insist on its own way; it is not irritable or resentful;

It does not rejoice at wrong, but rejoices in the right.

Love bears all things, believes all things, hopes all things, endures all things.

Love never ends; as for prophecy, it will pass away; as for tongues, they will cease; as for knowledge, it will pass away.

So faith, hope, love abide, these three; but the greatest of these is love.

1 Corinthians 13

IN MEMORIAM 21

OLD TESTAMENT

LORD, thou hast been our dwelling place
in all generations.

Before the mountains were brought forth,
or ever thou hadst formed the earth and the world,
from everlasting to everlasting thou art God.

For a thousand years in thy sight
are but as yesterday when it is past,
or as a watch in the night.

Thou dost sweep men away; they are like a dream,
like grass which is renewed in the morning:

In the morning it flourishes and is renewed;
in the evening it fades and withers.

The years of our life are threescore and ten,
or even by reason of strength fourscore;

Satisfy us in the morning with thy steadfast love,
that we may rejoice and be glad all our days.

Let thy work be manifest to thy servants,
and thy glorious power to their children.

Let the favor of the Lord our God be upon us,
and establish thou the work of our hands upon us,

Yea, the work of our hands establish thou it.

Psalm 90

NEW TESTAMENT

I appeal to you therefore, brethren, by the mercies of God, to present your bodies as a living sacrifice, holy and acceptable to God, which is your spiritual worship.

Do not be conformed to this world but be transformed by the renewal of your mind, that you may prove what is the will of God, what is good and acceptable and perfect.

After this I looked, and behold, a great multitude which no man could number, from every nation, from all tribes and peoples and tongues,

Standing before the throne and before the Lamb, clothed in white robes, with palm branches in their hands,

And crying out with a loud voice,

"Salvation belongs to our God who sits upon the throne, and to the Lamb!"

Then one of the elders addressed me, saying,

"Who are these, clothed in white robes, and whence have they come?"

I said to him, "Sir, you know."

And he said to me, "These are they who have come out of the great tribulation;

They have washed their robes and made them white in the blood of the Lamb.

Therefore are they before the throne of God,
and serve him day and night."

Romans 12
Revelation 7

22 CHILDREN'S DAY

OLD TESTAMENT

Hear, O sons, a father's instructions,
for I give you good precepts:
do not forsake my teaching.

**When I was a son with my father,
he taught me, and said to me,
"Let your heart hold fast my words;
keep my commandments, and live;**

Do not forget, and do not turn away from the words of my mouth.

**Get wisdom; get insight.
Do not forsake her, and she will keep you;
love her, and she will guard you."**

Incline your ear, and hear the words of the wise,
and apply your mind to my knowledge;

**For it will be pleasant if you keep them within you,
if all of them are ready on your lips.**

Come, O sons, listen to me,
I will teach you the fear of the LORD.

**Keep your tongue from evil,
and your lips from speaking deceit.**

Depart from evil, and do good;
seek peace, and pursue it.

**The eyes of the LORD are toward the righteous,
and his ears toward their cry.
The face of the LORD is against evildoers.**

Proverbs 4
Proverbs 22
Psalm 34

NEW TESTAMENT

At that time the disciples came to Jesus, saying, "Who is the greatest in the kingdom of heaven?"

And calling to him a child, he put him in the midst of them,

And said, "Truly, I say to you, unless you turn and become like children, you will never enter the kingdom of heaven.

Whoever humbles himself like this child, he is the greatest in the kingdom of heaven.

"Whoever receives one such child in my name receives me;

But whoever causes one of these little ones who believe in me to sin,

It would be better for him to have a great millstone fastened round his neck and to be drowned in the depth of the sea."

Then children were brought to him that he might lay his hands on them and pray.

The disciples rebuked the people; but Jesus said, "Let the children come to me, and do not hinder them;

For to such belongs the kingdom of heaven."

And he laid his hands on them and went away.

And the child grew and became strong, filled with wisdom; and the favor of God was upon him.

Matthew 18
Matthew 19
Luke 2

PENTECOST
(Whitsunday)

23

OLD TESTAMENT

"Behold, the days are coming, says the LORD, when I will make a new covenant with the house of Israel and the house of Judah,

This is the covenant which I will make with the house of Israel after those days, says the LORD:

I will put my law within them, and I will write it upon their hearts; and I will be their God, and they shall be my people.

And no longer shall each man teach his neighbor and each his brother, saying, 'Know the LORD,'

For they shall all know me, from the least of them to the greatest, says the LORD; for I will forgive their iniquity, and I will remember their sin no more."

"And I will give them one heart, and put a new spirit within them;

I will take the stony heart out of their flesh and give them a heart of flesh,

That they may walk in my statutes and keep my ordinances and obey them; and they shall be my people, and I will be their God."

For as the earth brings forth its shoots,
and as a garden causes what is sown in it to spring up,

So the Lord GOD will cause righteousness and praise
to spring forth before all the nations.

Jeremiah 31
Ezekiel 11
Isaiah 61

NEW TESTAMENT

When the day of Pentecost had come, they were all together in one place.

And suddenly a sound came from heaven like the rush of a mighty wind, and it filled all the house where they were sitting.

And there appeared to them tongues as of fire, distributed and resting on each one of them.

And they were all filled with the Holy Spirit and began to speak in other tongues, as the Spirit gave them utterance.

And they were amazed and wondered, saying, "Are not all these who are speaking Galileans?

And how is it that we hear, each of us in his own native language?"

But Peter, standing with the eleven, lifted up his voice and addressed them,

"Men of Judea and all who dwell in Jerusalem, give ear to my words.

This is what was spoken by the prophet Joel:
'And in the last days it shall be, God declares,
that I will pour out my Spirit upon all flesh,

And your sons and your daughters shall prophesy.
And it shall be that whoever calls on the name of the Lord shall be saved.'"

Acts 2

24 CHRISTIAN UNITY

OLD TESTAMENT

Behold, how good and pleasant it is
when brothers dwell in unity!

It is like the precious oil upon the head,

It is like the dew of Hermon,
which falls on the mountains of Zion!

For there the LORD has commanded the blessing,
life for evermore,

Praise the LORD, for the LORD is good;

Sing to his name, for he is gracious!

Give praise, O servants of the LORD,

You that stand in the house of the LORD,
in the courts of the house of our God!

Strengthen the weak hands,
and make firm the feeble knees.

Say to those who are of a fearful heart,
"Be strong, fear not!

Behold, your God
. . . will come and save you."

And a highway shall be there,
and it shall be called the Holy Way;
the unclean shall not pass over it,
and fools shall not err therein.

Psalm 133
Psalm 135
Isaiah 35

NEW TESTAMENT

I therefore, a prisoner for the Lord, beg you to lead a life worthy of the calling to which you have been called,

With all lowliness and meekness, with patience, forbearing one another in love,

Eager to maintain the unity of the Spirit in the bond of peace.

There is one body and one Spirit, just as you were called to the one hope that belongs to your call.

One Lord, one faith, one baptism, one God and Father of us all, who is above all and through all and in all.

I appeal to you, brethren, by the name of our Lord Jesus Christ, that all of you agree that there be no dissensions among you,

But that you be united in the same mind and the same judgment.

Let all bitterness and wrath and anger and clamor and slander be put away from you, with all malice,

And be kind to one another, tenderhearted, forgiving one another, as God in Christ forgave you.

And walk in love, as Christ loved us and gave himself up for us, a fragrant offering and sacrifice to God.

Ephesians 4
1 Corinthians 1
Ephesians 5

NEW LIFE 25

OLD TESTAMENT

Blessed is the man
who walks not in the counsel of the wicked,
nor stands in the way of sinners,
nor sits in the seat of scoffers;

But his delight is in the law of the LORD,
and on his law he meditates day and night.

He is like a tree
planted by streams of water,

That yields its fruit in its season,
and its leaf does not wither.
In all that he does, he prospers.

The wicked are not so,
but are like chaff which the wind drives away.

Therefore the wicked will not stand in the judgment,
nor sinners in the congregation of the righteous;

For the LORD knows the way of the righteous,
but the way of the wicked will perish.

"For as the heavens are higher than the earth,
so are my ways higher than your ways
and my thoughts than your thoughts."

"Incline your ear, and come to me;
hear, that your soul may live;

And I will make with you an everlasting covenant,
my steadfast, sure love for David."

Psalm 1
Isaiah 55

NEW TESTAMENT

Therefore, if any one is in Christ, he is a new creation; the old has passed away, behold, the new has come.

"Abide in me, and I in you. As the branch cannot bear fruit by itself, unless it abides in the vine, neither can you, unless you abide in me.

I am the vine, you are the branches.

He who abides in me, and I in him, he it is that bears much fruit,

For apart from me you can do nothing.

If a man does not abide in me, he is cast forth as a branch and withers; and the branches are gathered, thrown into the fire and burned.

If you abide in me, and my words abide in you, ask whatever you will, and it shall be done for you.

By this my Father is glorified, that you bear much fruit, and so prove to be my disciples.

If you keep my commandments, you will abide in my love, just as I have kept my Father's commandments and abide in his love.

"This is my commandment, that you love one another as I have loved you. Greater love has no man than this, that a man lay down his life for his friends."

2 Corinthians 5
John 15

26 TEMPERANCE

OLD TESTAMENT

Blessed is every one who fears the LORD,

Who walks in his ways!

Woe to those who rise early in the morning,
that they may run after strong drink,

Who tarry late into the evening till wine inflames them!

Woe to him who makes his neighbors drink
. . . and makes them drunk,
to gaze on their shame!

Wine is a mocker, strong drink a brawler;
and whoever is led astray by it is not wise.

Hear, my son, and be wise,
and direct your mind in the way.
Be not among winebibbers,
or among gluttonous eaters of meat;

For the drunkard and the glutton will come to poverty,
and drowsiness will clothe a man with rags.

Do not look at wine when it is red,
when it sparkles in the cup
and goes down smoothly.

At the last it bites like a serpent, and stings like an adder.

Be wise, my son, and make my heart glad,

A prudent man sees danger and hides himself.

Psalm 128
Isaiah 5
Habakkuk 2
Proverbs 20
Proverbs 23
Proverbs 27

NEW TESTAMENT

Look carefully then how you walk, not as unwise men but as wise, making the most of the time because the days are evil.

Therefore do not be foolish, but understand what the will of the Lord is.

And do not get drunk with wine, for that is debauchery; but be filled with the Spirit,

Walk by the Spirit, and do not gratify the desires of the flesh.

For the desires of the flesh are against the Spirit, and the desires of the Spirit are against the flesh;

For these are opposed to each other, to prevent you from doing what you would.

But the fruit of the Spirit is love, joy, peace, patience, kindness,

Goodness, faithfulness, gentleness, self-control; against such there is no law.

And those who belong to Christ Jesus have crucified the flesh with its passions and desires.

If we live by the Spirit, let us also walk by the Spirit.

Do you not know that you are God's temple and that God's Spirit dwells in you? If any one destroys God's temple, God will destroy him.

For God's temple is holy, and that temple you are.

Ephesians 5
Galatians 5
1 Corinthians 3

FOREFATHERS' DAY

Independence

27

OLD TESTAMENT

We have heard with our ears, O God,
our fathers have told us,
what deeds thou didst perform in their days,

But them thou didst set free.

"Return to the LORD your God, you and your children, and obey his voice in all that I command you this day, with all your heart and with all your soul;

And the LORD your God will bring you into the land which your fathers possessed, that you may possess it.

If you obey the commandments of the LORD your God which I command you this day, by loving the LORD your God, by walking in his ways, and by keeping his commandments and his statutes and his ordinances,

Then you shall live and multiply, and the LORD your God will bless you in the land."

"For this commandment which I command you this day is not too hard for you, neither is it far off."

But the word is very near you; it is in your mouth and in your heart, so that you can do it."

"The secret things belong to the LORD our God;

But the things that are revealed belong to us and to our children for ever, that we may do all the words of this law."

Psalm 44
Deuteronomy 29
Deuteronomy 30

NEW TESTAMENT

Now faith is the assurance of things hoped for, the conviction of things not seen.

For by it the men of old received divine approval.

By faith Abraham obeyed when he was called to go out to a place which he was to receive as an inheritance; and he went out not knowing where he was to go.

By faith Moses, when he was grown up, refused to be called the son of Pharaoh's daughter,

Choosing rather to share ill-treatment with the people of God than to enjoy the fleeting pleasures of sin.

By faith the people crossed the Red Sea as if on dry land:

And what more shall I say? For time would fail me to tell of Gideon, Barak, Samson, Jephthah, of David and Samuel and the prophets—

Who through faith conquered kingdoms, enforced justice, received promises, stopped the mouths of lions,

Others suffered mocking and scourging, and even chains and imprisonment.

And all these, though well attested by their faith, did not receive what was promised, since God had foreseen something better for us, that apart from us they should not be made perfect.

Hebrews 11

28 SOCIAL JUSTICE

OLD TESTAMENT

"For I know how many are your transgressions,
and how great are your sins—

You who afflict the righteous, who take a bribe,
and turn aside the needy in the gate.

You have built houses of hewn stone,
but you shall not dwell in them;

You have planted pleasant vineyards,
but you shall not drink their wine.

Seek good, and not evil,
that you may live;
and so the LORD, the God of hosts,
will be with you . . ."

O LORD, thou wilt hear the desire of the meek;
thou wilt strengthen their heart,
thou wilt incline thy ear

To do justice to the fatherless and the oppressed,
so that man who is of the earth may strike terror no more.

For thou hast maintained my just cause;
thou has sat on the throne giving righteous judgment.

I will give thanks to the LORD
with my whole heart;
I will tell of all thy wonderful deeds.

I will be glad and exult in thee,
I will sing praise to thy name, O Most High.

Amos 5
Psalm 9
Psalm 10

NEW TESTAMENT

Let love be genuine; hate what is evil, hold fast to what is good; love one another with brotherly affection; outdo one another in showing honor,

Bless those who persecute you; bless and do not curse them.

Rejoice with those who rejoice, weep with those who weep.

Live in harmony with one another; do not be haughty, but associate with the lowly; never be conceited.

Repay no one evil for evil, but take thought for what is noble in the sight of all.

If possible, so far as it depends upon you, live peacably with all.

No, "if your enemy is hungry, feed him; if he is thirsty, give him drink;

For by so doing you will heap burning coals upon his head."

Do not be overcome by evil, but overcome evil with good.

Owe no one anything, except to love one another; for he who loves his neighbor has fulfilled the law.

The commandments, "You shall not commit adultery, You shall not kill, You shall not steal, You shall not covet," and any other commandment, are summed up in this sentence,

"You shall love your neighbor as yourself." Love does no wrong to a neighbor; therefore love is the fulfilling of the law.

Romans 12
Romans 13

CHURCH UNIVERSAL 29

OLD TESTAMENT

As a hart longs
for flowing streams,
so longs my soul
for thee, O God.

**My soul thirsts for God,
for the living God.**

God is our refuge and strength,
a very present help in trouble.
Therefore we will not fear though the earth should change,

**Though the mountains shake in the heart of the sea;
though its waters roar and foam,
though the mountains tremble with its tumult.**

There is a river whose streams make glad the city of God,
the holy habitation of the Most High.

**God is in the midst of her, she shall not be moved;
God will help her right early.**

"Be still, and know that I am God.
I am exalted among the nations,
I am exalted in the earth!"

**Great is the LORD and greatly to be praised
in the city of our God!**

We have thought on thy steadfast love, O God,
in the midst of thy temple.

**As thy name, O God,
so thy praise reaches to the ends of the earth.**

Psalm 42
Psalm 46
Psalm 48

NEW TESTAMENT

He said to them, "But who do you say that I am?" Simon Peter replied, "You are the Christ, the Son of the living God."

And Jesus answered him, "Blessed are you, Simon Bar-Jona! For flesh and blood has not revealed this to you, but my Father who is in heaven.

And I tell you, you are Peter, and on this rock I will build my church, and the powers of death shall not prevail against it.

I will give you the keys of the kingdom of heaven, and whatever you bind on earth shall be bound in heaven, and whatever you loose on earth shall be loosed in heaven."

And I saw the holy city, new Jerusalem, coming down out of heaven from God, prepared as a bride adorned for her husband;

And I heard a great voice from the throne saying, "Behold, the dwelling of God is with men. He will dwell with them, and they shall be his people,

He will wipe away every tear from their eyes, and death shall be no more, neither shall there be mourning nor crying nor pain any more, for the former things have passed away."

The Spirit and the Bride say, "Come." And let him who hears say, "Come." And let him who is thirsty come, let him who desires take the water of life without price.

Matthew 16
Revelation 21
Revelation 22

30 INNER PURITY

OLD TESTAMENT

Who shall ascend the hill of the LORD?

And who shall stand in his holy place?

He who has clean hands and a pure heart,

Who does not lift up his soul to what is false,
and does not swear deceitfully.

He will receive blessing from the LORD,

And vindication from the God of his salvation.

With my whole heart I seek thee;
let me not wander from thy commandments!

Unison

Have mercy on me, O God,
according to thy steadfast love;
according to thy abundant mercy
blot out my transgressions.
Wash me thoroughly from my iniquity,
and cleanse me from my sin!
Purge me with hyssop, and I shall be clean;
wash me, and I shall be whiter than snow.
Create in me a clean heart, O God,
and put a new and right spirit within me.
Restore to me the joy of thy salvation,
and uphold me with a willing spirit.
a broken and contrite heart, O God, thou wilt not despise.

Psalm 24
Psalm 119
Psalm 51

NEW TESTAMENT

And he opened his mouth and taught them, saying:

Unison

"Blessed are the poor in spirit, for theirs is the kingdom of heaven.

"Blessed are those who mourn, for they shall be comforted.

"Blessed are the meek, for they shall inherit the earth.

"Blessed are those who hunger and thirst for righteousness, for they shall be satisfied.

"Blessed are the merciful, for they shall obtain mercy.

"Blessed are the pure in heart, for they shall see God.

"Blessed are the peacemakers, for they shall be called sons of God.

"Blessed are those who are persecuted for righteousness' sake, for theirs is the kingdom of heaven.

"Blessed are you when men revile you and persecute you and utter all kinds of evil against you falsely on my account. Rejoice and be glad, for your reward is great in heaven, for so men persecuted the prophets who were before you.

"You are the light of the world.

A city set on a hill cannot be hid.

Nor do men light a lamp and put it under a bushel, but on a stand, and it gives light to all in the house.

Let your light so shine before men, that they may see your good works and give glory to your Father who is in heaven."

Matthew 5

TRUST IN GOD 31

OLD TESTAMENT

O LORD, our Lord,
how majestic is thy name in all the earth!

**When I look at thy heavens, the work of thy fingers,
the moon and the stars which thou hast established;**

What is man that thou art mindful of him,
and the son of man that thou dost care for him?

**Yet thou hast made him little less than God,
and dost crown him with glory and honor.**

Thou hast given him dominion over the works of thy hands;
thou hast put all things under his feet,

**O LORD, our Lord,
how majestic is thy name in all the earth!**

When evildoers assail me,
they shall stumble and fall.

**Though a host encamp against me,
my heart shall not fear;
though war arise against me,
yet I will be confident.**

One thing have I asked of the LORD,
that will I seek after;

**That I may dwell in the house of the LORD
all the days of my life,**

For he will hide me in his shelter in the day of trouble;

**He will conceal me under the cover of his tent,
he will set me high upon a rock.**

Psalm 8
Psalm 27

NEW TESTAMENT

Command and teach these things. Let no one despise your youth,

But set the believers an example in speech and conduct, in love, in faith, in purity.

Till I come, attend to the public reading of scripture, to preaching, to teaching.

Do not neglect the gift you have, which was given you by prophetic utterance when the elders laid their hands upon you.

Practice these duties, devote yourself to them, so that all may see your progress.

Take heed to yourself and to your teaching;

Hold to that, for by so doing you will save both yourself and your hearers.

Now may the Lord make you increase and abound in love to one another and to all men, as we do to you,

So that he may establish your hearts unblamable in holiness before our God and Father, at the coming of our Lord Jesus with all his saints.

May the God of peace himself sanctify you wholly; and may your spirit and soul and body be kept sound and blameless at the coming of our Lord Jesus Christ.

1 Timothy 4
1 Thessalonians 3
1 Thessalonians 5

32 ENDURING LIFE

OLD TESTAMENT

I love thee, O LORD, my strength.
The LORD is my rock, and my fortress, and my deliverer,

my God, my rock, in whom I take refuge,
my shield, and the horn of my salvation, my stronghold.

I call upon the LORD, who is worthy to be praised,
and I am saved from my enemies.

The cords of death encompassed me, the torrents of perdition assailed me;

In my distress I called upon the LORD;
to my God I cried for help.

From his temple he heard my voice, and my cry to him reached his ears.
The LORD was my stay.

He brought me forth into a broad place;
he delivered me,

The LORD rewarded me according to my righteousness;
according to the cleanness of my hands he recompensed me.

The LORD lives; and blessed be my rock,
and exalted be the God of my salvation,

For this I will extol thee, O LORD, among the nations,
and sing praises to thy name.

Psalm 18

NEW TESTAMENT

"As Moses lifted up the serpent in the wilderness, so must the Son of man be lifted up,

That whoever believes in him may have eternal life.

For God so loved the world that he gave his only Son, that whoever believes in him should not perish but have eternal life."

For God sent the Son into the world, not to condemn the world, but that the world might be saved through him.

In this is love, not that we loved God but that he loved us and sent his Son to be the expiation for our sins.

He who has the Son has life; he who has not the Son has not life.

Jesus said to her, "Your brother will rise again."

Martha said to him, "I know that he will rise again in the resurrection at the last day."

Jesus said to her, "I am the resurrection and the life; he who believes in me, though he die, yet shall he live, and whoever lives and believes in me shall never die. Do you believe this?"

She said to him, "Yes, Lord; I believe that you are the Christ, the Son of God, he who is coming into the world."

John 3
John 11
1 John 4
1 John 5

LONGING FOR GOD

OLD TESTAMENT

I waited patiently for the LORD;
he inclined to me and heard my cry.

He drew me up from the desolate pit,
out of the miry bog,
and set my feet upon a rock,
making my steps secure.

He put a new song in my mouth,
a song of praise to our God.
Many will see and fear,
and put their trust in the Lord.

Blessed is the man who makes the LORD his trust,
who does not turn to the proud,
to those who go astray after false gods!

Thou hast multiplied, O LORD my God,
thy wondrous deeds and thy thoughts toward us;
none can compare with thee!

Were I to proclaim and tell of them,
they would be more than can be numbered.
may those who love thy salvation
say continually, "Great is the LORD!"

As for me, I am poor and needy;
but the Lord takes thought for me.
Thou art my help and my deliverer;
do not tarry, O my God!

Blessed be the LORD, the God of Israel,
from everlasting to everlasting!
Amen and Amen.

Psalm 40
Psalm 41

NEW TESTAMENT

Jesus said to him, "I am the way, and the truth, and the life; no one comes to the Father, but by me. If you had known me, you would have known my Father also;"

Philip said to him, "Lord, show us the Father, and we shall be satisfied."

Jesus said to him, "Have I been with you so long, and yet you do not know me, Philip? He who has seen me has seen the Father;

How can you say, 'Show us the Father'?

Do you not believe that I am in the Father and the Father in me?

The words that I say to you I do not speak on my own authority; but the Father who dwells in me does his works.

Believe me that I am in the Father and the Father in me; or else believe me for the sake of the works themselves.

"Truly, truly, I say to you, he who believes in me will also do the works that I do;

And greater works than these will he do, because I go to the Father.

Whatever you ask in my name, I will do it, that the Father may be glorified in the Son;"

"He who has my commandments and keeps them, he it is who loves me.

He who loves me will be loved by my Father, and I will love him and manifest myself to him."

John 14

34 FRIENDSHIP

OLD TESTAMENT

What is desired in a man is loyalty,
and a poor man is better than a liar.

There are friends who pretend to be friends,
but there is a friend who sticks closer than a brother.

A fool takes no pleasure in understanding,
but only in expressing his opinion.

The words of a man's mouth are deep water;
the fountain of wisdom is a gushing stream.

Your friend, and your father's friend, do not forsake;
and do not go to your brother's house in the day of your calamity.

Better is a neighbor who is near than a brother who is far away.

Be wise, my son, and make my heart glad,
that I may answer him who reproaches me.

He who is kind to the poor lends to the LORD,
and he will repay him for his deed.

He who gets wisdom loves himself;
he who keeps understanding will prosper.

He who trusts in his own mind is a fool;
but he who walks in wisdom will be delivered.

Proverbs 18
Proverbs 19
Proverbs 27
Proverbs 28

NEW TESTAMENT

"If you keep my commandments, you will abide in my love, just as I have kept my Father's commandments and abide in his love.

These things I have spoken to you that my joy may be in you, and that your joy may be full.

"This is my commandment, that you love one another as I have loved you.

Greater love has no man than this, that a man lay down his life for his friends.

You are my friends if you do what I command you. No longer do I call you servants, for the servant does not know what his master is doing;

But I have called you friends, for all that I have heard from my Father I have made known to you.

You did not choose me, but I chose you and appointed you that you should go and bear fruit and that your fruits should abide;

So that whatever you ask the Father in my name, he may give it to you.

"Remember the word that I said to you, 'A servant is not greater than his master.' "

"**But whoever would be great among you must be your servant, and whoever would be first among you must be slave of all. For the Son of man also came not to be served but to serve, and to give his life as a ranson for many.**"

John 15
Mark 10

LABOR DAY 35

OLD TESTAMENT

For everything there is a season,

And a time for every matter under heaven:

He has made everything beautiful in its time; also he has put eternity into man's mind,

There is nothing better for them than to be happy and enjoy themselves as long as they live;

It is God's gift to man that every one should eat and drink and take pleasure in all his toil.

There is nothing better than that a man should enjoy his work, for that is his lot;

They shall build houses and inhabit them;

They shall plant vineyards and eat their fruit.

They shall not build and another inhabit;

They shall not plant and another eat;

For like the days of a tree shall the days of my people be,

And my chosen shall long enjoy the work of their hands.

They shall not labor in vain,
or bear children for calamity;

**For they shall be the offspring of the blessed of the LORD,
and their children with them.**

Isaiah 65
Ecclesiastes 3

NEW TESTAMENT

"Do you not say, 'There are yet four months, then comes the harvest?' I tell you, lift up your eyes, and see how the fields are already white for harvest.

He who reaps receives wages, and gathers fruit for eternal life, so that sower and reaper may rejoice together.

For here the saying holds true, 'One sows and another reaps.'

I sent you to reap that for which you did not labor; others have labored, and you have entered into their labor."

For you yourselves know how you ought to imitate us; we were not idle when we were with you,

We did not eat any one's bread without paying, but with toil and labor we worked night and day, that we might not burden any of you.

For even when we were with you, we gave you this command: If any one will not work, let him not eat.

For we hear that some of you are living in idleness, mere busybodies, not doing any work.

"We must work the works of him who sent me, while it is day; night comes, when no one can work."

And let us not grow weary in well-doing, for in due season we shall reap, if we do not lose heart.

John 4
2 Thessalonians 3
John 9
Galatians 6

36 LORD'S DAY

OLD TESTAMENT

O give thanks to the LORD, for he is good;
his steadfast love endures for ever!

Let Israel say,
"His steadfast love endures for ever."

Let the house of Aaron say,
"His steadfast love endures for ever."

Let those who fear the LORD say,
"His steadfast love endures for ever."

The LORD is my strength and my song;
he has become my salvation.

Open to me the gates of righteousness,
that I may enter through them and give thanks to the LORD.

This is the day which the LORD has made;
let us rejoice and be glad in it.

Blessed be he who enters in the name of the LORD!
We bless you from the house of the LORD.

The LORD is God,
and he has given us light.

O give thanks to the LORD, for he is good;
for his steadfast love endures for ever!

Psalm 118

NEW TESTAMENT

On the sabbath they rested according to the commandment. But on the first day of the week, at early dawn, they went to the tomb, taking the spices which they had prepared.

And they found the stone rolled away from the tomb, but when they went in they did not find the body.

And he said to them, "O foolish men, and slow of heart to believe all that the prophets have spoken!

Was it not necessary that the Christ should suffer these things and enter into his glory?"

And beginning with Moses and all the prophets,

He interpreted to them in all the scriptures the things concerning himself.

I was in the Spirit on the Lord's day, and I heard behind me a loud voice like a trumpet

Saying, "Write what you see in a book and send it to the seven churches."

When I saw him, I fell at his feet as though dead.

But he laid his right hand upon me, saying, "Fear not,

I am the first and the last, and the living one;

I died, and behold I am alive for evermore, and I have the keys of Death and Hades. Now write what you see, what is and what is to take place hereafter."

Luke 24
Revelation 1

WISDOM 37

OLD TESTAMENT

"Surely there is a mine for silver,
and a place for gold which they refine.

**Iron is taken out of the earth,
and copper is smelted from the ore.**

"But where shall wisdom be found?
And where is the place of understanding?

**Man does not know the way to it,
and it is not found in the land of the living.**

The deep says, 'It is not in me,'
and the sea says, 'It is not with me.'

**It cannot be gotten for gold,
and silver cannot be weighed as its price.**

"Whence then comes wisdom?
And where is the place of understanding?

**It is hid from the eyes of all living,
and concealed from the birds of the air.**

"God understands the way to it,
and he knows its place.

**For he looks to the ends of the earth,
and sees everything under the heavens.**

And he said to man,
'Behold, the fear of the Lord, that is wisdom;

And to depart from evil is understanding.' "

Job 28

NEW TESTAMENT

If any of you lacks wisdom, let him ask God who gives to all men generously and without reproaching, and it will be given him.

But let him ask in faith, with no doubting, for he who doubts is like a wave of the sea that is driven and tossed by the wind.

For that person must not suppose that a double-minded man, unstable in all his ways, will receive anything from the Lord.

"Every one then who hears these words of mine and does them will be like a wise man who built his house upon the rock;

And the rain fell, and the floods came, and the winds blew and beat upon that house, but it did not fall, because it had been founded on the rock.

And every one who hears these words of mine and does not do them will be like a foolish man who built his house upon the sand;

And the rain fell, and the floods came, and the winds blew and beat against that house, and it fell; and great was the fall of it."

"Not every one who says to me, 'Lord, Lord,' shall enter the kingdom of heaven, but he who does the will of my Father who is in heaven."

James 1
Matthew 7

38 TRUE RICHES

OLD TESTAMENT

Men . . . trust in their wealth
and boast of the abundance of their riches — —
Truly no man can ransom himself,
or give to God the price of his life,
that he should continue to live on for ever.

The fool and the stupid alike must perish
and leave their wealth to others.

Be not afraid when one becomes rich,

When the glory of his house increases.

For when he dies he will carry nothing away;

His glory will not go down after him.

Put no confidence in extortion,
if riches increase, set not your heart on them.

For God alone my soul waits in silence,
for my hope is from him.

He only is my rock and my salvation,
my fortress; I shall not be shaken.

On God rests my deliverance and my honor;
my mighty rock, my refuge is God.

"Hear, O my people, and I will speak,

Offer to God a sacrifice of thanksgiving,
and pay your vows to the Most High."

Psalm 49
Psalm 62
Psalm 50

NEW TESTAMENT

And Jesus looked around and said to his disciples, "How hard it will be for those who have riches to enter the kingdom of God!"

"It is easier for a camel to go through the eye of a needle than for a rich man to enter the kingdom of God."

And they were exceedingly astonished, and said to him, "Then who can be saved?"

Jesus looked at them and said, "With men it is impossible, but not with God;

For all things are possible with God."

Jesus said, "Truly, I say to you, there is no one who has left house or brothers or sisters or mother or father or children or lands, for my sake and for the gospel,

Who will not receive a hundredfold now in this time, houses and brothers and sisters and mothers and children and lands, with persecutions, and in the age to come eternal life."

"Lay up for yourselves treasures in heaven, where neither moth nor rust consumes and where thieves do not break in and steal.

For where your treasure is, there will your heart be also."

For you know the grace of our Lord Jesus Christ, that though he was rich, yet for your sake he became poor, so that by his poverty you might become rich.

Mark 10
Matthew 6
2 Corinthians 8

SECURITY 39

OLD TESTAMENT

I love the LORD, because he has heard
my voice and my supplications.

**Because he inclined his ear to me,
therefore I will call on him as long as I live.**

Gracious is the LORD, and righteous;
our God is merciful.

The LORD has dealt bountifully.

I will lift up the cup of salvation
and call on the name of the LORD,

**I will pay my vows to the LORD
in the presence of all his people.**

Be surety for thy servant;
let not the godless oppress me.

My eyes fail with watching for thy salvation,

And for the fulfillment of thy righteous promise.

**Deal with thy servant according to thy steadfast love,
and teach me thy statutes.**

From the end of the earth I call to thee,
when my heart is faint.

**Lead thou me
to the rock that is higher than I;**

For thou art my refuge,
a strong tower against the enemy.

**Let me dwell in thy tent for ever!
Oh to be safe under the shelter of thy wings!**

Psalm 116
Psalm 119
Psalm 61

NEW TESTAMENT

"Come to me, all who labor and are heavy-laden, and I will give you rest.

Take my yoke upon you, and learn from me; for I am gentle and lowly in heart, and you will find rest for your souls.

For my yoke is easy, and my burden is light."

There is therefore now no condemnation for those who are in Christ Jesus.

For the law of the Spirit of life in Christ Jesus has set me free from the law of sin and death.

To set the mind on the flesh is death, but to set the mind on the Spirit is life and peace.

Any one who does not have the Spirit of Christ does not belong to him.

But if Christ is in you, although your bodies are dead because of sin, your spirits are alive because of righteousness.

So then, brethren, we are debtors, not to the flesh, to live according to the flesh—

For if you live according to the flesh you will die,

But you have received the spirit of sonship.

When we cry, Father! it is the Spirit himself bearing witness with our spirit that we are children of God, and if children, then heirs, heirs of God and fellow heirs with Christ.

Matthew 11
Romans 8

40 CHRISTIAN MINISTRY

OLD TESTAMENT

The Spirit of the Lord GOD is upon me,
because the LORD has anointed me
to bring good tidings to the afflicted;

He has sent me to bind up the brokenhearted,

To proclaim liberty to the captives,

And the opening of the prison to those who are bound;

To proclaim the year of the Lord's favor,

And the day of vengeance of our God;

To comfort all who mourn; . . .

To give them a garland instead of ashes,

The oil of gladness instead of mourning,

The mantle of praise instead of a faint spirit;

That they may be called oaks of righteousness,

The planting of the LORD, that he may be glorified.

But you shall be called the priests of the LORD,
men shall speak of you as the ministers of our God;
you shall eat the wealth of the nations,
and in their riches you shall glory.

I will greatly rejoice in the LORD, my soul shall exult in my God.

Isaiah 61

NEW TESTAMENT

For, "every one who calls upon the name of the Lord will be saved."

But how are men to call upon him in whom they have not believed? And how are they to believe in him of whom they have never heard?

And how are they to hear without a preacher? And how can men preach unless they are sent?

As it is written, "How beautiful are the feet of those who preach good news!"

So faith comes from what is heard, and what is heard comes by the preaching of Christ.

For the word of the cross is folly to those who are perishing, but to us who are being saved it is the power of God.

For I am not ashamed of the gospel: it is the power of God for salvation to every one who has faith, to the Jew first and also to the Greek.

For in it the righteousness of God is revealed through faith for faith; as it is written, "He who through faith is righteous shall live."

We preach Christ crucified, a stumbling-block to Jews and folly to Gentiles,

But to those who are called, both Jews and Greeks, Christ the power of God and the wisdom of God.

Romans 10
Romans 1
1 Corinthians 1

STEWARDSHIP 41

OLD TESTAMENT

He has showed you, O man, what is good;
and what does the LORD require of you

But to do justice, and to love kindness,
and to walk humbly with your God?

"From the days of your fathers you have turned aside from my statutes and have not kept them. Return to me, and I will return to you, says the LORD of hosts.

But you say, 'How shall we return?' Will man rob God?

Yet you are robbing me. But you say, 'How are we robbing thee?'

In your tithes and offerings. You are cursed with a curse, for you are robbing me; the whole nation of you.

Bring the full tithes into the storehouse, that there may be food in my house;

And thereby put me to the test, says the LORD of hosts, if I will not open the windows of heaven for you and pour down for you an overflowing blessing.

I will rebuke the devourer for you, so that it will not destroy the fruits of your soil; and your vine in the field shall not fail to bear, says the LORD of hosts.

Then all nations will call you blessed, for you will be a land of delight, says the LORD of hosts."

Micah 6
Malachi 3

NEW TESTAMENT

Having gifts that differ according to the grace given to us, let us use them:

If prophecy, in proportion to our faith; if service, in our serving; he who teaches, in his teaching;

He who exhorts, in his exhortation;

He who contributes, in liberality;

He who gives aid, with zeal;

He who does acts of mercy, with cheerfulness.

The point is this: he who sows sparingly will also reap sparingly, and he who sows bountifully will also reap bountifully.

Each one must do as he has made up his mind, not reluctantly or under compulsion,

For God loves a cheerful giver.

Let love be genuine.

Now the company of those who believed were of one heart and soul, and no one said that any of the things which he possessed was his own, but they had everything in common.

For as many as were possessors of lands or houses sold them, and brought the proceeds of what was sold and laid it at the apostles' feet; and distribution was made to each as any had need.

Romans 12
2 Corinthians 9
Acts 4

42 LOVE FOR ONE ANOTHER

OLD TESTAMENT

Give ear to my words, O LORD;
Hearken to the sound of my cry,
my King and my God,
for to thee do I pray.

O LORD, in the morning thou dost hear my voice;
in the morning I prepare a sacrifice for thee, and watch.

For thou art not a God who delights in wickedness;
evil may not sojourn with thee.

But I through the abundance of thy steadfast love
will enter thy house,
I will worship toward thy holy temple
in the fear of thee.

For thou dost bless the righteous, O Lord;
thou dost cover him with favor as with a shield.

Thou art my hiding-place and my shield;
I hope in thy word.

Depart from me, you evildoers,
that I may keep the commandments of my God.

Hear my voice in thy steadfast love;
O LORD, in thy justice preserve my life.

What man is there who desires life,
and covets many days, that he may enjoy good?

Happy is the man who takes refuge in the LORD.

Psalm 5
Psalm 119
Psalm 34

NEW TESTAMENT

For this is the message which you have heard from the beginning that we should love one another,

Beloved, let us love one another; for love is of God, and he who loves is born of God and knows God.

He who does not love does not know God; for God is love.

If any one says, "I love God," and hates his brother, he is a liar;

For he who does not love his brother whom he has seen, cannot love God whom he has not seen.

Do not love the world or the things in the world. If any one loves the world, love for the Father is not in him.

Do not wonder, brethren, that the world hates you.

We know that we have passed out of death into life, because we love the brethren. He who does not love remains in death.

Greater love has no man than this, that a man lay down his life for his friends.

A new commandment I give to you, that you love one another; even as I have loved you, that you also love one another.

1 John 2
1 John 3
1 John 4
John 13
John 15

GRATITUDE 43

OLD TESTAMENT

O give thanks to the LORD, for he is good;
for his steadfast love endures for ever!

Let the redeemed of the LORD say so,
whom he has redeemed from trouble.

Then they cried to the LORD in their trouble,
and he delivered them from their distress;

Let them thank the LORD for his steadfast love,
for his wonderful works to the sons of men!

For he satisfies him who is thirsty,
and the hungry he fills with good things.

Let them thank the LORD for his steadfast love,
for his wonderful works to the sons of men!

For he shatters the doors of bronze,
and cuts in two the bars of iron.

Let them thank the LORD for his steadfast love,
for his wonderful works to the sons of men!

And let them offer sacrifices of thanksgiving,
and tell of his deeds in songs of joy!

Whoever is wise, let him give heed to these things;
let men consider the steadfast love of the LORD.

Psalm 107

NEW TESTAMENT

And as he entered a village, he was met by ten lepers,

Who stood at a distance and lifted up their voices and said, "Jesus, Master, have mercy on us."

When he saw them he said to them, "Go and show yourselves to the priests."

And as they went they were cleansed.

Then one of them, when he saw that he was healed, turned back, praising God with a loud voice;

And he fell on his face at Jesus' feet, giving him thanks.

Now he was a Samaritan. Then said Jesus,

"Were not ten cleansed? Where are the nine? Was no one found to return and give praise to God except this foreigner?"

And he said to him, "Rise and go your way; your faith has made you well."

"Ask, and it will be given you; seek and you will find; knock, and it will be opened to you.

For every one who asks receives, and he who seeks finds, and to him who knocks it will be opened.

If you then, who are evil, know how to give good gifts to your children, how much more will your Father who is in heaven give good things to those who ask him?"

Luke 17
Matthew 7

44 ALL SAINTS

OLD TESTAMENT

May God be gracious to us and bless us
and make his face to shine upon us,

That thy way may be known upon earth,
thy saving power among all nations.

Let the peoples praise thee, O God;
let all the peoples praise thee!

Let the nations be glad and sing for joy,

For thou dost judge the peoples with equity
and guide the nations upon earth.

Let the peoples praise thee, O God;
let all the peoples praise thee!

The earth has yielded its increase;
God, our God, has blessed us.

God has blessed us;
let all the ends of the earth fear him!

"Fear not, for I have redeemed you;
I have called you by name, you are mine.

When you pass through the waters I will be with you;
and through the rivers, they shall not overwhelm you;

When you walk through fire you shall not be burned,
and the flame shall not consume you.

For I am the LORD your God,
the Holy One of Israel, your Savior.

Fear not, for I am with you."

Psalm 67
Isaiah 43

NEW TESTAMENT

Therefore, since we are surrounded by so great a cloud of witnesses,

Let us run with perseverance the race that is set before us, looking to Jesus the pioneer and perfecter of our faith.

For all who are led by the Spirit of God are sons of God.

The Spirit himself bearing witness with our spirit that we are children of God, and if children, then heirs, heirs of God and fellow heirs with Christ.

After this I looked, and behold, a great multitude which no man could number,

From every nation, from all tribes and peoples and tongues, standing before the throne and before the Lamb, clothed in white robes, with palm branches in their hands.

"These are they who have come out of the great tribulation; they have washed their robes and made them white in the blood of the Lamb.

Therefore are they before the throne of God.

They shall hunger no more, neither thirst any more;

For the Lamb in the midst of the throne will be their shepherd,
and he will guide them to springs of living water;
and God will wipe away every tear from their eyes."

Hebrews 12
Romans 8
Revelation 7

PEACE 45

OLD TESTAMENT

"Seek the LORD while he may be found,

Call upon him while he is near;

Let the wicked forsake his way,

And the unrighteous man his thoughts;

Let him return to the LORD, that he may have mercy on him,

And to our God, for he will abundantly pardon.

For my thoughts are not your thoughts,
neither are your ways my ways, says the LORD.

For as the heavens are higher than the earth,
so are my ways higher than your ways
and my thoughts than your thoughts."

"They shall beat their swords into plowshares,
and their spears into pruning hooks;
nation shall not lift up sword against nation,
neither shall they learn war any more;

But they shall sit every man under his vine and under his fig tree, and none shall make them afraid; for the mouth of the Lord of hosts has spoken."

"For behold, I create new heavens and a new earth;

But be glad and rejoice for ever in that which I create."

Isaiah 55
Micah 4
Isaiah 65

NEW TESTAMENT

And behold, a lawyer stood up to put him to the test, saying, "Teacher, what shall I do to inherit eternal life?"

And he answered, "You shall love the Lord your God with all your heart, and with all your soul, and with all your strength, and with all your mind; and your neighbor as yourself."

"You have heard that it was said, 'An eye for an eye and a tooth for a tooth.' But I say to you, Do not resist one who is evil.

But if any one strikes you on the right cheek, turn to him the other also."

"You have heard that it was said, 'You shall love your neighbor and hate your enemy.' But I say to you, Love your enemies and pray for those who persecute you,

So that you may be sons of your Father who is in heaven."

Then Jesus said to him, "Put your sword back into its place; for all who take the sword will perish by the sword."

"If any man would come after me, let him deny himself and take up his cross and follow me.

For what will it profit a man, if he gains the whole world and forfeits his life?

For whoever would save his life will lose it, and whoever loses his life for my sake will find it."

Luke 10
Matthew 5
Matthew 26
Matthew 16

46 THANKSGIVING

OLD TESTAMENT

Praise the LORD!
For it is good to sing praises to our God;

For he is gracious, and a song of praise is seemly.

The LORD builds up Jerusalem;
he gathers the outcasts of Israel.

**He heals the brokenhearted,
and binds up their wounds.**

He determines the number of the stars,
he gives to all of them their names.

**Great is our LORD, and abundant in power;
his understanding is beyond measure.**

Praise the LORD!
For it is good to sing praises to our God;

**Sing to the LORD with thanksgiving;
make melody to our God upon the lyre!**

Praise the LORD, O Jerusalem!
Praise your God, O Zion!

**For he strengthens the bars of your gates;
he blesses your sons within you.**

He makes peace in your borders;
he fills you with the finest of the wheat.

**He has not dealt thus with any other nation; . . .
Praise the Lord!**

Psalm 147

NEW TESTAMENT

Rejoice always, pray constantly, give thanks in all circumstances; for this is the will of God in Christ Jesus for you.

Addressing one another in psalms and hymns and spiritual songs, singing and making melody to the Lord with all your heart,

Always and for everything giving thanks in the name of our Lord Jesus Christ to God the Father.

We give thanks to God always for you all, constantly mentioning you in our prayers,

Remembering before our God and Father your work of faith and labor of love and steadfastness of hope in our Lord Jesus Christ.

Thanks be to God for his inexpressible gift!

Thanks be to God, who gives us the victory through our Lord Jesus Christ.

Let the peace of Christ rule in your hearts. And be thankful.

Let the word of Christ dwell in you richly, as you teach and admonish one another in all wisdom, and as you sing psalms and hymns and spiritual songs with thankfulness in your hearts to God.

And whatever you do, in word or deed, do everything in the name of the Lord Jesus, giving thanks to God the Father through him.

1 Thessalonians 1
1 Thessalonians 5
Colossians 3
Ephesians 5
1 Corinthians 15
2 Corinthians 9

HOME MISSIONS 47

OLD TESTAMENT

In the year that King Uzziah died I saw the Lord sitting upon a throne, high and lifted up; and his train filled the temple.

Above him stood the seraphim; each had six wings:

With two he covered his face, and with two he covered his feet, and with two he flew.

And one called to another and said:

"Holy, holy, holy is the LORD of hosts;
the whole earth is full of his glory."

And I said: "Woe is me! For I am lost; for I am a man of unclean lips, and I dwell in the midst of a people of unclean lips;

For my eyes have seen the King, the LORD of hosts!"

Then flew one of the seraphim to me, having in his hand a burning coal which he had taken with tongs from the altar.

And he touched my mouth, and said: "Behold, this has touched your lips; your guilt is taken away, and your sin forgiven."

And I heard the voice of the Lord saying, "Whom shall I send, and who will go for us?"

Then I said, "Here I am! Send me."

Isaiah 6

NEW TESTAMENT

But he, desiring to justify himself, said to Jesus, "And who is my neighbor?"

Unison

Jesus replied, "A man was going down from Jerusalem to Jericho, and he fell among robbers, who stripped him and beat him, and departed, leaving him half-dead. Now by chance a priest was going down that road; and when he saw him he passed by on the other side. So likewise a Levite, when he came to the place and saw him, passed by on the other side. But a Samaritan, as he journeyed, came to where he was; and when he saw him, he had compassion, and went to him and bound up his wounds, pouring on oil and wine; then he set him on his own beast and brought him to an inn, and took care of him. And the next day he took out two denarii and gave them to the innkeeper, saying, 'Take care of him; and whatever more you spend, I will repay you when I come back.'

Which of these three, do you think, proved neighbor to the man who fell among the robbers?"

He said, "The one who showed mercy on him."

Unison

And Jesus said to him, "Go and do likewise."

"You shall love the Lord your God with all your heart, and with all your soul, and with all your strength, and with all your mind; and your neighbor as yourself."

Luke 10

48 GOD'S WORD

OLD TESTAMENT

Oh, how I love thy law!
It is my meditation all the day.
How sweet are thy words to my taste,
sweeter than honey to my mouth!

Through thy precepts I get understanding;
therefore I hate every false way.

Thy word is a lamp to my feet
and a light to my path.

Thy testimonies are my heritage for ever;
yea, they are the joy of my heart.

Thou hast multiplied, O LORD my God,
thy wondrous deeds and thy thoughts toward us;
none can compare with thee!

Were I to proclaim and tell of them,
they would be more than can be numbered.

I have not hid thy saving help within my heart,
I have spoken of thy faithfulness and thy salvation;

I have not concealed thy steadfast love and thy faithfulness
from the great congregation.

Do not thou, O LORD, withhold
thy mercy from me,
let thy steadfast love and thy faithfulness
ever preserve me!

Let the words of my mouth and the meditation of my heart
be acceptable in thy sight,
O LORD, my rock and my redeemer.

Psalm 19
Psalm 40
Psalm 119

NEW TESTAMENT

I charge you in the presence of God and of Christ Jesus who is to judge the living and the dead, and by his appearing and his kingdom: preach the word,

Be urgent in season and out of season, convince, rebuke, and exhort, be unfailing in patience and in teaching.

For the time is coming when people will not endure sound teaching, but having itching ears they will accumulate for themselves teachers to suit their own likings,

And will turn away from listening to the truth and wander into myths.

As for you, always be steady, endure suffering,

Do the work of an evangelist, fulfil your ministry.

All scripture is inspired by God and profitable for teaching, for reproof, for correction, and for training in righteousness,

That the man of God may be complete, equipped for every good work.

I have fought the good fight, I have finished the race, I have kept the faith.

Henceforth there is laid up for me the crown of righteousness, which the Lord, the righteous judge, will award to me on that Day, and not only to me but also to all who have loved his appearing.

2 Timothy 4
2 Timothy 3

THE ADVENT OF JESUS 49

OLD TESTAMENT

"Behold, the days are coming, says the LORD, when I will raise up for David a righteous Branch,"

And the Spirit of the LORD shall rest upon him,
the spirit of wisdom and understanding,
the spirit of counsel and might,
the spirit of knowledge and the fear of the LORD.

And his delight shall be in the fear of the LORD.

He shall not judge by what his eyes see,
or decide by what his ears hear;

But with righteousness he shall judge the poor,
and decide with equity for the meek of the earth;

Righteousness shall be the girdle of his waist,
and faithfulness the girdle of his loins.

Behold my servant, whom I uphold,
my chosen, in whom my soul delights;

I have put my spirit upon him,
he will bring forth justice to the nations.

He will faithfully bring forth justice.

He will not fail or be discouraged till he has established justice in the earth;
and the coastlands wait for his law.

Jeremiah 23
Isaiah 11
Isaiah 42

NEW TESTAMENT

In the sixth month the angel Gabriel was sent from God to a city of Galilee named Nazareth,

And he came to her and said, "Hail, O favored one, the Lord is with you!" "Do not be afraid, Mary, for you have found favor with God.

And behold, you will conceive and bear a son, and you shall call his name Jesus.

He will be great, and will be called the Son of the Most High;

And of his kingdom there will be no end."

And Mary said,
"My soul magnifies the Lord,
and my spirit rejoices in God my Savior,
for he has regarded the low estate of his handmaiden.

For behold, henceforth all generations will call me blessed;

For he who is mighty has done great things for me,
and holy is his name.

He has shown strength with his arm,
and exalted those of low degree;

He has helped his servant Israel,
in remembrance of his mercy,
as he spoke to our fathers,
to Abraham and to his posterity for ever."

Luke 1

50 CHRISTMAS

OLD TESTAMENT

But you, O Bethlehem Ephrathah,
who are little to be among the clans of Judah,
from you shall come forth for me one who is to be ruler in Israel,

Whose origin is from of old,
from ancient days.

And he shall stand and feed his flock in the strength of the LORD,
in the majesty of the name of the LORD his God.

And they shall dwell secure, for now he shall be great
to the ends of the earth.
And this shall be peace,

For to us a child is born,
to us a son is given;
and the government will be upon his shoulder,

And his name will be called
"Wonderful Counselor, Mighty God,
Everlasting Father, Prince of Peace."

Of the increase of his government and of peace
there will be no end,
upon the throne of David, and over his kingdom,

To establish it, and to uphold it
with justice and with righteousness
from this time forth and for evermore.

Make a joyful noise to the LORD, all the lands!

Enter his gates with thanksgiving,
and his courts with praise!
Give thanks to him, bless his name!

Micah 5
Isaiah 9
Psalm 100

NEW TESTAMENT

Now when Jesus was born in Bethlehem of Judea in the days of Herod the king,

Behold, wise men from the East came to Jerusalem, saying, "Where is he who has been born king of the Jews? For we have seen his star in the East, and have come to worship him."

When Herod the king heard this, he was troubled, and all Jerusalem with him;

And assembling all the chief priests and scribes of the people, he inquired of them where the Christ was to be born.

They told him, "In Bethlehem of Judea;

For so it is written by the prophet:
'And you, O Bethlehem, in the land of Judah,
are by no means least among the rulers of Judah;

For from you shall come a ruler who will govern my people Israel.' "

And going into the house they saw the child with Mary his mother, and they fell down and worshiped him.

Then, opening their treasures, they offered him gifts, gold and frankincense and myrrh.

"Blessed be the Lord God of Israel, for he has visited and redeemed his people."

Matthew 2
Luke 1

THE SAVIOR OF THE WORLD 51

OLD TESTAMENT

For to us a child is born,
to us a son is given;
and the government will be upon his shoulder,

And his name will be called "Wonderful Counselor, Mighty God, Everlasting Father, Prince of Peace."

In his days may righteousness flourish,
and peace abound, till the moon be no more!

May all kings fall down before him, all nations serve him!

For he delivers the needy when he calls,
the poor and him who has no helper.

**He has pity on the weak and the needy,
and saves the lives of the needy.
From oppression and violence he redeems their life;**

May prayer be made for him continually,
and blessings invoked for him all the day!

**May his name endure for ever,
his fame continue as long as the sun!**

May men bless themselves by him,
all nations call him blessed!

**Blessed be the LORD, the God of Israel,
who alone does wondrous things.
Blessed be his glorious name for ever;
may his glory fill the whole earth!**

Isaiah 9
Psalm 72

NEW TESTAMENT

"He who is mighty has done great things for me,
and holy is his name."

"You shall call his name Jesus, for he will save his people from their sins."

As Moses lifted up the serpent in the wilderness, so must the Son of man be lifted up,

That whoever believes in him may have eternal life.

For God sent the Son into the world, not to condemn the world, but that the world might be saved through him.

For God so loved the world that he gave his only Son, that whoever believes in him should not perish but have eternal life.

"The thief comes only to steal and kill and destroy; I came that they may have life, and have it abundantly."

"For the Son of man came to seek and to save the lost."

"Thus it is written, that the Christ should suffer and on the third day rise from the dead,

And that repentance and forgiveness of sins should be preached in his name to all nations, beginning from Jerusalem."

Matthew 1
Luke 1
John 3
John 10
Luke 19
Luke 24

52 THE BLESSED LIFE

OLD TESTAMENT

Blessed are those whose way is blameless,
who walk in the law of the LORD!

Blessed are those who keep his testimonies,
who seek him with their whole heart,

With my whole heart I seek thee;
let me not wander from thy commandments!

O that my ways may be steadfast in keeping thy statutes!
Then I shall not be put to shame,
having my eyes fixed on all thy commandments.

I will meditate on thy precepts,
and fix my eyes on thy ways.

I will delight in thy statutes;
I will not forget thy word.

Teach me, O LORD, the way of thy statutes;
and I will keep it to the end.

Give me understanding, that I may keep thy law
and observe it with my whole heart.

Let thy steadfast love come to me, O LORD,
thy salvation according to thy promise;

Then shall I have an answer for those who taunt me,
for I trust in thy word.
Great peace have those who love thy law;
nothing can make them stumble.

Psalm 119

NEW TESTAMENT

Now those who were scattered went about preaching the word.

Philip went down to a city of Samaria, and proclaimed to them the Christ.

And the multitudes with one accord gave heed to what was said by Philip.

For unclean spirits came out of many; and many who were paralyzed or lame were healed.

So there was much joy in that city.

Make every effort to supplement your faith with virtue, and virtue with knowledge,

And knowledge with self-control, and self-control with steadfastness, and steadfastness with godliness,

And godliness with brotherly affection, and brotherly affection with love.

For if these things are yours and abound, they keep you from being ineffective or unfruitful in the knowledge of our Lord Jesus Christ.

For whoever lacks these things is blind and shortsighted and has forgotten that he was cleansed from his old sins.

Therefore, brethren, be the more zealous to confirm your call and election, for if you do this you will never fall;

So there will be richly provided for you an entrance into the eternal kingdom of our Lord and Savior Jesus Christ.

Acts 8
2 Peter 1

Calls to Worship

53

OLD TESTAMENT

The LORD is in his holy temple;
let all the earth keep silence befor him.

Habakkuk 2:20

"How awesome is this place! This is none other than the house of God, and this is the gate of heaven."

Genesis 28:17

54

O come, let us sing to the LORD;
let us make a joyful noise to the rock of our salvation!
Let us come into his presence with thanksgiving;
let us make a joyful noise to him with songs of praise!
O come, let us worship and bow down,
let us kneel before the LORD, our Maker!
For he is our God,
and we are the people of his pasture,
and the sheep of his hand.

Psalm 95:1-2, 6-7

55

Make a joyful noise to the LORD, all the lands!
Serve the LORD with gladness!
Come into his presence with singing!
Know that the LORD is God!
It is he that made us, and we are his;
we are his people, and the sheep of his pasture.

Psalm 100:1-2

56

Enter his gates with thanksgiving,
and his courts with praise!
Give thanks to him, bless his name!
For the LORD is good;
his steadfast love endures for ever,
and his faithfulness to all generations.

Psalm 100:4-5

57

I was glad when they said to me,
"Let us go to the house of the LORD!"
Our feet have been standing
within your gates, O Jerusalem!
Jerusalem, built as a city
which is bound firmly together,
to which the tribes go up,
the tribes of the LORD,
to give thanks to the name of the LORD.

Psalm 122:1-4

58

Ascribe to the LORD the glory of his name;
worship the LORD in holy array.

Psalm 29:2

Every day I will bless thee,
and praise thy name for ever and ever.

Psalm 145:2

59

This is the day which the LORD has made;
let us rejoice and be glad in it.

Psalm 118:24

60

"Seek the LORD while he may be found,
call upon him while he is near;
let the wicked forsake his way,
and the unrighteous man his thoughts;
let him return to the LORD, that he may have mercy on him,
and to our God, for he will abundantly pardon."

Isaiah 55:6-7

NEW TESTAMENT

61

"Come to me, all who labor and are heavy-laden, and I will give you rest. Take my yoke upon you, and learn from me; for I am gentle and lowly in heart, and you will find rest for your souls. For my yoke is easy, and my burden is light."

Matthew 11:28-30

62

But the hour is coming, and now is, when the true worshipers will worship the Father in spirit and truth, for such the Father seeks to worship him. God is spirit, and those who worship him must worship in spirit and truth.

John 4:23-24

63

The Spirit and the Bride say, "Come." And let him who hears say, "Come." And let him who is thirsty come, let him who desires take the water of life without price.

Revelation 22:17

Invocations

64

Almighty God, before whom all hearts are open, all desires known, and from whom no secrets are hid; cleanse the thoughts of our hearts by the inspiration of the Holy Spirit, that we may perfectly love thee and worthily magnify thy holy name; through Christ our Lord. Amen.

Gregorian Sacramentary, 7th Century

65

Almighty God, from whom every good prayer cometh, and who pourest out on all who desire it the spirit of grace and supplication; deliver us, when we draw nigh to thee, from coldness of heart and wanderings of mind, that with steadfast thoughts and kindled affections we may worship thee in spirit and in truth; through Jesus Christ our Lord. Amen.

William Bright

66

Almighty and everlasting God, in whom we live and move and have our being, who hast created us for thyself, so that our hearts are restless, till they find rest in thee; grant us purity of heart and strength of purpose so that no selfish passion may hinder us from knowing thy will, and no weakness from doing it. In thy light may we see life clearly and in thy service find perfect freedom; for thy mercy's sake. Amen.

Edward Caird (adapted)

67

Almighty God, who hast given us grace at this time with one accord to make our common supplications to thee, and dost promise that when two or three are gathered together in thy name thou wilt grant their requests; fulfill now, O Lord, the desires and petitions of thy servants, as may be most expedient for them; granting us in this world knowledge of thy truth, and in the world to come life everlasting. Amen.

St. Chrysostom

68

Lord of life and love and beauty, help us to worship thee in the beauty of holiness, that some beauty of holiness may appear in us. Quiet our souls before thee with the stillness of a wise trust, and a sense of being not in our hands, but in thine. Lift us above dark moods and the shadows of sin, that we may begin today, from the height of a prayer, to live as becomes sons and daughters of the Most High. Amen.

Newton's "Altar Stairs"

69

O Lord, renew our spirits and draw our hearts to thyself, that our work may not be in us a burden but a delight; and give us such a mighty love for thee as may sweeten our obedience. Oh, let us not serve thee with the spirit of bondage, as slaves, but with the cheerfulness and gladness of children, delighting ourselves in thee and rejoicing in thy work. Amen.

Benjamin Jencks

70

From the night our spirit awakens to thee, O God, for thy precepts are a light to us. Teach us thy righteousness, thy commandments, and thy judgments. Enlighten the eyes of our mind, that we sleep not in sin to death. Cause to rise upon us the sun of righteousness, and drive away from our hearts all dark and evil imaginings. Guard our life from reproach; guide our steps in the way of peace. Grant us to behold with joyfulness the dawning of this day, and at eventide to send up to thee our prayer of thanksgiving. Amen.

Ancient Collect

71

O God of peace, who hast taught us that in returning and rest we shall be saved, in quietness and confidence shall be our strength; by the might of thy spirit lift us, we pray thee, to thy presence, where we may be still and know that thou art God; through Jesus Christ our Lord. Amen.

Book of Common Prayer

72

O God, author of eternal light, lead us in our worshiping this day; that our lips may praise thee, our lives may bless thee, our meditations may glorify thee; through Jesus Christ our Lord. Amen.

Sarum Breviary, 11th Century (adapted)

Baptism

73

Then Jesus came from Galilee to the Jordan to John, to be baptized by him. John would have prevented him, saying, "I need to be baptized by you, and do you come to me?"

But Jesus answered him, "Let it be so now; for thus it is fitting for us to fulfil all righteousness." Then he consented.

And when Jesus was baptized, he went up immediately from the water, and behold, the heavens were opened and he saw the Spirit of God descending like a dove, and alighting on him;

And lo, a voice from heaven, saying, "This is my beloved Son, with whom I am well pleased."

Matthew 3:13-17

74

Jesus came and said to them, "All authority in heaven and on earth has been given to me.

Go therefore and make disciples of all nations, baptizing them in the name of the Father and of the Son and of the Holy Spirit,

Teaching them to observe all that I have commanded you;

And lo, I am with you always, to the close of the age."

Matthew 28:18-20

75

Do you not know that all of us who have been baptized into Christ Jesus were baptized into his death?

We were buried therefore with him by baptism into death,

So that as Christ was raised from the dead by the glory of the Father, we too might walk in newness of life.

For if we have been united with him in a death like his, we shall certainly be united with him in a resurrection like his.

We know that our old self was crucified with him so that the sinful body might be destroyed, and we might no longer be enslaved to sin.

For he who has died is freed from sin.

But if we have died with Christ, we believe that we shall also live with him.

For we know that Christ being raised from the dead will never die again; death no longer has dominion over him.

Romans 6:3-9

76

And as they went along the road they came to some water, and the eunuch said, "See, here is water! What is to prevent my being baptized?"

And he commanded the chariot to stop, and they both went down into the water, Philip and the eunuch, and he baptized him.

And when they came up out of the water, the Spirit of the Lord caught up Philip;

And the eunuch saw him no more, and went on his way rejoicing.

Acts 8:36-39

77

For in Christ Jesus you are all sons of God, through faith.

For as many of you as were baptized into Christ have put on Christ.

For you are all one in Christ Jesus.

For by one Spirit we were all baptized into one body.

Galatians 3:26-28b
1 Corinthians 12:13a

78

If then you have been raised with Christ, seek the things that are above, where Christ is, seated at the right hand of God.

Set your minds on things that are above, not on things that are on earth.

For you have died, and your life is hid with Christ in God.

When Christ who is our life appears, then you also will appear with him in glory.

Colossians 3:1-4

79

THE INSTITUTION

And when the hour came, he sat at table, and the apostles with him.

And he said to them, "I have earnestly desired to eat this passover with you before I suffer; for I tell you I shall not eat it until it is fulfilled in the kingdom of God."

And he took bread, and when he had given thanks he broke it and gave it to them, saying, "This is my body, which is given for you. Do this in remembrance of me."

And likewise the cup after supper, saying, "This cup which is poured out for you is the new covenant in my blood. Do this in remembrance of me."

Luke 22:14-20

80

SAINT PAUL

For I received from the Lord what I also delivered to you, that the Lord Jesus on the night when he was betrayed took bread,

And when he had given thanks, he broke it, and said, "This is my body which is for you.

Do this in remembrance of me."

In the same way also the cup, after supper,

Saying, "This cup is the new covenant in my blood. Do this, as often as you drink it, in remembrance of me."

For as often as you eat this bread and drink the cup, you proclaim the Lord's death until he comes.

1 Corinthians 11:23-28

81

IN CHRISTIAN LIFE

Jesus said to them, "I am the bread of life; he who comes to me shall not hunger, and he who believes in me shall never thirst."

"I am the living bread which came down from heaven; if any one eats of this bread, he will live for ever; and the bread which I shall give for the life of the world is my flesh."

"He who eats my flesh and drinks my blood abides in me, and I in him.

As the living Father sent me, and I live because of the Father, so he who eats me will live because of me."

John 6:35, 51, 56-57

82

"I am the bread of life. If any one eats of this bread, he will live for ever; and the bread which I shall give for the life of the world is my flesh."

John 6:48, 51

"If any one thirst, let him come to me and drink."

John 7:37

83

"Truly, truly, I say to you, unless a grain of wheat falls into the earth and dies, it remains alone; but if it dies, it bears much fruit.

He who loves his life loses it, and he who hates his life in this world will keep it for eternal life."

John 12:24-25

84

"I am the vine, you are the branches. As the branch cannot bear fruit by itself, unless it abides in the vine, neither can you, unless you abide in me.

He who abides in me, and I in him, he it is that bears much fruit, for apart from me you can do nothing."

John 15:4-5

Benedictions

85

"The LORD bless you and keep you:
The LORD make his face to shine upon you, and be gracious to you:
The LORD lift up his countenance upon you, and give you peace."

Numbers 6:24-26

86

May God be gracious to us and bless us
and make his face to shine upon us,
that thy way may be known upon earth,
thy saving power among all nations.

Psalm 67:1-2

87

Let the words of my mouth and the meditation of my heart
be acceptable in thy sight,
O LORD, my rock and my redeemer.

Psalm 19:14

88

The grace of the Lord Jesus Christ and the love of God and the fellowship of the Holy Spirit be with you all.

2 Corinthians 13:14

89

Now to him who is able to keep you from falling and to present you without blemish before the presence of his glory with rejoicing, to the only God, our Savior through Jesus Christ our Lord, be glory, majesty, dominion, and authority, before all time and now and for ever. Amen.

Jude 1:24-25

90

To the King of ages, immortal, invisible, the only God, be honor and glory for ever and ever. Amen.

1 Timothy 1:17

91

Now may the God of peace who brought again from the dead our Lord Jesus, the great shepherd of the sheep, by the blood of the eternal covenant, equip you with everything good that you may do his will, working in you that which is pleasing in his sight, through Jesus Christ; to whom be glory for ever and ever. Amen.

Hebrews 13:20-21

92

The peace of God, which passes all understanding, will keep your hearts and your minds in Christ Jesus.

Philippians 4:7

93

Now to him who by the power at work within us is able to do far more abundantly than all that we ask or think, to him be glory in the church and in Christ Jesus to all generations, for ever and ever. Amen.

Ephesians 3:20-21

CHRISTIAN WORSHIP

A HYMNAL

MUSIC SECTION

General Classification of Hymns

I. WORSHIP

	Hymn		*Hymn*
Adoration and Praise	94-113	Morning	132-137
Opening	114-124	Evening	138-150
Closing	125-131		

II. GOD THE FATHER

Majesty and Power	151-159	Providence and Care	165-171
Creator and Ruler	160-164	Love and Mercy	172-181

III. JESUS CHRIST, THE LORD

Advent and Nativity	182-206	Resurrection	238-248
Life and Ministry	207-220	The Everliving Christ	249-258
Suffering and Death	221-237	Praise to Christ	259-269

IV. THE HOLY SPIRIT

270-276

V. THE CHRISTIAN LIFE

The Call of Christ	277-287	Conflict and Courage	358-378
Acceptance of Christ	288-299	Love and Gratitude	379-392
Consecration and Service	300-316	Trust and Confidence	393-411
Aspiration and Vision	317-323	Joy and Peace	412-420
Prayer and Intercession	324-346	Stewardship	421-422
Faith and Hope	347-357		

VI. THE CHURCH OF THE LIVING GOD

The Church	423-433	The Lord's Supper	451-469
The Bible	434-442	The Ministry	470-474
The Lord's Day	443-448	Christian Fellowship	475-485
Baptism	449-450		

VII. THE KINGDOM OF GOD AND CHRISTIAN SOCIETY

Social Aspiration and Service	486-505	Our Nation	541-551
Brotherhood	506-522	World Friendship and Peace	552-567
World Missions	523-540		

VIII. THE LIFE ETERNAL

568-582

IX. SPECIAL SEASONS AND SERVICES

The Changing Year	583-592	Mother's Day	604
Thanksgiving	593-598	Dedications	605-606
The Home	599-602	School and College	607-608
Memorial Day	603	Travelers	609-610

RESPONSES

Doxology and Glorias	611-614	Offertory	634-638
Opening	615-624	Closing	639-644
After Prayer	625-633	Amens	645-650

CHRISTIAN WORSHIP

A Hymnal

ADORATION AND PRAISE

O Worship the King

LYONS. 10. 10. 11. 11.

94

ROBERT GRANT, 1785-1838

With dignity but joyously

J. MICHAEL HAYDN, 1770

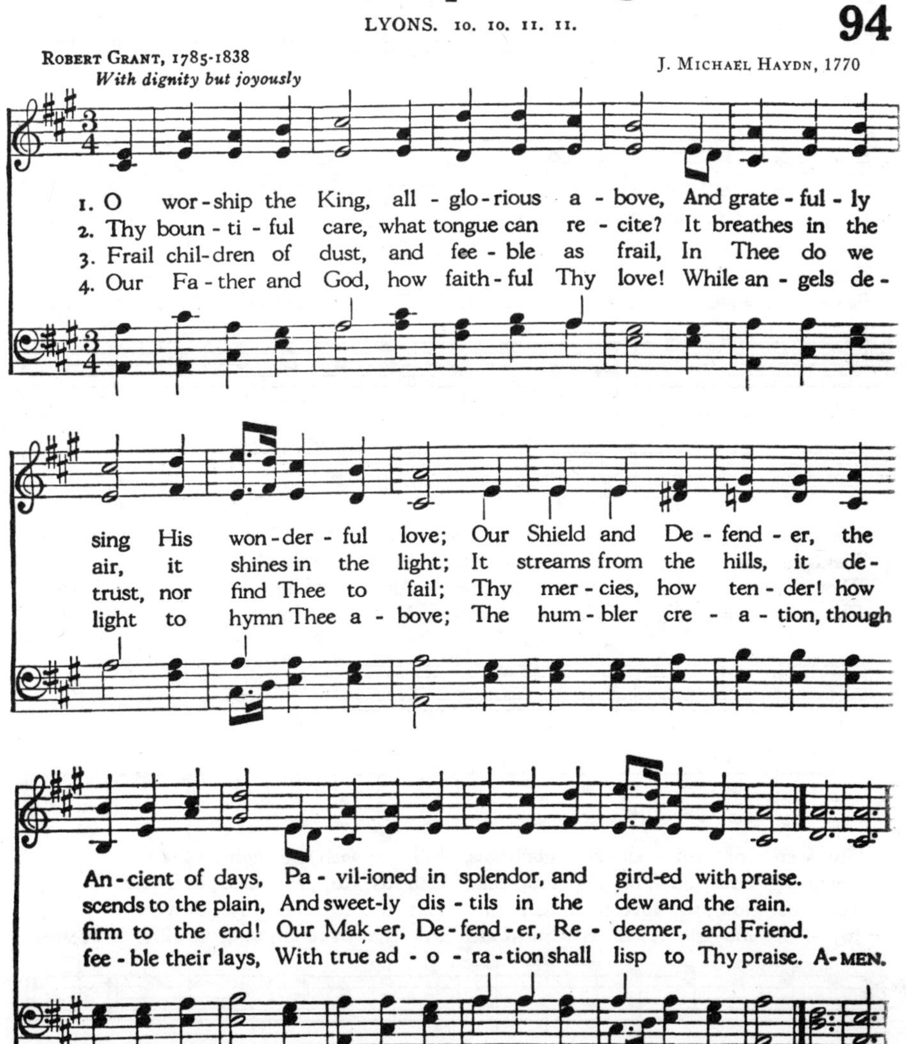

1. O wor-ship the King, all-glo-rious a-bove, And grate-ful-ly sing His won-der-ful love; Our Shield and De-fend-er, the An-cient of days, Pa-vil-ioned in splendor, and gird-ed with praise.
2. Thy boun-ti-ful care, what tongue can re-cite? It breathes in the air, it shines in the light; It streams from the hills, it de-scends to the plain, And sweet-ly dis-tils in the dew and the rain.
3. Frail chil-dren of dust, and fee-ble as frail, In Thee do we trust, nor find Thee to fail; Thy mer-cies, how ten-der! how firm to the end! Our Mak-er, De-fend-er, Re-deemer, and Friend.
4. Our Fa-ther and God, how faith-ful Thy love! While an-gels de-light to hymn Thee a-bove; The hum-bler cre-a-tion, though fee-ble their lays, With true ad-o-ra-tion shall lisp to Thy praise. A-MEN.

Joyful, Joyful, We Adore Thee

95

HYMN TO JOY. 8. 7. 8. 7. D.

HENRY VAN DYKE, 1852-1933 | LUDWIG VAN BEETHOVEN, 1770-1827

With exultation

1. Joy - ful, joy - ful, we a - dore Thee, God of glo - ry, Lord of love;
2. All Thy works with joy sur-round Thee, Earth and heaven re - flect Thy rays,
3. Thou art giv - ing and for - giv - ing, Ev - er bless - ing, ev - er blest,
4. Mor- tals, join the hap - py cho - rus Which the morn-ing stars be - gan;

Hearts un - fold like flowers be - fore Thee, Open-ing to the sun a - bove.
Stars and an - gels sing a-round Thee, Cen - ter of un - bro - ken praise.
Well - spring of the joy of liv - ing, O - cean depth of hap - py rest!
Fa - ther love is reign - ing o'er us, Broth-er love binds man to man.

Melt the clouds of sin and sad-ness, Drive the dark of doubt a - way;
Field and for - est, vale and mountain, Flow - ery meadow, flash - ing sea,
Thou our Fa - ther, Christ our Broth-er, All who live in love are Thine;
Ev - er sing - ing, march we on - ward, Vic - tors in the midst of strife,

Giv - er of im - mor - tal glad-ness, Fill us with the light of day.
Chant-ing bird and flow - ing foun-tain, Call us to re - joice in Thee.
Teach us how to love each oth - er, Lift us to the Joy di- vine.
Joy - ful mu - sic leads us Sun-ward In the tri-umph song of life. A-MEN.

Men and Children Everywhere

ROCK OF AGES. 7. 7. 7. 7. 5. 7. with Refrain.

96

JOHN J. MOMENT

Ancient Hebrew melody; arr. by CHARLOTTE MATHEWSON LOCKWOOD

Majestically
1. Men and chil-dren ev-ery-where, With sweet mu-sic fill the air!
2. Morn-ing, eve-ning, bless His name, Skies with crim-son clouds a-flame,
3. Storm and flood and o-cean's roar, Break-ers crash-ing on the shore,
Na-tions, come, your voi-ces raise To the Lord in hymns of praise!
Rain-bow arch, His cove-nant sign, Countless stars by night that shine!
Wa-ter-falls that nev-er sleep, Towering moun-tain, can-yon deep,
Join the an-gel song, All the worlds to Him be-long!
Through His far do-main, Love is King where He doth reign!
Tell ye forth His might, Lord of life and truth and right!
REFRAIN
Ho-ly, ho-ly, To our God all glo-ry be! A-MEN.

Holy, Holy, Holy Is the Lord

97

SABAOTH. 9. 10. 9. D. with Refrain.

FANNY J. CROSBY, 1823–1915

WILLIAM B. BRADBURY, 1816–1868

Joyously

1. Ho - ly, ho - ly ho - ly is the Lord! Sing, O ye peo - ple,
2. Praise Him, praise Him! shout a - loud for joy, Watchman of Zi - on,
3. King e - ter - nal, bless - ed be His name! So may His chil - dren
glad - ly a - dore Him; Let the moun-tains trem - ble at His word;
her - ald the sto - ry; Sin and death His king-dom shall de - stroy;
glad - ly a - dore Him; When in heav'n we join the hap - py strain,
Let the hills be joy - ful be - fore Him: Might - y in wis - dom,
All the earth shall sing of His glo - ry: Praise Him, ye an - gels,
When we cast our bright crowns be - fore Him: There in His like - ness
bound - less in mer - cy, Great is Je - ho - vah, King o - ver all.
ye who be - hold Him, Robed in His splen - dor, match - less, di - vine.
joy - ful a - wak - ing, There we shall see Him, there we shall sing:
CHORUS
Ho - ly, ho - ly, ho - ly is the Lord! Let the hills be joy - ful be - fore Him. A - MEN.

Praise to the Lord, the Almighty

LOBE DEN HERREN. 14. 14. 4. 7. 8.

98

JOACHIM NEANDER, 1650–1680
Tr. by CATHERINE WINKWORTH, 1829–1878

STRALSUND GESANGBUCH, 1665
Arr. in PRAXIS PIETATIS MELICA, 1668

Majestically

1. Praise to the Lord, the Al - might - y, the King of cre - a - tion!
O my soul, praise Him, for He is thy health and sal - va - tion!
All ye who hear, Now to His tem - ple draw near;
Join me in glad ad - o - ra - - tion!

2. Praise to the Lord, who o'er all things so won-drous - ly reign - eth,
Shield-eth thee un - der His wings, yea, so gen - tly sus - tain - eth!
Hast thou not seen How thy de - sires e'er have been
Grant - ed in what He or - dain - eth?

3. Praise to the Lord, who doth pros - per thy work and de - fend thee;
Sure - ly His good - ness and mer - cy here dai - ly at - tend thee.
Pon - der a - new What the Al - might - y can do,
If with His love He be - friend thee.

A - MEN.

Ancient of Days, Who Sittest Throned

99

ANCIENT OF DAYS. 11. 10. 11. 10.

WILLIAM C. DOANE, 1832-1913
Stanza 4, alt.

J. ALBERT JEFFERY, 1854-1929

With marked rhythm

1. An - cient of Days, who sit - test throned in glo - ry,
2. O Ho - ly Fa - ther, who hast led Thy chil - dren
3. O Ho - ly Je - sus, Prince of Peace and Sav - iour,
4. O Ho - ly Spir - it, Com - fort - er, Light Giv - er,

To Thee all knees are bent, all voic - es pray;
In all the a - ges, with the fire and cloud,
To Thee we owe the peace that still pre - vails,
Shine in our hearts with lib - er - at - ing power;

Thy love has blessed the wide world's won - drous sto - ry
Through seas dry shod, through wea - ry wastes be - wil - dering;
Still - ing the rude wills of men's wild be - ha - vior,
From haunt - ing dark - ness of the mind de - liv - er,

With light and life since E - den's dawn - ing day.
To Thee in rev - erent love, our hearts are bowed.
And calm - ing pas - sion's fierce and storm - y gales.
Grant truth's in - creas - ing ra - diance from this hour. A - MEN.

Glory Be to God on High

GWALCHMAI. 7. 4. 7. 4. D.

100

THEODORE C. WILLIAMS, 1855-1915

Welsh melody
Arr. by J. D. JONES, 1827–1879

With dignity

1. Glo - ry be to God on high, Al - le - lu - ia!
2. Crea-tures of the field and flood, Al - le - lu - ia!
3. Stars that have no voice to sing Al - le - lu - ia!

Let the whole cre - a - tion cry Al - le - lu - ia!
Earth and sea cry "God is good," Al - le - lu - ia!
Give their glo - ry to our King, Al - le - lu - ia!

Peace and bless - ing He has given, Al - le - lu - ia!
Toil - ing pil - grims raise the song, Al - le - lu - ia!
Si - lent powers and an - gels' song, Al - le - lu - ia!

Earth re - peat the songs of heaven, Al - le - lu - ia!
Saints in light the strain pro - long, Al - le - lu - ia!
All un - to our God be - long, Al - le - lu - ia! A - MEN.

Angel Voices, Ever Singing

101
ANGEL VOICES. 8. 5. 8. 5. 8. 4. 3.
Francis Pott, 1832-1909
Arthur S. Sullivan, 1842-1900
Joyfully
1. An - gel voic - es, ev - er sing - ing Round Thy throne of light,
2. Thou who art be - yond the far - thest Mor - tal eye can scan,
3. Yea, we know that Thou re - joic - est O'er each work of Thine;
4. Here, great God, to - day we of - fer Of Thine own to Thee;
An - gel harps for ev - er ring - ing, Rest not day nor night;
Can it be that Thou re - gard - est Songs of sin - ful man?
Thou didst ears and hands and voic - es For Thy praise de - sign;
And for Thine ac - cept - ance prof - fer, All un - wor - thi - ly,
Thou-sands on - ly live to bless Thee, And con - fess Thee Lord of might.
Can we feel that Thou art near us And wilt hear us? Yea, we can.
Crafts-man's art and mu - sic's meas-ure For Thy pleas-ure All com-bine.
Hearts and minds, and hands and voices, In our choic - est Mel - o - dy. A - MEN.
Father, We Praise Thee, Now the Night Is Over
102
CHRISTE SANCTORUM. 11. 11. 11. 5.
Gregory the Great, 540-604
Tr. by Percy Dearmer, 1867-1936
Melody from La Feillée's
Méthode du plain-chant, 1808
In moderate time
1. Fa - ther, we praise Thee, now the night is o - ver; Ac - tive and
2. Mon - arch of all things, fit us for Thy man - sions; Ban - ish our
3. All - ho - ly Fa - ther, Son and e - qual Spir - it, Trin - i - ty

watch-ful, stand we all be-fore Thee; Sing-ing, we of-fer
weak-ness, health and whole-ness send-ing; Bring us to heav-en,
bless-ed, send us Thy sal-va-tion; Thine is the glo-ry,
prayer and med-i-ta-tion: Thus we a-dore Thee.
where Thy saints u-nit-ed Joy with-out end-ing.
gleam-ing and re-sound-ing Through all cre-a-tion. A-MEN.

From "Enlarged Songs of Praise." By permission of the Oxford University Press.

Let the Whole Creation Cry

103

VIENNA. 7. 7. 7. 7.

STOPFORD A. BROOKE, 1832-1916

JUSTIN H. KNECHT, 1752-1817

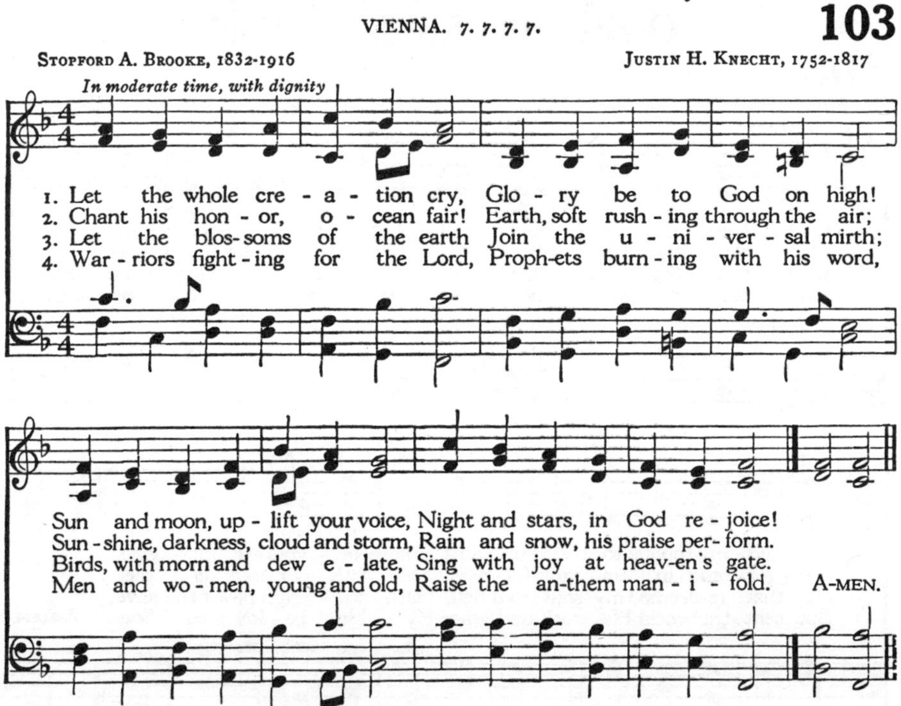
In moderate time, with dignity
1. Let the whole cre-a-tion cry, Glo-ry be to God on high!
2. Chant his hon-or, o-cean fair! Earth, soft rush-ing through the air;
3. Let the blos-soms of the earth Join the u-ni-ver-sal mirth;
4. War-riors fight-ing for the Lord, Proph-ets burn-ing with his word,
Sun and moon, up-lift your voice, Night and stars, in God re-joice!
Sun-shine, darkness, cloud and storm, Rain and snow, his praise per-form.
Birds, with morn and dew e-late, Sing with joy at heav-en's gate.
Men and wo-men, young and old, Raise the an-them man-i-fold. A-MEN.

Words used by permission of Miss Evelyn Brooke.

From All That Dwell Below the Skies

104
OLD 100TH. L. M.
From the Genevan Psalter,
Arr. by Louis Bourgeois, 1551
Isaac Watts, 1674-1748
With dignity
1. From all that dwell be - low the skies, Let the Cre - a - tor's praise a - rise:
2. E - ter - nal are thy mer -cies, Lord; E - ter - nal truth at - tends thy word;
Let the Re - deem-er's name be sung Thro' ev - 'ry land, by ev - 'ry tongue.
Thy praise shall sound from shore to shore Till suns shall rise and set no more. A-men.
O Bless the Lord, my Soul
105
ST. THOMAS. S. M.
Isaac Watts, 1674-1748
Aaron Williams, 1731-1776
Joyfully
1. O bless the Lord, my soul! Let all with - in me join,
2. O bless the Lord, my soul! Nor let His mer - cies lie
3. He crowns thy life with love, When ran - somed from the grave;
4. His won - drous works and ways He made by Mo - ses known;
And aid my tongue to bless His Name, Whose fa - vors are di - vine.
For - got - ten in un-thank-ful - ness, And with - out prais - es die.
He that re-deemed my soul from hell, Hath sov - 'reign pow'r to save.
But sent the world His truth and grace By His be - lov - ed Son. A-men.

Worship the Lord in the Beauty of Holiness

MONSELL. 12. 10. 12. 10.

106

JOHN S. B. MONSELL, 1811-1875 — WILLIAM F. SHERWIN, 1826-1888

In moderate, dignified time

1. Wor - ship the Lord in the beau - ty of ho - li - ness,
2. Low at His feet lay thy bur - den of care - ful - ness,
3. Fear not to en - ter His courts in the slen - der - ness

Bow down be - fore Him, His glo - ry pro - claim;
High on His heart He will bear it for thee;
Of the poor wealth thou wouldst reck - on as thine;

Gold of o - be - dience and in - cense of low - li - ness,
Com - fort thy sor - rows and an - swer thy pray'r - ful - ness,
Truth in its beau - ty, and love in its ten - der - ness,

Bring and a - dore Him,—the Lord is His name.
Guid - ing thy steps as may best for thee be.
These are the of - f'rings to lay on His shrine.

A - MEN.

Holy, Holy, Holy, Lord God Almighty

107
NICAEA. 11. 12. 12. 10.
REGINALD HEBER, 1783-1826, Alt.
JOHN B. DYKES, 1823-1876
With exaltation
1. Ho - ly, ho - ly, ho - ly, Lord God Al-might - y! Ear - ly in the
2. Ho - ly, ho - ly, ho - ly! all the saints a - dore Thee, Cast-ing down their
3. Ho - ly, ho - ly, ho - ly! tho' the dark-ness hide Thee, Tho' the eye of
4. Ho - ly, ho - ly, ho - ly, Lord God Al-might - y! All Thy works shall
morn - ing our song shall rise to Thee; Ho - ly, ho - ly, ho - ly,
gold-en crowns a-round the crys - tal sea; Cher-u - bim and sera - phim
sin-ful men Thy glo - ry may not see; On - ly Thou art ho - ly;
praise Thy name, in earth, and sky, and sea; Ho - ly, ho - ly, ho - ly,
mer - ci - ful and might-y! God in Three Per- sons, blessed Trin-i-ty!
fall-ing down be-fore Thee, Who wast, and art, and ev-er-more shalt be.
there is none be-side Thee, Per-fect in pow'r, in love, and pu-ri - ty.
mer - ci - ful and might-y! God in Three Per- sons, blessed Trin-i-ty! A-MEN.
108
To Thee, my Heart, Eternal King
GERMANY. L. M.
EXETER COLLECTION
In moderate time
Adapted from SACRED MELODIES
WILLIAM GARDINER, 1770-1853
1. To Thee, my heart, e - ter - nal King, Would now its thank-ful trib - ute bring;
2. All na - ture shows Thy boundless love, In worlds be - low and worlds a - bove;
3. Here what de-light-ful truths are giv'n; Here Je - sus shows the way to heav'n;
4. For love like this, O may our song Thro' end-less years Thy praise pro-long;

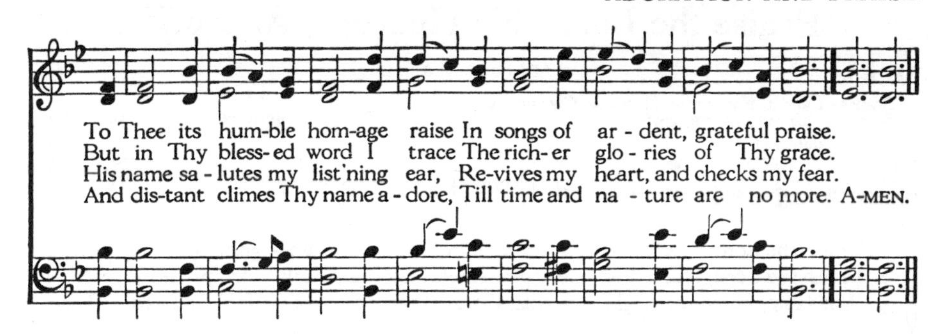
To Thee its hum-ble hom-age raise In songs of ar - dent, grateful praise.
But in Thy bless-ed word I trace The rich-er glo - ries of Thy grace.
His name sa - lutes my list'ning ear, Re-vives my heart, and checks my fear.
And dis-tant climes Thy name a - dore, Till time and na - ture are no more. A-MEN.

My God, I Thank Thee, Who Hast Made

109

WENTWORTH. 8. 4. 8. 4. 8. 4.

ADELAIDE A. PROCTER, 1825-1864 — FREDERICK C. MAKER, 1844-1927

With dignity and joy
1. My God, I thank Thee, who hast made The earth so bright,
2. I thank Thee, too, that Thou hast made Joy to a - bound,
3. I thank Thee, Lord, that Thou hast kept The best in store;
So full of splen - dor and of joy, Beau - ty and light;
So man - y gen - tle thoughts and deeds Cir - cling us 'round,
We have e - nough, yet not too much, To long for more;
So man - y glo - rious things are here, No - ble and right.
That in the dark - est spot of earth Some love is found.
A yearn-ing for a deep - er peace Not known be - fore. A - MEN.

Praise the Lord: Ye Heavens, Adore Him

110

FABEN. 8. 7. 8. 7. D.

Stanzas 1 and 2, FOUNDLING HOSPITAL COLLECTION, 1796
Stanza 3, EDWARD OSLER, 1798–1863

JOHN H. WILLCOX, 1827–1875

In stately rhythm

1. Praise the Lord: ye heavens, a - dore Him; Praise Him, an - gels in the height;
2. Praise the Lord, for He is glo - rious; Nev - er shall His prom - ise fail:
3. Wor - ship, hon - or, glo - ry, bless - ing, Lord, we of - fer un - to Thee;

Sun and moon, re - joice be - fore Him, Praise Him, all ye stars of light.
God hath made His saints vic - to - rious; Sin and death shall not pre - vail.
Young and old, Thy praise ex - press - ing, In glad hom - age bend the knee.

Praise the Lord, for He hath spo - ken; Worlds His might - y voice o - beyed:
Praise the God of our sal - va - tion; Hosts on high, His power pro - claim;
All the saints in heaven a - dore Thee; We would bow be - fore Thy throne:

Laws which nev - er shall be bro - ken For their guid-ance He hath made.
Heaven and earth and all cre - a - tion, Laud and mag - ni - fy His Name.
As Thine an - gels serve be - fore Thee, So on earth Thy will be done. A - MEN.

Come, Thou Fount of Every Blessing

111

NETTLETON. 8. 7. 8. 7. D.

ROBERT ROBINSON, 1735-1790 — JOHN WYETH (?), 1770-1858

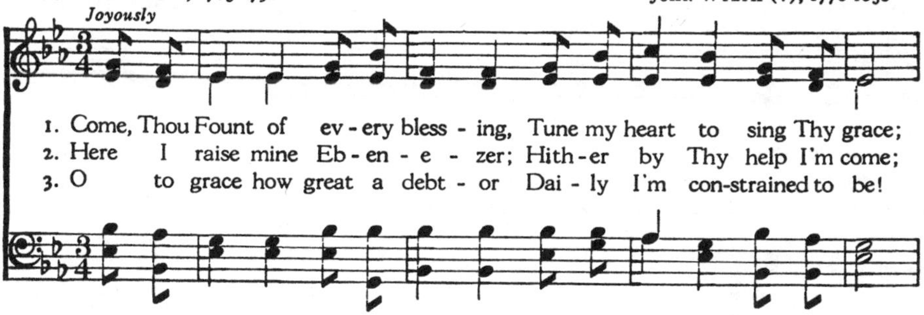

Joyously

1. Come, Thou Fount of ev - ery bless - ing, Tune my heart to sing Thy grace;
2. Here I raise mine Eb - en - e - zer; Hith - er by Thy help I'm come;
3. O to grace how great a debt - or Dai - ly I'm con-strained to be!

Streams of mer - cy, nev - er ceas - ing, Call for songs of loud - est praise.
And I hope, by Thy good pleas - ure, Safe - ly to ar - rive at home.
Let Thy good - ness, like a fet - ter, Bind my wan - dering heart to Thee:

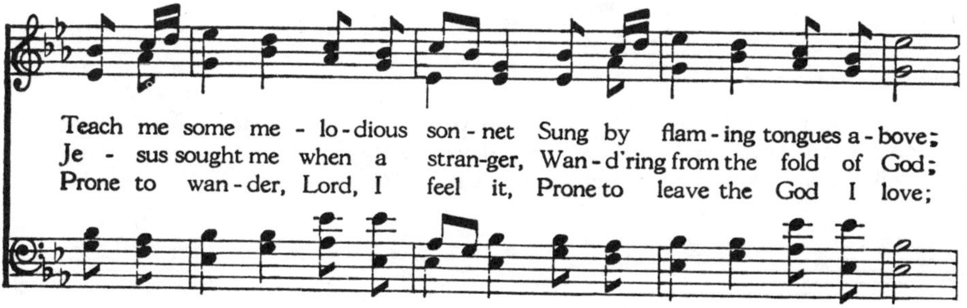

Teach me some me - lo - dious son - net Sung by flam - ing tongues a - bove;
Je - sus sought me when a stran-ger, Wan - d'ring from the fold of God;
Prone to wan - der, Lord, I feel it, Prone to leave the God I love;

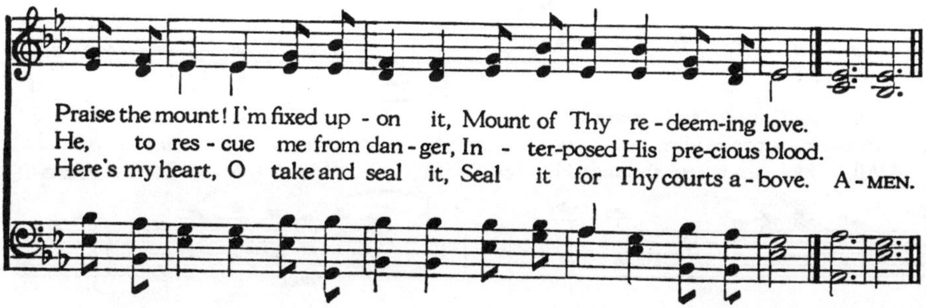

Praise the mount! I'm fixed up - on it, Mount of Thy re - deem-ing love.
He, to res - cue me from dan - ger, In - ter-posed His pre-cious blood.
Here's my heart, O take and seal it, Seal it for Thy courts a - bove. A - MEN.

Praise the Lord, His Glories Show

112
LLANFAIR. 7. 7. 7. 7. with Alleluias.
From Psalm cl
HENRY F. LYTE, 1793-1847
ROBERT WILLIAMS, c. 1781-1821
Joyously
1. Praise the Lord, His glo - ries show, Al - le - lu - ia!
2. Earth to heaven, and heaven to earth, Al - le - lu - ia!
3. Praise the Lord, His mer - cies trace, Al - le - lu - ia!
Saints with - in His courts be - low, Al - le - lu - ia!
Tell His won - ders, sing His worth, Al - le - lu - ia!
Praise His prov - i - dence and grace, Al - le - lu - ia!
An - gels round His throne a - bove, Al - le - lu - ia!
Age to age and shore to shore, Al - le - lu - ia!
All that He for man hath done, Al - le - lu - ia!
All that see and share His love, Al - le - lu - ia!
Praise Him, praise Him ev - er - more! Al - le - lu - ia!
All He sends us through His Son. Al - le - lu - ia!
A-MEN.

With Happy Voices Ringing

113

TOURS. 7. 6. 7. 6. D.
William G. Tarrant, 1853-1928
Berthold Tours, 1838-1897
Joyfully
1. With hap - py voic - es ring - ing, Thy chil - dren, Lord, ap - pear;
2. What though no eye be - holds Thee, No hand Thy hand may feel,
3. And shall we not a - dore Thee, With more than joy - ous song,
Their joy - ous prais - es bring - ing In an - thems sweet and clear.
Thy u - ni - verse un - folds Thee, Thy star - ry heavens re - veal,
And live in truth be - fore Thee, All beau - ti - ful and strong?
For skies of gold - en splen - dor, For az - ure, roll - ing sea,
The earth and all its glo - ry, Our homes and all we love,
Lord, bless our souls en - deav - or Thy ser - vants true to be,
For blos - soms sweet and ten - der, O Lord, we wor - ship Thee.
Tell forth the won - drous sto - ry Of One who reigns a - bove.
And through all life, for - ev - er, To live our praise to Thee. A-men.

As the Sun Doth Daily Rise

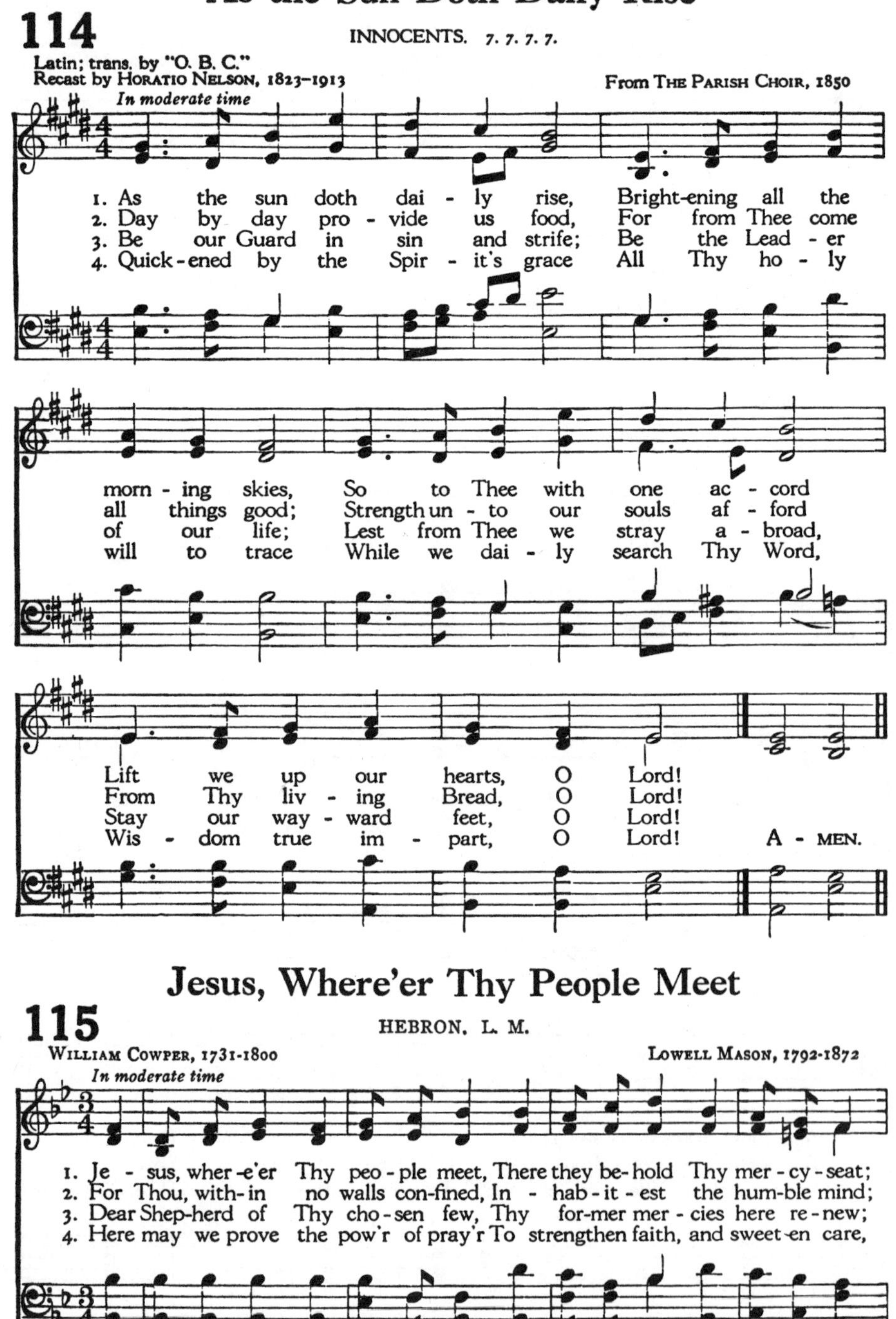
114
INNOCENTS. 7. 7. 7. 7.
Latin; trans. by "O. B. C."
Recast by Horatio Nelson, 1823-1913
From The Parish Choir, 1850
In moderate time
1. As the sun doth dai - ly rise, Bright-ening all the morn - ing skies, So to Thee with one ac - cord Lift we up our hearts, O Lord!
2. Day by day pro - vide us food, For from Thee come all things good; Strength un - to our souls af - ford From Thy liv - ing Bread, O Lord!
3. Be our Guard in sin and strife; Be the Lead - er of our life; Lest from Thee we stray a - broad, Stay our way - ward feet, O Lord!
4. Quick - ened by the Spir - it's grace All Thy ho - ly will to trace While we dai - ly search Thy Word, Wis - dom true im - part, O Lord!
A - men.
Jesus, Where'er Thy People Meet
115
HEBRON. L. M.
William Cowper, 1731-1800
Lowell Mason, 1792-1872
In moderate time
1. Je - sus, wher - e'er Thy peo - ple meet, There they be - hold Thy mer - cy - seat;
2. For Thou, with - in no walls con - fined, In - hab - it - est the hum - ble mind;
3. Dear Shep - herd of Thy cho - sen few, Thy for - mer mer - cies here re - new;
4. Here may we prove the pow'r of pray'r To strengthen faith, and sweet - en care,

Where er they seek Thee, Thou art found, And ev - ry place is hallowed ground.
Such ev- er bring Thee where they come, And go - ing, take Thee to their home.
Here to our wait - ing hearts pro-claim The sweetness of Thy sav-ing name.
To teach our faint de - sires to rise, And bring all heav'n be- fore our eyes. A - MEN.
Lord, We Come Before Thee Now
HENDON. 7. 7. 7. 7. 7.
116
William Hammond, 1719-1783
H. A. Caesar Malan, 1787-1864
In moderate time
1. Lord, we come be - fore Thee now, At Thy feet we humbly bow; O do not our suit dis - dain! Shall we seek Thee, Lord, in vain? Shall we seek Thee, Lord, in vain?
2. Lord, on Thee our souls de - pend: In com - pas - sion now de - scend; Fill our hearts with Thy rich grace, Tune our lips to sing Thy praise, Tune our lips to sing Thy praise.
3. In Thine own ap - point - ed way, Now we seek Thee; here we stay; Lord, we know not how to go, Till a bless - ing Thou be - stow, Till a bless - ing Thou be - stow.
4. Grant that all may seek and find Thee a God su - preme-ly kind; Heal the sick, the cap- tive free; Let us all re - joice in Thee, Let us all re - joice in Thee. A - MEN.

We Gather Together to Ask the Lord's Blessing

117

KREMSER. Irregular.

Anonymous
Tr. by THEODORE BAKER

Netherland folk song, 1625
Arr. by EDWARD KREMSER, 1838-1914

In moderate time
1. We gath - er to - geth - er to ask the Lord's bless - ing;
2. Be - side us to guide us, our God with us join - ing,
3. We all do ex - tol Thee, Thou Lead - er tri - um - phant,
He chas - tens and has - tens His will to make known;
Or - dain - ing, main - tain - ing His king - dom di - vine;
And pray that Thou still our De - fend - er wilt be.
The wick - ed op - press - ing now cease from dis - tress - ing,
So from the be - gin - ning the fight we were win - ning:
Let Thy con - gre - ga - tion es - cape trib - u - la - tion:
Sing prais - es to His Name: He for - gets not His own.
Thou, Lord, wast at our side, all glo - ry be Thine!
Thy Name be ev - er praised! O Lord, make us free! A - MEN.

Come, Sound His Praise Abroad

118

SILVER STREET. S. M.
ISAAC WATTS, 1674-1748
ISAAC SMITH, 1735-1800
In stately, moderate time
1. Come, sound His praise a - broad And hymns of glo - ry sing: Je - hovah is the sov - ereign God, The u - ni - ver - sal King.
2. He formed the deeps un-known; He gave the seas their bound; The wa-tery worlds are all His own, And all the sol - id ground.
3. Come, wor - ship at His throne, Come, bow be - fore the Lord: We are His works and not our own; He formed us by His word.
4. To - day at - tend His voice, Nor dare pro - voke His rod; Come, like the peo - ple of His choice, And own your gra - cious God. A - MEN.
Come, We That Love the Lord
119
ST. THOMAS. S. M.
ISAAC WATTS, 1674-1748
AARON WILLIAMS, 1731-1776
In moderate time
1. Come, we that love the Lord, And let our joys be known; Join in a song of sweet ac - cord, And thus surround the throne.
2. Let those re - fuse to sing Who nev - er knew our God; But chil-dren of the heav'n-ly King Should speak their joys a - broad.
3. The hill of Zi - on yields A thou - sand sa - cred sweets Be - fore we reach the heav'n-ly fields, Or walk the gold - en streets.
4. Then let our songs a - bound, And ev - 'ry tear be dry; We're marching thro' Emmanuel's ground, To fair - er worlds on high. A-MEN.

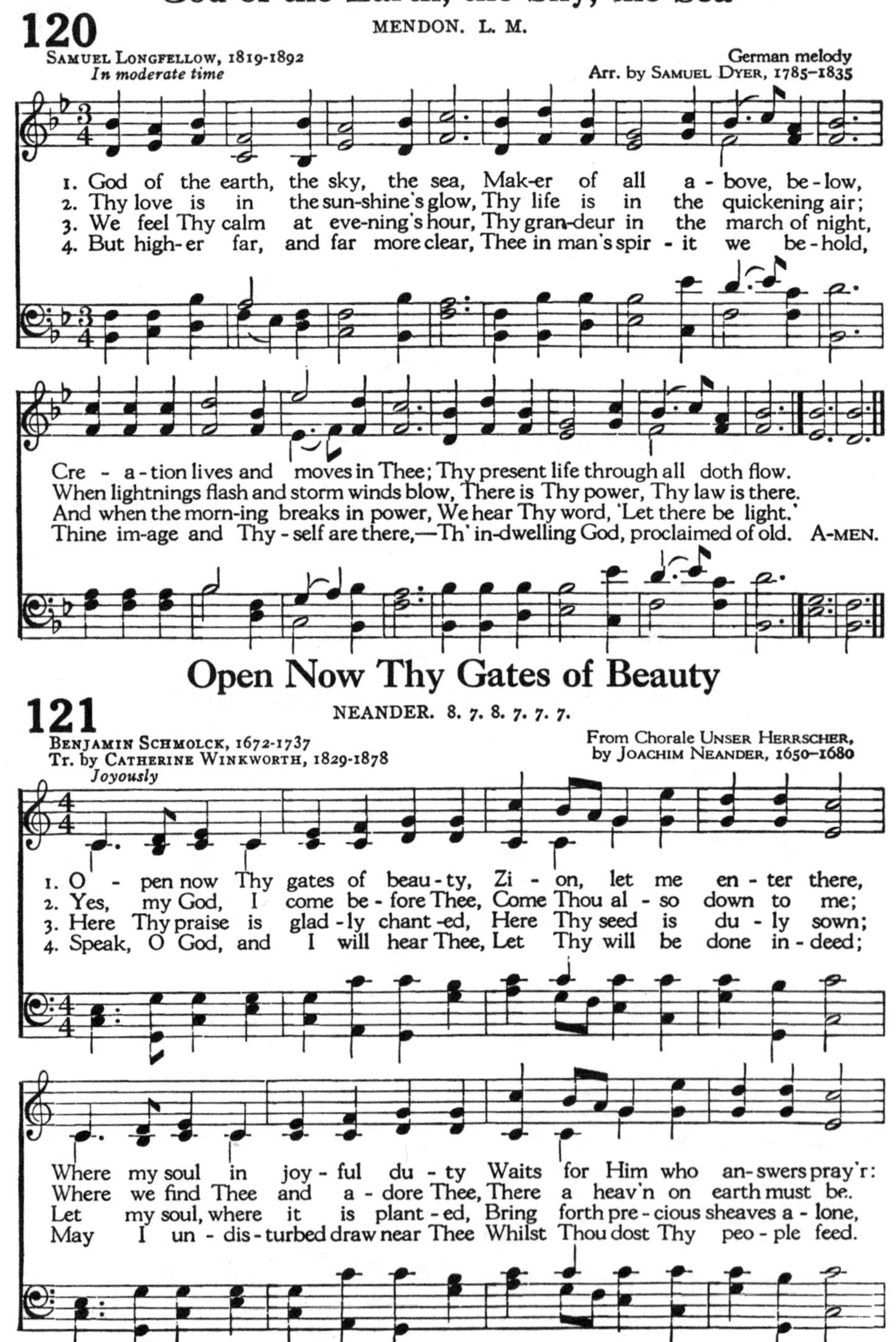

God of the Earth, the Sky, the Sea
120
MENDON. L. M.
Samuel Longfellow, 1819-1892
In moderate time
German melody
Arr. by Samuel Dyer, 1785–1835
1. God of the earth, the sky, the sea, Mak-er of all a - bove, be-low,
2. Thy love is in the sun-shine's glow, Thy life is in the quickening air;
3. We feel Thy calm at eve-ning's hour, Thy gran-deur in the march of night,
4. But high-er far, and far more clear, Thee in man's spir - it we be-hold,
Cre - a-tion lives and moves in Thee; Thy present life through all doth flow.
When lightnings flash and storm winds blow, There is Thy power, Thy law is there.
And when the morn-ing breaks in power, We hear Thy word, 'Let there be light.'
Thine im-age and Thy-self are there,—Th' in-dwelling God, proclaimed of old. A-men.
Open Now Thy Gates of Beauty
121
NEANDER. 8. 7. 8. 7. 7. 7.
Benjamin Schmolck, 1672-1737
Tr. by Catherine Winkworth, 1829-1878
Joyously
From Chorale Unser Herrscher,
by Joachim Neander, 1650-1680
1. O - pen now Thy gates of beau-ty, Zi - on, let me en - ter there,
2. Yes, my God, I come be-fore Thee, Come Thou al - so down to me;
3. Here Thy praise is glad-ly chant-ed, Here Thy seed is du - ly sown;
4. Speak, O God, and I will hear Thee, Let Thy will be done in-deed;
Where my soul in joy - ful du - ty Waits for Him who an-swers pray'r:
Where we find Thee and a - dore Thee, There a heav'n on earth must be.
Let my soul, where it is plant-ed, Bring forth pre-cious sheaves a - lone,
May I un - dis-turbed draw near Thee Whilst Thou dost Thy peo-ple feed.

O how bless-ed is this place, Filled with sol-ace, light, and grace.
To my heart, O en-ter Thou, Let it be Thy tem-ple now.
So that all I hear may be Fruit-ful un-to life in me.
Here of life the foun-tain flows, Here is balm for all our woes. A-MEN.

Come, Thou Almighty King

ITALIAN HYMN (TRINITY). 6. 6. 4. 6. 6. 6. 4.

122

Anonymous

FELICE DE GIARDINI, 1716-1796

Joyously, with dignity

1. Come, Thou al-might-y King, Help us Thy name to sing, Help us to praise! Fa-ther all-glo-ri-ous, O'er all vic-to-ri-ous, Come, and reign o-ver us, An-cient of Days!
2. Come, Thou In-car-nate Word, Gird on Thy might-y sword, Our pray'r at-tend; Come, and Thy peo-ple bless, And give Thy word suc-cess; Spir-it of ho-li-ness, On us de-scend!
3. Come, Ho-ly Com-fort-er, Thy sa-cred wit-ness bear, In this glad hour: Thou who al-might-y art, Now rule in ev-ery heart, And ne'er from us de-part, Spir-it of power!
4. To Thee, great One in Three, E-ter-nal prais-es be Hence, ev-er-more: Thy sov-'reign maj-es-ty May we in glo-ry see, And to e-ter-ni-ty Love and a-dore! A-MEN.

God Himself Is with Us

123

ARNSBERG. 6. 6. 8. D. 3. 3. 6. 6.

Gerhard Tersteegen, 1697–1769
Tr. by Frederick W. Foster, 1760–1835
and John Miller, d. 1810; alt., 1932

Joachim Neander's Bundes-Lieder, 1680

Not too fast; reverently

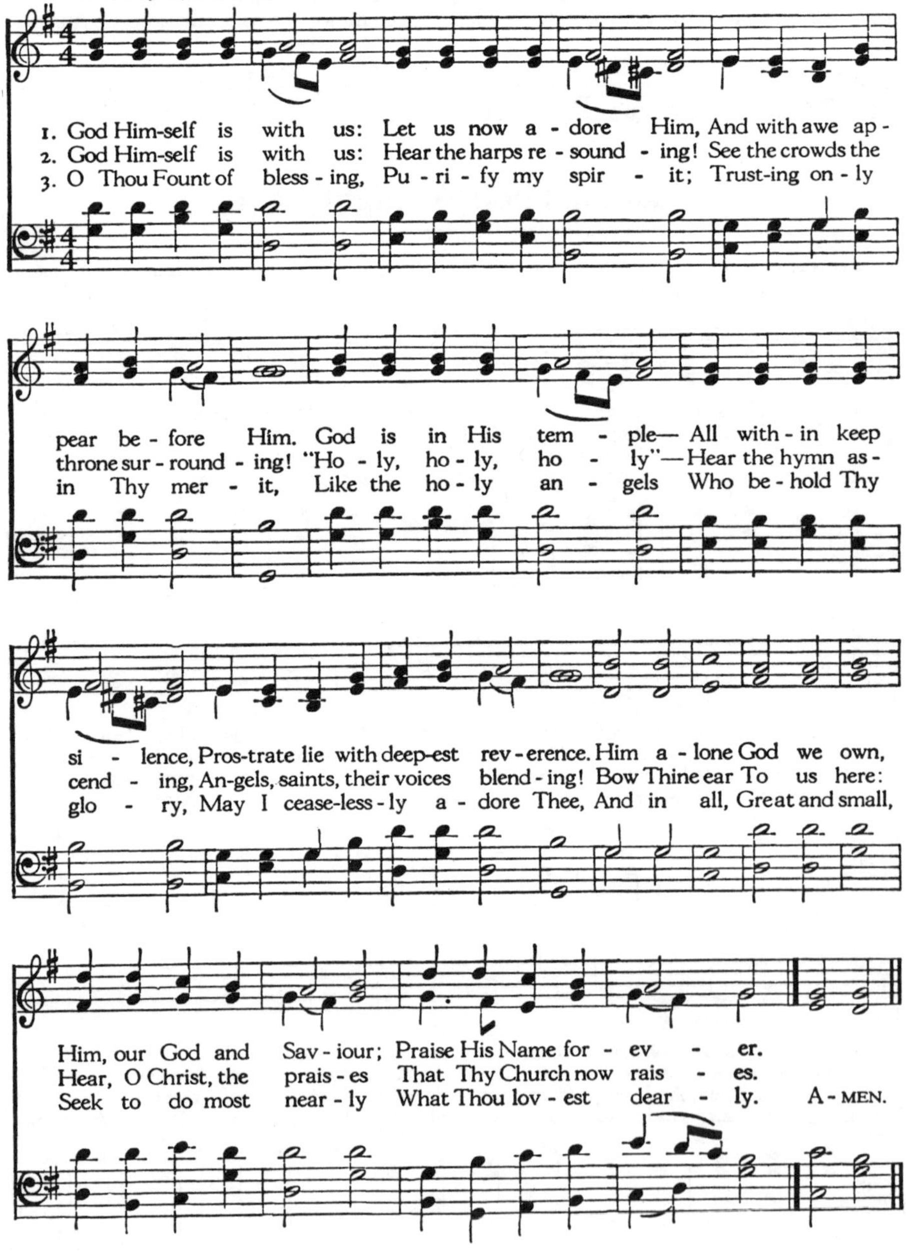

1. God Him-self is with us: Let us now a - dore Him, And with awe ap - pear be - fore Him. God is in His tem - ple— All with - in keep si - lence, Pros-trate lie with deep-est rev - erence. Him a - lone God we own, Him, our God and Sav - iour; Praise His Name for - ev - er.
2. God Him-self is with us: Hear the harps re - sound - ing! See the crowds the throne sur - round - ing! "Ho - ly, ho - ly, ho - ly"—Hear the hymn as - cend - ing, An-gels, saints, their voices blend - ing! Bow Thine ear To us here: Hear, O Christ, the prais - es That Thy Church now rais - es.
3. O Thou Fount of bless - ing, Pu - ri - fy my spir - it; Trust-ing on - ly in Thy mer - it, Like the ho - ly an - gels Who be - hold Thy glo - ry, May I cease-less - ly a - dore Thee, And in all, Great and small, Seek to do most near - ly What Thou lov - est dear - ly. A - men.

Praise to the Living God

LEONI (YIGDAL) 6. 6. 8. 4. D

124

Daniel Ben Judah, 14th century
Revised Version of The Yigdal
Majestically
Arr. from a Hebrew melody
1. Praise to the liv-ing God. All prais-ed be His Name,
2. His spir-it flow-eth free, High surg-ing where it will:
3. He hath e-ter-nal life Im-plant-ed in the soul;
Who was, and is, and is to be, And still the same!
In proph-et's word He spoke of old— He speak-eth still.
His love shall be our strength and stay, While a-ges roll.
The one e-ter-nal God, Ere aught that now ap-pears;
Es-tab-lished is His law, And change-less it shall stand,
Praise to the liv-ing God! All prais-ed be His Name
The First, the Last: be-yond all thought His time-less years!
Deep writ up-on the hu-man heart, On sea, or land.
Who was, and is, and is to be, And still the same!
A-MEN.

The Lord Be with Us As Each Day

125

BELMONT. C. M.

JOHN ELLERTON, 1826–1893, alt.

Adapted from SACRED MELODIES, WILLIAM GARDINER, 1770–1853

Reverently

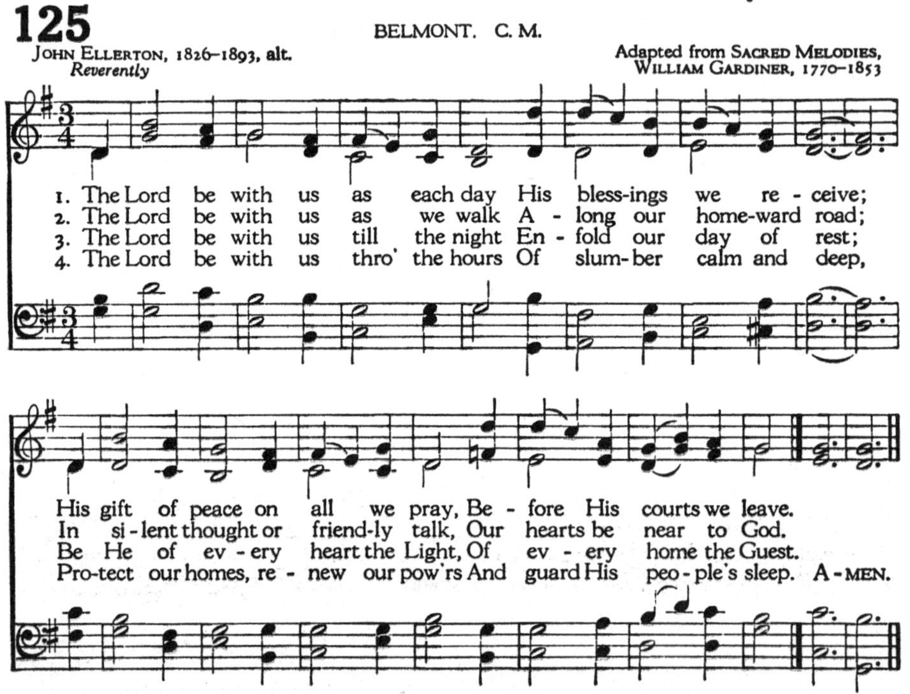
1. The Lord be with us as each day His bless-ings we re - ceive;
2. The Lord be with us as we walk A - long our home-ward road;
3. The Lord be with us till the night En - fold our day of rest;
4. The Lord be with us thro' the hours Of slum-ber calm and deep,
His gift of peace on all we pray, Be - fore His courts we leave.
In si-lent thought or friend-ly talk, Our hearts be near to God.
Be He of ev - ery heart the Light, Of ev - ery home the Guest.
Pro-tect our homes, re - new our pow'rs And guard His peo-ple's sleep. A-MEN.

May the Grace of Christ Our Saviour

126

STOCKWELL. 8. 7. 8. 7.

JOHN NEWTON, 1725-1807

DARIUS E. JONES, 1815-1881

In moderate time

1. May the grace of Christ our Sav - iour, And the Fa - ther's bound-less love,
2. Thus may we a - bide in un - ion With each oth - er and the Lord,
With the Ho - ly Spir-it's fa - vor, Rest up-on us from a - bove.
And pos-sess, in sweet commun - ion, Joys which earth can-not af - ford. A - MEN.

Lord, Dismiss Us with Thy Blessing

127

SICILIAN MARINERS. 8. 7. 8. 7. 8. 7.

Ascribed to JOHN FAWCETT, 1740-1817
Stanza 1, line 6, alt.;
stanza 3 recast by GODFREY THRING, 1823-1903
Arr. from a Sicilian melody
In moderate time
1. Lord, dis - miss us with Thy bless - ing; Fill our hearts with joy and peace; Let us each, Thy love pos - sess - ing, Tri - umph in re - deem - ing grace: O re - fresh us, O re - fresh us, Trav - eling through this wil - der - ness.
2. Thanks we give and ad - o - ra - tion For Thy gos - pel's joy - ful sound; May the fruits of Thy sal - va - tion In our hearts and lives a - bound: Ev - er faith - ful, Ev - er faith - ful To the truth may we be found;
3. So that when Thy love shall call us, Sav - iour, from the world a - way, Let no fear of death ap - pall us, Glad Thy sum - mons to o - bey: May we ev - er, May we ev - er Reign with Thee in end - less day.
A-MEN.

Saviour, Again to Thy Dear Name We Raise

128

ELLERS. 10. 10. 10. 10.

JOHN ELLERTON, 1826-1893

EDWARD J. HOPKINS, 1818-1901

Not too fast

1. Sav - iour, a - gain to Thy dear Name we raise
2. Grant us Thy peace up - on our home - ward way;
3. Grant us Thy peace, Lord, through the com - ing night,
4. Grant us Thy peace through - out our earth - ly life,
With one ac - cord our part - ing hymn of praise;
With Thee be - gan, with Thee shall end the day:
Turn Thou for us its dark - ness in - to light;
Our balm in sor - row, and our stay in strife;
We stand to bless Thee ere our wor - ship cease,
Guard Thou the lips from sin, the hearts from shame,
From harm and dan - ger keep Thy chil - dren free,
Then, when Thy voice shall bid our con - flict cease,
And still our hearts to wait Thy word of peace.
That in this house have called up - on Thy Name.
For dark and light are both a - like to Thee.
Call us, O Lord, to Thine e - ter - nal peace. A - MEN.

God Be with You Till We Meet Again

129

FAREWELL. 9. 8. 8. 9. with Refrain.

JEREMIAH E. RANKIN, 1828–1904 — WILLIAM G. TOMER, 1833–1896

In moderate time
1. God be with you till we meet a - gain, By His counsels guide, uphold you,
2. God be with you till we meet a - gain, Neath His wings securely hide you,
3. God be with you till we meet a - gain, When life's perils thick confound you,
4. God be with you till we meet a - gain, Keep love's banner floating o'er you,
With His sheep se-cure - ly fold you, God be with you till we meet a - gain.
Dai - ly man -na still pro- vide you, God be with you till we meet a - gain.
Put His arms un- fail - ing round you, God be with you till we meet a - gain.
Smite death's threat'ning wave before you, God be with you till we meet a - gain.
CHORUS
Till we meet till we meet, Till we meet at Je - sus' feet;
Till we meet, till we meet, till we meet;
Till we meet, Till we meet, God be with you till we meet a-gain. A-MEN.
Till we meet, till we meet,

We Leave Thy House but Leave Not Thee

130

STIREWALT. L. M.

THOMAS TIPLADY, 1882-

ROB ROY PEERY 1900-

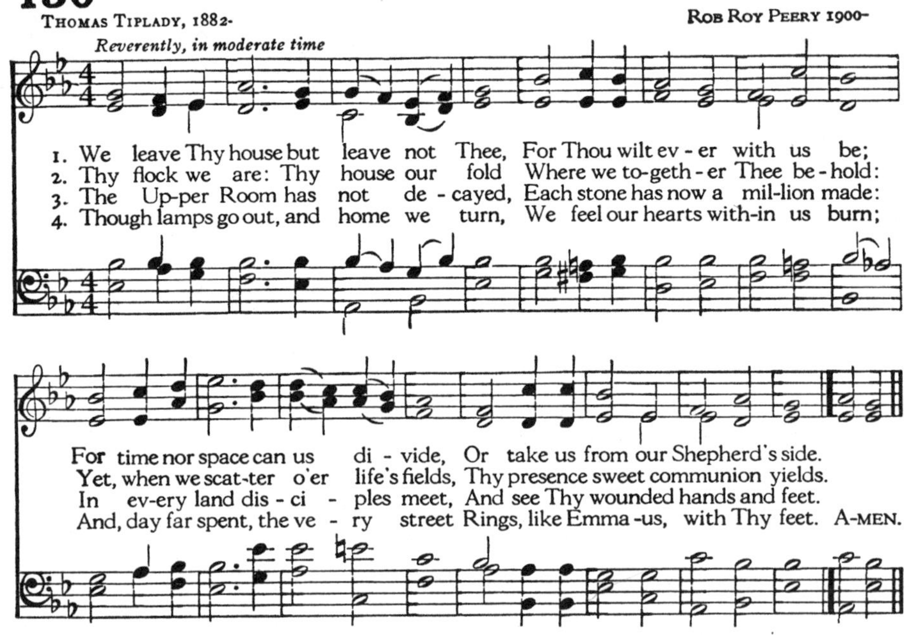
Reverently, in moderate time
1. We leave Thy house but leave not Thee, For Thou wilt ev - er with us be;
2. Thy flock we are: Thy house our fold Where we to-geth - er Thee be - hold:
3. The Up-per Room has not de - cayed, Each stone has now a mil-lion made:
4. Though lamps go out, and home we turn, We feel our hearts with-in us burn;
For time nor space can us di - vide, Or take us from our Shepherd's side.
Yet, when we scat-ter o'er life's fields, Thy presence sweet communion yields.
In ev-ery land dis - ci - ples meet, And see Thy wounded hands and feet.
And, day far spent, the ve - ry street Rings, like Emma -us, with Thy feet. A-MEN.

Lord, at This Closing Hour

131

BOYLSTON. S. M.

ELEAZOR T. FITCH

LOWELL MASON, 1792-1872

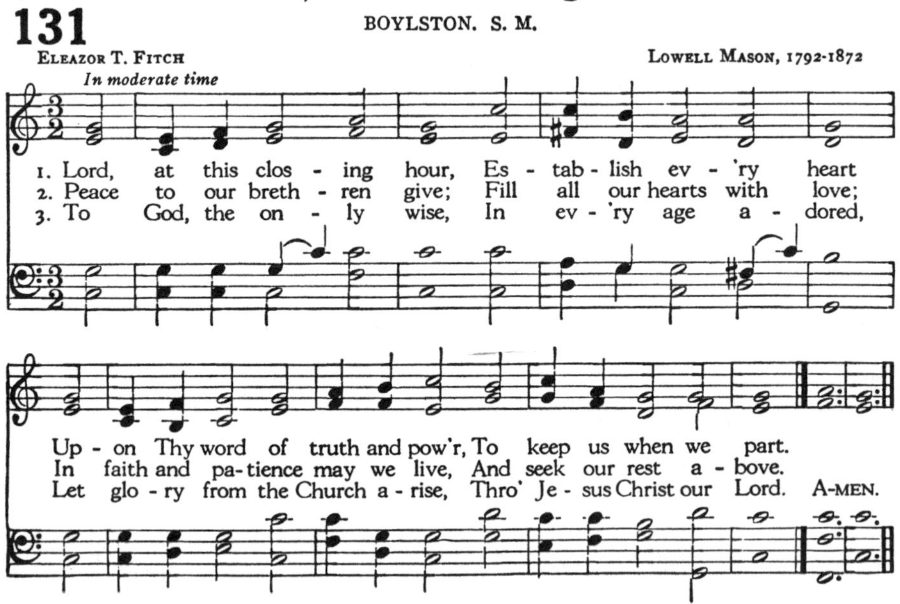
In moderate time
1. Lord, at this clos - ing hour, Es - tab - lish ev - 'ry heart
2. Peace to our breth - ren give; Fill all our hearts with love;
3. To God, the on - ly wise, In ev - 'ry age a - dored,
Up - on Thy word of truth and pow'r, To keep us when we part.
In faith and pa - tience may we live, And seek our rest a - bove.
Let glo - ry from the Church a - rise, Thro' Je - sus Christ our Lord. A-MEN.

O Lord of Life, Thy Quick'ning Voice

JACKSON. C. M.

132

GEORGE MACDONALD, 1824-1905

THOMAS JACKSON, c. 1715-1781

In moderate time
1. O Lord of life, thy quick-ning voice A-wakes my morn-ing song!
2. I see thy light, I feel thy wind; The world, it is thy word;
3. There-fore I choose my high-est part, And turn my face to Thee;
In glad-some words I would re-joice That I to thee be-long.
What-ev-er wakes my heart and mind Thy pre-sence is, my Lord.
Therefore I stir my in-most heart To wor-ship fer-vent-ly.
A-MEN.

O God, Thy World Is Sweet with Prayer

CANONBURY. L. M.

133

LUCY LARCOM, 1826–1893

ROBERT SCHUMANN, 1810-1856

Not too fast
1. O God, thy world is sweet with pray'r; The breath of Christ is in the air;
2. Thou art our Morn-ing and our Sun, Our work is glad, in thee be-gun;
3. O God, with-in us and a-bove, Close to us in the Christ we love,
We rise on thy free Spir-it's wings, And ev-'ry tho't with-in us sings.
Our foot-worn path is fresh with dew, For thou cre-a-test all things new.
Thro' him, our on-ly guide and way, May heav'nly life be ours to-day!
A-MEN.

Come, My Soul, Thou Must Be Waking

134

HAYDN. 8. 4. 7. 8. 4. 7.

FRIEDRICH R. L. VON CANITZ, 1654-1699
Tr. by HENRY J. BUCKOLL, 1803-1871

FRANZ JOSEPH HAYDN, 1732-1809

In moderate time

1. Come, my soul, thou must be waking; Now is breaking O'er the earth another day:
Come to Him who made this splendor; See thou render All thy feeble strength can pay.

2. Gladly hail the sun returning; Ready burning Be the incense of thy powers;
For the night is safely ended; God hath tended With His care thy helpless hours.

3. Pray that He may prosper ever Each endeavor, When thine aim is good and true;
But that He may ever thwart thee, And convert thee, When thou evil wouldst pursue.

4. Our God's bounteous gifts abuse not, Light refuse not, But His Spirit's voice obey;
Thou with Him shalt dwell, beholding Light enfolding All things in unclouded day.

A - MEN.

When Morning Gilds the Skies

135

LAUDES DOMINI. 6. 6. 6. 6. 6. 6.

German, c. 1800
Tr. by Edward Caswall, 1814-1878

Joseph Barnby, 1838-1896

Joyously and with dignity

1. When morn - ing gilds the skies, My heart a -
2. When - e'er the sweet church bell Peals o - ver
3. The night be - comes as day, When from the
4. Ye na - tions of man - kind, In this your

wak - ing cries, May Je - sus Christ be praised!
hill and dell, May Je - sus Christ be praised!
heart we say, May Je - sus Christ be praised!
con - cord find, May Je - sus Christ be praised!

A - like at work and prayer, To Je - sus I re -
O hark to what it sings, As joy - ous - ly it
The powers of dark - ness fear, When this sweet chant they
Let all the earth a - round Ring joy - ous with the

pair; May Je - sus Christ be praised!
rings, May Je - sus Christ be praised!
hear, May Je - sus Christ be praised!
sound, May Je - sus Christ be praised! A - men.

Still, Still with Thee

136

CONSOLATION. 11. 10. 11. 10.

HARRIET B. STOWE, 1812–1896 — FELIX MENDELSSOHN, 1809-1847

In moderate time

1. Still, still with Thee, when pur - ple morn - ing break - eth,
2. A - lone with Thee, a - mid the mys - tic shad - ows,
3. When sinks the soul, sub - dued by toil, to slum - ber,
4. So shall it be at last, in that bright morn - ing,

When the bird wak - eth, and the shad - ows flee;
The sol - emn hush of na - ture new - ly born;
Its clos - ing eyes look up to Thee in prayer;
When the soul wak - eth, and life's shad - ows flee;

Fair - er than morn - ing, love - li - er than day - light,
A - lone with Thee in breath - less ad - o - ra - tion,
Sweet the re - pose be - neath Thy wings o'er - shad - ing,
O in that hour, fair - er than day - light dawn - ing,

Dawns the sweet con - scious - ness, I am with Thee.
In the calm dew and fresh - ness of the morn.
But sweet - er still, to wake and find Thee there.
Shall rise the glo - rious thought, I am with Thee.

A - MEN.

At Thy Feet, Our God and Father

ST. ASAPH. 8. 7. 8. 7. D.

137

JAMES D. BURNS, 1823–1864 — WILLIAM S. BAMBRIDGE, 1842–1923

In moderate time

1. At Thy feet, our God and Father, Who hast blessed us all our days,
2. Je - sus, for Thy love most ten - der On the cross for sin - ners shown,
3. Ev - ery day will be the bright - er When Thy gra - cious face we see;
We with grate - ful hearts would gath-er To be - gin the day with praise;
We would praise Thee and sur - ren - der All our hearts to be Thine own.
Ev - 'ry bur - den will be light - er When we know it comes from Thee.
Praise for light so bright - ly shin - ing On our steps from heaven a - bove;
With so blest a Friend pro - vid - ed, We up - on our way would go,
Spread Thy love's broad ban - ner o'er us; Give us strength to serve and wait,
Praise for mer - cies dai - ly twin - ing Round us gold - en cords of love.
Sure of be - ing safe - ly guid - ed, Guard-ed well from ev-ery foe.
Till Thy glo - ry breaks be - fore us Thro' the cit - y's o - pen gate. A - MEN.

Abide with Me! Fast Falls the Eventide

138
EVENTIDE. 10. 10. 10. 10.
Henry F. Lyte, 1793-1847
William H. Monk, 1823-1889
In moderate time
1. A - bide with me! fast falls the e - ven - tide; The dark-ness deep - ens— Lord, with me a - bide! When oth - er help - ers fail, and com-forts flee, Help of the help-less, O a - bide with me!
2. Swift to its close ebbs out life's lit - tle day; Earth's joys grow dim, its glo - ries pass a - way; Change and de - cay in all a - round I see; O Thou, who changest not, a - bide with me!
3. I need Thy pres - ence ev - 'ry pass - ing hour; What but Thy grace can foil the temp - ter's pow'r? Who, like Thy - self, my guide and stay can be? Thro' cloud and sunshine, O a - bide with me!
4. Hold Thou Thy cross be - fore my clos - ing eyes; Shine through the gloom and point me to the skies; Heav'n's morn - ing breaks, and earth's vain shadows flee; In life, in death, O Lord, a - bide with me! A-MEN.
Again, as Evening's Shadow Falls
139
CANONBURY. L. M.
Samuel Longfellow, 1819-1892
Robert Schumann, 1810-1856
In moderate time
1. A - gain, as eve - ning's shad-ow falls, We gath - er in these hallowed walls;
2. May struggling hearts, that seek re - lease, Here find the rest of God's own peace;
3. O God our Light, to Thee we bow; With - in all shad-ows stand-est thou;
4. Life's tu - mult we must meet a - gain, We can - not at the shrine re - main;

And ves-per hymn and ves - per pray'r Rise mingling on the ho - ly air.
And, strengthened here by hymn and pray'r, Lay down the bur-den and the care.
Give deep-er calm than night can bring, Give sweeter songs than lips can sing.
But in the spir-it's se - cret cell May hymn and pray'r for-ev-er dwell. A-MEN.

The Day Thou Gavest, Lord, Is Ended

ST. CLEMENT. 9. 8. 9. 8.

140

JOHN ELLERTON, 1826-1893 — CLEMENT C. SCHOLEFIELD, 1839-1904

In moderate time; with flowing rhythm

1. The day Thou gav - est, Lord, is end - ed, The dark - ness
2. We thank Thee that Thy Church un - sleep - ing, While earth rolls
3. As o'er each con - ti - nent and is - land The dawn leads
4. So be it, Lord; Thy throne shall nev - er, Like earth's proud
falls at Thy be - hest; To Thee our morn - ing hymns as -
on - ward in - to light, Through all the world her watch is
on an - oth - er day, The voice of prayer is nev - er
em - pires, pass a - way; Thy king - dom stands, and grows for
cend - ed, Thy praise shall hal - low now our rest.
keep - ing, And rests not now by day or night.
si - lent, Nor die the strains of praise a - way.
ev - er, Till all Thy crea - tures own Thy sway. A - MEN.

Now, on Land and Sea Descending

141

VESPER HYMN. 8. 7. 8. 7. 8. 6. 8. 7.

SAMUEL LONGFELLOW, 1819–1892, alt.
DIMITRI S. BORTNIANSKY, 1752–1825
In moderate time
1. Now, on land and sea de-scend-ing, Brings the night its peace pro-found;
2. Soon as dies the sun-set glo-ry, Stars of heaven shine out a-bove,
3. Now, our wants and bur-dens leav-ing To His care who cares for all,
4. As the dark-ness deep-ens o'er us, Lo! e-ter-nal stars a-rise;
Let our ves-per hymn be blend-ing With the ho-ly calm a-round.
Tell-ing still the an-cient sto-ry—Their Cre-a-tor's change-less love.
Cease we fear-ing, cease we griev-ing: At His touch our bur-dens fall.
Hope and faith and love rise glo-rious, Shin-ing in the spir-it's skies.
Ju-bi-la-te! Ju-bi-la-te! Ju-bi-la-te! A-men!
Let our ves-per hymn be blend-ing With the ho-ly calm a-round.
Tell-ing still the an-cient sto-ry—Their Cre-a-tor's changeless love.
Cease we fear-ing, cease we griev-ing: At His touch our bur-dens fall.
Hope and faith and love rise glo-rious, Shin-ing in the spir-it's skies. A-MEN.

The Shadows of the Evening Hours

ST. LEONARD (Hiles). C. M. D.

ADELAIDE A. PROCTER, 1825–1864
Stanza 3, line 7, alt.

HENRY HILES, 1826–1904

In moderate time

1. The shad-ows of the eve - ning hours Fall from the dark-ening sky;
2. Slow - ly the rays of day - light fade: So fade with - in our heart
3. Let peace, O Lord, Thy peace, O God, Up - on our souls de - scend;

Up - on the fra - grance of the flowers The dews of eve - ning lie:
The hopes in earth - ly love and joy, That one by one de - part.
From mid-night fears and per - ils, Thou Our trem - bling hearts de - fend.

Be - fore Thy throne, O Lord of heaven, We kneel at close of day;
Slow - ly the bright stars, one by one, With - in the heav - ens shine:
Give us a res - pite from our toil, Calm and sub - due our woes;

Look on Thy chil-dren from on high, And hear us while we pray.
Give us, O Lord, fresh hopes in heav'n, And trust in things di - vine.
Through the long day we la - bor, Lord, O give us now re - pose. A-MEN.

For lower key, see No. 273

God, That Madest Earth and Heaven

143

AR HYD Y NOS. 8. 4. 8. 4. 8. 8. 8. 4.

Reginald Heber, 1783–1826
Frederick L. Hosmer, 1840–1928

Welsh traditional melody
Harmonized by L. O. Emerson, 1820–1916

In flowing rhythm

1. God, that mad-est earth and heav-en, Dark-ness and light;
2. When the con-stant sun re-turn-ing Un-seals our eyes,
Who the day for toil hast giv-en, For rest the night;
May we, born a-new like morn-ing, To la-bor rise;
May Thine an-gel guards de-fend us, Slum-ber sweet Thy mer-cy send us;
Gird us for the task that calls us, Let not ease and self en-thrall us,
Ho-ly dreams and hopes at-tend us, This live-long night.
Strong thro' Thee what-e'er be-fall us, O God most wise!
A-MEN.

Day Is Dying in the West

CHAUTAUQUA. 7. 7. 7. 7. 4. with Refrain **144**

MARY A. LATHBURY, 1841–1913 WILLIAM F. SHERWIN, 1826–1888

Quietly and reverently

1. Day is dy - ing in the west, Heav'n is touching earth with rest; Wait and
2. Lord of life, be-neath the dome Of the u - ni-verse, Thy home, Gath - er
3. While the deep-'ning shad-ows fall, Heart of Love, en - fold - ing all, Thro' the
4. When for - ev - er from our sight Pass the stars, the day, the night, Lord of

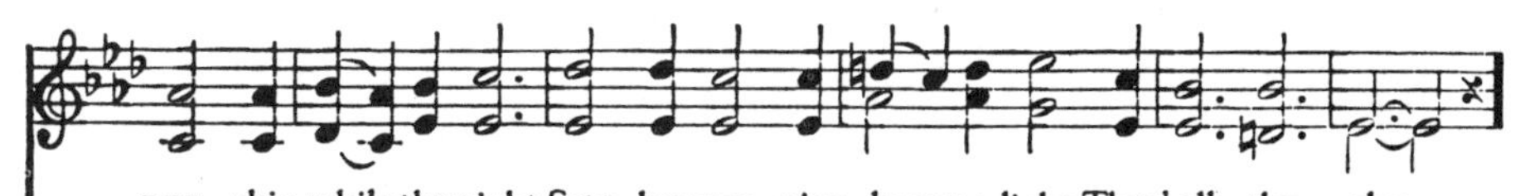

wor - ship while the night Sets her eve - ning lamps a-light Thro' all the sky.
us, who seek Thy face, To the fold of Thy embrace; For Thou art nigh.
glo - ry and the grace Of the stars that veil Thy face, Our hearts as - cend.
an - gels, on our eyes Let e - ter - nal morn-ing rise, And shad-ows end!

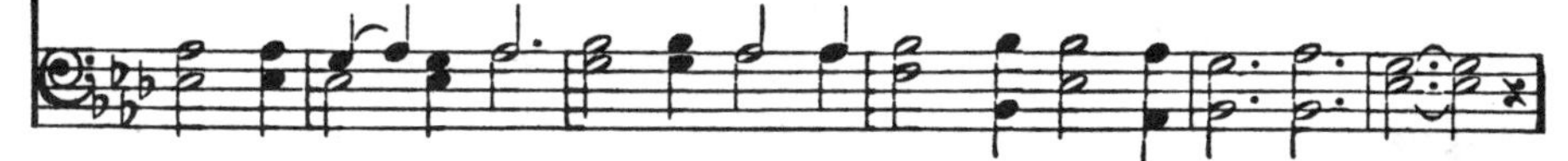

REFRAIN

Ho - ly, ho - ly, ho - ly, Lord God of Hosts! Heav'n and earth are full of Thee!

Heav'n and earth are prais - ing Thee, O Lord most high! A - MEN.

Courtesy of the Chautauqua Institution, Chautauqua, N. Y.

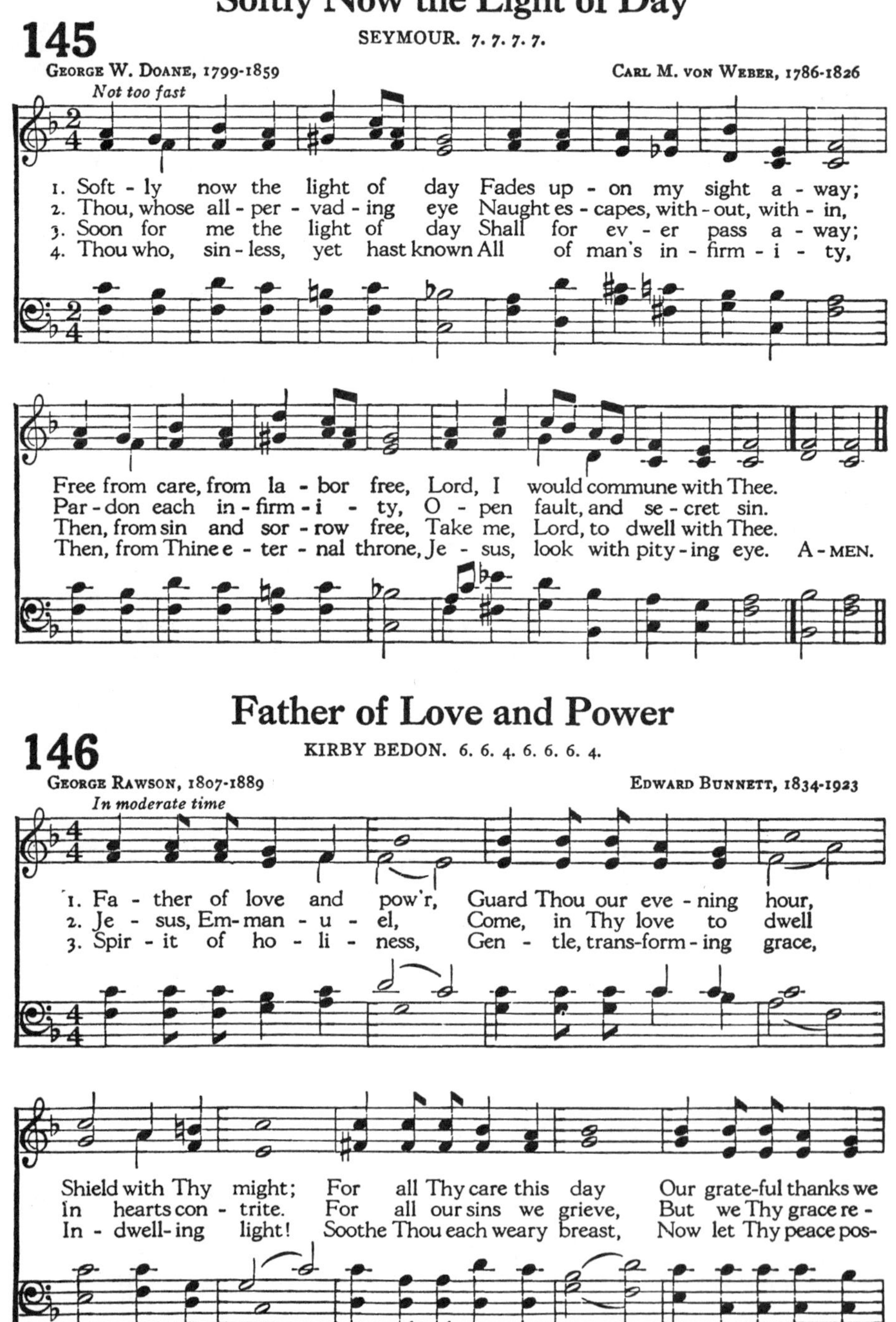
Softly Now the Light of Day
145
SEYMOUR. 7. 7. 7. 7.
GEORGE W. DOANE, 1799-1859
CARL M. VON WEBER, 1786-1826
Not too fast
1. Soft - ly now the light of day Fades up - on my sight a - way;
2. Thou, whose all - per - vad - ing eye Naught es - capes, with - out, with - in,
3. Soon for me the light of day Shall for ev - er pass a - way;
4. Thou who, sin - less, yet hast known All of man's in - firm - i - ty,
Free from care, from la - bor free, Lord, I would commune with Thee.
Par - don each in - firm - i - ty, O - pen fault, and se - cret sin.
Then, from sin and sor - row free, Take me, Lord, to dwell with Thee.
Then, from Thine e - ter - nal throne, Je - sus, look with pity - ing eye. A - MEN.
Father of Love and Power
146
KIRBY BEDON. 6. 6. 4. 6. 6. 6. 4.
GEORGE RAWSON, 1807-1889
EDWARD BUNNETT, 1834-1923
In moderate time
1. Fa - ther of love and pow'r, Guard Thou our eve - ning hour,
2. Je - sus, Em - man - u - el, Come, in Thy love to dwell
3. Spir - it of ho - li - ness, Gen - tle, trans-form - ing grace,
Shield with Thy might; For all Thy care this day Our grate-ful thanks we
In hearts con - trite. For all our sins we grieve, But we Thy grace re -
In - dwell - ing light! Soothe Thou each weary breast, Now let Thy peace pos-

pay, And to our Fa - ther pray, Bless us to - night!
ceive, And in Thy word be - lieve; Bless us to - night!
sessed Calm us to per - fect rest; Bless us to - night! A - MEN.

Now God Be with Us, for the Night Is Closing

147

FLEMMING. 11. 11. 11. 5.

PETRUS HERBERT, ? -1571
Tr. by CATHERINE WINKWORTH, 1829-1878

FRIEDRICH F. FLEMMING, 1778-1813

Reverently, in moderate time

1. Now God be with us, for the night is clos - ing: The light and
2. Let peace-ful tho'ts be ours when sleep o'er-takes us, Our ear- liest
3. We have no ref - uge, none on earth to aid us, Save thee, O
4. Fa - ther, thy name be prais'd, thy king-dom giv - en, Thy will be
dark - ness are of his dis - pos - ing, And 'neath his shad - ow
tho'ts be thine when morn-ing wakes us, All day serve thee, in
Fa - ther, who thine own hast made us; But thy dear pres - ence
done on earth as 'tis in heav - en; Keep us in life, for -
here to rest we yield us, For he will shield us.
all that we are do - ing, Thy praise pur - su - ing.
will not leave them lone - ly Who seek thee on - ly.
give our sins, de - liv - er Us now and ev - er! A - MEN.

All Praise to Thee, My God, This Night

148

TALLIS' CANON. L. M.

THOMAS KEN, 1637-1711 — THOMAS TALLIS, c. 1520-1585

With dignity

1. All praise to Thee, my God, this night,
2. For - give me, Lord, for Thy dear Son,
3. Teach me to live, that I may dread
4. O may my soul on Thee re - pose,
5. Praise God, from whom all bless - ings flow;

For all the bless - ings of the light; Keep me, O keep me,
The ill that I this day have done, That with the world, my -
The grave as lit - tle as my bed; Teach me to die, that
And with sweet sleep mine eye - lids close; Sleep that may me more
Praise Him, all crea - tures here be - low; Praise Him a - bove, ye

King of kings, Be - neath Thine own al - might - y wings.
self, and Thee, I, ere I sleep, at peace may be.
so I may Rise glo - rious at the aw - ful day.
vig - orous make To serve my God when I a - wake.
heaven-ly host; Praise Fa - ther, Son, and Ho - ly Ghost. A - MEN.

Now the Day Is Over

MERRIAL. 6. 5. 6. 5.

149

Sabine Baring-Gould, 1834-1924
Joseph Barnby, 1838-1896
With graceful rhythm
1. Now the day is over, Night is drawing nigh,
2. Jesus, give the weary Calm and sweet repose;
3. Thro' the long night-watches May Thine angels spread
4. When the morning wakens, Then may I arise,
Shadows of the evening Steal across the sky.
With Thy ten-d'rest blessing May our eyelids close.
Their white wings above me, Watching round my bed.
Pure, and fresh, and sinless In Thy holy eyes.
A-men.
evening Steal a-cross the sky.
Sun of My Soul, Thou Saviour Dear
150
HURSLEY. L. M.
John Keble, 1792–1866
Katholisches Gesangbuch, Vienna, c. 1774
In moderate time
1. Sun of my soul, Thou Saviour dear, It is not night if Thou be near,
2. When soft the dews of kindly sleep My wearied eyelids gently steep,
3. Abide with me from morn till eve, For without Thee I cannot live;
4. Be near to bless me when I wake, Ere thro' the world my way I take;
O may no earth-born cloud arise To hide Thee from Thy servant's eyes.
Be my last tho't—how sweet to rest For-ever on my Saviour's breast.
Abide with me when night is nigh, For without Thee I dare not die.
Abide with me till, in Thy love, I lose myself in heav'n above.
A-men.

151 Lord of All Being, Throned Afar

LOUVAN. L. M.

OLIVER W. HOLMES, 1809-1896 — VIRGIL C. TAYLOR, 1817-1891, Alt. by B. F. W.

In moderate time, with dignity

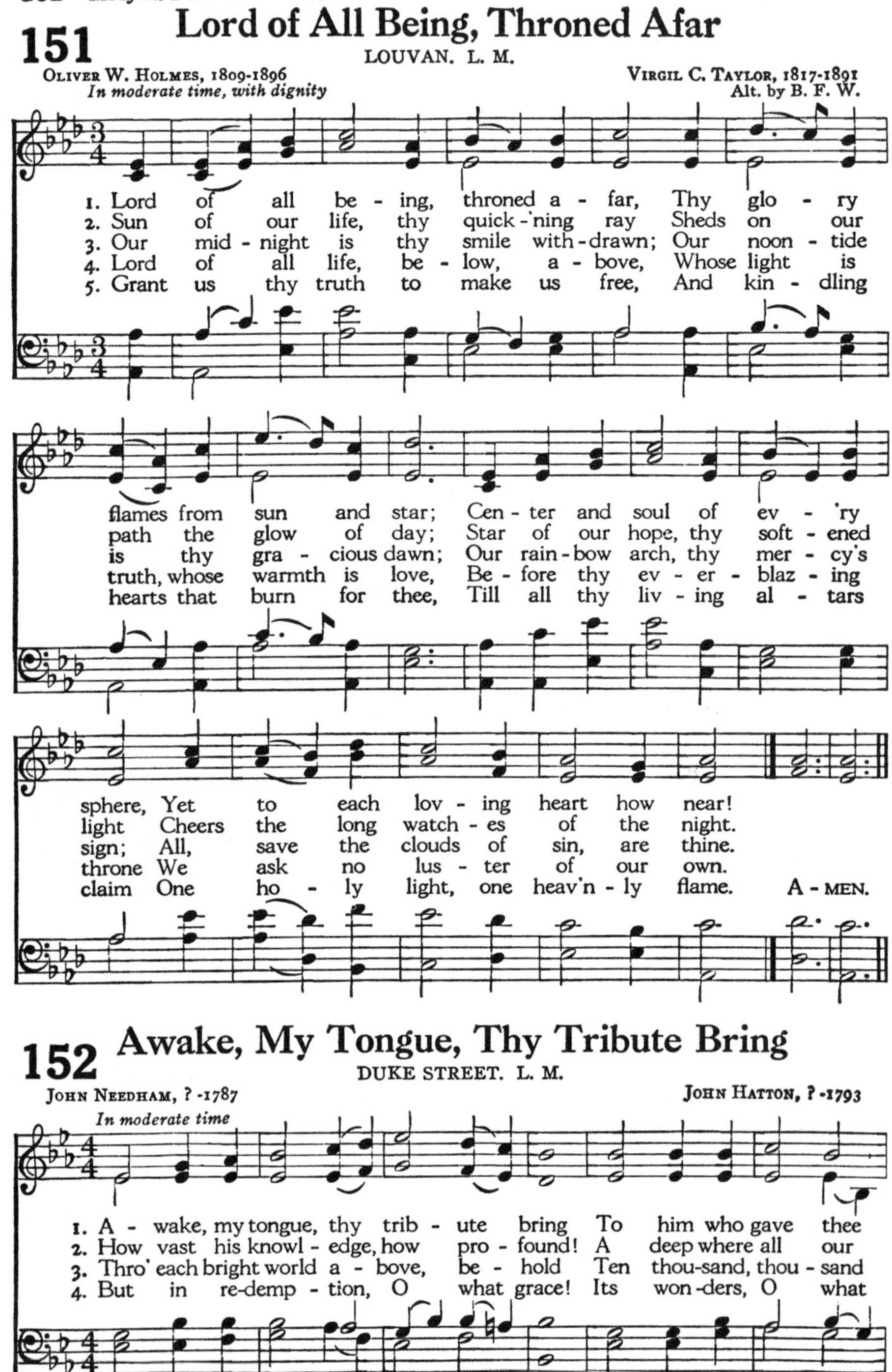
1. Lord of all be - ing, throned a - far, Thy glo - ry
2. Sun of our life, thy quick - 'ning ray Sheds on our
3. Our mid - night is thy smile with - drawn; Our noon - tide
4. Lord of all life, be - low, a - bove, Whose light is
5. Grant us thy truth to make us free, And kin - dling
flames from sun and star; Cen - ter and soul of ev - 'ry
path the glow of day; Star of our hope, thy soft - ened
is thy gra - cious dawn; Our rain - bow arch, thy mer - cy's
truth, whose warmth is love, Be - fore thy ev - er - blaz - ing
hearts that burn for thee, Till all thy liv - ing al - tars
sphere, Yet to each lov - ing heart how near!
light Cheers the long watch - es of the night.
sign; All, save the clouds of sin, are thine.
throne We ask no lus - ter of our own.
claim One ho - ly light, one heav'n - ly flame.
A - MEN.

152 Awake, My Tongue, Thy Tribute Bring

DUKE STREET. L. M.

JOHN NEEDHAM, ? -1787 — JOHN HATTON, ? -1793

In moderate time

1. A - wake, my tongue, thy trib - ute bring To him who gave thee
2. How vast his knowl - edge, how pro - found! A deep where all our
3. Thro' each bright world a - bove, be - hold Ten thou-sand, thou - sand
4. But in re-demp - tion, O what grace! Its won-ders, O what

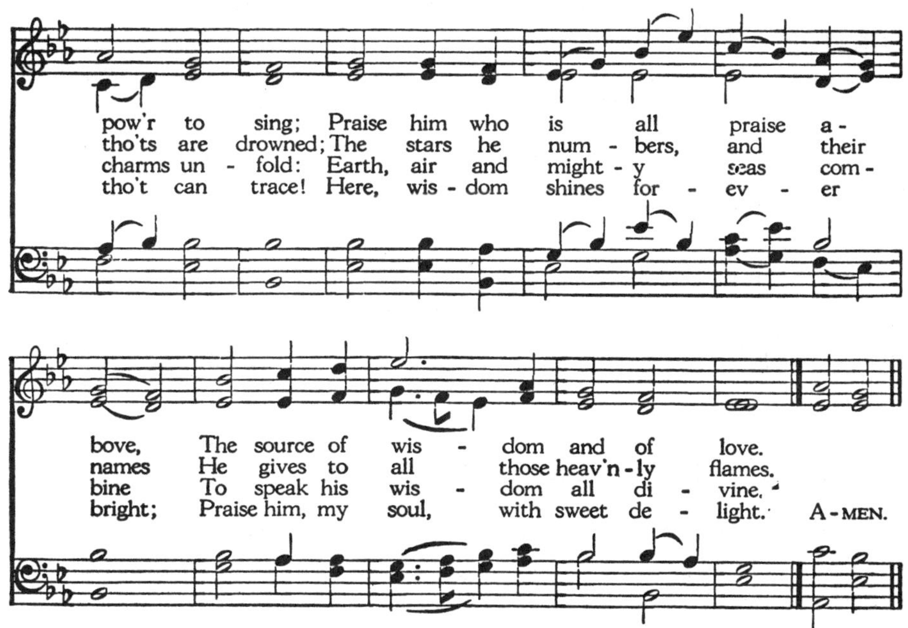
pow'r to sing; Praise him who is all praise a - bove, The source of wis - dom and of love.
tho'ts are drowned; The stars he num - bers, and their names He gives to all those heav'n - ly flames.
charms un - fold: Earth, air and might - y seas com - bine To speak his wis - dom all di - vine.
tho't can trace! Here, wis - dom shines for - ev - er bright; Praise him, my soul, with sweet de - light.
A - MEN.

Begin My Tongue, Some Heavenly Theme

MANOAH. C. M.

153

Isaac Watts, 1674–1748

From Henry W. Greatorex's Collection, 1851

In moderate time
1. Be - gin, my tongue, some heav'nly theme, And speak some boundless thing, The might-y works, or might-ier name, Of our e - ter - nal King.
2. Tell of His won-drous faith - ful - ness, And sound His pow'r a - broad; Sing the sweet prom-ise of His grace, The love and truth of God.
3. His ver - y word of grace is strong As that which built the skies; The voice that rolls the stars a - long Speaks all the prom-is - es.
4. O might I hear Thy heav'n-ly tongue But whis - per "Thou art mine!" Those gen-tle words should raise my song To notes al - most di - vine.
A - MEN.

O God, the Rock of Ages

154

MIRIAM. 7. 6. 7. 6. D.

EDWARD H. BICKERSTETH, 1825–1906
JOSEPH P. HOLBROOK, 1822–1888
In moderate time, with dignity
1. O God, the Rock of A - ges, Who ev - er-more has been,
2. Our years are like the shad - ows On sun - ny hills that lie,
3. O thou, who canst not slum - ber, Whose light grows nev - er pale,
4. Lord, crown our faith's en - deav - or With beau - ty and with grace,
What time the tem - pest ra - ges, Our dwell - ing-place se - rene:
Or grass - es in the mead - ows That blos - som but to die:
Teach us a - right to num - ber Our years be - fore they fail.
Till, clothed in light for - ev - er, We see thee face to face:
Be - fore thy first cre - a - tions, O Lord, the same as now,
A sleep, a dream, a sto - ry, By stran - gers quick - ly told,
On us thy mer - cy light - en, On us thy good - ness rest,
A joy no lan - guage meas - ures, A foun - tain brim - ming o'er,
To end - less gen - er - a - tions, The Ev - er - last - ing Thou!
An un - re-main - ing glo - ry Of things that soon are old.
And let thy Spir - it bright - en The hearts thy - self hath blessed.
An end - less flow of pleas - ures, An o - cean with - out shore. A - MEN.

A Mighty Fortress Is Our God

EIN' FESTE BURG. 8. 7. 8. 7. 6. 6. 6. 6. 7.

155

Martin Luther, 1483–1546
Tr. by Frederick H. Hedge, 1805–1890

Martin Luther, 1483–1546

In moderate time, with great dignity

1. A might-y for-tress is our God, A bul-wark nev-er fail-ing;
2. Did we in our own strength con-fide, Our striv-ing would be los-ing;
3. And though this world, with dev-ils filled, Should threat-en to un-do us,
4. That word a-bove all earth-ly powers, No thanks to them, a-bid-eth;
Our help-er He, a-mid the flood Of mor-tal ills pre-vail-ing:
Were not the right Man on our side, The Man of God's own choos-ing:
We will not fear, for God hath willed His truth to tri-umph through us:
The Spir-it and the gifts are ours Through Him who with us sid-eth:
For still our an-cient foe Doth seek to work us woe; His craft and power are great,
Dost ask who that may be? Christ Je-sus, it is He; Lord Sa-ba-oth, His name,
The Prince of Dark-ness grim—We trem-ble not for him; His rage we can en-dure,
Let goods and kin-dred go, This mor-tal life al-so; The bod-y they may kill:
And, armed with cru-el hate, On earth is not his e-qual.
From age to age the same, And He must win the bat-tle.
For lo, his doom is sure, One lit-tle word shall fell him.
God's truth a-bid-eth still, His king-dom is for-ev-er. A-MEN.

Lord, Thy Glory Fills the Heaven

156

FABEN. 8. 7. 8. 7. D.

RICHARD MANT, 1776-1848
JOHN H. WILLCOX, 1827-1875
Joyously
1. Lord, Thy glo - ry fills the heav - en; Earth is with its ful - ness stored;
2. Ev - er thus in God's high prais - es, Breth-ren, let our tongues u - nite,
3. Lord, Thy glo - ry fills the heav - en; Earth is with its ful - ness stored;
Un - to Thee be glo - ry giv - en, Ho - ly, ho - ly, ho - ly Lord!
While our tho'ts His greatness rais - es, And our love His gifts ex - cite:
Un - to Thee be glo - ry giv - en, Ho - ly, ho - ly, ho - ly Lord!
Heav'n is still with an-thems ring - ing; Earth takes up the an - gels' cry,
With His ser - aph train be - fore Him, With His ho - ly Church be - low,
Thus Thy glo - rious name con - fess - ing, We a - dopt the an - gels' cry,
Ho - ly, ho - ly, ho - ly, sing - ing, Lord of hosts, Thou Lord most high.
Thus u - nite we to a - dore Him, Bid we thus our an - them flow.
Ho - ly, ho - ly, ho - ly, bless - ing Thee, the Lord our God most high!
A - MEN.

All Creatures of Our God and King

LASST UNS ERFREUEN. 8. 8. 4. 4. 8. 8. with Alleluias **157**

ST. FRANCIS OF ASSISI, 1182–1226
Tr. by WILLIAM H. DRAPER, 1855–1933

Melody from GEISTLICHE KIRCHENGESÄNG, 1623

With dignity, in moderate time

1. All crea-tures of our God and King, Lift up your voice and with us sing Al-le-lu-ia! Al-le-lu-ia! Thou burn-ing sun with gold-en beam, Thou sil-ver moon with soft-er gleam! O praise Him, O praise Him! Al-le-lu-ia! Al-le-lu-ia! Al-le-lu-ia!
2. Thou rush-ing wind that art so strong, Ye clouds that sail in heaven a-long, O praise Him! Al-le-lu-ia! Thou ris-ing morn, in praise re-joice, Ye lights of eve-ning, find a voice! O praise Him,
3. Dear moth-er earth, who day by day Un-fold-est bless-ings on our way, O praise Him! Al-le-lu-ia! The flowers and fruits that in thee grow, Let them His glo-ry al-so show! O praise Him,
4. And all ye men of ten-der heart, For-giv-ing oth-ers, take your part, O sing ye! Al-le-lu-ia! Ye who long pain and sor-row bear, Praise God and on Him cast your care! O praise Him,
A-MEN.

God of Our Fathers, the Strength of Our People

158

LOBE DEN HERREN. 14. 14. 4. 7. 8.

WINFRED E. GARRISON, 1874-

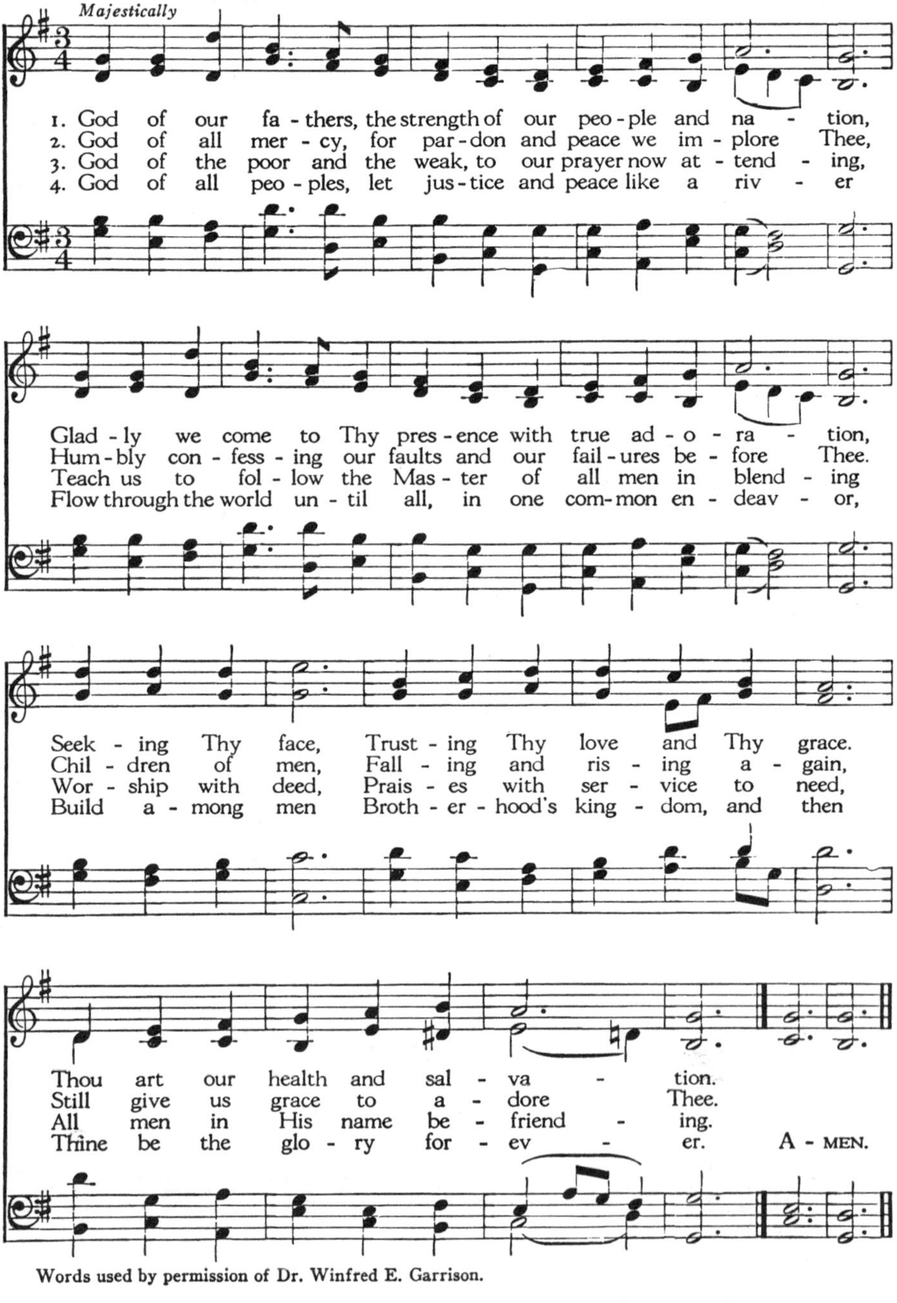

STRALSUND GESANGBUCH, 1665
Arr. in PRAXIS PIETATIS MELICA, 1668

Majestically

1. God of our fa - thers, the strength of our peo - ple and na - tion,
2. God of all mer - cy, for par - don and peace we im - plore Thee,
3. God of the poor and the weak, to our prayer now at - tend - ing,
4. God of all peo - ples, let jus - tice and peace like a riv - er

Glad - ly we come to Thy pres - ence with true ad - o - ra - tion,
Hum - bly con - fess - ing our faults and our fail - ures be - fore Thee.
Teach us to fol - low the Mas - ter of all men in blend - ing
Flow through the world un - til all, in one com - mon en - deav - or,

Seek - ing Thy face, Trust - ing Thy love and Thy grace.
Chil - dren of men, Fall - ing and ris - ing a - gain,
Wor - ship with deed, Prais - es with ser - vice to need,
Build a - mong men Broth - er - hood's king - dom, and then

Thou art our health and sal - va - tion.
Still give us grace to a - dore Thee.
All men in His name be - friend - ing.
Thine be the glo - ry for - ev - er. A - MEN.

Immortal, Invisible, God Only Wise

JOANNA. 11. 11. 11. 11.
159
Walter Chalmers Smith, 1824–1908
Welsh hymn melody
In moderate time, with flowing rhythm
1. Im - mor - tal, in - vis - i - ble, God on - ly wise,
2. Un - rest - ing, un - hast - ing, and si - lent as light,
3. To all, life Thou giv - est— to both great and small;
4. Great Fa - ther of Glo - ry, pure Fa - ther of Light,
In light in - ac - ces - si - ble hid from our eyes,
Nor want - ing nor wast - ing, Thou rul - est in might;
In all life Thou liv - est, the true life of all;
Thine an - gels a - dore Thee, all veil - ing their sight;
Most bless - ed, most glo - rious, the An - cient of Days,
Thy jus - tice like moun - tains high soar - ing a - bove
We blos - som and flour - ish as leaves on the tree,
All praise we would ren - der; O help us to see
Al - might - y, vic - to - rious, Thy great Name we praise.
Thy clouds which are foun - tains of good - ness and love.
And with - er and per - ish—but naught chang - eth Thee.
'Tis on - ly the splen - dor of light hid - eth Thee!
A - men.

Mighty God, While Angels Bless Thee

160

AUTUMN. 8. 7. 8. 7. D.

ROBERT ROBINSON, 1735–1790

Adapted from the GENEVAN PSALTER, 1551

In moderate time

1. Might - y God, while an - gels bless Thee, May a mor - tal sing Thy name?
2. For the gran - deur of Thy na - ture, Grand be - yond a ser - aph's thought;
3. Brightness of the Fa - ther's glo - ry, Shall Thy praise un - ut - tered lie?

Lord of men as well as an - gels, Thou art ev - 'ry crea - ture's theme.
For the won - ders of cre - a - tion, Works with skill and kind - ness wrought;
Break, my tongue, such guilt - y si - lence! Sing the Lord who came to die.

Lord of ev - 'ry land and na - tion, An - cient of e - ter - nal days,
For Thy prov - i - dence, that gov - erns, Thro' Thine em - pire's wide do - main,
From the high - est throne of glo - ry To the cross of deep - est woe,

Sound - ed thro' the wide cre - a - tion Be Thy just and end - less praise.
Wings an an - gel, guides a spar - row, Bless - ed be Thy gen - tle reign.
All to ran - som guilt - y cap - tives; Flow my praise, for - ev - er flow! A - MEN.

Eternal Spirit, Evermore Creating

FINLANDIA. 11. 10. 11. 10. 11. 10.

161

HENRY B. ROBINS — JEAN SIBELIUS, 1865-1957.

In moderate time
1. E - ter - nal Spir - it, ev - er-more cre - at - ing, Through-out Thy liv - ing
2. O Thou in Whom a ho - ly full - ness dwell-eth, Who hast the mys - tic
3. Lost in the maze of pur - pos - es con - tend-ing, In the dark night of
4. O Thou on Whom our hu - man good de - pend-eth, Who from of old hath
u - ni-verse far - flung Thy pur-pose throbs in puls - es un - a - bat-ing,
fount of life with-in, Whose quick'ning Spir - it where it list - eth tell-eth
mor-tal strife and pain, Spread Thou the man - tle of Thy love un - end-ing,
been Thy peo-ple's stay, Whose boun-ty like the gen - tle rain de-scend-eth,
Thy glo - ry by the morn-ing star is sung— Yet this fair earth is
How man may tri - umph o - ver death and sin— Flood Thou our souls, Thou
Round the be - wil - dered, and their way make plain! Gird those brave souls, up -
And like the dew is fresh from day to day, Quicken our spir - its,
in the shad-ow wait-ing Where hu-man hearts by bit - ter - ness are wrung!
pres-ence pu - ri - fy - ing, Help us our bat - tle for the right to win!
on Thy will de-pend-ing, Who rise to build the com-mon weal a - gain!
as we wait ex-pect-ant, That we may go in strength up - on our way! A-MEN.

Words used by permission of the author, Henry B. Robins. Music used by permission of the Presbyterian Board of Christian Education, owner of the special arrangement of this tune, made in 1932.

God Moves in a Mysterious Way

162

DUNDEE. C. M.

William Cowper, 1731–1800

Scottish Psalter, 1615

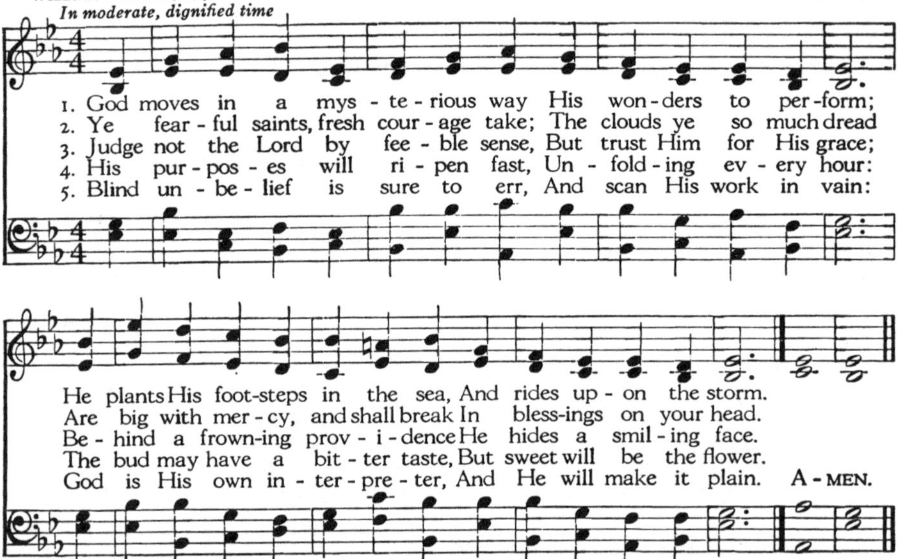

In moderate, dignified time

1. God moves in a mys - te - rious way His won-ders to per-form;
He plants His foot-steps in the sea, And rides up - on the storm.
2. Ye fear - ful saints, fresh cour - age take; The clouds ye so much dread
Are big with mer - cy, and shall break In bless-ings on your head.
3. Judge not the Lord by fee - ble sense, But trust Him for His grace;
Be - hind a frown-ing prov - i - dence He hides a smil - ing face.
4. His pur - pos - es will ri - pen fast, Un - fold - ing ev - ery hour:
The bud may have a bit - ter taste, But sweet will be the flower.
5. Blind un - be - lief is sure to err, And scan His work in vain:
God is His own in - ter - pre - ter, And He will make it plain. A - men.

O God, Whose Smile Is in the Sky

163

AVON (MARTYRDOM). C. M.

John Haynes Holmes, 1879–

Hugh Wilson, 1766–1824

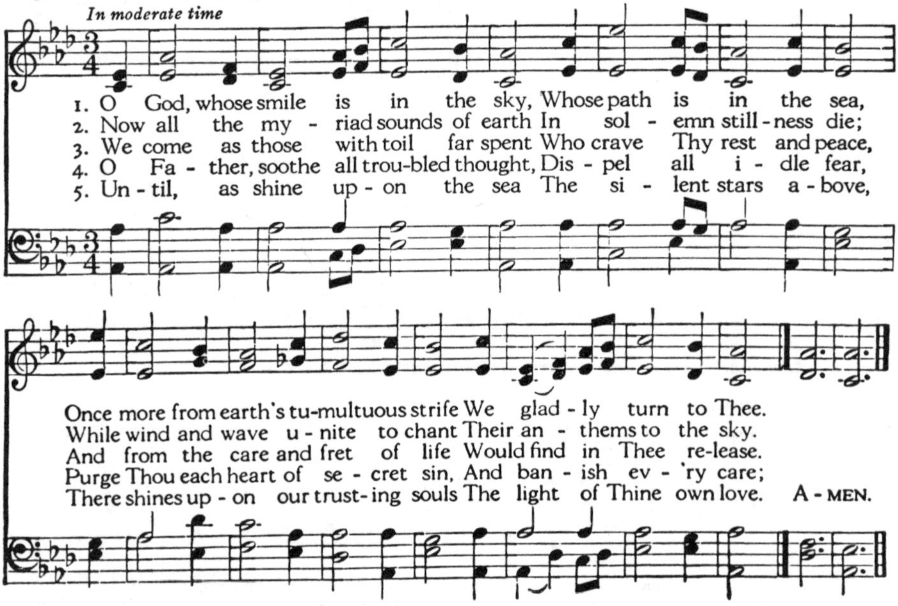

In moderate time

1. O God, whose smile is in the sky, Whose path is in the sea,
Once more from earth's tu-multuous strife We glad - ly turn to Thee.
2. Now all the my - riad sounds of earth In sol - emn still - ness die;
While wind and wave u - nite to chant Their an - thems to the sky.
3. We come as those with toil far spent Who crave Thy rest and peace,
And from the care and fret of life Would find in Thee re-lease.
4. O Fa - ther, soothe all trou-bled thought, Dis - pel all i - dle fear,
Purge Thou each heart of se - cret sin, And ban - ish ev - 'ry care;
5. Un - til, as shine up - on the sea The si - lent stars a - bove,
There shines up - on our trust - ing souls The light of Thine own love. A - men.

The Spacious Firmament on High

CREATION. L. M. D.

164

JOSEPH ADDISON, 1672–1719

FRANZ JOSEPH HAYDN, 1732–1809

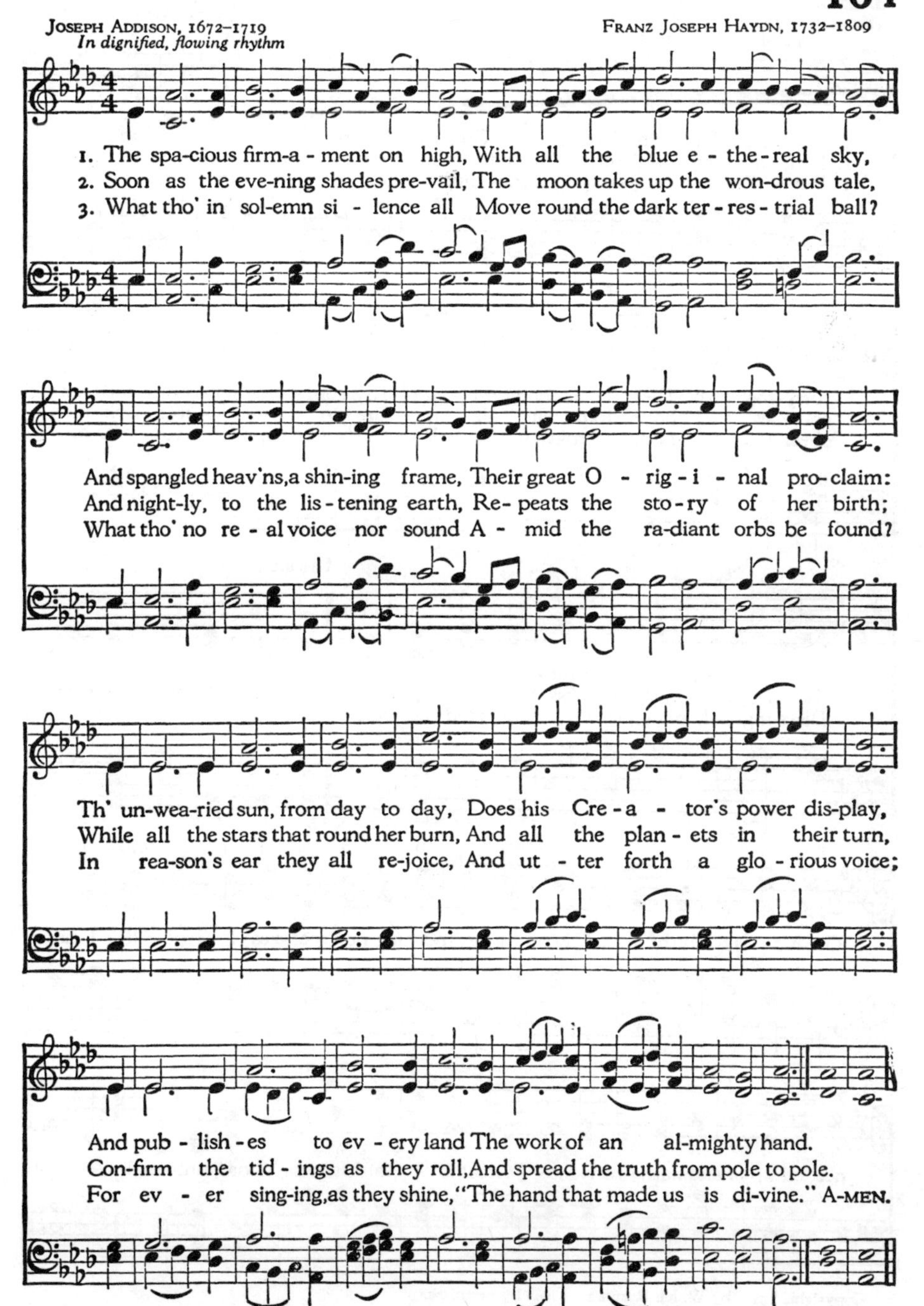
In dignified, flowing rhythm
1. The spa-cious firm-a - ment on high, With all the blue e - the - real sky,
2. Soon as the eve-ning shades pre-vail, The moon takes up the won-drous tale,
3. What tho' in sol-emn si - lence all Move round the dark ter - res - trial ball?
And spangled heav'ns, a shin-ing frame, Their great O - rig - i - nal pro-claim:
And night-ly, to the lis - tening earth, Re - peats the sto - ry of her birth;
What tho' no re - al voice nor sound A - mid the ra-diant orbs be found?
Th' un-wea-ried sun, from day to day, Does his Cre - a - tor's power dis-play,
While all the stars that round her burn, And all the plan - ets in their turn,
In rea-son's ear they all re-joice, And ut - ter forth a glo - rious voice;
And pub - lish - es to ev - ery land The work of an al-mighty hand.
Con-firm the tid - ings as they roll, And spread the truth from pole to pole.
For ev - er sing-ing, as they shine, "The hand that made us is di-vine." A-MEN.

Great Is Thy Faithfulness

165

FAITHFULNESS. 11. 10. 11. 10. with Refrain

THOMAS O. CHISHOLM, 1866–

WILLIAM M. RUNYAN, 1870–

In moderate time, with dignity

1. "Great is Thy faith-ful-ness," O God my Fa-ther, There is no shad-ow of
2. Sum-mer and win-ter, and springtime and harvest, Sun, moon and stars in their
3. Par-don for sin and a peace that en-dur-eth, Thy own dear pres-ence to
turn-ing with Thee; Thou chang-est not, Thy com-pas-sions, they fail not;
cours-es a-bove, Join with all na-ture in man-i-fold wit-ness
cheer and to guide; Strength for to-day and bright hope for to-mor-row,
As Thou hast been Thou for-ev-er wilt be.
To Thy great faith-ful-ness, mer-cy and love.
Bless-ings all mine, with ten thou-sand be-side!
CHORUS
"Great is Thy faith-ful-ness!
Great is Thy faithfulness!" Morning by morning new mer-cies I see; All I have
needed Thy hand hath pro-vided—"Great is Thy faithfulness," Lord, unto me! A-MEN.

Unto the Hills Around Do I Lift Up

SANDON. 10. 4. 10. 4. 10. 10.

166

From Psalm cxxi. JOHN CAMPBELL, DUKE OF ARGYLL, 1845-1914

CHARLES HENRY PURDAY, 1799-1885

In moderate time

1. Unto the hills around do I lift up My longing eyes; O whence for me shall my salvation come, From whence arise? From God the Lord doth come my certain aid, From God the Lord who heaven and earth hath made.

2. He will not suffer that thy foot be moved: Safe shalt thou be. No careless slumber shall His eyelids close, Who keepeth thee. Behold, He sleepeth not, He slumbereth ne'er, Who keepeth Israel in His holy care.

3. Jehovah is Himself thy keeper true, Thy changeless shade; Jehovah thy defense on thy right hand Himself hath made. And thee no sun by day shall ever smite; No moon shall harm thee in the silent night.

4. From every evil shall He keep thy soul, From every sin; Jehovah shall preserve thy going out, Thy coming in. Above thee watching, He whom we adore Shall keep thee henceforth, yea, forevermore. A-MEN.

For the Beauty of the Earth

167

DIX. 7. 7. 7. 7. 7. 7.

Folliott S. Pierpoint, 1835-1917

From a chorale by
Conrad Kocher, 1786-1872

Joyfully
1. For the beau - ty of the earth, For the glo - ry of the skies,
2. For the beau - ty of each hour Of the day and of the night,
3. For the joy of ear and eye; For the heart and mind's de - light;
4. For the joy of hu - man love, Broth - er, sis - ter, par - ent, child,
For the love which from our birth O - ver and a - round us lies:
Hill and vale, and tree and flower, Sun and moon, and stars of light:
For the mys - tic har - mo - ny Link - ing sense to sound and sight:
Friends on earth, and friends a - bove; For all gen - tle thoughts and mild:
Lord of all, to Thee we raise This our hymn of grate - ful praise. A-men.

From "Enlarged Songs of Praise." Permission Estate of F. S. Pierpont and Oxford University Press.

How Strong and Sweet My Father's Care

168

EUDORA. 8. 8. 8. 4.

Anonymous

J. R. Murray

Like a prayer
1. How strong and sweet my Fa-ther's care, That round a - bout me, like the air,
2. O keep me ev - er in Thy love, Dear Fa - ther, watching from a - bove;

Is with me al-ways, ev-ery - where! He cares for me.
And let me still Thy mer-cy prove, And care for me. A - MEN.

The King of Love my Shepherd Is

DOMINUS REGIT ME. 8. 7. 8. 7.

169

HENRY W. BAKER, 1821–1877 JOHN B. DYKES, 1823–1876

In moderate time
1. The King of love my Shep - herd is,
2. Where streams of liv - ing wa - ter flow
3. Per - verse and fool - ish oft I strayed,
4. In death's dark vale I fear no ill
5. Thou spread'st a ta - ble in my sight;
6. And so through all the length of days
Whose good - ness fail - eth nev - er; I noth - ing lack if
My ran - somed soul He lead - eth, And where the ver - dant
But yet in love He sought me, And on His shoul - der
With Thee, dear Lord, be - side me; Thy rod and staff my
Thy unc - tion grace be - stow - eth; And O what trans-port
Thy good - ness fail - eth nev - er: Good Shep - herd, may I
I am His And He is mine for - ev - er.
pas - tures grow, With food ce - les - tial feed - eth.
gen - tly laid, And home, re - joic - ing, brought me.
com - fort still, Thy cross be - fore to guide me.
of de - light From Thy pure chal - ice flow - eth.
sing Thy praise With - in Thy house for - ev - er. A - MEN.

The Lord Is My Shepherd

170

POLAND (KOSCHAT). 11. 11. 11. 11.

JAMES MONTGOMERY, 1771–1854

THOMAS KOSCHAT, 1845–1914

In moderate time

1. The Lord is my Shep-herd, no want shall I know; I feed in green
pas-tures, safe-fold-ed I rest; He lead-eth my soul where the
still wa-ters flow, Re-stores me when wan-d'ring, re-deems when op-
pressed, Re-stores me when wand'ring, re-deems when op-pressed.

2. Thro' the val-ley and shad-ow of death tho' I stray, Since Thou art my
Guard-ian, no e-vil I fear; Thy rod shall de-fend me, Thy
staff be my stay; No harm can be-fall with my Com-fort-er
near, No harm can be-fall with my Com-fort-er near.

3. In the midst of af-flic-tion my ta-ble is spread; With bless-ings un-
meas-ured my cup run-neth o'er; With per-fume and oil Thou a-
noint-est my head: O what shall I ask of Thy prov-i-dence
more? O what shall I ask of Thy prov-i-dence more?

4. Let good-ness and mer-cy, my boun-ti-ful God, Still fol-low my
steps till I meet Thee a-bove; I seek, by the path which my
fore-fa-thers trod Thro' the land of their so-journ, Thy king-dom of
love, Thro' the land of their so-journ, Thy king-dom of love.

A-MEN.

This Is My Father's World

TERRA PATRIS. S. M. D.

171

MALTBIE D. BABCOCK, 1858–1901

FRANKLIN L. SHEPPARD, 1852–1930
Har. by EDWARD SHIPPEN BARNES, 1887–

Joyfully

1. This is my Fa - ther's world, And to my lis - tening ears,
2. This is my Fa - ther's world, The birds their car - ols raise,
3. This is my Fa - ther's world, O let me ne'er for - get

All na - ture sings, and round me rings The mu - sic of the spheres.
The morn - ing light, the lil - y white, De - clare their Mak - er's praise.
That though the wrong seems oft so strong, God is the Rul - er yet.

This is my Fa-ther's world: I rest me in the thought Of
This is my Fa-ther's world: He shines in all that's fair; In the
This is my Fa-ther's world: The bat - tle is not done; Je -

rocks and trees, of skies and seas; His hand the won - ders wrought.
rus - tling grass I hear Him pass, He speaks to me ev-ery-where.
sus who died shall be sat - is - fied, And earth and heaven be one. A-MEN.

There's a Wideness in God's Mercy

172

RICHARDS. 8. 7. 8. 7. D.

FREDERICK W. FABER, 1814-1863 (*First Tune*) Arranged from EMMELAR

In moderate time
1. There's a wide - ness in God's mer - cy, Like the wide - ness of the sea:
2. Was there ev - er kind - est shep - herd Half so gen - tle, half so sweet
3. There is no place where earth's sor - rows Are more felt than up in heav'n;
4. For the love of God is broad - er Than the meas - ure of man's mind;
There's a kind - ness in His jus - tice, Which is more than lib - er - ty.
As the Sav - iour, who would have us Come and gath - er round His feet?
There is no place where earth's fail - ings Have such kind - ly judg - ment giv'n.
And the heart of the E - ter - nal Is most won - der - ful - ly kind.
There is wel - come for the sin - ner, And more gra - ces for the good;
It is God; His love looks might - y, But is might - ier than it seems;
There is plen - ti - ful re - demp - tion In the blood that has been shed;
If our love were but more sim - ple, We should take Him at His word;
There is mer - cy with the Sav - iour; There is heal - ing in His blood.
'Tis our Fa - ther; and His fond - ness Goes far out be - yond our dreams.
There is joy for all the mem - bers In the sor - rows of the Head.
And our lives would be all sun - shine In the sweet - ness of our Lord. A - MEN.

There's a Wideness in God's Mercy

WELLESLEY. 8. 7. 8. 7.
173
FREDERICK W. FABER, 1814–1863
(Second Tune)
In moderate time
LIZZIE S. TOURJEE, 1858–1913
1. There's a wide-ness in God's mer-cy, Like the wide-ness of the sea;
2. There is wel-come for the sin-ner, And more grac-es for the good;
3. For the love of God is broad-er Than the meas-ure of man's mind,
4. If our love were but more sim-ple, We should take Him at His word;
There's a kind-ness in His jus-tice, Which is more than lib-er-ty.
There is mer-cy with the Sav-iour; There is heal-ing in His blood.
And the heart of the E-ter-nal Is most won-der-ful-ly kind.
And our lives would be all sun-shine In the sweet-ness of our Lord. A-MEN.
O God of Bethel, by Whose Hand
PHILLIP DODDRIDGE, 1702–1751
JOHN LOGAN, 1748–1788
As in SCOTTISH PARAPHRASES, 1781
DUNDEE. C. M.
174
SCOTTISH PSALTER, 1615
With stately rhythm
1. O God of Beth-el, by whose hand Thy peo-ple still are fed;
2. Our vows, our prayers, we now pre-sent Be-fore Thy throne of grace;
3. Through each per-plex-ing path of life Our wan-dering foot-steps guide;
4. O spread Thy cov-ering wings a-round Till all our wan-derings cease,
5. Such bless-ings from Thy gra-cious hand Our hum-ble prayers im-plore;
Who through this wea-ry pil-grim-age Hast all our fa-thers led,
God of our fa-thers, be the God Of their suc-ceed-ing race.
Give us each day our dai-ly bread, And rai-ment fit pro-vide.
And at our Fa-ther's loved a-bode Our souls ar-rive in peace.
And Thou shalt be our cho-sen God, And por-tion ev-er-more. A-MEN.

O God, Whose Love Is Over All

175

DENVER. C. M. D.

John Haynes Holmes, 1879–   H. Houseley

In moderate time

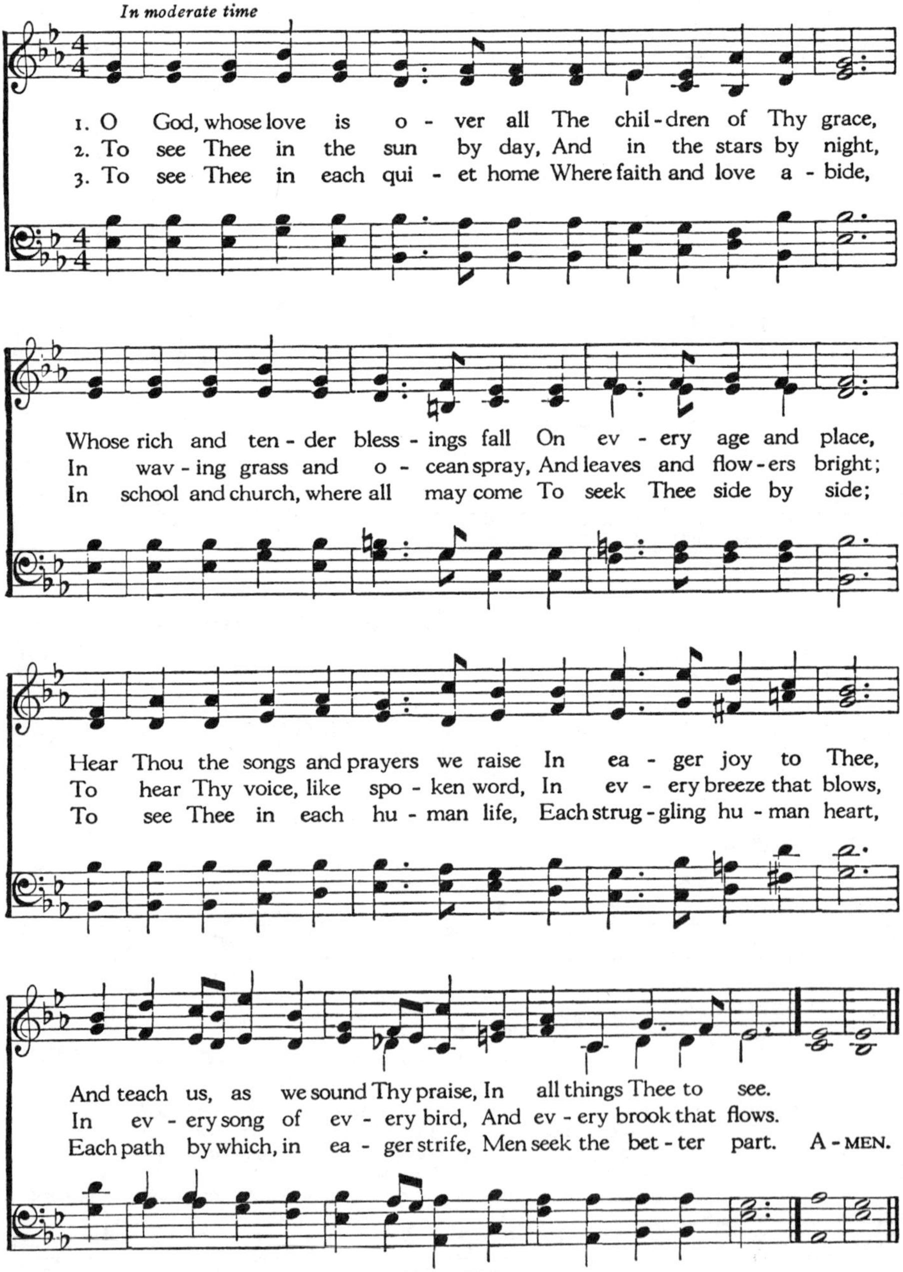

1. O God, whose love is o - ver all The chil - dren of Thy grace,
2. To see Thee in the sun by day, And in the stars by night,
3. To see Thee in each qui - et home Where faith and love a - bide,

Whose rich and ten - der bless - ings fall On ev - ery age and place,
In wav - ing grass and o - cean spray, And leaves and flow - ers bright;
In school and church, where all may come To seek Thee side by side;

Hear Thou the songs and prayers we raise In ea - ger joy to Thee,
To hear Thy voice, like spo - ken word, In ev - ery breeze that blows,
To see Thee in each hu - man life, Each strug - gling hu - man heart,

And teach us, as we sound Thy praise, In all things Thee to see.
In ev - ery song of ev - ery bird, And ev - ery brook that flows.
Each path by which, in ea - ger strife, Men seek the bet - ter part. A - MEN.

To God Our Hearts We Lift

NUN DANKET. 6. 7. 6. 7. 6. 6. 6. 6.

176

THOMAS TIPLADY, 1882–

In moderate time

JOHANN CRÜGER, 1598–1662

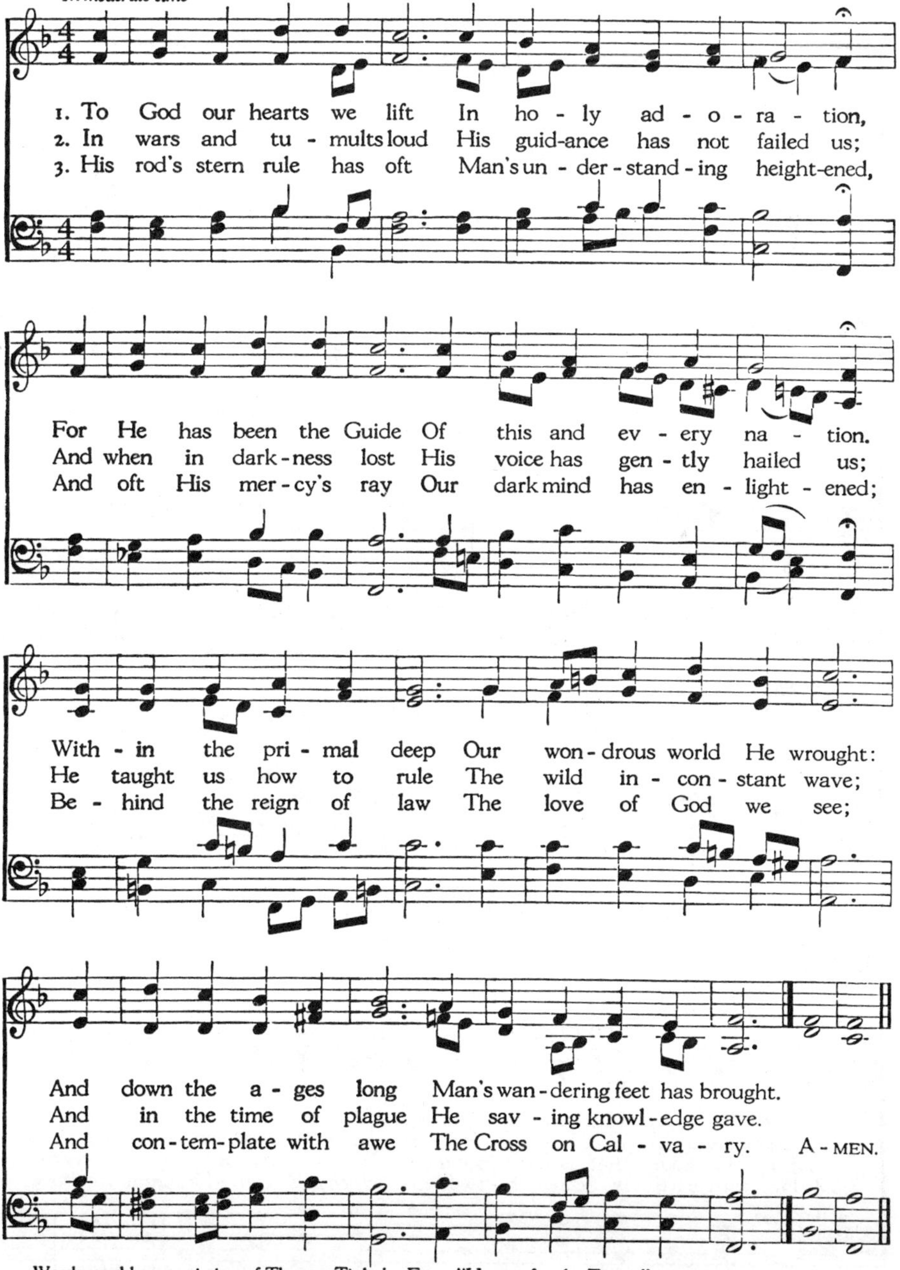

1. To God our hearts we lift In ho - ly ad - o - ra - tion,
2. In wars and tu - mults loud His guid-ance has not failed us;
3. His rod's stern rule has oft Man's un - der - stand - ing height-ened,

For He has been the Guide Of this and ev - ery na - tion.
And when in dark - ness lost His voice has gen - tly hailed us;
And oft His mer - cy's ray Our dark mind has en - light - ened;

With - in the pri - mal deep Our won - drous world He wrought:
He taught us how to rule The wild in - con - stant wave;
Be - hind the reign of law The love of God we see;

And down the a - ges long Man's wan - dering feet has brought.
And in the time of plague He sav - ing knowl - edge gave.
And con - tem - plate with awe The Cross on Cal - va - ry. A - MEN.

Life of Ages, Richly Poured

177
POSEN. 7. 7. 7. 7.
Samuel Johnson, 1822–1882
George C. Strattner, 1650–1705
With dignity
1. Life of a - ges, rich - ly poured, Love of God, un - spent and free, Flow - ing in the proph - et's word And the peo - ple's lib - er - ty,—
2. Breath - ing in the think-er's creed, Puls - ing in the he - ro's blood, Nerv - ing sim - plest thought and deed, Fresh - 'ning time with truth and good,
3. Con - se - crat - ing art and song, Ho - ly book and pil - grim track, Hurl - ing floods of ty - rant wrong From the sa - cred lim - its back,—
4. Life of a - ges, rich - ly poured, Love of God, un - spent and free, Flow still in the proph - et's word And the peo - ple's lib - er - ty!
A - MEN.
God Is Love; His Mercy Brightens
178
CARTER. 8. 7. 8. 7.
John Bowring, 1792–1872
Edmund S. Carter, 1845–?
In moderate time
1. God is love; His mer - cy bright-ens All the path in which we rove;
2. Chance and change are bus - y ev - er; Man de - cays, and a - ges move;
3. E'en the hour that dark-est seem-eth Will His change-less good-ness prove;
4. He with earth - ly cares en - twin-eth Hope and com - fort from a - bove;

Bliss He wakes and woe He lightens; God is wis-dom, God is love.
But His mer-cy wan-eth nev-er; God is wis-dom, God is love.
From the mist His brightness streameth; God is wis-dom, God is love.
Ev-ery-where His glo-ry shin-eth; God is wis-dom, God is love. A-MEN.

O God, in Whom We Live and Move

179

BELOIT. L. M.

SAMUEL LONGFELLOW, 1819–1892

CARL G. REISSIGER, 1798–1859

In moderate time
1. O God, in whom we live and move, Thy love is law, Thy law is love; Thy present Spirit waits to fill The soul which comes to do Thy will.
2. Unto Thy children's spirits teach Thy love, beyond the powers of speech; And make them know, with joyful awe, Th'encircling presence of Thy law.
3. Its patient working doth fulfil Man's hope, and God's all-perfect will, Nor suffers one true word or thought, Or deed of love, to come to nought.
4. Such faith, O God, our spirits fill, That we may work in patience still. Who works for justice, works for Thee; Who works in love, Thy child shall be. A-MEN.

God Speaks to Us in Bird and Song

180

CHILDHOOD. 8. 8. 8. 6.

J. JOHNSON, 1849–1926 — From A STUDENTS' HYMNAL, University of Wales, 1923

In moderate time

1. God speaks to us in bird and song; In winds that drift the clouds a - long; A - bove the din of toil and wrong, A mel - o - dy of love.
2. God speaks to us in far and near; In peace of home and friends most dear; From the dim past, and pres - ent clear, A mel - o - dy of love.
3. God speaks to us in dark - est night; By qui-et ways through morn-ings bright, When shad - ows fall with eve - ning light, A mel - o - dy of love.
4. God speaks to us in ev - ery land, On wave-lapped shore and si - lent strand; By kiss of child, and touch of hand, A mel - o - dy of love.
5. O voice di - vine, speak Thou to me! Be - yond the earth, be - yond the sea; First let me hear, then sing to Thee A mel - o - dy of love. A-MEN.

Music from "A Students' Hymnal." By permission of the Oxford University Press. Words from "The Christian Hymnary." Copyright owned by Miss E. R. Johnson. Used by permission.

Let Us with a Gladsome Mind

181

INNOCENTS. 7. 7. 7. 7.

JOHN MILTON, 1608–1674 — From THE PARISH CHOIR, 1850

Joyously

1. Let us with a glad - some mind Praise the Lord, for He is kind;
2. He, with all com-mand - ing might, Filled the new-made world with light;
3. All things liv - ing He doth feed; His full hand sup - plies their need:

For His mer - cies aye en - dure, Ev - er faith-ful, ev - er sure. A-MEN.

O Come, O Come, Emmanuel

VENI EMMANUEL. 8. 8. 8. 8. 8. 8.

182

From Latin, 12th century
Stanza 1 Tr. by JOHN M. NEALE, 1818–1866
Stanzas 2, 3 Tr. by HENRY S. COFFIN, 1877-1954
Ancient plain song, 13th century
Unison; with spirit
1. O come, O come, Em - man - - - u - el, And ran - som cap - tive
2. O come, Thou Wis - dom from on high, And or - der all things,
3. O come, De - sire of na - tions, bind All peo - ples in one
Is - - - ra - el, That mourns in lone - ly ex - - ile here
far and nigh; To us the path of know - ledge show,
heart and mind; Bid en - vy, strife, and quar - rels cease;
Un - til the Son of God ap - pear. Re - joice! Re - joice! Em -
And cause us in her ways to go. Re - joice! Re - joice! Em -
Fill the whole world with heav - en's peace. Re - joice! Re - joice! Em -
man - u - el Shall come to thee, O Is - - - ra - el!
man - u - el Shall come to thee, O Is - - - ra - el!
man - u - el Shall come to thee, O Is - - - ra - el! A - MEN.

Watchman, Tell Us of the Night

183

WATCHMAN. 7. 7. 7. 7. D.

JOHN BOWRING, 1792–1872
In moderate time
LOWELL MASON, 1792–1872
1. Watch-man, tell us of the night, What its signs of prom - ise are.
2. Watch-man, tell us of the night; High - er yet that star as - cends.
3. Watch-man, tell us of the night, For the morn - ing seems to dawn.
Trav - eler, o'er yon moun-tain's height See that glo - ry-beam - ing star!
Trav - eler, bless - ed - ness and light, Peace and truth, its course por - tends.
Trav - eler, dark - ness takes its flight; Doubt and ter - ror are with-drawn.
Watch-man, doth its beau - teous ray Aught of joy or hope fore - tell?
Watch-man, will its beams a - lone Gild the spot that gave them birth?
Watch-man, let thy wan-dering cease; Hie thee to thy qui - et home!
Trav-eler, yes; it brings the day, Prom-ised day of Is - ra - el.
Trav-eler, a - ges are its own; See, it bursts o'er all the earth!
Trav-eler, lo, the Prince of Peace, Lo, the Son of God is come!
A-MEN.

O Little Town of Bethlehem

ST. LOUIS. 8. 6. 8. 6. 7. 6. 8. 6.

PHILLIPS BROOKS, 1835–1893
With joy and serenity
LEWIS H. REDNER, 1831–1908
1. O lit - tle town of Beth - le - hem, How still we see thee lie!
2. For Christ is born of Ma - ry, And gath - ered all a - bove,
3. How si - lent - ly, how si - lent - ly The won - drous gift is given!
4. O ho - ly Child of Beth - le - hem! De - scend to us, we pray;
A - bove thy deep and dream - less sleep The si - lent stars go by;
While mor - tals sleep, the an - gels keep Their watch of won-dering love.
So God im - parts to hu - man hearts The bless-ings of His heaven.
Cast out our sin, and en - ter in, Be born in us to - day.
Yet in thy dark streets shin - eth The ev - er - last - ing Light;
O morn - ing stars, to - geth - er Pro - claim the ho - ly birth,
No ear may hear His com - ing, But in this world of sin,
We hear the Christ - mas an - gels The great glad tid - ings tell;
The hopes and fears of all the years Are met in thee to - night.
And prais - es sing to God the King, And peace to men on earth!
Where meek souls will re - ceive Him still, The dear Christ en - ters in.
O come to us, a - bide with us, Our Lord Im - man - u - el!
A - MEN.

While Shepherds Watched Their Flocks by Night

185

CHRISTMAS. C. M.

NAHUM TATE, 1652–1715
With joyous rhythm
GEORGE FREDERICK HANDEL, 1685–1759
1. While shep - herds watched their flocks by night, All
2. "Fear not!" said he— for might - y dread Had
3. "To you, in Da - vid's town this day, Is
4. "The heaven - ly Babe you there shall find To
seat - ed on the ground, The an - gel of the Lord came down,
seized their trou - bled mind— "Glad tid - ings of great joy I bring,
born of Da - vid's line, The Sav - iour, who is Christ the Lord;
hu - man view dis - played, All mean - ly wrapped in swath - ing bands,
And glo - ry shone a - round, And glo - ry shone a - round.
To you and all man - kind, To you and all man - kind.
And this shall be the sign, And this shall be the sign:
And in a man - ger laid, And in a man - ger laid." A-MEN.

5 Thus spake the seraph; and forthwith
Appeared a shining throng
Of angels praising God on high,
Who thus addressed their song:

6 "All glory be to God on high,
And to the earth be peace:
Good will henceforth from heaven to men,
Begin and never cease!"

All My Heart This Night Rejoices

EBELING (BONN). 8. 3. 3. 6. D.

PAUL GERHARDT, 1607–1676
Tr. by CATHERINE WINKWORTH, 1829–1878

JOHANN G. EBELING, 1620–1676

Like a carol

1. All my heart this night re - joi - ces, As I hear,
2. Hark! a voice from yon - der man - ger, Soft and sweet,
3. Come, then, let us has - ten yon - der; Here let all,

Far and near, Sweet - est an - gel voi - ces;
Doth en - treat, "Flee from woe and dan - ger;
Great and small, Kneel in awe and won - der,

"Christ is born," the choirs are sing - ing, Till the air,
Breth - ren, come; from all that grieves you You are freed;
Love Him who with love is yearn - ing; Hail the Star

Ev - ery - where, Now with joy is ring - ing.
All you need I will sure - ly give you."
That from far Bright with hope is burn - ing. A - MEN.

Angels We Have Heard on High

187

ANGELS WE HAVE HEARD. 7. 7. 7. 7. with Refrain

Traditional

Old French-English Carol

Joyously

1. An - gels we have heard on high, Sweet - ly sing - ing o'er the plains.
2. Shep-herds, why this ju - bi - lee? Why your joy - ous strains pro - long?
3. Come to Beth - le - hem, and see Him whose birth the an - gels sing;
4. See Him in a man - ger laid, Whom the choirs of an - gels praise;

And the moun-tains in re - ply, Ech - o - ing their joy - ous strains.
What the glad-some ti - dings be Which in - spire your heav'n - ly song?
Come, a - dore on bend - ed knee, Christ the Lord, the new - born King.
Ma - ry, Jo - seph, lend your aid, While our hearts in love we raise.

Soprano only, or unison ad lib.

Glo - - - - - - ri - a

in ex - cel - sis De - o Glo - - - -

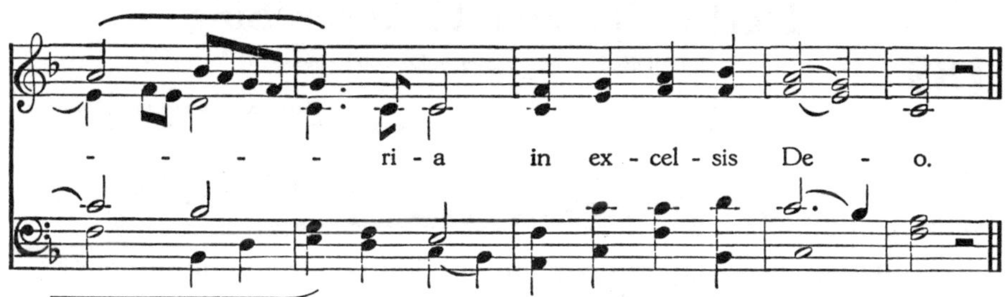
- - - - ri - a in ex - cel - sis De - o.

Silent Night, Holy Night

STILLE NACHT. Irregular

188

JOSEPH MOHR, 1792–1848
Tr. compiled from various sources

FRANZ GRUBER, 1787–1863

In moderate flowing rhythm

1. Si - lent night, ho - ly night, All is calm, all is bright;
2. Si - lent night, ho - ly night, Dark-ness flies, all is light;
3. Si - lent night, ho - ly night, Son of God, love's pure light;
4. Si - lent night, ho - ly night, Won-drous Star, lend thy light;
Round yon Vir - gin Moth-er and Child! Ho - ly In - fant, so ten-der and mild,
Shep-herds hear the an - gels sing, "Al - le - lu - ia! hail the King!
Ra - diant beams from Thy ho - ly face, With the dawn of re - deem-ing grace,
With the an - gels let us sing, Al - le - lu - ia to our King;
Sleep in heav-en - ly peace, Sleep in heav - en - ly peace.
Christ the Sav-iour is born, Christ the Sav - iour is born."
Je - sus, Lord, at Thy birth, Je - sus, Lord, at Thy birth.
Christ the Sav-iour is born, Christ the Sav - iour is born.
A - MEN.

Hark! The Herald Angels Sing

189

MENDELSSOHN. 7. 7. 7. 7. D. with Refrain

CHARLES WESLEY, 1707–1788
Alt. by GEORGE WHITEFIELD, 1714–1770

FELIX MENDELSSOHN, 1809–1847
Adapted by WILLIAM H. CUMMINGS, 1831–1918

Joyously

1. Hark! the her - ald an - gels sing, "Glo - ry to the new - born King;
2. Christ, by high - est heaven a - dored, Christ, the ev - er - last - ing Lord:
3. Hail the heav'n-born Prince of Peace! Hail the Sun of right-eous - ness!

Peace on earth, and mer - cy mild; God and sin - ners rec - on - ciled."
Long de - sired, be - hold Him come, Find - ing here His hum - ble home.
Light and life to all He brings, Risen with heal - ing in His wings.

Joy - ful, all ye na - tions, rise, Join the tri - umph of the skies;
Veiled in flesh the God - head see, Hail th' in - car - nate De - i - ty!
Mild He lays His glo - ry by, Born that man no more may die,

With an - gel - ic hosts pro - claim, "Christ is born in Beth - le - hem!"
Pleased as man with men to dwell, Je - sus our Im - man - u - el.
Born to raise the sons of earth, Born to give them sec - ond birth.

Hark! the her - ald an - gels sing, "Glo - ry to the new - born King." A - MEN.

Joy to the World! The Lord Is Come

ANTIOCH. C. M.

190

ISAAC WATTS, 1674–1748

GEORGE F. HANDEL, 1685–1759

With joy

1. Joy to the world! the Lord is come: Let earth re -
2. Joy to the world! the Sav - iour reigns: Let men their
3. No more let sins and sor - rows grow, Nor thorns in -
4. He rules the world with truth and grace, And makes the

ceive her King; Let ev - ery heart pre - pare Him room,
songs em - ploy; While fields and floods, rocks, hills and plains,
fest the ground; He comes to make His bless - ings flow
na - tions prove The glo - ries of His right - eous - ness,

And heaven and na - ture sing, And heaven and na - ture
Re - peat the sound - ing joy, Re - peat the sound - ing
Far as the curse is found, Far as the curse is
And won - ders of His love, And won - ders of His

And heaven and na - ture sing,
Re - peat the sound - ing joy,
Far as the curse is found,
And won - ders of His love,

And
Re -
Far
And

sing, And heaven, and heaven and na - ture sing.
joy, Re - peat, re - peat the sound - ing joy.
found, Far as, far as the curse is found.
love, And won - ders, won - ders of His love. A-MEN.

heaven and na - ture sing,
peat the sound - ing joy,
as the curse is found,
won - ders of His love,

It Came upon the Midnight Clear

191

CAROL. C. M. D

EDMUND H. SEARS, 1810–1876

RICHARD S. WILLIS, 1819–1900

In the style of a carol

1. It came up-on the mid-night clear, That glo-rious song of old,
From an-gels bend-ing near the earth, To touch their harps of gold:
"Peace on the earth, good will to men, From heaven's all-gra-cious King."
The world in sol-emn still-ness lay, To hear the an-gels sing.

2. Still thro the clo-ven skies they come, With peace-ful wings un-furled,
And still their heaven-ly mu-sic floats O'er all the wea-ry world:
A-bove its sad and low-ly plains They bend on hov-ering wing,
And ev-er o'er its Ba-bel sounds The bless-ed an-gels sing.

3. And ye, be-neath life's crush-ing load, Whose forms are bend-ing low,
Who toil a-long the climb-ing way With pain-ful steps and slow,
Look now! for glad and gold-en hours Come swift-ly on the wing:
O rest be-side the wea-ry road, And hear the an-gels sing!

4. For lo! the days are has-tening on, By pro-phet-bards fore-told,
When with the ev-er-cir-cling years Comes round the age of gold;
When peace shall o-ver all the earth Its an-cient splen-dors fling,
And the whole world send back the song Which now the an-gels sing.

A-MEN.

Angels, from the Realms of Glory

REGENT SQUARE. 8. 7. 8. 7. 8. 7.

192

JAMES MONTGOMERY, 1771–1854

With spirit and joy

HENRY SMART, 1813–1879

1. An - gels, from the realms of glo - ry, Wing your flight o'er
2. Shep - herds, in the field a - bid - ing, Watch - ing o'er your
3. Sa - ges, leave your con - tem - pla - tions, Bright - er vi - sions
4. Saints, be - fore the al - tar bend - ing, Watch - ing long in

all the earth; Ye who sang cre - a - tion's sto - ry,
flocks by night, God with man is now re - sid - ing;
beam a - far; Seek the great De - sire of na - tions;
hope and fear, Sud - den - ly the Lord, de - scend - ing,

Now pro - claim Mes - si - ah's birth: Come and wor - ship,
Yon - der shines the in - fant Light: Come and wor - ship,
Ye have seen His na - tal star: Come and wor - ship,
In His tem - ple shall ap - pear: Come and wor - ship,

Come and wor - ship, Wor - ship Christ, the new - born King.
Come and wor - ship, Wor - ship Christ, the new - born King.
Come and wor - ship, Wor - ship Christ, the new - born King.
Come and wor - ship, Wor - ship Christ, the new - born King. A - MEN.

Good Christian Men, Rejoice

193

IN DULCI JUBILO. Irregular

Mediaeval Latin Carol
Tr. by JOHN M. NEALE, 1818–1866

14th century German melody

Joyfully

1. Good Chris-tian men, re - joice With heart and soul and voice!
2. Good Chris-tian men, re - joice With heart and soul and voice!
3. Good Chris-tian men, re - joice With heart and soul and voice!

Give ye heed to what we say: News! News! Je - sus Christ is born to - day.
Now ye hear of end-less bliss: Joy! Joy! Je - sus Christ was born for this.
Now ye need not fear the grave: Peace! Peace! Je - sus Christ was born to save;

Ox and ass be - fore Him bow, And He is in the man - ger now:
He hath oped the heaven - ly door, And man is blessed for ev - er - more.
Calls you one, and calls you all, To gain His ev - er - last - ing hall.

Christ is born to - day, Christ is born to - day!
Christ was born for this, Christ was born for this!
Christ was born to save, Christ was born to save!

A - MEN.

Lo, How a Rose E'er Blooming

PRAETORIUS. Irregular

194

Traditional
Tr. by THEODORE BAKER

16th century melody
Har. by MICHAEL PRAETORIUS, 1571–1621

In moderate time

1. Lo, how a Rose e'er bloom - ing From ten - der stem . . . hath sprung! Of Jes - se's lin - eage com ing As men of . . old have sung. It came, a flow'r - et bright, A - mid the cold of win - ter, When half spent was . the night.

2. I - sa - iah 'twas fore - told it, The Rose I have . . . in mind, With Ma - ry we be - hold it, The Vir - gin Moth - er kind. To show God's love a - right, She bore to men a Sav - iour, When half spent was . the night. A-MEN.

Hush, All Ye Sounds of War

195

THE PRINCE OF PEACE. 6. 6. 12. 12. 12.

WILLIAM H. DRAPER, 1855– 1933 — CYRIL BARKER

In the style of a carol

1. Hush, all ye sounds of war, Ye na - tions all be still, A
2. No more di - vid - ed be, Ye fam - i - lies of men, Old

voice of heav'n - ly joy steals o - ver vale and hill, O
en - mi - ty for - get, Old friend-ship knit a - gain, In

hear the an - gels sing the cap - tive world's re - lease, This
the new year of God let broth - ers' love in - crease, This

day is born in Beth - le - hem the Prince of Peace. A - MEN.

As with Gladness Men of Old

DIX. 7. 7. 7. 7. 7. 7.

196

WILLIAM C. DIX, 1837–1898

From a chorale by
CONRAD KOCHER, 1786–1872

Joyfully

1. As with glad - ness men of old Did the guid - ing
2. As with joy - ous steps they sped To that low - ly
3. As they of - fered gifts most rare At that man - ger

star be - hold; As with joy they hailed its light,
man - ger bed, There to bend the knee be - fore
rude and bare, So may we with ho - ly joy,

Lead - ing on - ward, beam - ing bright; So, most gra - cious
Him whom heaven and earth a - dore; So may we with
Pure, and free from sin's al - loy, All our cost - liest

Lord, may we Ev - er - more be led to Thee.
will - ing feet Ev - er seek Thy mer - cy - seat.
treas - ures bring. Christ, to Thee, our heaven - ly King. A - MEN.

The First Noel, the Angel Did Say

197
THE FIRST NOEL. Irregular, with Refrain
Old English Carol
In moderate time
Traditional melody in
W. Sandys' "Christmas Carols," 1833
1. The first No - el, the an - gel did say, Was to
2. They look - ed up and saw a star Shin - ing
3. And by the light of that same star Three
4. This star drew nigh to the north - west, O'er
5. Then en - tered in those wise - men three, Full
cer - tain poor shep-herds in fields as they lay; In fields where
in the east, be - yond them far, And to the
wise - men came from coun - try far; To seek for a
Beth - le - hem it took its rest, And there it
rev - er - ent - ly up - on the knee, And of - fered
they lay keep - ing their sheep, On a cold win - ter's
earth it gave great light, And so it con -
king was their in - tent, And to fol - low the
did both stop and stay, Right o - ver the
there, in His pres - ence, Their gold and
night that was so deep.
tin-ued both day and night.
star wher - ev - er it went.
place where Je - sus lay.
myrrh and frank - in - cense.
Refrain
No - el, No - el, No -

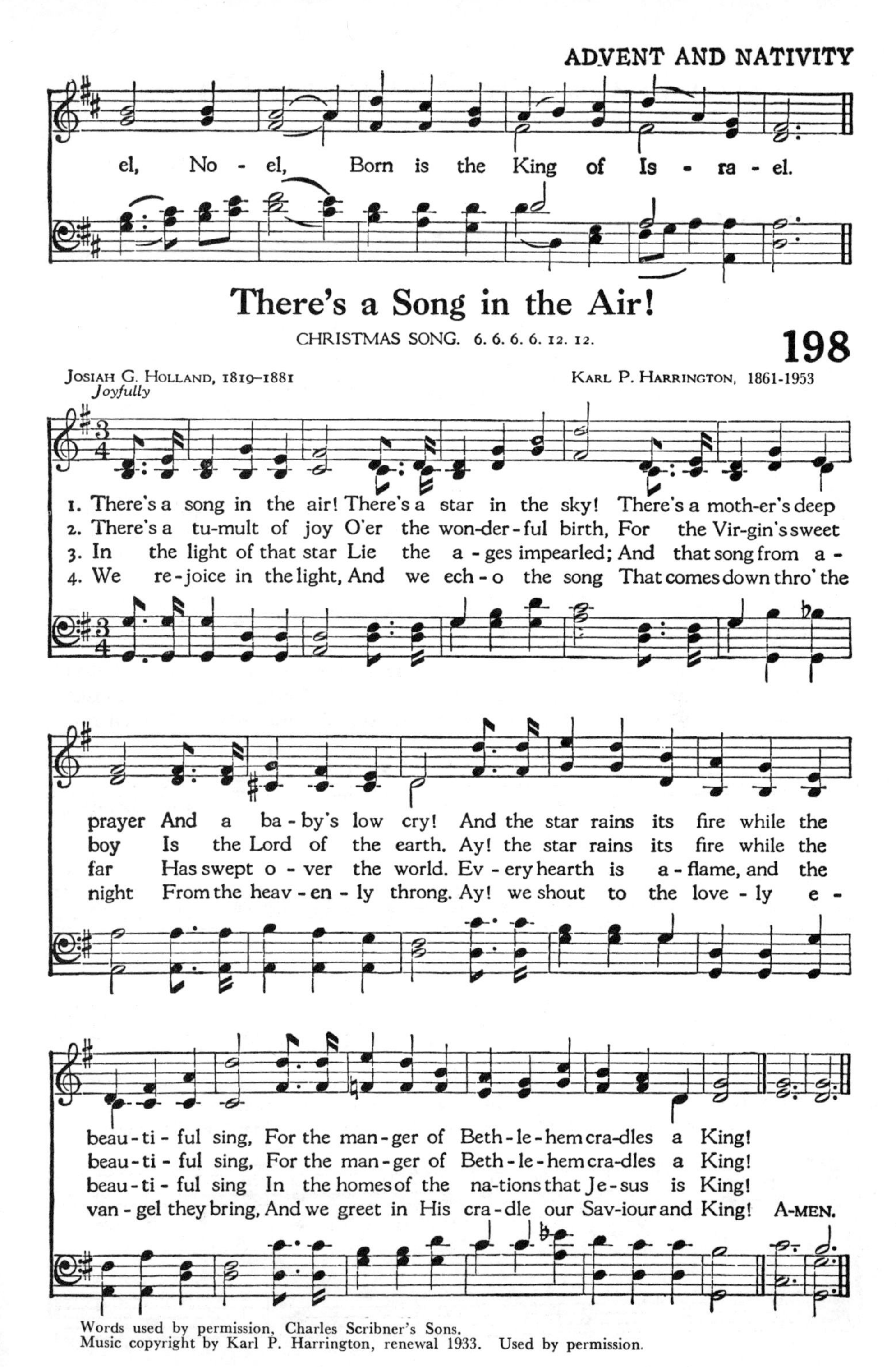
ADVENT AND NATIVITY
el, No - el, Born is the King of Is - ra - el.
There's a Song in the Air!
CHRISTMAS SONG. 6. 6. 6. 6. 12. 12.
198
Josiah G. Holland, 1819–1881
Karl P. Harrington, 1861-1953
Joyfully
1. There's a song in the air! There's a star in the sky! There's a moth-er's deep prayer And a ba - by's low cry! And the star rains its fire while the beau - ti - ful sing, For the man - ger of Beth - le - hem cra-dles a King!
2. There's a tu-mult of joy O'er the won-der - ful birth, For the Vir-gin's sweet boy Is the Lord of the earth. Ay! the star rains its fire while the beau - ti - ful sing, For the man - ger of Beth - le - hem cra-dles a King!
3. In the light of that star Lie the a - ges impearled; And that song from a - far Has swept o - ver the world. Ev - ery hearth is a - flame, and the beau - ti - ful sing In the homes of the na-tions that Je - sus is King!
4. We re - joice in the light, And we ech - o the song That comes down thro' the night From the heav - en - ly throng. Ay! we shout to the love - ly e - van - gel they bring, And we greet in His cra - dle our Sav-iour and King!
A-MEN.
Words used by permission, Charles Scribner's Sons.
Music copyright by Karl P. Harrington, renewal 1933. Used by permission.

Away in a Manger, No Crib for His Bed

199

MUELLER. 11. 11. 11. 11

MARTIN LUTHER, 1483–1546 | CARL MUELLER

In unison, in the style of a carol

1. A - way in a man - ger, no crib for a bed, The lit - tle Lord Je - sus laid down His sweet head. The stars in the sky looked down where He lay, The lit - tle Lord Je - sus, a - sleep on the hay.
2. The cat - tle are low - ing, the Ba - by a - wakes, But lit - tle Lord Je - sus, no cry - ing He makes. I love Thee, Lord Je - sus, look down from the sky, And stay by my cra - dle till morn - ing is nigh.
3. Be near me, Lord Je - sus, I ask Thee to stay Close by me for ev - er, and love me, I pray. Bless all the dear chil - dren in Thy ten - der care, And fit us for heav - en to live with Thee there.

What Child Is This, Who, Laid to Rest

GREENSLEEVES. 8. 7. 8. 7. with Refrain

200

WILLIAM C. DIX, 1837–1898

Old English melody

In unison

1. What Child is this, who, laid to rest, On Ma-ry's lap is sleep-ing?
2. Why lies He in such mean es-tate Where ox and ass are feed-ing?
3. So bring Him in-cense, gold and myrrh, Come, peas-ant, King to own Him;

Whom an-gels greet with an-thems sweet, While shep-herds watch are keep-ing?
Good Chris-tian, fear: for sin-ners here The si-lent Word is plead-ing.
The King of kings sal-va-tion brings, Let lov-ing hearts en-throne Him.

REFRAIN. *Unison or Harmony*

This, this is Christ the King, Whom shep-herds guard and an-gels sing:
Haste, haste to bring Him laud, The Babe, the Son of Ma-ry. A-MEN.

Calm on the List'ning Ear of Night
201
ST. AGNES. C. M.
Edmund H. Sears, 1810–1876
John B. Dykes, 1823–1876
In moderate time
1. Calm on the list - 'ning ear of night Come heav'n's me - lo - dious strains,
2. Ce - les - tial choirs, from courts a - bove, Shed sa - cred glo - ries there,
3. The an-sw'ring hills of Pal - es - tine Send back the glad re - ply,
4. "Glo - ry to God!" the sounding skies Loud with their an - thems ring:
Where wild Ju - de - a stretch - es far Her sil - ver - man-tled plains.
And an - gels, with their spark - ling lyres, Make mu - sic on the air.
And greet from all their ho - ly heights The Day-spring from on high.
"Peace on the earth, good-will to men, From heav'n's e - ter - nal King." A - men.
Brightest and Best of the Sons of the Morning
202
MORNING STAR. 11. 10. 11. 10.
Reginald Heber, 1783–1826
John P. Harding, 1850–1911
In the style of a carol
1. Bright - est and best of the sons of the morn - ing, Dawn on our
2. Cold on His cra - dle the dew-drops are shin - ing; Low lies His
3. Say, shall we yield Him, in cost - ly de - vo - tion, O - dors of
4. Vain - ly we of - fer each am - ple ob - la - tion; Vain - ly with
5. Bright - est and best of the sons of the morn - ing, Dawn on our
dark - ness and lend us Thine aid; Star of the East, the ho - ri - zon a -
head with the beasts of the stall; An - gels a - dore Him in slum - ber re -
E - dom and of - ferings di - vine, Gems of the moun-tain, and pearls of the
gifts would His fa - vor se - cure: Rich - er by far is the heart's ad - o -
dark - ness and lend us Thine aid; Star of the East, the ho - ri - zon a -

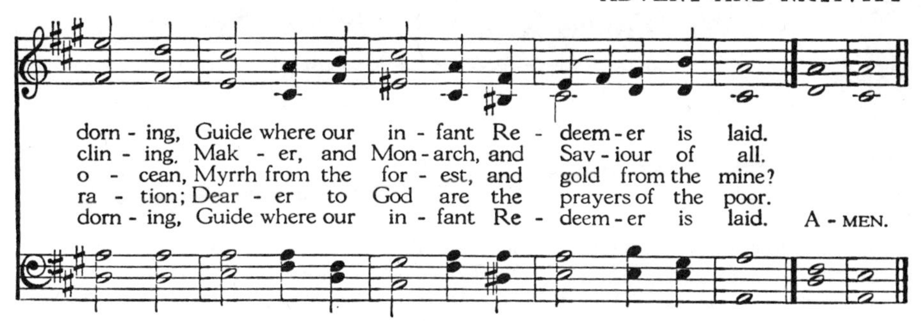
dorn - ing, Guide where our in - fant Re - deem - er is laid.
clin - ing, Mak - er, and Mon - arch, and Sav - iour of all.
o - cean, Myrrh from the for - est, and gold from the mine?
ra - tion; Dear - er to God are the prayers of the poor.
dorn - ing, Guide where our in - fant Re - deem - er is laid. A - MEN.

Wise Men Seeking Jesus

LONELY MIDNIGHT. 6. 5. 6. 5. D.

203

JAMES EAST, 1926 — ALONZO POTTER HOWARD, 1838–1902

To be sung in unison

1. Wise men seek-ing Je - sus Trav-eled from a - far, Guid-ed on their
2. Prayer-ful souls may find Him By our qui - et lakes, Meet Him on our
3. Ev - 'ry peace-ful vil - lage In our land might be, Made by Je - sus'
jour - ney By a beau-teous star. But if we de - sire Him, He is
hill - sides Where the morn-ing breaks. In our fer - tile corn - fields While the
pres - ence Like sweet Beth-a - ny. He is more than near us, If we
close at hand; For our na - tive coun - try Is our Ho - ly Land.
sheaves are bound, In our bus - y mar - kets Je - sus may be found.
love Him well; For He seek - eth ev - er In our hearts to dwell. A-MEN.

We Three Kings of Orient Are

204

KINGS OF ORIENT. 8. 8. 8. 6. with Refrain

JOHN H. HOPKINS, 1820–1891 — JOHN H. HOPKINS, 1820–1891

In unison

1. We three kings of O - ri - ent are; Bear - ing gifts we trav-erse a - far
Field and foun - tain, moor and moun-tain, Fol - low - ing yon - der star.
2. Born a King on Beth - le-hem's plain, Gold I bring to crown Him a - gain,
King for ev - er, ceas - ing nev - er O - ver us all to reign.
3. Frank-in - cense to of - fer have I; In - cense owns a De - i - ty nigh;
Prayer and prais - ing all men rais - ing, Wor - ship Him, God on high.
4. Myrrh is mine: its bit - ter per - fume Breathes a life of gath - er - ing gloom:
Sor - rowing, sigh - ing, bleed - ing, dy - ing, Sealed in the stone - cold tomb.
5. Glo-rious now be - hold Him a - rise, King and God and Sac - ri - fice;
Al - le - lu - ia, Al - le - lu - ia! Sounds thro' the earth and skies.

REFRAIN

O star of won - der, star of night, Star with roy - al beau - ty bright,
West-ward lead - ing, still pro-ceed- ing, Guide us to Thy per - fect light. A - MEN.

O Come, All Ye Faithful

ADESTE FIDELES. Irregular, with Refrain

205

Anonymous, Latin, 18th century
Tr. by FREDERICK OAKELEY, 1802–1880

From J. F. WADE'S
CANTUS DIVERSI, 1751

Joyously
1. O come, all ye faith - ful, joy - ful and tri - um - phant,
2. Sing, choirs of an - gels, sing in ex - ul - ta - tion,
3. Yea, Lord, we greet Thee, born this hap - py morn - ing,
O come ye, O come ye to Beth - le-hem! Come and be - hold Him,
O sing, all ye cit - i-zens of heav'n a-bove! Glo - ry to God, all
Je - sus, to Thee be all glo - ry giv'n; Word of the Fa - ther,
born the King of an - gels!
glo - ry in the high - est!
now in flesh ap - pear - ing!
REFRAIN
O come, let us a-dore Him, O come let us a - dore Him, O come, let us a - dore Him, Christ, the Lord! A-MEN.

I Know Not How That Bethlehem's Babe

206

SHIRLEYN. C. M.

HARRY WEBB FARRINGTON, 1880–1931

EARL E. HARPER, 1895–

In moderate time

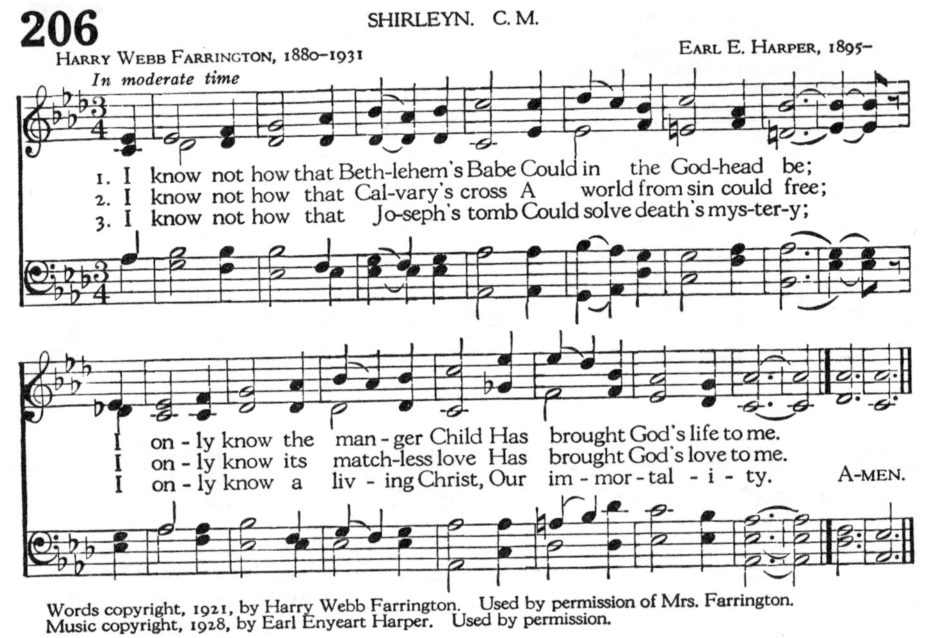
1. I know not how that Beth-lehem's Babe Could in the God-head be;
2. I know not how that Cal-vary's cross A world from sin could free;
3. I know not how that Jo-seph's tomb Could solve death's mys-ter-y;
I on - ly know the man - ger Child Has brought God's life to me.
I on - ly know its match-less love Has brought God's love to me.
I on - ly know a liv - ing Christ, Our im - mor - tal - i - ty.
A-MEN.

My Dear Redeemer and My Lord

207

FEDERAL STREET. L. M.

ISAAC WATTS, 1674–1748

HENRY K. OLIVER, 1800–1885

In a reverent manner

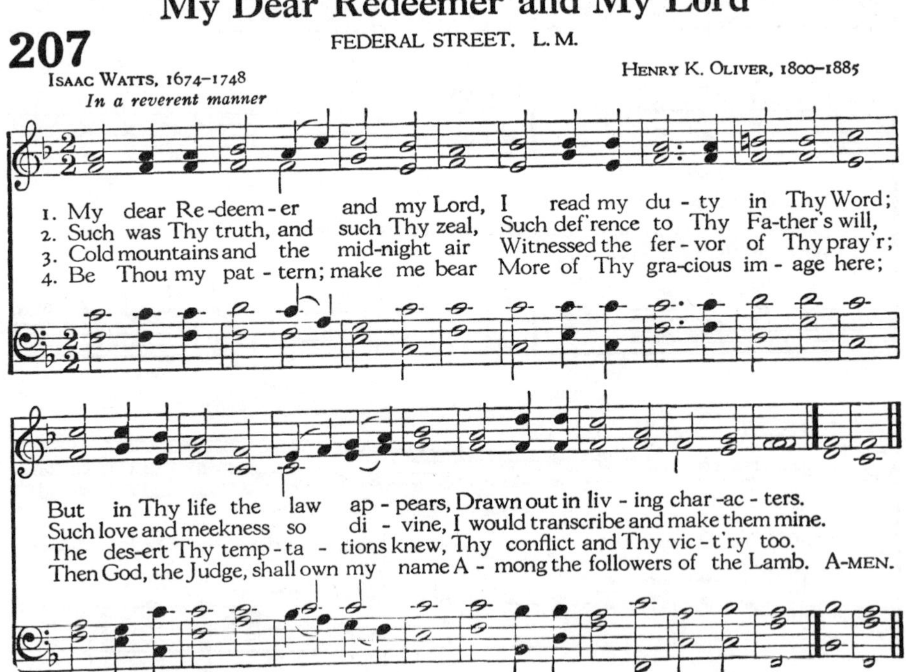
1. My dear Re-deem-er and my Lord, I read my du - ty in Thy Word;
2. Such was Thy truth, and such Thy zeal, Such def'rence to Thy Fa-ther's will,
3. Cold mountains and the mid-night air Witnessed the fer - vor of Thy pray'r;
4. Be Thou my pat - tern; make me bear More of Thy gra-cious im - age here;
But in Thy life the law ap - pears, Drawn out in liv - ing char -ac - ters.
Such love and meekness so di - vine, I would transcribe and make them mine.
The des-ert Thy temp - ta - tions knew, Thy conflict and Thy vic - t'ry too.
Then God, the Judge, shall own my name A - mong the followers of the Lamb. A-MEN.

Light of the World, We Hail Thee

SALVE DOMINE. 7. 6. 7. 6. D.

208

JOHN S. B. MONSELL, 1811–1875
LAWRENCE W. WATSON, 1860–1927
In moderate time
1. Light of the world, we hail Thee, Flush-ing the east-ern skies;
2. Light of the world, Thy beau-ty Steals in-to ev-ery heart,
3. Light of the world, il-lu-mine This dark-ened earth of Thine,
Nev-er shall dark-ness veil Thee A-gain from hu-man eyes;
And glo-ri-fies with du-ty Life's poor-est, hum-blest part;
Till ev-ery-thing that's hu-man Be filled with the di-vine;
Too long, a-las, with-hold-en, Now spread from shore to shore;
Thou rob-est in Thy splen-dor The sim-plest ways of men,
Till ev-ery tongue and na-tion, From sin's do-min-ion free,
Thy light, so glad and gold-en, Shall set on earth no more.
And help-est them to ren-der Light back to Thee a-gain.
Rise in the new cre-a-tion Which springs from love and Thee. A-MEN.

We Would See Jesus; Lo! His Star

209

CUSHMAN. 11. 10. 11. 10.

J. EDGAR PARK, 1879–

HERBERT B. TURNER, 1852–1927

In moderate time

1. We would see Je - sus; lo! His star is shin - ing
A - bove the sta - ble while the an - gels sing;
There in a man - ger on the hay re - clin - ing;
Haste, let us lay our gifts be - fore the King.

2. We would see Je - sus, Ma - ry's Son most ho - ly,
Light of the vil - lage life from day to day;
Shin - ing re - vealed through ev - ery task most low - ly,
The Christ of God, the Life, the Truth, the Way.

3. We would see Je - sus, on the moun - tain teach - ing,
With all the lis - tening peo - ple gath - ered round;
While birds and flowers and sky a - bove are preach - ing,
The bless - ed - ness which sim - ple trust has found.

4. We would see Je - sus, in His work of heal - ing,
At ev - en - tide be - fore the sun was set;
Di - vine and hu - man, in His deep re - veal - ing,
Of God and man in lov - ing serv - ice met.

5. We would see Je - sus; in the ear - ly morn - ing
Still as of old He call - eth, "Fol - low me";
Let us a - rise, all mean - er serv - ice scorn - ing:
Lord, we are Thine, we give our - selves to Thee.

A - MEN.

O Master Workman of the Race

AMESBURY. C. M. D.

210

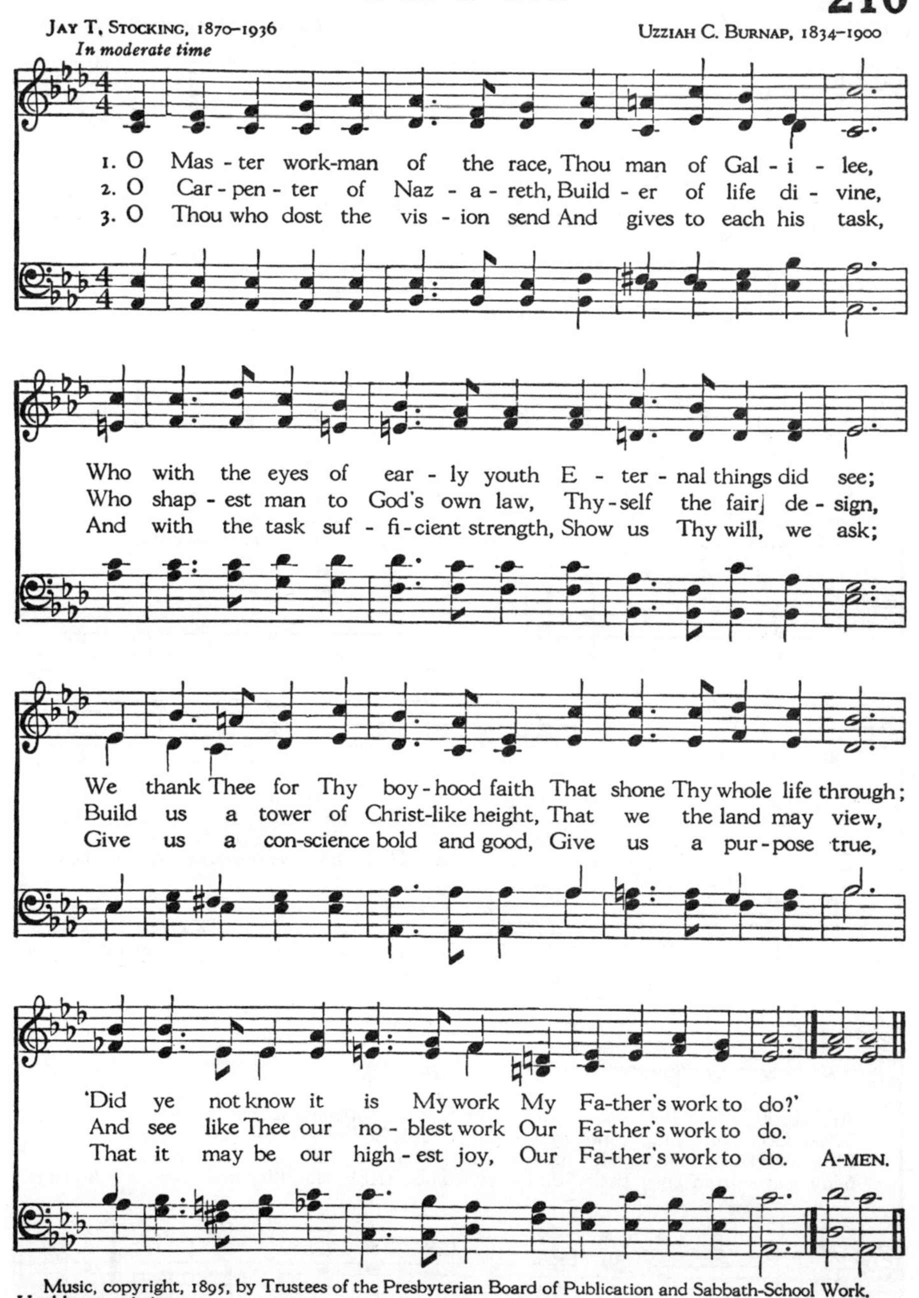
Jay T. Stocking, 1870–1936
Uzziah C. Burnap, 1834–1900
In moderate time
1. O Mas - ter work-man of the race, Thou man of Gal - i - lee,
2. O Car - pen - ter of Naz - a - reth, Build - er of life di - vine,
3. O Thou who dost the vis - ion send And gives to each his task,
Who with the eyes of ear - ly youth E - ter - nal things did see;
Who shap - est man to God's own law, Thy-self the fair de - sign,
And with the task suf - fi-cient strength, Show us Thy will, we ask;
We thank Thee for Thy boy-hood faith That shone Thy whole life through;
Build us a tower of Christ-like height, That we the land may view,
Give us a con-science bold and good, Give us a pur-pose true,
'Did ye not know it is My work My Fa-ther's work to do?'
And see like Thee our no - blest work Our Fa-ther's work to do.
That it may be our high - est joy, Our Fa-ther's work to do.
A-men.

O Son of God Incarnate

211

CHENIES. 7. 6. 7. 6. D.

WILBUR FISK TILLETT, 1854–1936

TIMOTHY R. MATTHEWS, 1826–1910

In moderate time

1. O Son of God in - car - nate, O Son of man di - vine!
2. O Mind of God in - car - nate, O Thought in flesh en - shrined!
3. O Heart of God in - car - nate, Love - bear - er to man - kind!
4. O Will of God in - car - nate, So hu - man, so di - vine!

In whom God's glo - ry dwell - eth, In whom man's vir - tues shine;
In hu - man form Thou speak - est To men the Fa - ther's mind:
From Thee we learn what love is, In Thee love's ways we find:
Free wills to us Thou giv - est, That we may make them Thine:

God's light to earth Thou bring - est To drive sin's night a - way,
God's thought to earth Thou bring - est That men in Thee may see
God's love to earth Thou bring - est In liv - ing deeds that prove
God's will to earth Thou bring - est That all who would o - bey,

And through Thy life, so ra - diant, Earth's dark-ness turns to day.
What God is like, and see - ing, Think God's tho'ts aft - er Thee.
How sweet to serve all oth - ers, When we all oth - ers love.
May learn from Thee their du - ty, The truth, the life, the way. A - MEN.

When the Golden Evening Gathered

STOCKWELL, NEW. 8. 7. 11. 8. 7. 11.

212

William J. Dawson, 1854–1928
Calvin W. Laufer, 1874–1938
In moderate time
1. When the gold - en eve-ning gath-ered On the shore of Gal - i - lee,
2. Not in robes of pur - ple splen-dor, Not in silk - en soft-ness shod,
3. For He healed their sick at e - ven, And He cured the le - per's sore,
4. Not in robes of pur - ple splen-dor, But in lives that do His will,
When the fish - ing boats lay qui - et by the sea,
But in rai - ment worn with trav - el came their God;
So that sin - ful men and wom - en sinned no more;
And in pa - tient acts of kind - ness He comes still;
Long a - go the peo - ple won-dered, Though no sign was in the sky,
And the peo - ple knew His pres - ence By the heart that ceased to sigh
And the world grew mirth - ful - heart - ed, And for - got its mis - er - y
And the peo - ple cry with won - der, Though no sign is in the sky,
For the glo - ry of the Lord was pass - ing by.
When the glo - ry of the Lord was pass - ing by.
When the glo - ry of the Lord was pass - ing by.
That the glo - ry of the Lord is pass - ing by.
A - MEN.

I Think When I Read that Sweet Story of Old

213
SWEET STORY. Irregular
A Greek folk song
JEMIMA T. LUKE, 1813–1906
Arr. by WILLIAM B. BRADBURY, 1816–1868
In moderate time
1. I think when I read that sweet sto - ry of old,
2. I wish that His hands had been placed on my head,
When Je - sus was here a - mong men,
That His arms had been thrown a - round me,
How He called lit - tle chil - dren as lambs to His fold,
And that I might have seen His kind look when He said,
I should like to have been with them then.
"Let the lit - tle ones come un - to me."
A - MEN.

Tell Me the Stories of Jesus

STORIES OF JESUS. 8. 4. 8. 4. 5. 4. 5. 4.

214

WILLIAM H. PARKER, 1845–1929

FREDERIC A. CHALLINOR, 1866-1952

Unison or duet
1. Tell me the sto - ries of Je - sus I love to hear;
2. First let me hear how the chil - dren Stood round His knee,
3. In - to the cit - y I'd fol - low The chil - dren's band,
Things I would ask Him to tell me If He were here:
And I shall fan - cy His bless - ing Rest - ing on me;
Wav - ing a branch of the palm - tree High in my hand;
Scenes by the way - side, Tales of the sea,
Words full of kind - ness, Deeds full of grace,
One of His her - alds, Yes, I would sing
Sto - ries of Je - sus, Tell them to me.
All in the love - light Of Je - sus' face.
Loud - est ho - san - nas, "Je - sus is King!"
A - MEN.

When the Lord of Love Was Here
215
SALVATOR. 7. 7. 5. 7. 7. 5.
Stopford A. Brooke, 1832–1916
M. B. Foster, 1851–1922
In moderate time
1. When the Lord of love was here, Hap-py hearts to Him were dear, Though His heart was sad; Worn and lone-ly for our sake, Yet He turned a-side to make All the wea-ry glad.
2. Meek and low-ly were His ways, From His lov-ing grew His praise, From His giv-ing, prayer; All the out-cast thronged to hear, All the sor-row-ful drew near To en-joy His care.
3. When He walked the fields, He drew From the flowers and birds and dew, Par-a-bles of God; For with-in His heart of love All the soul of man did move,—God had His a-bode.
4. Lord, be ours Thy power to keep In the ver-y heart of grief, And in tri-al, love; In our meek-ness to be wise, And through sor-row to a-rise To our God a-bove.
A-men.
Music from the Christian Hymnary Tune Book.
My Master Was So Very Poor
216
HERONGATE. L.M.
Harry Lee
Traditional melody
Arr. by R. Vaughan Williams, 1872–
In moderate time
1. My Mas-ter was so ver-y poor, A man-ger was His cra-dling place;
2. My Mas-ter was so ver-y poor, And with the poor He broke the bread;
3. My Mas-ter was so ver-y poor, They nailed Him na-ked to a cross;

So very-y rich my Mas-ter was, Kings came from far to gain His grace.
So ver-y rich my Mas-ter was, That mul-ti-tudes by Him were fed.
So ver-y rich my Mas-ter was, He gave His all and knew no loss.
A-MEN.

Words copyright by Harry Lee.
Music from "The English Hymnal." Used by permission of the Oxford University Press.

O Jesus, Youth of Nazareth

BROOKFIELD. L. M.

217

FERDINAND Q. BLANCHARD, 1876–

THOMAS B. SOUTHGATE, 1814–1868

In moderate time
1. O Je-sus, youth of Na-za-reth, Pre-par-ing for the bit-ter strife, Wilt thou im-part to ev-ery heart Thy per-fect pur-i-ty of life?
2. O Christ whose words make dear the fields And hill-sides green of Gal-i-lee, Grant us to find, with rev-erent mind, The truth thou saidst should make us free.
3. O suf-fering Lord on Cal-va-ry, Whom love led on to mor-tal pain, We know thy cross is not a loss If we thy love shall tru-ly gain.
4. O Mas-ter of a-bun-dant life From na-tal morn to vic-tory's hour, We look to thee, heed thou our plea, Teach us to share thy age-less power.
A-MEN.

O Jesus, When I Think of Thee

218

PARACLETE. C. M.

GEORGE W. BETHUNE, 1805–1862 — FREDERICK C. MAKER, 1844–1927

In moderate time

1. O Jesus, when I think of Thee, Thy manger, cross, and throne,
My spirit trusts exultingly In Thee, and Thee alone.
2. I see Thee in Thy weakness first; Then, glorious from Thy shame,
I see Thee death's strong fetters burst, And reach heaven's mightiest name.
3. O let me share Thy holy birth, Thy faith, Thy death to sin!
And, strong amidst the toils of earth, My heavenly life begin.
4. Then shall I know what means the strain Triumphant of Saint Paul:
"To live is Christ, to die is gain;" "Christ is my all in all." A-MEN.
What Grace, O Lord, and Beauty Shone
219
DALEHURST. C. M.
EDWARD DENNY, 1796–1889
ARTHUR COTTMAN, 1842–1879
In moderate time
1. What grace, O Lord, and beauty shone Around Thy steps below;
2. Thy foes might hate, despise, revile, Thy friends unfaithful prove;
3. O give us hearts to love like Thee! Like Thee, O Lord, to grieve
4. One with Thyself, may every eye In us, Thy brethren, see

What patient love was seen in all Thy life and death of woe.
Unwearied in forgiveness still, Thy heart could only love.
Far more for others' sin than all The wrongs that we receive.
The gentleness and grace that spring From union, Lord, with Thee. A-MEN.

O Son of Man, Our Hero Strong and Tender

WINDSOR. 11. 10. 11. 10.

220

FRANK FLETCHER, 1870-1954 — JOSEPH BARNBY, 1838-1896

In moderate time

1. O Son of Man, our He - ro strong and ten - der,
2. O feet so strong to climb the path of du - ty,
3. Lov - er of chil - dren, boy - hood's in - spi - ra - tion.
4. Not in our fail - ures on - ly and our sad - ness

Whose serv - ants are the brave in all the earth,
O lips di - vine that taught the words of truth,
Of all man - kind the Serv - ant and the King;
We seek Thy pres - ence, Com - fort - er and Friend;

Our liv - ing sac - ri - fice to Thee we ren - der,
Kind eyes that marked the li - lies in their beau - ty,
O Lord of joy and hope and con - so - la - tion,
O rich man's Guest, be with us in our glad - ness,

Who shar - est all our sor - rows, all our mirth.
And heart that kin - dled at the zeal of youth;
To Thee our fears and joys and hopes we bring.
O poor man's Mate, our low - liest tasks at - tend.

A-MEN.

All Glory, Laud, and Honor

221

ST. THEODULPH. 7. 6. 7. 6. D.

THEODULPH OF ORLEANS, ? – 821
Tr. by JOHN M. NEALE, 1818–1866

MELCHIOR TESCHNER, d. c. 1615

Joyfully

1. All glo - ry, laud, and hon - or, To Thee, Re - deem - er, King,
2. The com - pa - ny of an - gels Are prais - ing Thee on high,
3. To Thee, be - fore Thy pas - sion They sang their hymns of praise;
To whom the lips of chil - dren Made sweet ho - san - nas ring.
And mor - tal men and all things Cre - a - ted make re - ply.
To Thee, now high ex - alt - ed, Our mel - o - dy we raise.
Thou art the King of Is - ra - el, Thou Da - vid's roy - al Son,
The peo - ple of the He - brews With palms be - fore Thee went;
Thou didst ac - cept their prais - es; Ac - cept the praise we bring,
Who in the Lord's Name com - est, The King and Bless - ed One.
Our praise and prayer and an - thems Be - fore Thee we pre - sent.
Who in all good de - light - est, Thou good and gra - cious King.
A-MEN.

From Bethany, the Master

DAY OF REST. 7. 6. 7. 6. D.

222

Marion Franklin Ham, 1867–
James W. Elliott, 1833–1915
In moderate march rhythm
1. From Beth - a - ny, the Mas - ter Comes down Mt. Ol - ive's slope,
2. The king of Love, in tri - umph Rides through the ci - ty's gate;
3. Not of this world his king - dom; His power is from a - bove;
And all the world is sing - ing A glad new song of hope;
Re - ject - ed, scorned—yet vic - tor, The con - quer - or of Hate;
His realm is of the spir - it, His scep - ter—Truth and Love;
Cry out, O state - ly ce - dars, A - long the rug - ged way!
O wave your green palm - branch-es! Ex - alt his match-less worth!
He calls us to his serv - ice, His ban - ner is un - furled;
Ye vine-yards, shout ho - san - nas, To greet this hap - py day!
This king of Love shall con - quer The na - tions of the earth.
With thee we march, O Mas - ter, To o - ver - come the world.
A - MEN.

Words used by permission of Marion Franklin Ham.

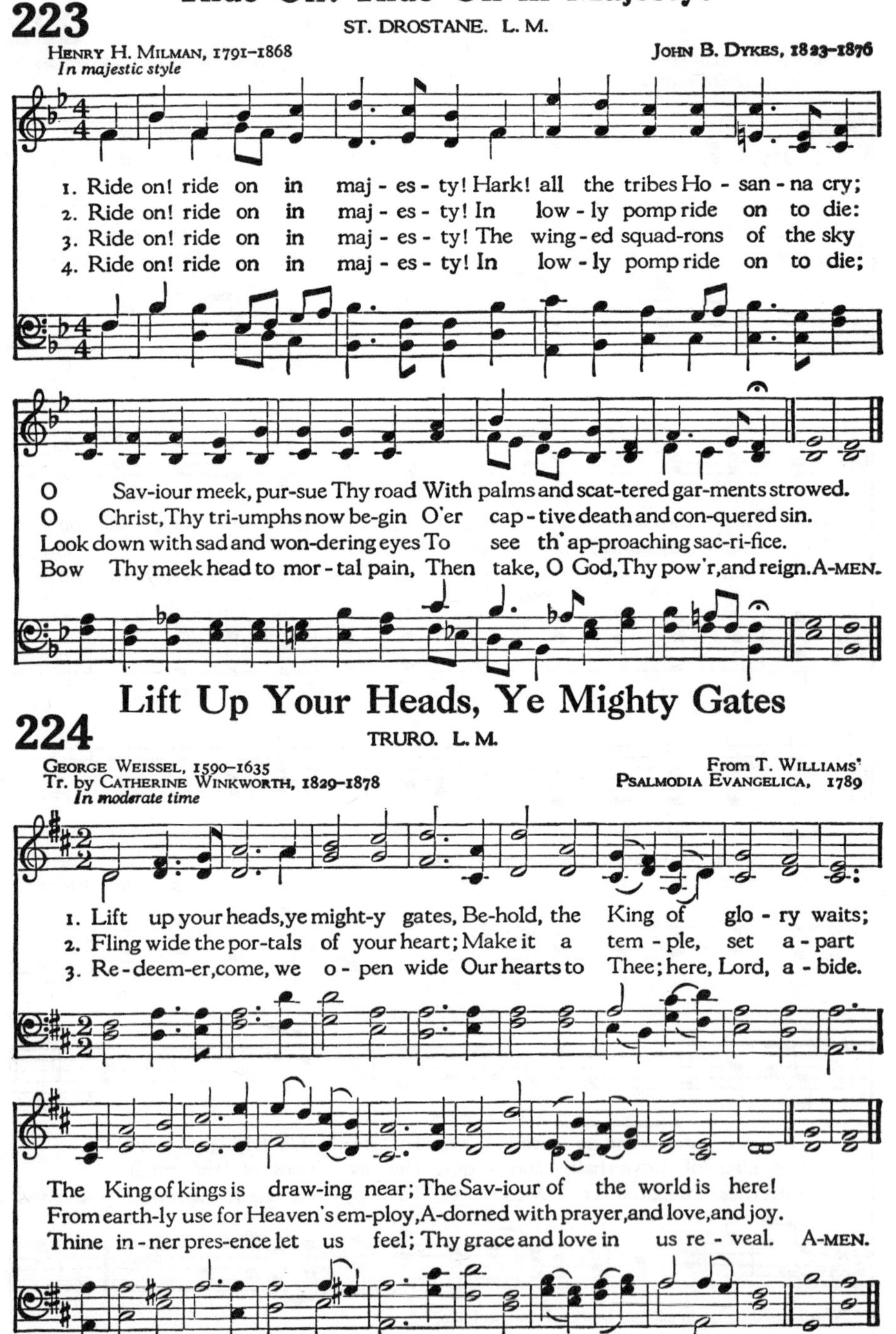
Ride On! Ride On in Majesty!
223
ST. DROSTANE. L. M.
HENRY H. MILMAN, 1791–1868
JOHN B. DYKES, 1823–1876
In majestic style
1. Ride on! ride on in maj - es - ty! Hark! all the tribes Ho - san - na cry;
2. Ride on! ride on in maj - es - ty! In low - ly pomp ride on to die:
3. Ride on! ride on in maj - es - ty! The wing - ed squad-rons of the sky
4. Ride on! ride on in maj - es - ty! In low - ly pomp ride on to die;
O Sav-iour meek, pur-sue Thy road With palms and scat-tered gar-ments strowed.
O Christ, Thy tri-umphs now be-gin O'er cap - tive death and con-quered sin.
Look down with sad and won-dering eyes To see th' ap-proaching sac-ri-fice.
Bow Thy meek head to mor - tal pain, Then take, O God, Thy pow'r, and reign. A-MEN.
Lift Up Your Heads, Ye Mighty Gates
224
TRURO. L. M.
GEORGE WEISSEL, 1590–1635
Tr. by CATHERINE WINKWORTH, 1829–1878
From T. WILLIAMS' PSALMODIA EVANGELICA, 1789
In moderate time
1. Lift up your heads, ye might-y gates, Be-hold, the King of glo - ry waits;
2. Fling wide the por-tals of your heart; Make it a tem - ple, set a - part
3. Re - deem-er, come, we o - pen wide Our hearts to Thee; here, Lord, a - bide.
The King of kings is draw-ing near; The Sav-iour of the world is here!
From earth-ly use for Heaven's em-ploy, A-dorned with prayer, and love, and joy.
Thine in - ner pres-ence let us feel; Thy grace and love in us re - veal. A-MEN.

Into the Woods my Master Went

LANIER. Irregular
Sidney Lanier, 1842–1881
Peter C. Lutkin, 1858–1931
In moderate time
1. In - to the woods my Mas - ter went, Clean for - spent, for - spent;
2. Out of the woods my Mas - ter went, And He was well con - tent;
In - to the woods my Mas - ter came, For - spent with love and shame. But the
Out of the woods my Mas - ter came, Con - tent with death and shame. When
ol - ives they were not blind to Him, The lit - tle gray leaves were kind to Him,
death and shame would woo Him last, From un - der the trees they drew Him last,
The thorn-tree had a mind to Him, When in - to the woods He came.
'Twas on a tree they slew Him last, When out of the woods He came.
A - men.

Night, with Ebon Pinion

226

SORROWS. 6. 5. 6. 5. 7. 6. 6. 5.

Love H. Jameson, 1811-1892 | Joseph P. Powell

In moderate time

1. Night, with eb-on pin-ion, Brood-ed o'er the vale; All a-round was si-lent, Save the night-wind's wail, When Christ, the Man of sor-rows, In tears, and sweat, and blood, Pros-trate in the gar-den, Raised His voice to God.
2. Smit-ten for of-fen-ses Which were not His own, He, for our transgressions, Had to weep a-lone; No friend with words to com-fort, Nor hand to help was there, When the Meek and Low-ly Hum-bly bowed in pray'r.
3. Ab-ba, Fa-ther, Fa-ther, If in-deed it may, Let this cup of an-guish Pass from me, I pray: Yet, if it must be suf-fered, By me, Thine on-ly Son, Ab-ba, Fa-ther, Fa-ther, Let Thy will be done. A-MEN.

Go to Dark Gethsemane

227

REDHEAD NO. 76 (AJALON). 7. 7. 7. 7. 7. 7.

James Montgomery, 1771–1854 | Richard Redhead, 1820–1901

In moderate time

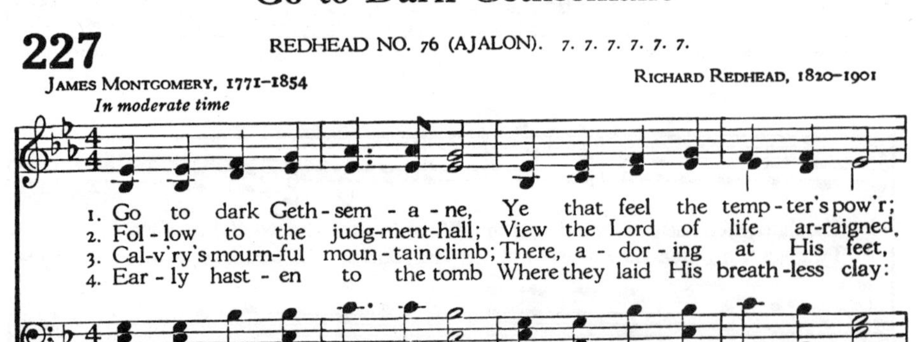

1. Go to dark Geth-sem-a-ne, Ye that feel the temp-ter's pow'r;
2. Fol-low to the judg-ment-hall; View the Lord of life ar-raigned,
3. Cal-v'ry's mourn-ful moun-tain climb; There, a-dor-ing at His feet,
4. Ear-ly hast-en to the tomb Where they laid His breath-less clay:

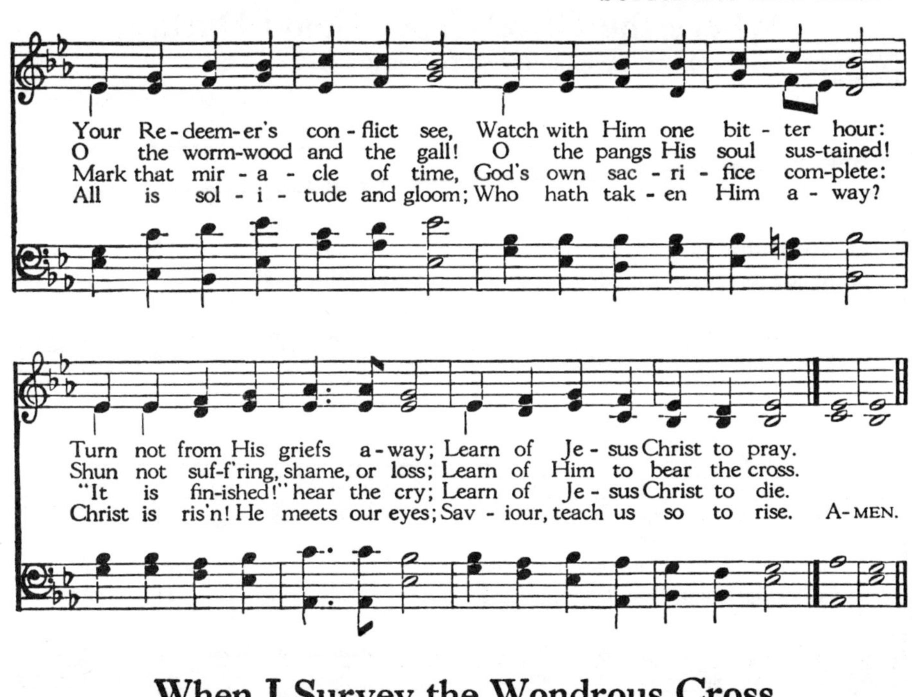
Your Re-deem-er's con-flict see, Watch with Him one bit-ter hour:
O the worm-wood and the gall! O the pangs His soul sus-tained!
Mark that mir-a-cle of time, God's own sac-ri-fice com-plete:
All is sol-i-tude and gloom; Who hath tak-en Him a-way?
Turn not from His griefs a-way; Learn of Je-sus Christ to pray.
Shun not suf-f'ring, shame, or loss; Learn of Him to bear the cross.
"It is fin-ished!" hear the cry; Learn of Je-sus Christ to die.
Christ is ris'n! He meets our eyes; Sav-iour, teach us so to rise. A-MEN.

When I Survey the Wondrous Cross

HAMBURG. L. M.

228

ISAAC WATTS, 1674–1748

LOWELL MASON, 1792–1872

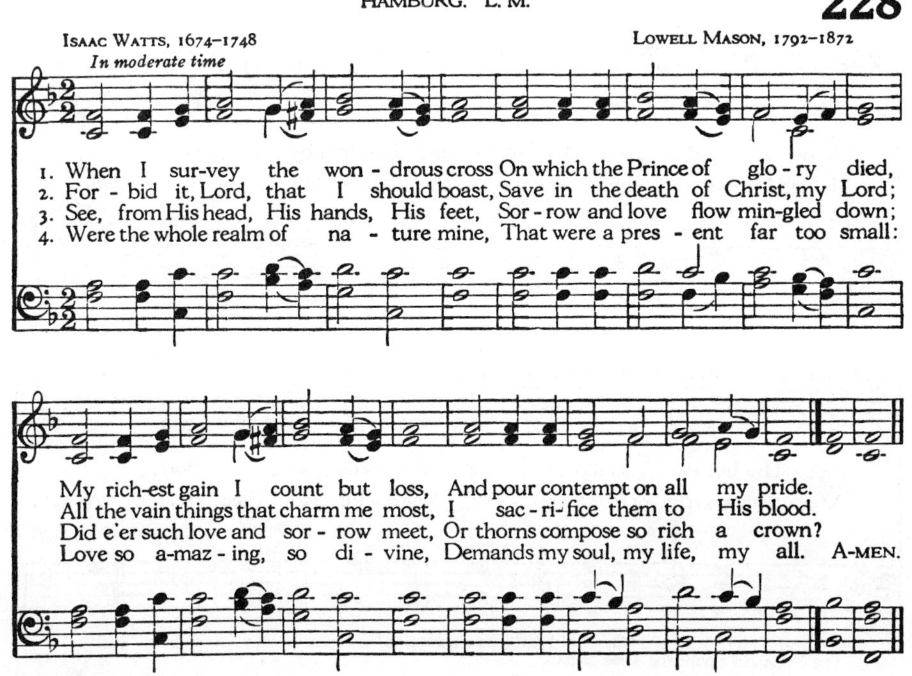
In moderate time
1. When I sur-vey the won-drous cross On which the Prince of glo-ry died,
2. For-bid it, Lord, that I should boast, Save in the death of Christ, my Lord;
3. See, from His head, His hands, His feet, Sor-row and love flow min-gled down;
4. Were the whole realm of na-ture mine, That were a pres-ent far too small:
My rich-est gain I count but loss, And pour contempt on all my pride.
All the vain things that charm me most, I sac-ri-fice them to His blood.
Did e'er such love and sor-row meet, Or thorns compose so rich a crown?
Love so a-maz-ing, so di-vine, Demands my soul, my life, my all. A-MEN.

Where the Olive Grove Stood Darkly

229

JESUS SAVIOUR, BLESSED CENTRE. 8. 5. 8. 5. D.

THOMAS TIPLADY, 1882–

JAMES MOUNTAIN, 1843–1933

In moderate time

1. Where the ol - ive grove stood dark - ly Thou, O Christ, didst pray;
And up - on Thine up-turned fea - tures Fell the moon's soft ray.
Drops of blood were on Thy fore - head, Brought by an - guish sore;
Yet Thy bur-den Thou didst shoul-der, Lord, Whom we a - dore.

2. When to fol - low Thee brings sor - row, Pain and so - cial loss;
Let us watch Thee in the gar - den Tak - ing up Thy cross.
Though for - sak - ings and be - tray - als Fol - low on Thy will,
May we tread the path of du - ty, Faith - ful to Thee still. A - MEN.

Words from "Hymns for the Times." Used by permission of Thomas Tiplady, the author. Music from "The Christian Hymnary Tune Book."

There Is a Green Hill Far Away

GREEN HILL. C. M. with Refrain

230

CECIL F. ALEXANDER, 1818–1895

GEORGE C. STEBBINS, 1846-1945

In moderate time
1. There is a green hill far a - way, With-out a cit - y wall,
2. We may not know, we can - not tell What pains He had to bear;
3. He died that we might be for-given, He died to make us good,
4. There was no oth - er good e - nough To pay the price of sin;
Where the dear Lord was cru - ci - fied, Who died to save us all.
But we be - lieve it was for us He hung and suf - fered there.
That we might go at last to heaven, Saved by His pre - cious blood.
He on - ly could un - lock the gate Of heaven and let us in.
CHORUS
Oh, dear - ly, dear - ly has He loved, And we must love Him, too;
Rit.
And trust in His re-deem-ing blood, And try His works to do. A - MEN.

O Sacred Head, Now Wounded

231

PASSION CHORALE. 7. 6. 7. 6. D.

Ascribed to BERNARD OF CLAIRVAUX, 1091-1153
Tr. by PAUL GERHARDT, 1607-1676
Tr. by JAMES W. ALEXANDER, 1804-1859

HANS LEO HASSLER, 1564-1612
Harmonized by J. S. BACH, 1685-1750

With great dignity

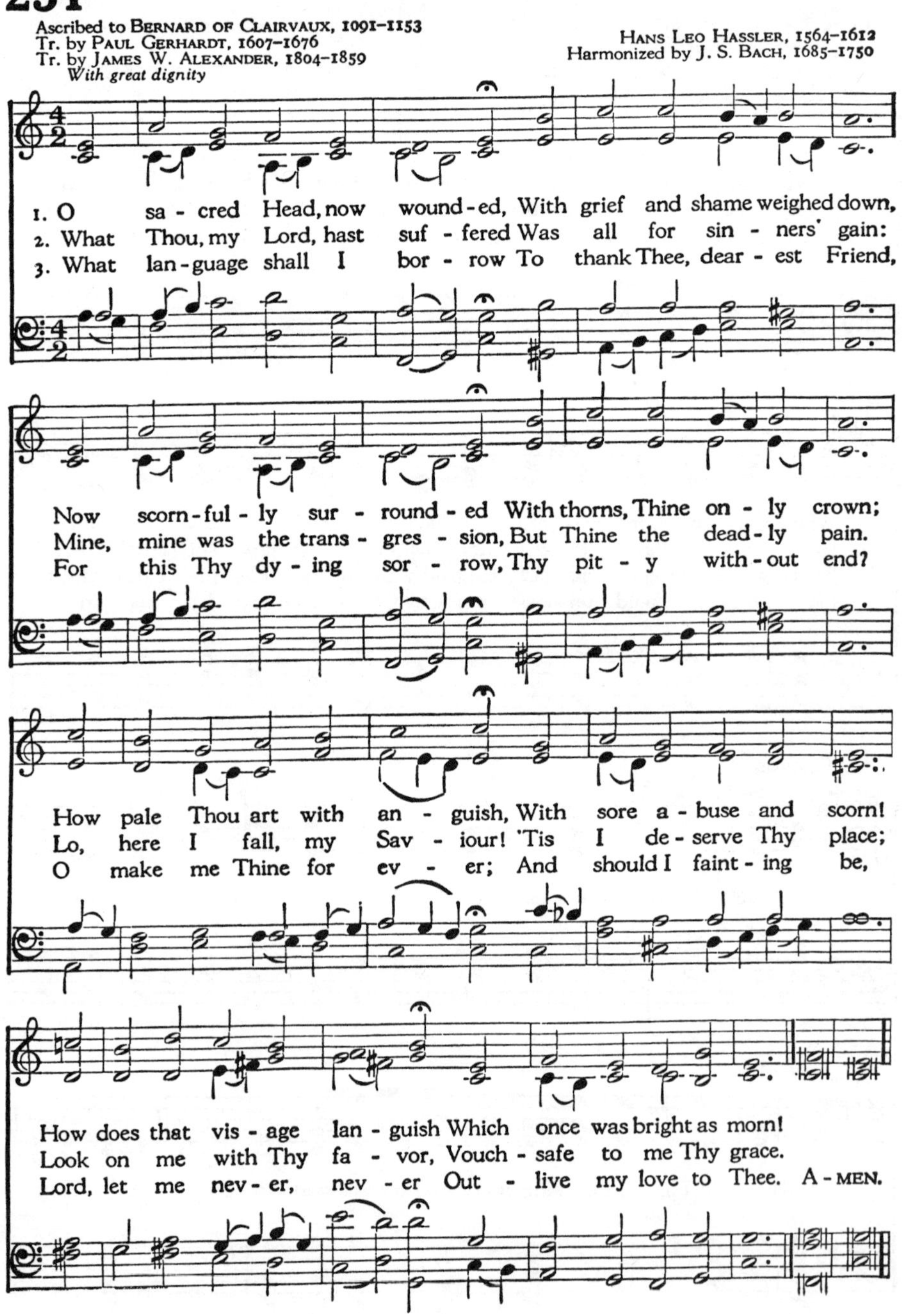
1. O sa - cred Head, now wound - ed, With grief and shame weighed down,
2. What Thou, my Lord, hast suf - fered Was all for sin - ners' gain:
3. What lan - guage shall I bor - row To thank Thee, dear - est Friend,
Now scorn - ful - ly sur - round - ed With thorns, Thine on - ly crown;
Mine, mine was the trans - gres - sion, But Thine the dead - ly pain.
For this Thy dy - ing sor - row, Thy pit - y with - out end?
How pale Thou art with an - guish, With sore a - buse and scorn!
Lo, here I fall, my Sav - iour! 'Tis I de - serve Thy place;
O make me Thine for ev - er; And should I faint - ing be,
How does that vis - age lan - guish Which once was bright as morn!
Look on me with Thy fa - vor, Vouch - safe to me Thy grace.
Lord, let me nev - er, nev - er Out - live my love to Thee. A - MEN.

'Tis Midnight; and on Olive's Brow

OLIVE'S BROW. L. M.

232

WILLIAM B. TAPPAN, 1794–1849 — WILLIAM B. BRADBURY, 1816–1868

Not too slowly

1. 'Tis mid-night; and on Ol - ive's brow The star is dimmed that late-ly shone:
2. 'Tis mid-night, and from all re-moved, The Sav-iour wres-tles lone with fears;
3. 'Tis mid-night, and for oth - ers' guilt The Man of Sor-rows weeps in blood;
4. 'Tis mid-night, and from heaven-ly plains Is borne the song that an - gels know;
'Tis mid-night; in the gar - den now, The suf-fering Sav-iour prays a - lone.
E'en that dis - ci-ple whom He loved Heeds not his Mas-ter's grief and tears.
Yet He that hath in an - guish knelt Is not for-sak - en by His God.
Un-heard by mor-tals are the strains That sweet-ly soothe the Sav-iour's woe. A-MEN.

O Come and Mourn with Me Awhile

ST. CROSS. L. M.

233

FREDERICK W. FABER, 1814–1863 — JOHN B. DYKES, 1823–1876

In moderate time

1. O come and mourn with me a - while; O come ye to the Sav-iour's side;
2. Have we no tears to shed for Him, While sol-diers scoff and foes de - ride?
3. Seven times He spake, seven words of love; And all three hours His si - lence cried
4. O love of God! O sin of man! In this dread act your strength is tried;
O come, to-geth-er let us mourn: Je - sus, our Lord, is cru - ci - fied!
Ah! look how pa-tient-ly He hangs: Je - sus, our Lord, is cru - ci - fied!
For mer-cy on the souls of men: Je - sus, our Lord, is cru - ci - fied!
And vic - to - ry re-mains with love: Je - sus, our Lord, is cru - ci - fied! A-MEN.

O Jesus, We Adore Thee

234

MEIRIONYDD. 7. 6. 7. 6. D.

ARTHUR T. RUSSELL, 1806–1874

Welsh hymn melody

With great reverence

1. O Je - sus, we a - dore Thee, Up - on the cross, our King!
2. Yet doth the world dis - dain Thee, Still pass - ing by the cross;
3. O glo - rious King, we bless Thee, No lon - ger pass Thee by;
We bow our hearts be - fore Thee, Thy gra - cious Name we sing.
Lord, may our hearts re - tain Thee; All else we count but loss.
O Je - sus, we con - fess Thee The Son en - throned on high.
That Name hath brought sal - va - tion, That Name in life our stay,
Ah, Lord, our sins ar-raigned Thee, And nailed Thee to the tree:
Lord, grant to us re - mis - sion; Life through Thy death re - store;
Our peace, our con - so - la - tion, When life shall fade a - way.
Our pride, our Lord, dis - dained Thee; Yet deign our Hope to be.
Yea, grant us the fru - i - tion Of life for - ev - er-more.
A - MEN.

Beneath the Cross of Jesus

ST. CHRISTOPHER. 7. 6. 8. 6. 8. 6. 8. 6.

235

Elizabeth C. Clephane, 1830–1869
Frederick C. Maker, 1844–1927
Not too fast
1. Be - neath the cross of Je - sus I fain would take my stand,
2. Up - on that cross of Je - sus Mine eye at times can see
3. I take, O cross, thy shad - ow For my a - bid - ing place;
The shad - ow of a might - y rock With - in a wea - ry land;
The ver - y dy - ing form of One Who suf - fered there for me;
I ask no oth - er sun - shine than The sun - shine of His face;
A home with - in the wil - der - ness, A rest up - on the way,
And from my strick - en heart with tears Two won - ders I con - fess:
Con - tent to let the world go by, To know no gain nor loss,
From the burn-ing of the noon-tide heat, And the bur - den of the day.
The won-ders of re-deem-ing love And my un-wor-thi - ness.
My sin - ful self my on - ly shame, My glo - ry all the cross. A - men.

Above the Hills of Time the Cross Is Gleaming

236

LONDONDERRY. 11. 10. 11. 10. D.

THOMAS TIPLADY, 1882–

In moderate time

Traditional Irish melody

1. A - bove the hills of time the cross is gleam-ing, Fair as the sun when night has turned to day; And from it love's pure light is rich - ly stream-ing, To cleanse the heart and ban - ish sin a - way. To this dear cross the eyes of men are turn - ing To - day as

2. The cross, O Christ, Thy won-drous love re - veal - ing, A - wakes our hearts as with the light of morn, And par-don o'er our sin - ful spir - its steal - ing Tells us that we, in Thee, have been re - born. Like ech - oes to sweet tem - ple bells re - ply - ing, Our hearts, O

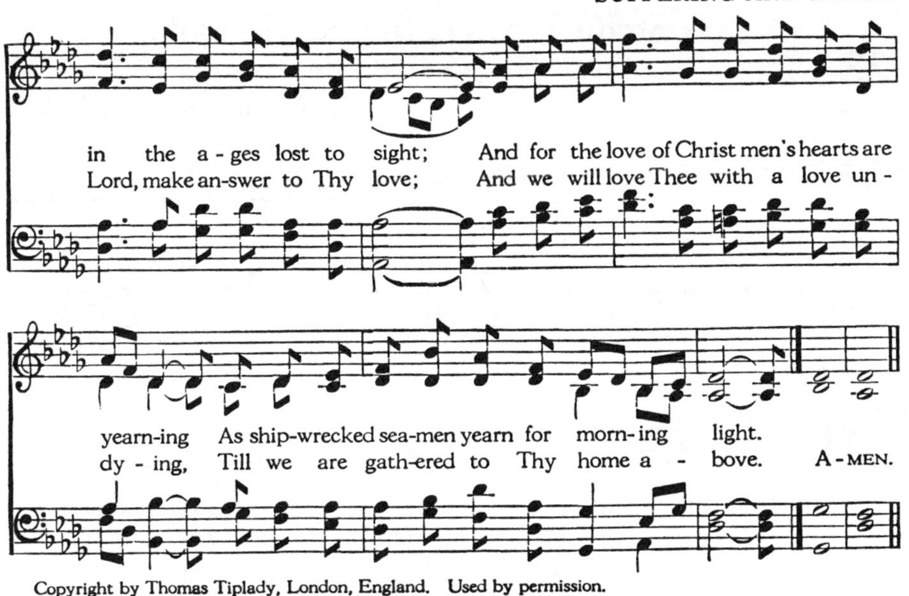
in the a-ges lost to sight; And for the love of Christ men's hearts are
Lord, make an-swer to Thy love; And we will love Thee with a love un-
yearn-ing As ship-wrecked sea-men yearn for morn-ing light.
dy-ing, Till we are gath-ered to Thy home a-bove. A-MEN.

In the Cross of Christ I Glory

RATHBUN. 8. 7. 8. 7.

237

JOHN BOWRING, 1792–1872 ITHAMAR CONKEY, 1815–1867

In moderate time

1. In the cross of Christ I glo-ry, Tow-'ring o'er the wrecks of time;
2. When the woes of life o'er-take me, Hopes de-ceive, and fears an-noy,
3. When the sun of bliss is beam-ing Light and love up-on my way,
4. Bane and bless-ing, pain and pleasure, By the cross are sanc-ti-fied;

All the light of sa-cred sto-ry Gath-ers round its head sub-lime.
Nev-er shall the cross for-sake me; Lo! it glows with peace and joy.
From the cross the ra-diance streaming Adds more lus-ter to the day.
Peace is there, that knows no meas-ure, Joys that thro' all time a-bide. A-MEN.

The Strife Is O'er, the Battle Done

238

PALESTRINA. 8. 8. 8. 4. with Alleluias

Latin; Tr. by FRANCIS POTT, 1832–1909

GIOVANNI P. DA PALESTRINA, 1526–1594
Adapted by W. H. MONK, 1823–1889

Jubilantly, with majesty

Al - le - lu - ia! Al - le - lu - ia! Al - le - lu - ia!

1. The strife is o'er, the bat - tle done;
2. The powers of death have done their worst,
3. The three sad days are quick - ly sped;
4. Lord, by the stripes which wound - ed Thee,

The vic - to - ry of life is won; The song of
But Christ their le - gions hath dis - persed; Let shouts of
He ris - es glo - rious from the dead; All glo - ry
From death's dread sting Thy serv - ants free, That we may

tri - umph has be - gun. Al - le - lu - ia!
ho - ly joy out - burst. Al - le - lu - ia!
to our ris - en Head! Al - le - lu - ia!
live and sing to Thee, Al - le - lu - ia! A - MEN.

Christ the Lord Is Risen Today

EASTER HYMN (WORGAN). 7. 7. 7. 7. with Alleluias

CHARLES WESLEY, 1707–1788, and others — From LYRA DAVIDICA, 1708

Joyously

1. Christ the Lord is risen to - day, Al - - - - le - lu - ia!
2. Lives a - gain our glo - rious King, Al - - - - le - lu - ia!
3. Love's re - deem - ing work is done, Al - - - - le - lu - ia!
4. Soar we now where Christ has led, Al - - - - le - lu - ia!

Sons of men and an - gels say, Al - - le - lu - ia!
Where, O death, is now thy sting? Al - - le - lu - ia!
Fought the fight, the bat - tle won, Al - - le - lu - ia!
Fol - lowing our ex - alt - ed Head, Al - - le - lu - ia!

Raise your joys and tri - umphs high, Al - - le - lu - ia!
Once He died, our souls to save, Al - - le - lu - ia!
Death in vain for - bids Him rise, Al - - le - lu - ia!
Made like Him, like Him we rise, Al - - le - lu - ia!

Sing, ye heavens, and earth re - ply, Al - le - lu - ia!
Where's thy vic-tory, boast-ing grave? Al - le - lu - ia!
Christ hath o - pened Par - a - dise, Al - le - lu - ia!
Ours the cross, the grave, the skies, Al - le - lu - ia! A-MEN.

Christ Is Risen, Christ Is Risen

240

RESURREXIT. 8. 7. 8. 7. 7. 5. 7. 5. with Refrain

A. T. Gurney, 1820–1887 — Arthur S. Sullivan, 1842–1900

Joyfully

1. Christ is ris - en, Christ is ris - en! He hath burst His bonds in twain;
2. See, the chains of death are bro - ken; Earth be - low and heav'n a - bove,
3. Glo - rious an - gels, downward thronging, Hail the Lord of all the skies;
Christ is ris - en, Christ is ris - en! Al - le - lu - ia! swell the strain!
Joy in each a - maz - ing to - ken Of His ris - ing, Lord of love:
Heav'n, with joy and ho - ly long - ing, For the Word in - car - nate, cries.
For our gain He suf - fered loss, By di - vine de - cree;
He for - ev - er - more shall reign By the Fa - ther's side,
"Christ is ris - en! earth re - joice! Gleam, ye star - ry train!
He hath died up - on the cross, But our God is He.
Till He comes to earth a - gain, Comes to claim His bride.
All cre - a - tion find a voice; He o'er all shall reign."

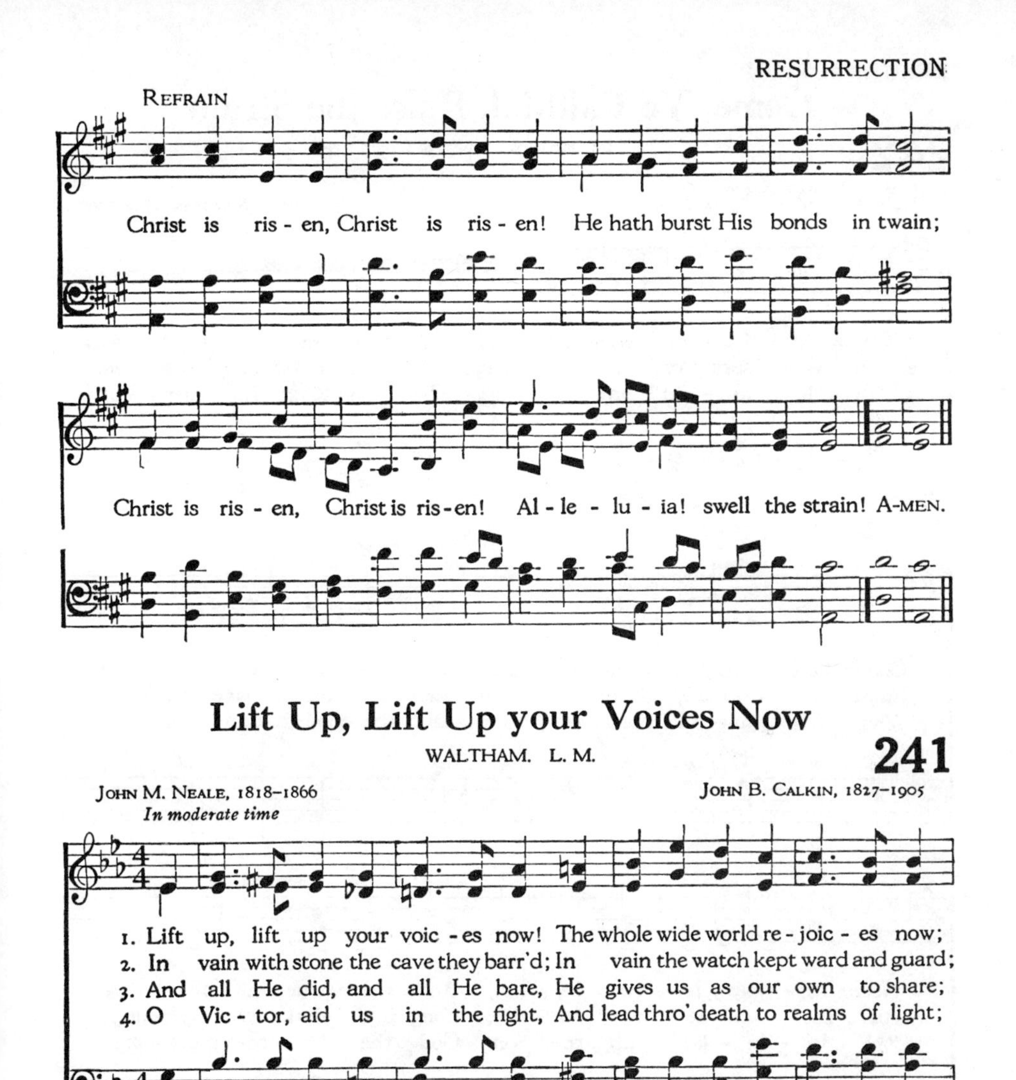
REFRAIN
Christ is ris - en, Christ is ris - en! He hath burst His bonds in twain;
Christ is ris - en, Christ is ris-en! Al - le - lu - ia! swell the strain! A-MEN.

Lift Up, Lift Up your Voices Now

241

WALTHAM. L. M.

JOHN M. NEALE, 1818–1866 — JOHN B. CALKIN, 1827–1905

In moderate time

1. Lift up, lift up your voic - es now! The whole wide world re - joic - es now;
The Lord hath triumph'd glo-rious-ly, The Lord shall reign vic - to - rious-ly.

2. In vain with stone the cave they barr'd; In vain the watch kept ward and guard;
Ma - jes - tic from the spoil-ed tomb, In pomp of tri-umph Christ is come.

3. And all He did, and all He bare, He gives us as our own to share;
And hope, and joy, and peace be -gin, For Christ has won, and man shall win.

4. O Vic - tor, aid us in the fight, And lead thro' death to realms of light;
We safe-ly pass where Thou hast trod; In Thee we die to rise to God. A-MEN.

Come, Ye Faithful, Raise the Strain

242

ST. KEVIN. 7. 6. 7. 6. D.

JOHN OF DAMASCUS, 8th century
Tr. by JOHN M. NEALE, 1818–1866
ARTHUR S. SULLIVAN, 1842–1900
In moderate time
1. Come, ye faith - ful, raise the strain Of tri - umph - ant glad - ness:
2. 'Tis the spring of souls to - day: Christ hath burst His pris - on,
3. "Al - le - lu - ia!" now we cry To our King Im - mor - tal,
God hath brought His peo - ple forth In - to joy from sad - ness.
From the frost and gloom of death Light and life have ris - en.
Who, tri - um-phant, burst the bars Of the tomb's dark por - tal;
Now re - joice, Je - ru - sa - lem, And with true af - fec - tion
All the win - ter of our sins, Long and dark, is fly - ing
"Al - le - lu - ia!" with the Son, God the Fa - ther prais - ing;
Wel - come in un - wea - ried strains Je - sus' res - ur - rec - tion.
From His light, to whom we give Thanks and praise un - dy - ing.
"Al - le - lu - ia!" yet a - gain To the Spir - it rais - ing. A - MEN.

On Wings of Living Light

MANSFIELD. 6. 6. 6. 6. 8. 8.

243

WILLIAM W. HOW, 1823–1897 JOSEPH BARNBY, 1838–1896

Joyfully

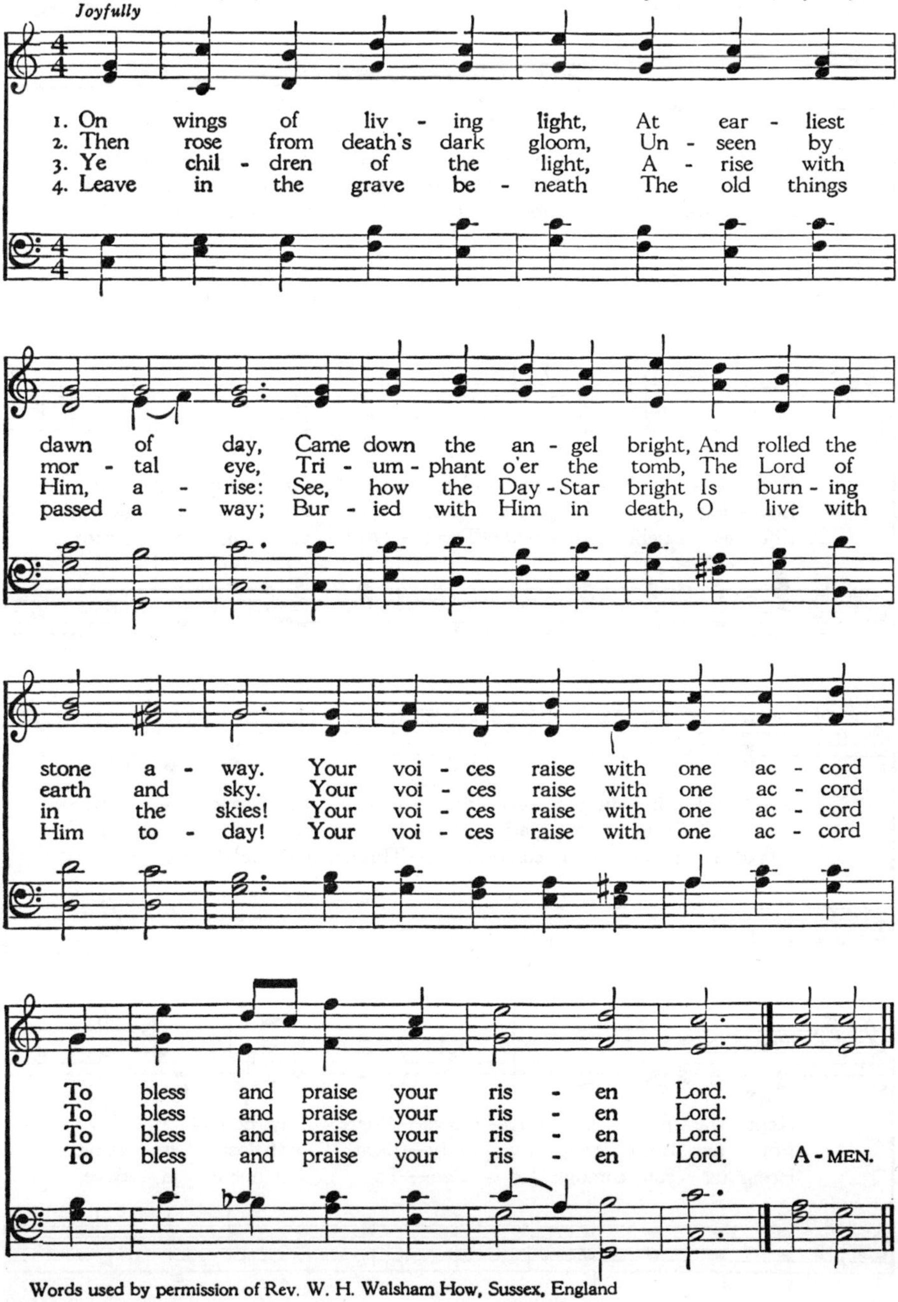

1. On wings of liv - ing light, At ear - liest
2. Then rose from death's dark gloom, Un - seen by
3. Ye chil - dren of the light, A - rise with
4. Leave in the grave be - neath The old things

dawn of day, Came down the an - gel bright, And rolled the
mor - tal eye, Tri - um - phant o'er the tomb, The Lord of
Him, a - rise: See, how the Day - Star bright Is burn - ing
passed a - way; Bur - ied with Him in death, O live with

stone a - way. Your voi - ces raise with one ac - cord
earth and sky. Your voi - ces raise with one ac - cord
in the skies! Your voi - ces raise with one ac - cord
Him to - day! Your voi - ces raise with one ac - cord

To bless and praise your ris - en Lord.
To bless and praise your ris - en Lord.
To bless and praise your ris - en Lord.
To bless and praise your ris - en Lord. A - MEN.

Thine Is the Glory

244

JUDAS MACCABEUS. 5. 5. 6. 5. 6. 5. 6. 5. with Refrain

Anonymous
Tr. by R. Birch Hoyle, 1923
George F. Handel, 1685–1759
With majestic rhythm
1. Thine is the glo - ry,— Ris - en, con - qu'ring Son,
2. Lo! Je - sus meets thee,— Ris - en from the tomb;
3. No more we doubt Thee,— Glo - rious Prince of Life!
End - less is the vic - t'ry— Thou o'er death hast won.
Lov - ing - ly He greets thee,— Scat - ters fear and gloom;
Life is nought with - out Thee;— Aid us in our strife;
An - gels in bright rai - ment—Rolled the stone a - way.
Let His Church with glad - ness— Hymns of tri - umph sing,
Make us more than con'qu'rors,— Through Thy death - less love.
Kept the fold - ed grave-clothes—Where Thy bod - y lay.
For her Lord now liv - eth;— Death hath lost its sting.
Bring us safe through Jor - dan— To Thy home a - bove.

REFRAIN
Thine is the glo - ry, Ris - en, con-qu'ring Son,
End - less is the vic - t'ry Thou o'er death hast won. A - MEN.

I Know that my Redeemer Lives

BRADFORD. C. M.

245

CHARLES WESLEY, 1707–1788 GEORGE F. HANDEL, 1685–1759

In moderate time
1. I know that my Re - deem - er lives; He lives, who once was dead;
2. He lives tri - um - phant o'er the grave, At God's right hand on high,
3. He lives, that I may al - so live, And now His grace pro-claim;
4. Let strains of heav'n - ly mu - sic rise, While all their an - them sing
To me in grief He com-fort gives; With peace He crowns my head.
My ran - somed soul to keep and save, To bless and glo - ri - fy.
He lives, that I may hon - or give To His most ho - ly Name.
To Christ, my pre - cious Sac - ri - fice, And ev - er - liv - ing King. A-MEN.

'Welcome, Happy Morning!' Age to Age Shall Say

246

FORTUNATUS. 11. 11. 11. 11. with Refrain

VENANTIUS FORTUNATUS, 530–609
Tr. by JOHN ELLERTON, 1826–1893

ARTHUR S. SULLIVAN, 1842–1900

In moderate time

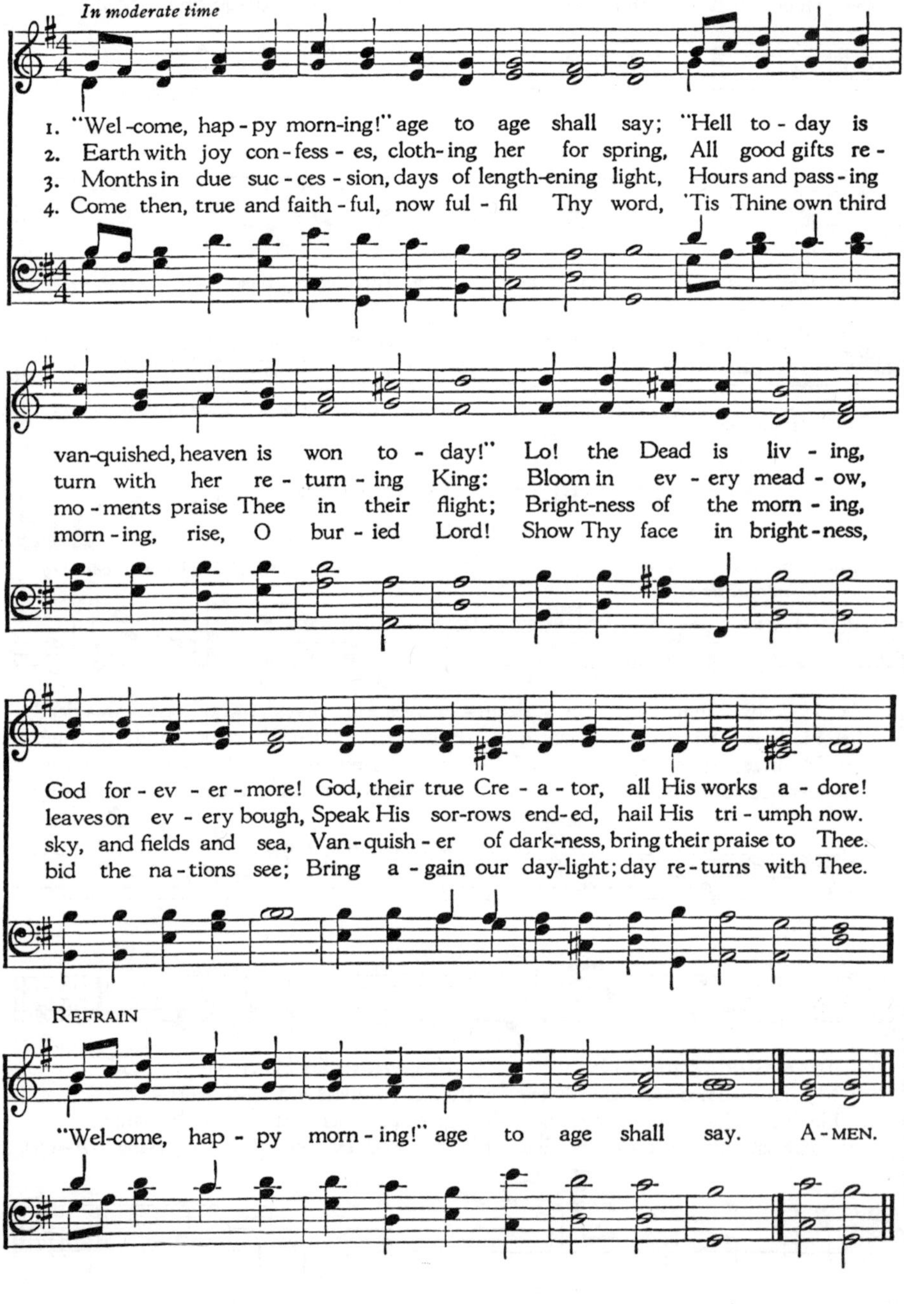

1. "Wel-come, hap-py morn-ing!" age to age shall say; "Hell to-day is
2. Earth with joy con-fess-es, cloth-ing her for spring, All good gifts re-
3. Months in due suc-ces-sion, days of length-ening light, Hours and pass-ing
4. Come then, true and faith-ful, now ful-fil Thy word, 'Tis Thine own third

van-quished, heaven is won to-day!" Lo! the Dead is liv-ing,
turn with her re-turn-ing King: Bloom in ev-ery mead-ow,
mo-ments praise Thee in their flight; Bright-ness of the morn-ing,
morn-ing, rise, O bur-ied Lord! Show Thy face in bright-ness,

God for-ev-er-more! God, their true Cre-a-tor, all His works a-dore!
leaves on ev-ery bough, Speak His sor-rows end-ed, hail His tri-umph now.
sky, and fields and sea, Van-quish-er of dark-ness, bring their praise to Thee.
bid the na-tions see; Bring a-gain our day-light; day re-turns with Thee.

REFRAIN

"Wel-come, hap-py morn-ing!" age to age shall say. A-MEN.

The Day of Resurrection

LANCASHIRE. 7. 6. 7. 6. D.

JOHN OF DAMASCUS, 8th century
Tr. by JOHN M. NEALE, 1818–1866

HENRY SMART, 1813–1879

Joyfully

1. The day of res-ur-rec-tion! Earth, tell it out a-broad
The Pass-o-ver of glad-ness, The Pass-o-ver of God.
From death to life e-ter-nal, From this world to the sky,
Our Christ hath brought us o-ver With hymns of vic-to-ry.

2. Our hearts be pure from e-vil, That we may see a-right
The Lord in rays e-ter-nal Of res-ur-rec-tion light;
And, lis-tening to His ac-cents, May hear, so calm and plain,
His own "All hail!" and, hear-ing, May raise the vic-tor strain.

3. Now let the heavens be joy-ful, Let earth her song be-gin;
Let the round world keep tri-umph, And all that is there-in;
Let all things seen and un-seen, Their notes of glad-ness blend,
For Christ the Lord hath ris-en, Our Joy that hath no end.

A-MEN.

RESURRECTION

Life Is Good, for God Contrives It

248

TREFAENAN. 8. 7. 8. 7. 8. 8. 8. 7.

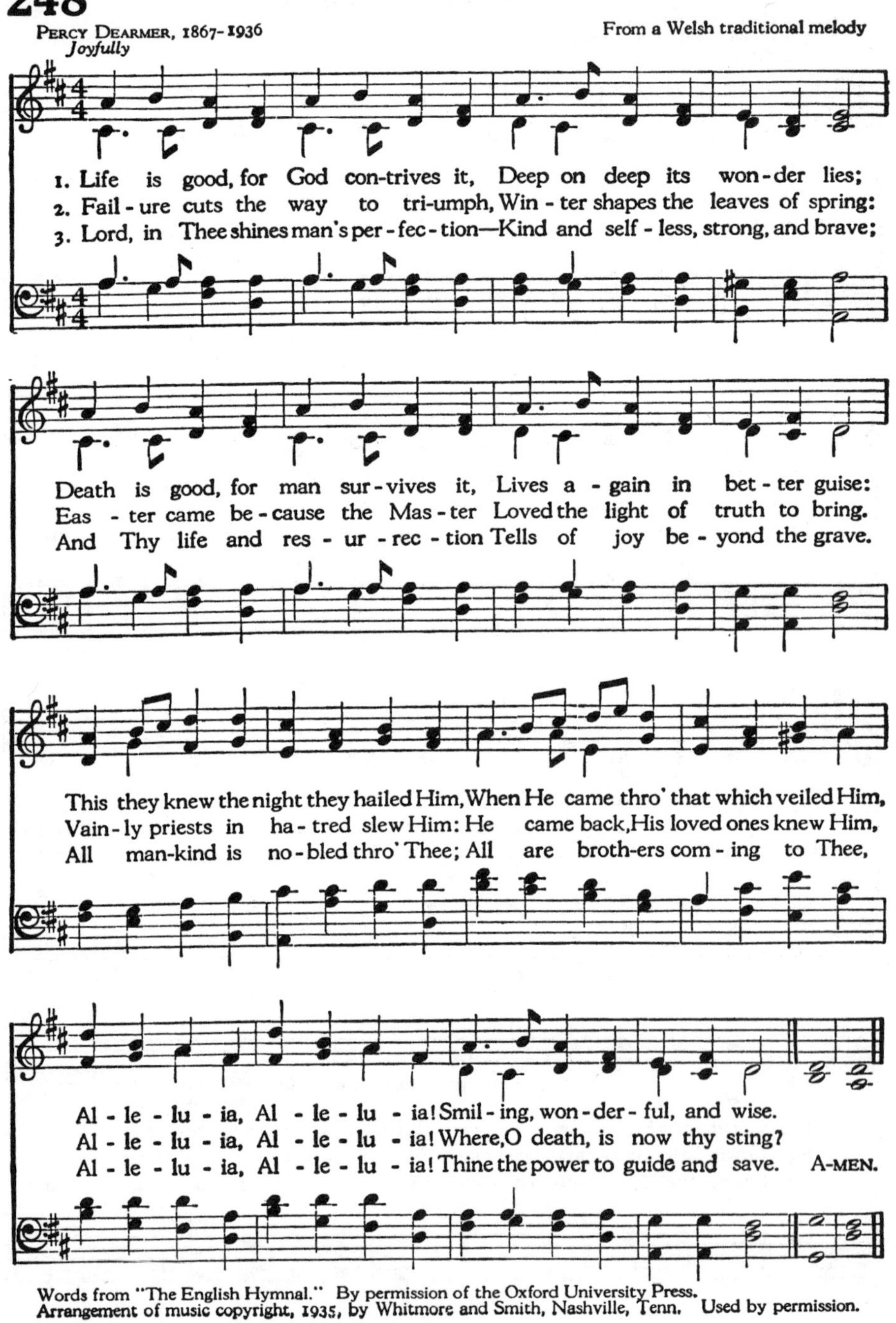

Percy Dearmer, 1867-1936
From a Welsh traditional melody
Joyfully
1. Life is good, for God con-trives it, Deep on deep its won-der lies;
2. Fail-ure cuts the way to tri-umph, Win-ter shapes the leaves of spring:
3. Lord, in Thee shines man's per-fec-tion—Kind and self-less, strong, and brave;
Death is good, for man sur-vives it, Lives a-gain in bet-ter guise:
Eas-ter came be-cause the Mas-ter Loved the light of truth to bring.
And Thy life and res-ur-rec-tion Tells of joy be-yond the grave.
This they knew the night they hailed Him, When He came thro' that which veiled Him,
Vain-ly priests in ha-tred slew Him: He came back, His loved ones knew Him,
All man-kind is no-bled thro' Thee; All are broth-ers com-ing to Thee,
Al-le-lu-ia, Al-le-lu-ia! Smil-ing, won-der-ful, and wise.
Al-le-lu-ia, Al-le-lu-ia! Where, O death, is now thy sting?
Al-le-lu-ia, Al-le-lu-ia! Thine the power to guide and save.
A-MEN.

There's a Light Upon the Mountains

MT. HOLYOKE. 8. 7. 8. 7. D.

249

Henry Burton, 1840–1930
In moderate time
Maurice L. Wostenholm, 1887–
1. There's a light up-on the moun-tains, And the day is at the spring,
2. In the fad-ing of the star-light We may see the com-ing morn;
3. There's a hush of ex-pec-ta-tion And a qui-et in the air,
4. He is break-ing down the bar-riers, He is cast-ing up the way;
5. Hark! we hear a dis-tant mu-sic, And it comes with full-er swell;
When our eyes shall see the beau-ty And the glo-ry of the King:
And the lights of men are pal-ing In the splen-dors of the dawn;
And the breath of God is mov-ing In the fer-vent breath of prayer;
He is call-ing for His an-gels To build up the gates of day:
'Tis the tri-umph-song of Je-sus, Of our King, Im-man-u-el!
Wea-ry was our heart with wait-ing, And the night-watch seemed so long,
For the east-ern skies are glow-ing As with light of hid-den fire,
For the suf-fering, dy-ing Je-sus Is the Christ up-on the throne,
But His an-gels here are hu-man, Not the shin-ing hosts a-bove;
Go ye forth with joy to meet Him! And, my soul, be swift to bring
But His tri-umph-day is break-ing, And we hail it with a song.
And the hearts of men are stir-ring With the throbs of deep de-sire.
And the tra-vail of our spir-it Is the tra-vail of His own.
For the drum-beats of His ar-my Are the heart-beats of our love.
All thy sweet-est and thy dear-est For the tri-umph of our King!
A-MEN.

Crown Him with Many Crowns

250

DIADEMATA. S. M. D.

MATTHEW BRIDGES, 1800–1894, and
GODFREY THRING, 1823–1903

GEORGE J. ELVEY, 1816–1893

Joyously

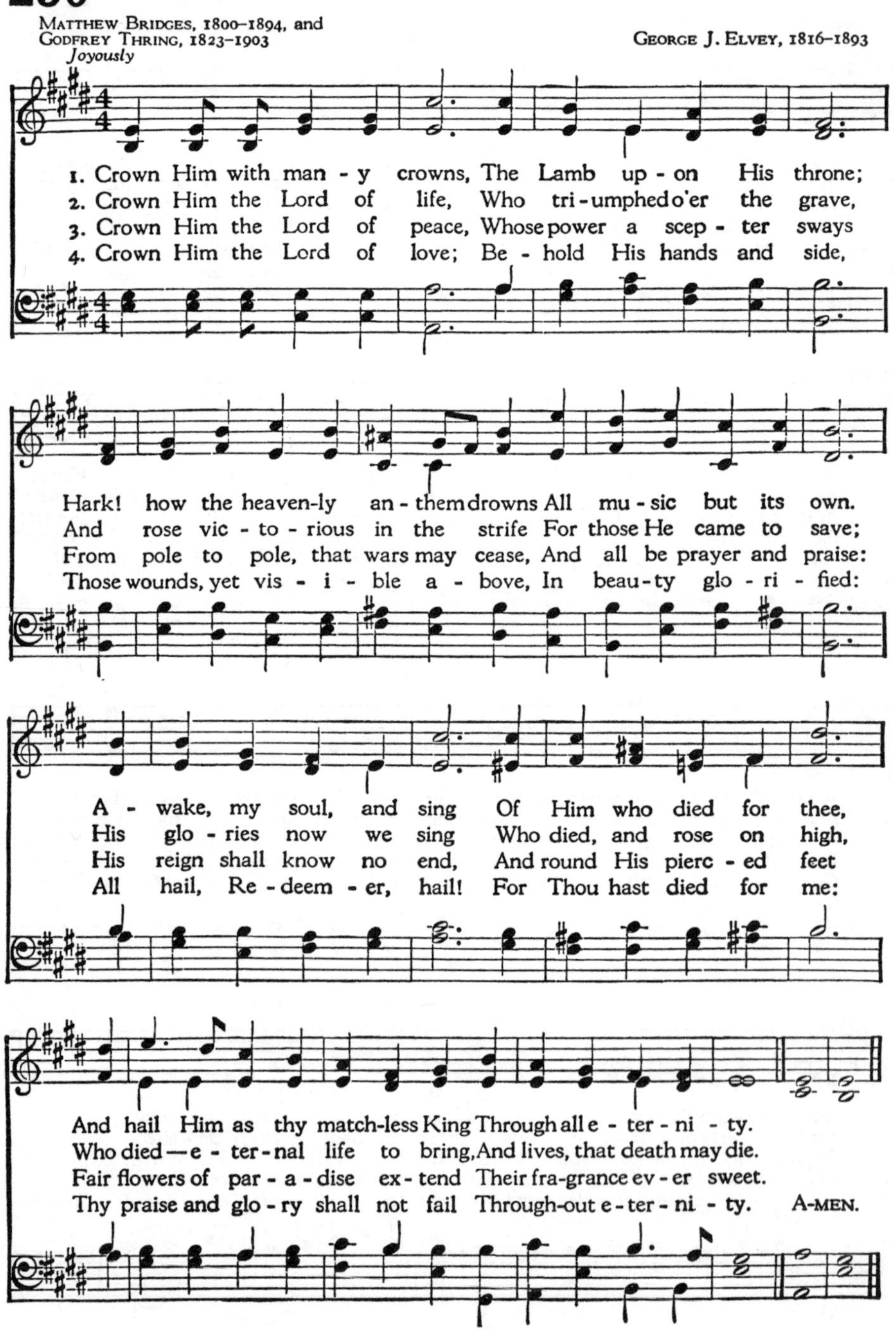
1. Crown Him with man - y crowns, The Lamb up - on His throne;
2. Crown Him the Lord of life, Who tri - umphed o'er the grave,
3. Crown Him the Lord of peace, Whose power a scep - ter sways
4. Crown Him the Lord of love; Be - hold His hands and side,
Hark! how the heaven-ly an - them drowns All mu - sic but its own.
And rose vic - to - rious in the strife For those He came to save;
From pole to pole, that wars may cease, And all be prayer and praise:
Those wounds, yet vis - i - ble a - bove, In beau - ty glo - ri - fied:
A - wake, my soul, and sing Of Him who died for thee,
His glo - ries now we sing Who died, and rose on high,
His reign shall know no end, And round His pierc - ed feet
All hail, Re - deem - er, hail! For Thou hast died for me:
And hail Him as thy match-less King Through all e - ter - ni - ty.
Who died—e - ter - nal life to bring, And lives, that death may die.
Fair flowers of par - a - dise ex - tend Their fra - grance ev - er sweet.
Thy praise and glo - ry shall not fail Through-out e - ter - ni - ty.
A-MEN.

All the Toil and Sorrow Done

251
LLANFAIR. 7. 7. 7. 7. with Alleluias
A. P. Stanley, 1815–1881
Robert Williams, c. 1781–1821
With joy and dignity
1. All the toil and sor - row done, Al - le - lu - ia!
2. Still His words be- fore us range, Al - le - lu - ia!
3. Ev - er - more in heart and mind, Al - le - lu - ia!
All the bat - tle fought and won, Al - le - lu - ia!
Through the a - ges as they change; Al - le - lu - ia!
We our life in Him will find; Al - le - lu - ia!
Now be - hind we leave the past, Al - le - lu - ia!
Where - so - e'er the truth will lead, Al - le - lu - ia!
To our own e - ter - nal Friend, Al - le - lu - ia!
For - ward be our glanc - es cast. Al - le - lu - ia!
He will give the light we need. Al - le - lu - ia!
Ev - er - more let us as - cend. Al - le - lu - ia! A-men.

Words from "The Christian Hymnary."

All Hail the Power of Jesus' Name

252

CORONATION. C. M.

(*First Tune*)

EDWARD PERRONET, 1726–1792
Alt. by JOHN RIPPON, 1751–1836

OLIVER HOLDEN, 1765–1844

With dignity, in moderate time

1. All hail the power of Je - sus' Name! Let an - gels pros - trate fall;
2. Ye cho - sen seed of Is - rael's race, Ye ran - somed from the fall,
3. Let ev - ery kin - dred, ev - ery tribe, On this ter - res - trial ball,
4. O that with yon - der sa - cred throng We at His feet may fall!

Bring forth the roy - al di - a - dem, And crown Him Lord of all;
Hail Him who saves you by His grace, And crown Him Lord of all;
To Him all maj - es - ty as - cribe, And crown Him Lord of all;
We'll join the ev - er - last - ing song, And crown Him Lord of all;

Bring forth the roy - al di - a - dem, And crown Him Lord of all.
Hail Him who saves you by His grace, And crown Him Lord of all.
To Him all maj - es - ty as - cribe, And crown Him Lord of all.
We'll join the ev - er - last - ing song, And crown Him Lord of all. A - MEN.

All Hail the Power of Jesus' Name

253

MILES' LANE. C. M.

(*Second Tune*)

EDWARD PERRONET, 1726–1792
Alt. by JOHN RIPPON, 1751–1836

WILLIAM SHRUBSOLE, 1760–1806

1. All hail the power of Je - sus' name! Let an - gels pros - trate fall;
2. Ye cho - sen seed of Is - rael's race, Ye ran - somed from the fall,
3. Let ev - ery kin - dred, ev - ery tribe, On this ter - res - trial ball,
4. O that with yon - der sa - cred throng We at His feet may fall!

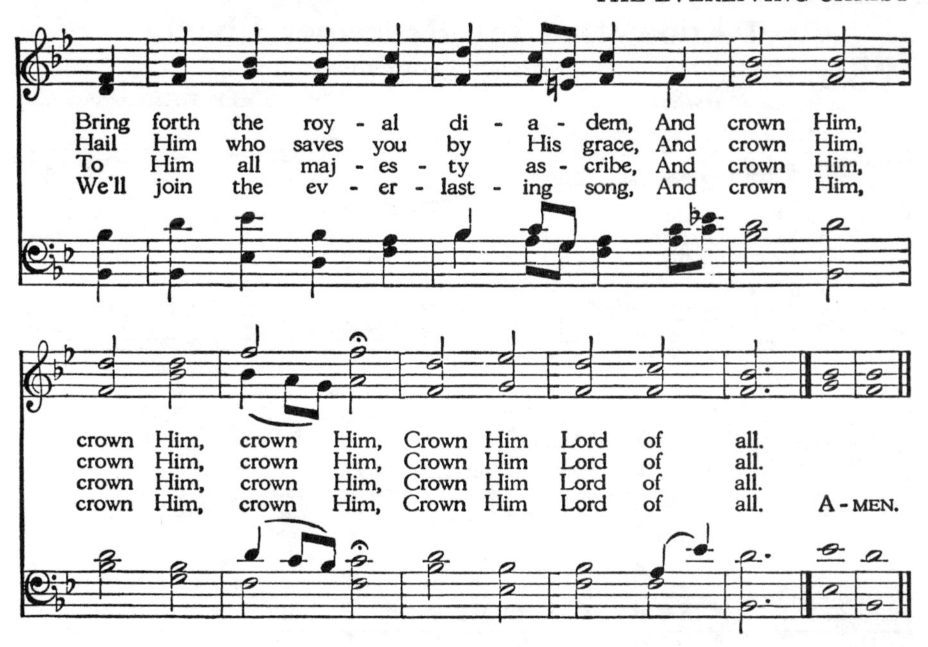
Bring forth the roy - al di - a - dem, And crown Him,
Hail Him who saves you by His grace, And crown Him,
To Him all maj - es - ty as - cribe, And crown Him,
We'll join the ev - er - last - ing song, And crown Him,
crown Him, crown Him, Crown Him Lord of all.
crown Him, crown Him, Crown Him Lord of all.
crown Him, crown Him, Crown Him Lord of all.
crown Him, crown Him, Crown Him Lord of all. A - MEN.

Immortal Love, Forever Full

SERENITY. C. M.

254

JOHN G. WHITTIER, 1807–1892 WILLIAM V. WALLACE, 1814–1865

In flowing rhythm, with dignity

1. Im - mor - tal Love, for - ev - er full, For - ev - er flow - ing free,
2. We may not climb the heaven-ly steeps To bring the Lord Christ down;
3. But warm, sweet, ten - der, e - ven yet A pres - ent help is He;
4. The heal - ing of His seam-less dress Is by our beds of pain;
5. O Lord and Mas - ter of us all, What-e'er our name or sign,

For - ev - er shared, for - ev - er whole, A nev - er - ebb - ing sea!
In vain we search the low - est deeps, For Him no depths can drown:
And faith has still its Ol - i - vet, And love its Gal - i - lee.
We touch Him in life's throng and press, And we are whole a - gain.
We own Thy sway, we hear Thy call, We test our lives by Thine. A - MEN.

I Know that my Redeemer Liveth

255
POUNDS. 9. 8. 9. 8. with Refrain
Jessie H. Brown, 1861-1921
James H. Fillmore, 1849-1941
With exultation
1. I know that my Re-deem-er liv - eth, And on the earth . . . . a-gain shall stand; . . . . I know e - ter - nal life He giv - eth, That grace and pow'r . . . . . are in His hand.
2. I know His promise nev - er fail - eth, The word He speaks, . . . it can-not die; . . . . Tho' cru - el death my flesh as - sail - eth, Yet I shall see . . . . . . Him by and by.
3. I know my mansion He pre - par - eth, That where He is, ... there I may be; . . . . O won-drous tho't, for me He car - eth, And He at last . . . . . . will come for me.
And on the earth
again shall stand;
That grace and pow'r
Chorus
I know, I know . . . . . that Je - sus liv - eth, And on the earth . . . . a - gain shall stand; I know, I know . . . that life He giv-eth, That grace and pow'r . . are in His hand. A-men.
I know, I know
And on the earth
I know, I know
That grace and pow'r

Look, Ye Saints! The Sight Is Glorious

CWM RHONDDA. 8. 7. 8. 7. 8. 7.

256

THOMAS KELLY, 1769–1854

Welsh hymn melody
JOHN HUGHES, 1873–1932

With exultation and joy

1. Look, ye saints! The sight is glo - rious: See the Man of Sor - rows now; From the fight re - turned vic-to - rious, Ev - ery knee to Him shall bow: Crown Him! Crown Him! Crown Him! Crown Him! Crowns be-come the Vic-tor's brow, Crowns be - come the Vic - tor's brow.
2. Crown the Sav - iour! An - gels, crown Him! Rich the tro - phies Je - sus brings; In the seat of power en-throne Him, While the vault of heav - en rings: Crown Him! Crown Him! Crown Him! Crown Him! Crown the Sav-iour King of kings, Crown the Sav - iour King of kings.
3. Sin - ners in de - ri - sion crowned Him, Mock - ing thus the Sav - iour's claim; Saints and an - gels crowd a - round Him, Own His ti - tle, praise His Name: Crown Him! Crown Him! Crown Him! Crown Him! Spread a-broad the Vic-tor's fame, Spread a - broad the Vic - tor's fame.
4. Hark, those bursts of ac - cla - ma - tion! Hark, those loud tri - um-phant chords! Je - sus takes the high - est sta - tion; O what joy the sight af - fords! Crown Him! Crown Him! Crown Him! Crown Him! King of kings, and Lord of lords! King of kings, and Lord of lords!
A-MEN.

Hail to the Lord's Anointed

257

SHEFFIELD. 7. 6. 7. 6. D.

JAMES MONTGOMERY, 1771–1854

English melody, arranged

With joy
1. Hail to the Lord's A - noint - ed, Great Da - vid's great - er Son!
2. He comes with suc - cor speed - y To those who suf - fer wrong,
3. He shall come down like show - ers Up - on the fruit - ful earth;
4. For him shall prayer un - ceas - ing And dai - ly vows as - cend,
Hail, in the time ap - point - ed, His reign on earth be - gun!
To help the poor and need - y, And bid the weak be strong;
And love, joy, hope, like flow - ers, Spring in His path to birth;
His king-dom still in - creas - ing, A king - dom with - out end:
He comes to break op - pres - sion, To set the cap - tive free;
To give them songs for sigh - ing, Their dark-ness turn to light,
Be - fore Him on the moun - tains Shall peace, the her - ald, go,
The tide of time shall nev - er His cov - e - nant re - move,
To take a - way trans-gres - sion, And rule in e - qui - ty.
Whose souls, con-demned and dy - ing, Were pre-cious in His sight.
And right-eous-ness, in foun - tains, From hill to val - ley flow.
His name shall stand for - ev - er— That name to us is Love.
A - MEN.

Ye Servants of God, Your Master Proclaim

HANOVER. 10. 10. 11. 11.

258

CHARLES WESLEY, 1707–1788 | WILLIAM CROFT, 1678–1727

In moderate time

1. Ye ser - vants of God, your Mas - ter pro - claim,
2. God rul - eth on high, al - might - y to save;
3. "Sal - va - tion to God, who sits on the throne!"
4. Then let us a - dore, and give Him His right,

And pub - lish a - broad His won - der - ful Name;
And still He is nigh, His pres - ence we have:
Let all cry a - loud, and hon - or the Son:
All glo - ry and power, all wis - dom and might,

The Name all - vic - to - rious of Je - sus ex - tol;
The great con - gre - ga - tion His tri - umph shall sing,
The prais - es of Je - sus the an - gels pro - claim,
All hon - or and bless - ing, with an - gels a - bove,

His king - dom is glo - rious, and rules o - ver all.
As - crib - ing sal - va - tion to Je - sus, our King.
Fall down on their fa - ces, and wor - ship the Lamb.
And thanks nev - er ceas - ing for in - fi - nite love. A - MEN.

Praise, my Soul, the King of Heaven

259
DULCE CARMEN. 8. 7. 8. 7. 8. 7.
From an ESSAY ON THE CHURCH PLAIN CHANT, 1782
Arr. by SAMUEL WEBBE, 1740–1816
HENRY F. LYTE, 1793–1847
Joyously
1. Praise, my soul, the King of heav - en, To His feet thy trib - ute bring; Ran - som'd, heal'd, re - stor'd, for - giv - en, Ev - er - more His prais - es sing; Al - le - lu - ia! Al - le - lu - ia! Praise the ev - er - last - ing King.
2. Praise Him for His grace and fa - vor To our fa - thers in dis - tress; Praise Him still the same as ev - er, Slow to chide, and swift to bless; Al - le - lu - ia! Al - le - lu - ia! Glo - rious in His faith - ful - ness.
3. Fa - ther - like, He tends and spares us, Well our fee - ble frame He knows; In His hands He gen - tly bears us, Res - cues us from all our foes; Al - le - lu - ia! Al - le - lu - ia! Wide - ly yet His mer - cy flows.
4. An - gels in the height, a - dore Him, Ye be - hold Him face to face; Saints tri - um - phant, bow be - fore Him, Gath - ered in from ev - 'ry race; Al - le - lu - ia! Al - le - lu - ia! Praise with us the God of grace.
A-MEN.

Rejoice, the Lord Is King

DARWALL'S 148TH. 6. 6. 6. 6. 8. 8.

260

CHARLES WESLEY, 1707–1788
JOHN DARWALL, 1731–1789
Jubilantly
1. Re - joice, the Lord is King: Your Lord and King a - dore!
2. Je - sus, the Sav - iour, reigns, The God of truth and love;
3. His King - dom can - not fail, He rules o'er earth and heaven;
Re - joice, give thanks, and sing, And tri - umph
When He had purged our stains, He took His
The keys of death and hell Are to our
ev - er - more: Lift up your heart, lift up your voice!
seat a - bove: Lift up your heart, lift up your voice!
Je - sus given: Lift up your heart, lift up your voice!
Re - joice, a - gain I say, re - joice!
Re - joice, a - gain I say, re - joice!
Re - joice, a - gain I say, re - joice! A - MEN.

Fairest Lord Jesus

261

CRUSADER'S HYMN. 5. 6. 8. 5. 5. 8.

German, 17th century

From SCHLESISCHE VOLKSLIEDER, 1842
Arr. by RICHARD S. WILLIS, 1819-1900

In moderate time, and graceful rhythm

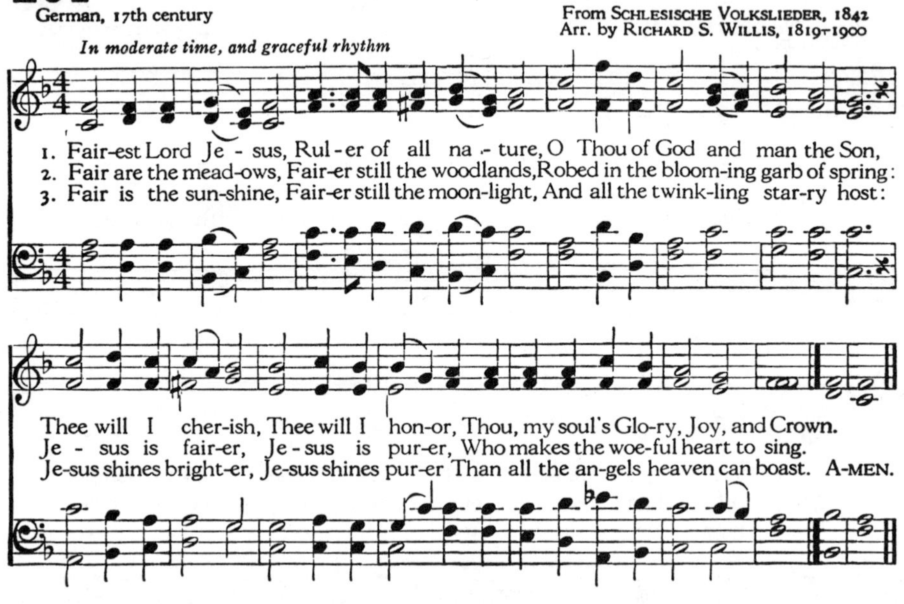
1. Fair-est Lord Je - sus, Rul - er of all na - ture, O Thou of God and man the Son,
2. Fair are the mead-ows, Fair-er still the woodlands, Robed in the bloom-ing garb of spring:
3. Fair is the sun-shine, Fair-er still the moon-light, And all the twink-ling star-ry host:
Thee will I cher-ish, Thee will I hon-or, Thou, my soul's Glo-ry, Joy, and Crown.
Je - sus is fair-er, Je - sus is pur-er, Who makes the woe-ful heart to sing.
Je-sus shines bright-er, Je-sus shines pur-er Than all the an-gels heaven can boast. A-MEN.

O for a Thousand Tongues to Sing

262

AZMON. C. M

CHARLES WESLEY, 1707-1788

CARL G. GLÄSER, 1784-1829
Arr. by LOWELL MASON, 1792-1872

In moderate time, with dignity

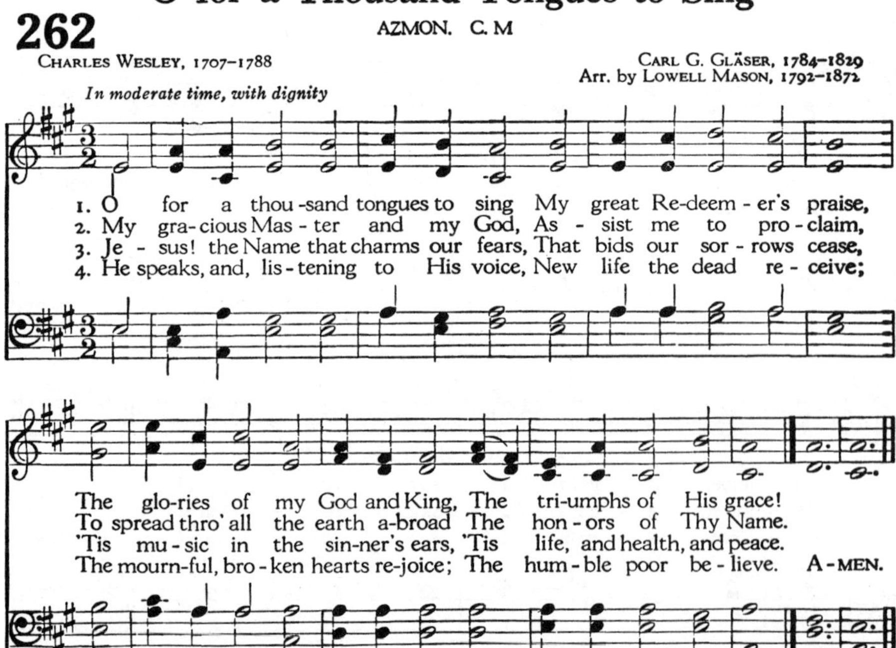
1. O for a thou-sand tongues to sing My great Re-deem - er's praise,
2. My gra-cious Mas - ter and my God, As - sist me to pro - claim,
3. Je - sus! the Name that charms our fears, That bids our sor - rows cease,
4. He speaks, and, lis - tening to His voice, New life the dead re - ceive;
The glo-ries of my God and King, The tri-umphs of His grace!
To spread thro' all the earth a-broad The hon - ors of Thy Name.
'Tis mu - sic in the sin-ner's ears, 'Tis life, and health, and peace.
The mourn-ful, bro - ken hearts re-joice; The hum - ble poor be - lieve. A - MEN.

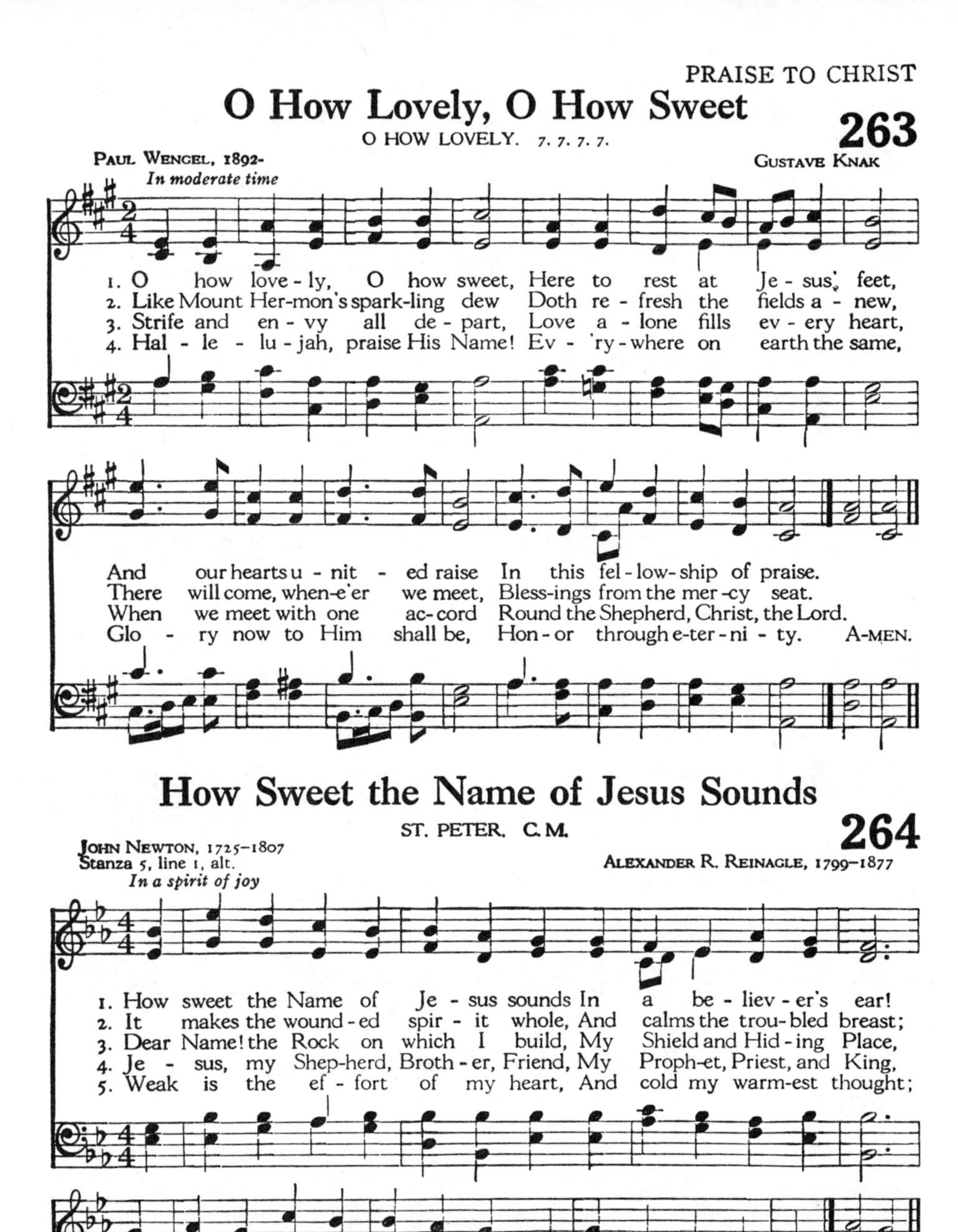
PRAISE TO CHRIST
O How Lovely, O How Sweet
263
O HOW LOVELY. 7. 7. 7. 7.
Paul Wengel, 1892-
Gustave Knak
In moderate time
1. O how love-ly, O how sweet, Here to rest at Je-sus' feet,
2. Like Mount Her-mon's spark-ling dew Doth re-fresh the fields a-new,
3. Strife and en-vy all de-part, Love a-lone fills ev-ery heart,
4. Hal-le-lu-jah, praise His Name! Ev-'ry-where on earth the same,
And our hearts u-nit-ed raise In this fel-low-ship of praise.
There will come, when-e'er we meet, Bless-ings from the mer-cy seat.
When we meet with one ac-cord Round the Shepherd, Christ, the Lord.
Glo-ry now to Him shall be, Hon-or through e-ter-ni-ty. A-men.
How Sweet the Name of Jesus Sounds
264
ST. PETER. C.M.
John Newton, 1725–1807
Stanza 5, line 1, alt.
Alexander R. Reinagle, 1799–1877
In a spirit of joy
1. How sweet the Name of Je-sus sounds In a be-liev-er's ear!
2. It makes the wound-ed spir-it whole, And calms the trou-bled breast;
3. Dear Name! the Rock on which I build, My Shield and Hid-ing Place,
4. Je-sus, my Shep-herd, Broth-er, Friend, My Proph-et, Priest, and King,
5. Weak is the ef-fort of my heart, And cold my warm-est thought;
It soothes his sor-rows, heals his wounds, And drives a-way his fear.
'Tis man-na to the hun-gry soul, And to the wea-ry rest.
My nev-er-fail-ing Treas-ury, filled With bound-less stores of grace;
My Lord, my Life, my Way, my End, Ac-cept the praise I bring.
But when I see Thee as Thou art, I'll praise Thee as I ought. A-men.

O Could I Speak the Matchless Worth

265

ARIEL. 8. 8. 6. D. with Repeat

SAMUEL MEDLEY, 1738–1799

Arr. from MOZART by LOWELL MASON, 1792–1872

Joyfully

1. O could I speak the match-less worth, O could I sound the glories forth, Which in my Sav-iour shine, I'd soar and touch the heav'nly strings, And vie with Gabriel while He sings In notes al-most di-vine, In notes al-most di-vine.
2. I'd sing the char-ac-ters He bears, And all the forms of love He wears, Ex-alt-ed on His throne; In loft-iest songs of sweetest praise, I would to ev-er-last-ing days Make all His glories known, Make all His glo-ries known.
3. Well—the de-light-ful day will come When my dear Lord will bring me home, And I shall see His face; Then, with my Saviour, Brother, Friend, A blest e-ter-ni-ty I'll spend, Tri-um-phant in His grace, Tri-um-phant in His grace. A-MEN.

Shepherd of Eager Youth

266

KIRBY BEDON. 6. 6. 4. 6. 6. 6. 4

CLEMENT OF ALEXANDRIA, c. 220
Tr. by HENRY M. DEXTER, 1821–1890

EDWARD BUNNETT, 1834–1923

In moderate time

1. Shep-herd of ea-ger youth, Guid-ing in love and truth,
2. Thou art our ho-ly Lord, The all-sub-du-ing Word,
3. Thou art the great High Priest; Thou hast pre-pared the feast
4. Ev-er be Thou our Guide, Our Shep-herd and our Pride,
5. So now, and till we die, Sound we Thy prais-es high,

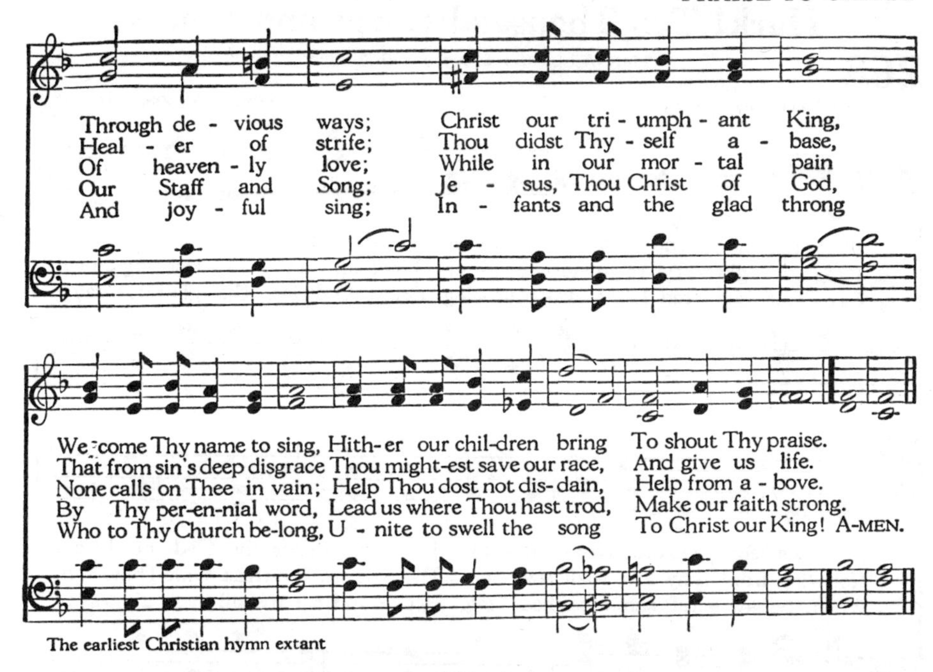
Through de - vious ways; Christ our tri - umph - ant King,
Heal - er of strife; Thou didst Thy - self a - base,
Of heaven - ly love; While in our mor - tal pain
Our Staff and Song; Je - sus, Thou Christ of God,
And joy - ful sing; In - fants and the glad throng
Welcome Thy name to sing, Hith-er our chil-dren bring To shout Thy praise.
That from sin's deep disgrace Thou might-est save our race, And give us life.
None calls on Thee in vain; Help Thou dost not dis-dain, Help from a - bove.
By Thy per-en-nial word, Lead us where Thou hast trod, Make our faith strong.
Who to Thy Church be-long, U - nite to swell the song To Christ our King! A-MEN.

The earliest Christian hymn extant

Children of the Heavenly King

PLEYEL'S HYMN. 7. 7. 7. 7.

267

JOHN CENNICK, 1718–1755

IGNACE J. PLEYEL, 1757–1831

In moderate time

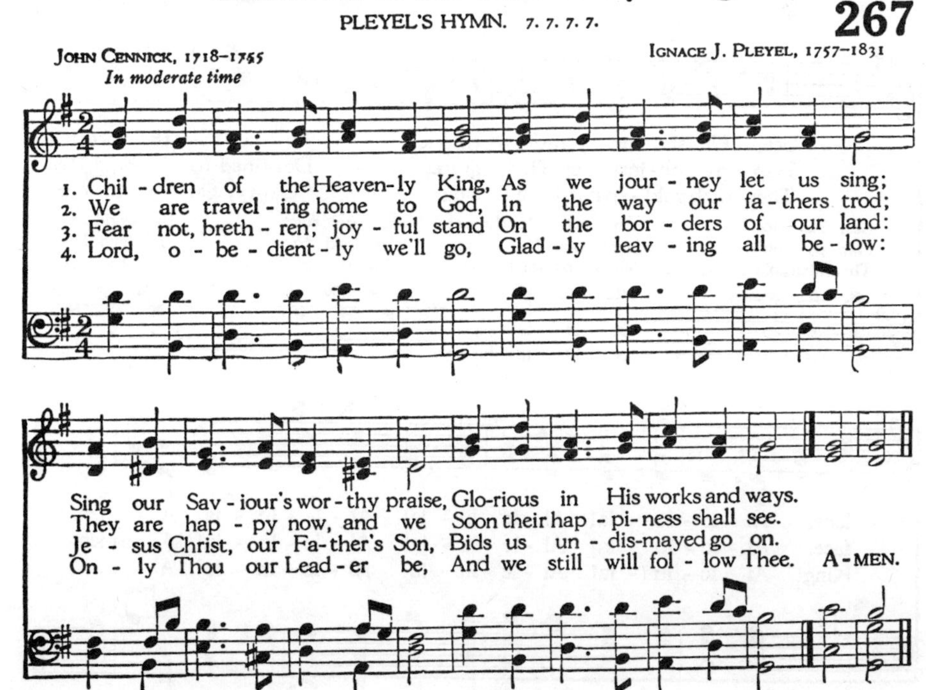
1. Chil - dren of the Heaven-ly King, As we jour - ney let us sing;
2. We are travel - ing home to God, In the way our fa - thers trod;
3. Fear not, breth - ren; joy - ful stand On the bor - ders of our land:
4. Lord, o - be - dient - ly we'll go, Glad - ly leav - ing all be - low:
Sing our Sav - iour's wor - thy praise, Glo-rious in His works and ways.
They are hap - py now, and we Soon their hap - pi-ness shall see.
Je - sus Christ, our Fa-ther's Son, Bids us un - dis-mayed go on.
On - ly Thou our Lead - er be, And we still will fol - low Thee. A - MEN.

Hark! Ten Thousand Harps and Voices

268

HARWELL. 8. 7. 8. 7. 7. 7. with Alleluias

THOMAS KELLY, 1769–1854

LOWELL MASON, 1792–1872

Joyously

1. Hark! ten thou - sand harps and voic - es Sound the note of praise a - bove;
2. King of glo - ry, reign for ev - er, Thine an ev - er - last - ing crown;
3. Sav - iour, has - ten Thine ap - pear - ing; Bring, O bring the glo-rious day

Je - sus reigns and heav'n re - joic - es, Je - sus reigns, the God of love:
Noth-ing from Thy love shall sev - er Those whom Thou hast made Thine own:
When, the aw - ful sum-mons hear - ing, Heav'n and earth shall pass a - way:

See, He sits on yon-der throne; Je - sus rules the world a -
Hap - py ob-jects of Thy grace, Des-tined to be-hold Thy
Then, with gold - en harps we'll sing, "Glo-ry, glo - ry to our

See, He sits on yon - der throne; Je - sus rules the world a -
Hap-py ob - - jects of Thy grace, Des-tined to be-hold Thy
Then, with gold - - en harps we'll sing, "Glo - ry, glo - - ry to our

lone. Al - le - lu - ia! Al - le - lu - ia! Al - le - lu - ia! A - men.
face. Al - le - lu - ia! Al - le - lu - ia! Al - le - lu - ia! A - men.
King!" Al - le - lu - ia! Al - le - lu - ia! Al - le - lu - ia! A - men.

Saviour, Blessed Saviour, Listen While We Sing

DAVID. 6. 5. 6. 5. D.
269
Godfrey Thring, 1823-1903
Thomas Morley, 1845-1891
In moderate time
1. Sav - iour, bless - ed Sav - iour, Lis - ten while we sing,
2. Near - er, ev - er near - er, Christ, we draw to Thee,
3. Clear - er still, and clear - er, Dawns the light from heaven,
4. Great, and ev - er great - er, Are Thy mer - cies here;
Hearts and voi - ces rais - ing Prais - es to our King.
Deep in ad - o - ra - tion Bend - ing low the knee:
In our sad - ness bring - ing News of sins for - given;
True and ev - er - last - ing Are the glo - ries there,
All we have we of - fer, All we hope to be,
Thou for our re - demp - tion Cam'st on earth to die:
Life has lost its shad - ows; Pure the light with - in;
Where no pain or sor - row, Toil or care, is known,
Bod - y, soul, and spir - it, All we yield to Thee.
Thou, that we might fol - low, Hast gone up on high.
Thou hast shed Thy ra - diance On a world of sin.
Where the an - gel le - gions Cir - cle round Thy throne.
A - men.

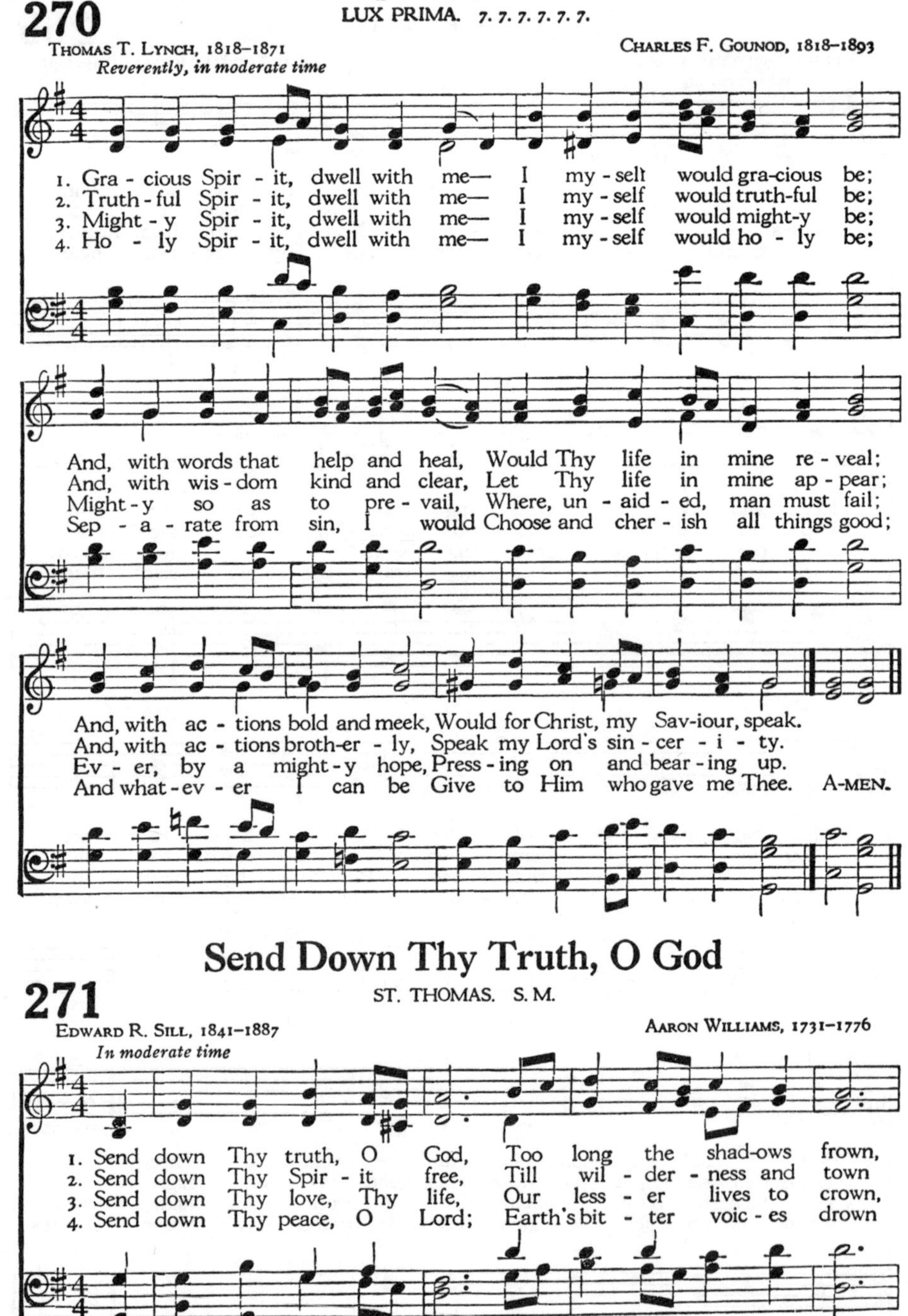
Gracious Spirit, Dwell with Me
270
LUX PRIMA. 7. 7. 7. 7. 7. 7.
THOMAS T. LYNCH, 1818–1871
CHARLES F. GOUNOD, 1818–1893
Reverently, in moderate time
1. Gra - cious Spir - it, dwell with me— I my - self would gra-cious be;
2. Truth - ful Spir - it, dwell with me— I my - self would truth-ful be;
3. Might - y Spir - it, dwell with me— I my - self would might-y be;
4. Ho - ly Spir - it, dwell with me— I my - self would ho - ly be;
And, with words that help and heal, Would Thy life in mine re - veal;
And, with wis - dom kind and clear, Let Thy life in mine ap - pear;
Might - y so as to pre - vail, Where, un - aid - ed, man must fail;
Sep - a - rate from sin, I would Choose and cher - ish all things good;
And, with ac - tions bold and meek, Would for Christ, my Sav-iour, speak.
And, with ac - tions broth-er - ly, Speak my Lord's sin - cer - i - ty.
Ev - er, by a might - y hope, Press - ing on and bear - ing up.
And what - ev - er I can be Give to Him who gave me Thee.
A-MEN.
Send Down Thy Truth, O God
271
ST. THOMAS. S. M.
EDWARD R. SILL, 1841–1887
AARON WILLIAMS, 1731–1776
In moderate time
1. Send down Thy truth, O God, Too long the shad-ows frown,
2. Send down Thy Spir - it free, Till wil - der - ness and town
3. Send down Thy love, Thy life, Our less - er lives to crown,
4. Send down Thy peace, O Lord; Earth's bit - ter voic - es drown

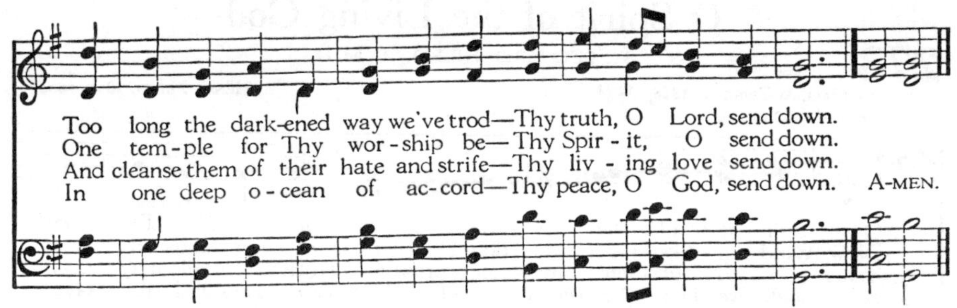
Too long the dark-ened way we've trod—Thy truth, O Lord, send down.
One tem-ple for Thy wor-ship be—Thy Spir-it, O send down.
And cleanse them of their hate and strife—Thy liv-ing love send down.
In one deep o-cean of ac-cord—Thy peace, O God, send down. A-MEN.

Spirit of God, Descend upon my Heart

272

MORECAMBE. 10. 10. 10. 10.

GEORGE CROLY, 1780–1860

FREDERICK C. ATKINSON, 1841–1897

Reverently, in moderate time
1. Spir-it of God, de-scend up-on my heart; Wean it from earth; thro all its puls-es move; Stoop to my weak-ness, might-y as Thou art, And make me love Thee as I ought to love.
2. I ask no dream, no proph-et ec-sta-sies, No sud-den rend-ing of the veil of clay, No an-gel vis-it-ant, no o-pening skies; But take the dim-ness of my soul a-way.
3. Hast Thou not bid me love Thee, God and King? All, all Thine own—soul, heart, and strength, and mind. I see Thy cross—there teach my heart to cling: O let me seek Thee, and O let me find!
4. Teach me to feel that Thou art al-ways nigh; Teach me the strug-gles of the soul to bear, To check the ris-ing doubt, the reb-el sigh; Teach me the pa-tience of un-an-swered prayer.
5. Teach me to love Thee as Thine an-gels love, One ho-ly pas-sion fill-ing all my frame; The kind-ling of the heaven-de-scend-ed Dove, My heart an al-tar, and Thy love the flame. A-MEN.

O Spirit of the Living God

273

ST. LEONARD (HILES). C. M. D.

HENRY HALLAM TWEEDY. 1868– 1953

HENRY HILES, 1826–1904

In moderate time

1. O Spir - it of the Liv - ing God, Thou Light and Fire Di - vine:
2. Blow, Wind of God! With wis - dom blow Un - til our minds are free
3. Teach us to ut - ter liv - ing words Of truth which all may hear,
4. So shall we know the power of Him Who came man-kind to save.

De - scend up - on Thy Church once more And make it tru - ly Thine!
From mists of er - ror, clouds of doubt, Which blind our eyes to Thee!
The lan - guage all men un - der-stand When love speaks, loud and clear;
So shall we rise with Him to life Which soars be - yond the grave;

Fill it with love and joy and power, With right - eous- ness and peace,
Burn, wing - ed fire! In - spire our lips With flam - ing love and zeal,
Till ev - ery age and race and clime Shall blend their creeds in one,
And earth shall win true ho - li - ness, Which makes Thy chil - dren whole,

Till Christ shall dwell in hu-man hearts, And sin and sor - row cease.
To preach to all Thy great Good News, God's glo-rious Com-mon-weal!
And earth shall form one broth- er - hood By whom Thy will is done.
Till, per - fect - ed by Thee, we preach Cre - a - tion's glo- rious goal! A - MEN.

Words used by permission of Henry H. Tweedy

Holy Spirit, Truth Divine
274
LAST HOPE (MERCY). 7. 7. 7. 7.
Samuel Longfellow, 1819–1892
Arr. from Louis M. Gottschalk, 1829–1869
In moderate time
1. Ho - ly Spir - it, Truth di - vine! Dawn up - on this soul of mine;
2. Ho - ly Spir - it, Love di - vine! Glow with-in this soul of mine;
3. Ho - ly Spir - it, Pow'r di - vine! Fill and nerve this will of mine;
4. Ho - ly Spir - it, Right di - vine! King with - in my con - science reign;
Word of God, be Thou my Light! Wake my spir - it, clear my sight.
Kin - dle ev - 'ry high de - sire; Per - ish self in Thy pure fire.
By Thee may I strong - ly live, Brave-ly bear and no - bly strive.
Be my Law, and I shall be Firm - ly bound, for-ev - er free. A-men.
Spirit Divine, Attend our Prayer
275
Andrew Reed, 1787–1862
Samuel Longfellow, 1819–1892
GRAFENBERG. C. M.
Johann Crüger's
Praxis Pietatis Melica, 1653
Rather slowly
1. Spir - it di - vine, at - tend our prayer, And make our hearts Thy home;
2. Come as the light; to wait - ing minds, That long the truth to know,
3. Come as the fire; en - kin - dle now The sac - ri - fi - cial flame,
4. Come as the dew; on hearts that pine De - scend in this still hour,
5. Come as the wind; sweep clean a - way What dead with - in us lies,
De - scend with all Thy gra-cious power; Come, Ho-ly Spir - it, come.
Re - veal the nar - row path of right, The way of du - ty show.
That all our souls an of-fering be To our Re-deem - er's name.
Till ev - ery bar - ren place shall own With joy Thy quick - ening power.
And search and fresh - en all our souls With liv - ing en - er - gies. A-men.

Holy Spirit, Faithful Guide

276

FAITHFUL GUIDE. 7. 7. 7. 7. D.

Marcus M. Wells, 1815–1895 | Marcus M. Wells, 1815–1895

Not too slowly
1. Ho - ly Spir - it, faith - ful Guide, Ev - er near the Chris-tian's side;
2. Ev - er pres - ent, tru - est Friend, Ev - er near Thine aid to lend,
3. When our days of toil shall cease, Wait-ing still for sweet re - lease,
Gen - tly lead us by the hand, Pil - grims in a des - ert land;
Leave us not to doubt and fear, Grop - ing on in dark - ness drear;
Noth - ing left but heav'n and pray'r, Won-d'ring if our names are there,
Wea - ry souls for - e'er re - joice, While they hear that sweet - est voice
When the storms are rag - ing sore, Hearts grow faint, and hopes give o'er,
Wad - ing deep the dis - mal flood, Plead - ing naught but Je - sus' blood,—
Whis-p'ring soft - ly, "Wand'rer, come! Fol - low Me, I'll guide thee home."
Whis - per soft - ly, "Wand'rer, come! Fol - low Me, I'll guide thee home."
Whis - per soft - ly, "Wand'rer, come! Fol - low Me, I'll guide thee home." A - men.

"Come unto Me, Ye Weary"

MEIRIONYDD. 7. 6. 7. 6. D.

277

William C. Dix, 1837–1898
In moderate time, with flowing rhythm
Welsh hymn melody
1. "Come un - to me, ye wea - ry, And I will give you rest."
2. "Come un - to me, ye faint - ing, And I will give you life."
3. "And who - so - ev - er com - eth, I will not cast him out."
O bless - ed voice of Je - sus, Which comes to hearts op-pressed!
O cheer - ing voice of Je - sus, Which comes to aid our strife!
O wel - come voice of Je - sus, Which drives a - way our doubt!
It tells of ben - e - dic - tion, Of par - don, grace, and peace,
The foe is stern and ea - ger, The fight is fierce and long;
Which calls us, ver - y sin - ners, Un - wor - thy though we be
Of joy that hath no end - ing, Of love which can - not cease.
But Thou hast made us might - y, And strong-er than the strong.
Of love so free and bound - less, To come, dear Lord, to Thee! A-MEN.
Music copyright by Dr. Basil Harwood, from the "Oxford Hymn Book." Used by permission.

Come to the Saviour Now

278

INVITATION. 6. 6. 6. 6. D.

JOHN M. WIGNER, 1844–?

FREDERICK C. MAKER, 1844–1927

In moderate time

1. Come to the Sav - iour now, He gen - tly call - eth thee;
In true re - pent - ance bow, Be - fore Him bend the knee;
He wait - eth to be - stow Sal - va - tion, peace, and love,
True joy on earth be - low, A home in heaven a - bove.

2. Come to the Sav - iour now, Ye who have wan-dered far;
Re - new your sol - emn vow, For His by right you are;
Come, like poor wan - dering sheep Re - turn - ing to His fold;
His arm will safe - ly keep, His love will ne'er grow cold.

3. Come to the Sav - iour, all, What-e'er your bur - dens be;
Hear now His lov - ing call, "Cast all your care on me."
Come, and for ev - ery grief In Je - sus you will find
A sure and safe re - lief, A lov - ing Friend and kind.

A-MEN.

O Jesus, Thou Art Standing

ST. HILDA. 7. 6. 7. 6. D.

279

WILLIAM W. HOW, 1823–1897

JUSTIN H. KNECHT, 1752–1817
EDWARD HUSBAND, 1843–1908

In moderate time
1. O Je - sus, Thou art stand - ing Out - side the fast-closed door,
2. O Je - sus, Thou art knock - ing: And lo, that hand is scarred,
3. O Je - sus, Thou art plead - ing In ac - cents meek and low,
In low - ly pa - tience wait - ing To pass the thresh - old o'er:
And thorns Thy brow en - cir - cle, And tears Thy face have marred.
"I died for you, my chil - dren, And will ye treat me so?"
Shame on us, Chris - tian breth - ren, His name and sign who bear;
O love that pass - eth know - ledge, So pa - tient - ly to wait!
O Lord, with shame and sor - row We o - pen now the door;
O shame, thrice shame up - on us, To keep Him stand-ing there!
O sin that hath no e - qual, So fast to bar the gate!
Dear Sav - iour, en - ter, en - ter, And leave us nev - er - more.
A-MEN.

Jesus Is Tenderly Calling Thee Home

280

STEBBINS. 10. 8. 10. 7. with Refrain

FANNY J. CROSBY, 1823–1915

GEORGE C. STEBBINS, 1846-1945

In moderate time
1. Je - sus is ten - der - ly call - ing thee home— Call - ing to - day,
2. Je - sus is call - ing the wea - ry to rest— Call - ing to - day,
3. Je - sus is wait - ing, O come to Him now— Wait - ing to - day,
4. Je - sus is plead - ing, O list to His voice— Hear Him to - day,
call - ing to - day; Why from the sun-shine of love wilt thou roam,
call - ing to - day; Bring Him thy bur - den and thou shalt be blest;
wait - ing to - day; Come with thy sins, at His feet low - ly bow,
hear Him to - day; They who be - lieve on His name shall re - joice;
Far - ther and far - ther a - way?
He will not turn thee a - way.
Come, and no long - er de - lay.
Quick-ly a - rise and o - bey.
REFRAIN.
Call - ing to - day, ...
Call-ing, call-ing to - day, to-day,
Call - - ing to - day; . . . .
Call - ing, call - ing to - day, to - day;
Je - - sus is
Je - sus is ten - der - ly
call - ing, Is ten - der - ly call - ing to - day.
call-ing to-day,
A - MEN.

Jesus Calls Us, O'er the Tumult

GALILEE. 8. 7. 8. 7.

281

CECIL F. ALEXANDER, 1818–1895 — WILLIAM H. JUDE, 1852–1892

In moderate time

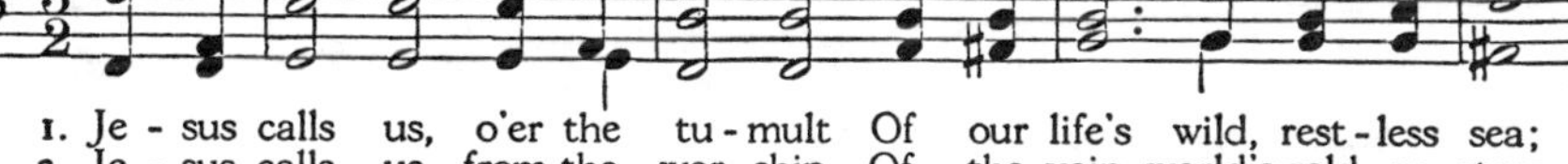

1. Je - sus calls us, o'er the tu - mult Of our life's wild, rest - less sea;
2. Je - sus calls us, from the wor - ship Of the vain world's gold - en store,
3. In our joys and in our sor - rows, Days of toil and hours of ease,
4. Je - sus calls us: by Thy mer - cies, Sav - iour, may we hear Thy call,

Day by day His sweet voice soundeth, Say-ing: "Chris-tian, fol - low me."
From each i - dol that would keep us, Say-ing: "Chris-tian, love me more."
Still He calls, in cares and pleasures: "Christian, love me more than these."
Give our hearts to Thy o - be-dience, Serve and love Thee best of all. A-MEN.

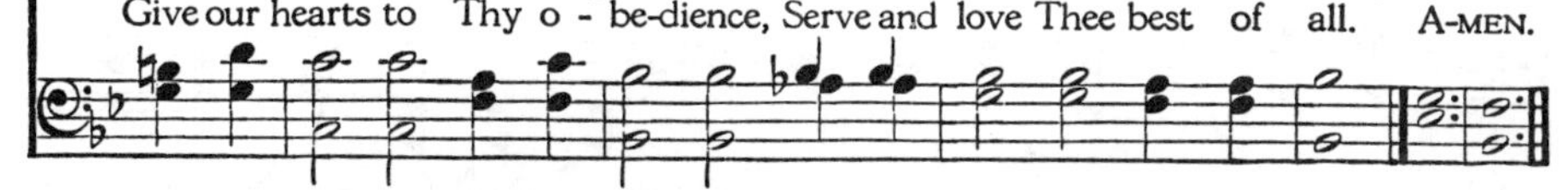

Come to Jesus, Ye Who Labor

BULLINGER. 8. 5. 8. 3.

282

EDWIN P. PARKER, 1836–1925 — ETHELBERT W. BULLINGER, 1837–1913

In moderate time

1. Come to Je - sus, ye who la - bor, From vain - striv - ings cease;
2. Come to Him, ye who, in sor - row, Vain - ly seek re - lief;
3. Come to Him, all ye who wan - der Wear - y and un - blest;
4. Come to Him, His yoke is eas - y, And His bur - den light;
5. Come to Him, all sweet - est voic - es Ten - der - ly en - treat;

Heav - y - la - den He will give you Rest and peace.
He has pre - cious balm and com - fort For each grief.
In His meek and low - ly serv - ice There is rest.
All your weak - ness He will strengthen With His might.
Lay your sins and cares and bur - dens At His feet. A - MEN.

Softly and Tenderly Jesus Is Calling

283

SOFTLY AND TENDERLY. 11. 7. 11. 7. with Refrain

WILL L. THOMPSON, 1847–1909 — WILL L. THOMPSON, 1847–1909

Not too slow

1. Soft - ly and ten - der - ly Je - sus is call - ing,
2. Why should we tar - ry when Je - sus is plead - ing,
3. O, for the won - der - ful love He has prom - ised,
Call - ing for you and for me; Pa - tient - ly Je - sus is
Plead-ing for you and for me? Why should we lin - ger and
Prom-ised for you and for me; Tho' we have sinned, He has
wait - ing and watch - ing, Watch - ing for you and for me.
heed not His mer - cies, Mer - cies for you and for me?
mer - cy and par - don, Par - don for you and for me.
REFRAIN
Come home, Come home, Ye who are wea-ry, come home;
Come home, Come home,
Ear-nest-ly, ten-der-ly, Je-sus is call-ing, Call-ing, O sin-ner, come home! A-MEN.

I Hear the Saviour Say

ALL TO CHRIST I OWE. 6. 6. 7. 7. with Refrain

284

ELVINA M. HALL, alt. JOHN T. GRAPE

In moderate time

1. I hear the Sav-iour say, Thy strength in-deed is small:
2. For noth-ing good have I Where-by Thy grace to claim;
3. And when, be-fore the throne, I stand in Him com-plete,
Come to me, I'll be thy stay; Find in me thine all in all.
Je-sus died my soul to save, And bless-ed be His name.
"Je-sus died my soul to save," My lips shall still re-peat.
CHORUS.
Je-sus died for me; All to Him I owe;
Sin had left a crim-son stain, He washed it white as snow. A-MEN.

"Take up thy Cross," the Saviour Said

285
WAREHAM. L. M.
CHARLES W. EVEREST, 1814–1877
WILLIAM KNAPP, 1698–1768
With a flowing rhythm
1. "Take up thy cross," the Saviour said, "If thou wouldst
2. Take up thy cross; let not its weight Fill thy weak
3. Take up thy cross, nor heed the shame; Nor let thy
4. Take up thy cross, and fol - low Christ; Nor think till
my dis - ci - ple be; De - ny thy - self, the
spir - it with a - larm; His strength shall bear thy
fool - ish pride re - bel: Thy Lord for thee the
death to lay it down; For on - ly he who
world for - sake, And hum - bly fol - low aft - er me."
spir - it up, And brace thy heart and nerve thine arm.
cross en - dured, To save thy soul from death and hell.
bears the cross May hope to wear the glo - rious crown. A - MEN.
286 Art Thou Weary, Art Thou Troubled
From the Greek, 8th century
JOHN M. NEALE, 1818–1866
STEPHANOS. 8. 5. 8. 3.
HENRY W. BAKER, 1821–1877
In moderate time
1. Art thou wea - ry, art thou trou - bled, Art thou sore dis - tressed?
2. Hath He marks to lead me to Him, If He be my Guide?
3. Hath He di - a - dem, as mon-arch, That His brow a - dorns?
4. If I find Him, if I fol - low, What His guer - don here?
5. If I still hold close - ly to Him, What hath He at last?
6. If I ask Him to re - ceive me, Will He say me nay?

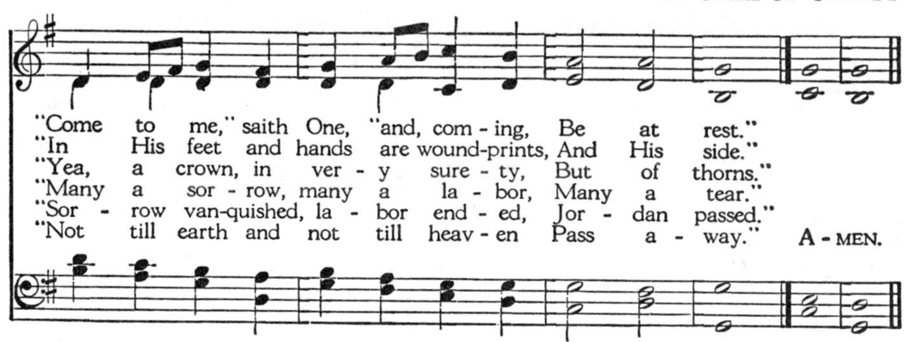
"Come to me," saith One, "and, com - ing, Be at rest."
"In His feet and hands are wound-prints, And His side."
"Yea, a crown, in ver - y sure - ty, But of thorns."
"Many a sor - row, many a la - bor, Many a tear."
"Sor - row van-quished, la - bor end - ed, Jor - dan passed."
"Not till earth and not till heav - en Pass a - way." A - MEN.

Unbar the Door! and Let the Lord Christ In!

PAX VERITATIS. 10. 10. 10. 10.

287

JOHN OXENHAM, d. 1941

FRANZ C. BORNSCHEIN, 1879–

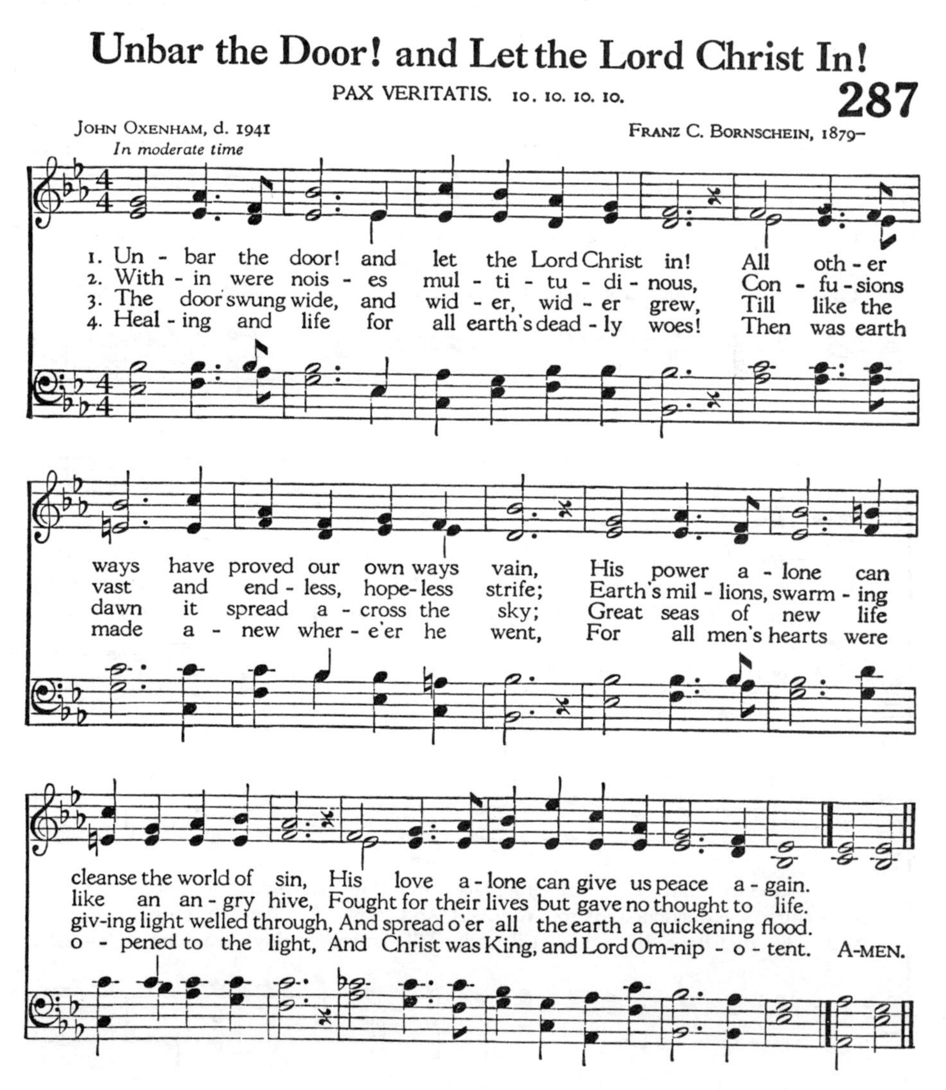
In moderate time
1. Un - bar the door! and let the Lord Christ in! All oth - er ways have proved our own ways vain, His power a - lone can cleanse the world of sin, His love a - lone can give us peace a - gain.
2. With - in were nois - es mul - ti - tu - di - nous, Con - fu - sions vast and end - less, hope - less strife; Earth's mil - lions, swarm - ing like an an - gry hive, Fought for their lives but gave no thought to life.
3. The door swung wide, and wid - er, wid - er grew, Till like the dawn it spread a - cross the sky; Great seas of new life giv-ing light welled through, And spread o'er all the earth a quickening flood.
4. Heal - ing and life for all earth's dead - ly woes! Then was earth made a - new wher - e'er he went, For all men's hearts were o - pened to the light, And Christ was King, and Lord Om-nip - o - tent. A-MEN.

I Heard the Voice of Jesus Say

288

VOX DILECTI. C. M. D.

HORATIUS BONAR, 1808–1889

JOHN B. DYKES, 1823–1876

In moderate time

1. I heard the voice of Je - sus say, "Come un - to me and rest;
2. I heard the voice of Je - sus say, "Be - hold, I free - ly give
3. I heard the voice of Je - sus say, "I am this dark world's light;
Lay down, thou wea - ry one, lay down Thy head up - on my breast."
The liv - ing wa - ter; thirst - y one, Stoop down, and drink, and live."
Look un - to me, thy morn shall rise, And all thy day be bright."
I came to Je - sus as I was, Wea - ry and worn and sad;
I came to Je - sus, and I drank Of that life - giv - ing stream;
I looked to Je - sus, and I found In Him my star, my sun;
I found in Him a rest - ing place, And He has made me glad.
My thirst was quenched, my soul re-vived, And now I live in Him.
And in that light of life I'll walk, Till travel-ing days are done.
A - MEN.

Thy Life Was Given for Me

KENOSIS. 6. 6. 6. 6. 8. 6. 8. 6.

289

FRANCES R. HAVERGAL, 1836–1879
PHILIP P. BLISS, 1838–1876
In moderate time
1. Thy life was giv'n for me, Thy blood, O Lord, was shed,
2. Long years were spent for me In wea - ri - ness and woe,
3. Thy Fa - ther's home of light, The rain - bow - cir - cled throne,
4. And Thou hast brought to me, Down from Thy home a - bove,
5. O let my life be giv'n, My years for Thee be spent;
That I might ran - somed be, And quick - ened from the dead;
That through e - ter - ni - ty Thy glo - ry I might know;
Were left for earth - ly night, For wan-d'rings sad and lone;
Sal - va - tion full and free, Thy par - don and Thy love;
World - fet - ters all be riv'n, And joy with suf - f'ring blent;
Thy life, thy life was giv'n for me; What have I giv'n for Thee?
Long years, long years were spent for me; Have I spent one for Thee?
Yea! all, Yea! all was left for me; Have I left aught for Thee?
Great gifts, great gifts Thou broughtest me; What have I brought to Thee?
Thou gav'st, Thou gav'st Thy-self for me, I give my - self to Thee.
Thy life, thy life was giv'n for me; What have I giv'n for Thee?
Long years, long years were spent for me; Have I spent one for Thee?
Yea! all, Yea! all was left for me; Have I left aught for Thee?
Great gifts, great gifts Thou broughtest me; What have I brought to Thee?
Thou gav'st, Thou gav'st Thyself for me, I give my - self to Thee. A - MEN.

I've Found a Friend, O Such a Friend

290

FRIEND. 8. 7. 8. 7. D.

JAMES G. SMALL, 1817–1888

GEORGE C. STEBBINS, 1846-1945

In moderate time

1. I've found a Friend, O such a Friend! He loved me ere I knew Him;
He drew me with the cords of love, And thus He bound me to Him.
And 'round my heart still close - ly twine Those ties which naught can sev - er,
For I am His, and He is mine, For ev - er and for ev - er.

2. I've found a Friend, O such a Friend! He bled, He died to save me;
And not a - lone the gift of life, But His own self He gave me.
Naught that I have my own I call, I hold it for the Giv - er;
My heart, my strength, my life, my all Are His, and His for ev - er.

3. I've found a Friend, O such a Friend! So kind, and true, and ten - der,
So wise a Coun - sel - or and Guide, So might - y a De - fend - er!
From Him who loves me now so well, What power my soul can sev - er?
Shall life or death, or earth or hell? No! I am His for ev - er.

A - MEN.

Dear God, Our Father, at Thy Knee Confessing

291

O PERFECT LOVE. 11. 10. 11. 10.

KATHARINE LEE BATES, 1859–1929 — JOSEPH BARNBY, 1838–1896

In moderate time
1. Dear God, our Father, at Thy knee confessing
Our sins and follies, close in Thine embrace,
Children forgiven, happy in Thy blessing,
Deepen our spirits to receive Thy grace.
2. Not for more beauty would our eyes entreat Thee,
Flooded with beauty, beauty ev'rywhere;
Only for keener vision that may greet Thee
In all Thy vestures of the earth and air.
3. The stars and rainbows are Thy wondrous wearing,
Sunlight and shadow moving on the hills;
Holy the meadow where Thy feet are faring,
Holy the brooklet that Thy laughter fills.
4. Not for more love our craving hearts implore Thee,
But for more power to love until they glow
Like hearths of comfort, eager to restore Thee
Hidden in human wretchedness and woe.
5. In souls most sullen Thou art softly dreaming
Of saints and heroes wrought from Thy divine
Pity and patience, still the lost redeeming;
Deepen our spirits for a love like Thine.
A-MEN.

Words used by permission of Mrs. George S. Burgess and reprinted by permission of "The Woman's Press."

Thou Didst Leave Thy Throne

292

MARGARET. Irregular

Emily E. S. Elliott, 1836-1897
Timothy R. Matthews, 1826-1910
In moderate time
1. Thou didst leave Thy throne and Thy king - ly crown, When Thou
2. Heav - en's arch - es rang when the an - gels sang, Pro -
3. The fox - es found rest, and the birds their nest In the
4. Thou cam'st, O Lord, with the liv - ing word That should
5. When heaven's arch - es shall ring and her choir shall sing At Thy
cam - est to earth for me; But in Beth - le - hem's home there was
claim - ing Thy roy - al de - gree; But in low - ly birth didst Thou
shade of the for - est tree; But Thy couch was the sod, O Thou
set Thy peo - ple free; But with mock - ing scorn, and with
com - ing to vic - to - ry, Let Thy voice call me home, say - ing,
found no room For Thy ho - ly Na - tiv - i - ty. O
come to earth, And in great hu - mil - i - ty. O
Son of God, In the des - erts of Gal - i - lee. O
crown of thorn, They bore Thee to Cal - va - ry. O
"Yet there is room, There is room at my side for thee!" And my
come to my heart, Lord Je - sus, There is room in my heart for Thee.
come to my heart, Lord Je - sus, There is room in my heart for Thee.
come to my heart, Lord Je - sus, There is room in my heart for Thee.
come to my heart, Lord Je - sus, There is room in my heart for Thee.
heart shall re-joice, Lord Je - sus, When Thou com-est and callest for me. A-MEN.

My Life, my Love I Give to Thee

I'LL LIVE FOR HIM. 8. 8. 8. 6. with Refrain

293

R. E. Hudson
C. R. Dunbar
In moderate time
1. My life, my love I give to Thee, Thou Lamb of God, who died for me;
2. I now be-lieve Thou dost re-ceive, For Thou hast died that I might live,
3. O Thou who died on Cal - va - ry To save my soul and make me free;
O may I ev - er faith - ful be, My Sav - iour and my God!
And now henceforth I'll trust in Thee, My Sav - iour and my God!
I'll con - se - crate my life to Thee, My Sav - iour and my God!
Refrain.
I'll live for Him who died for me, How hap - py then my life shall be!
I'll live for Him who died for me, My Sav - iour and my God! A - men.

294 Rock of Ages, Cleft for Me

TOPLADY. 7. 7. 7. 7. 7. 7.

AUGUSTUS M. TOPLADY, 1740–1778, alt. — THOMAS HASTINGS, 1784–1872

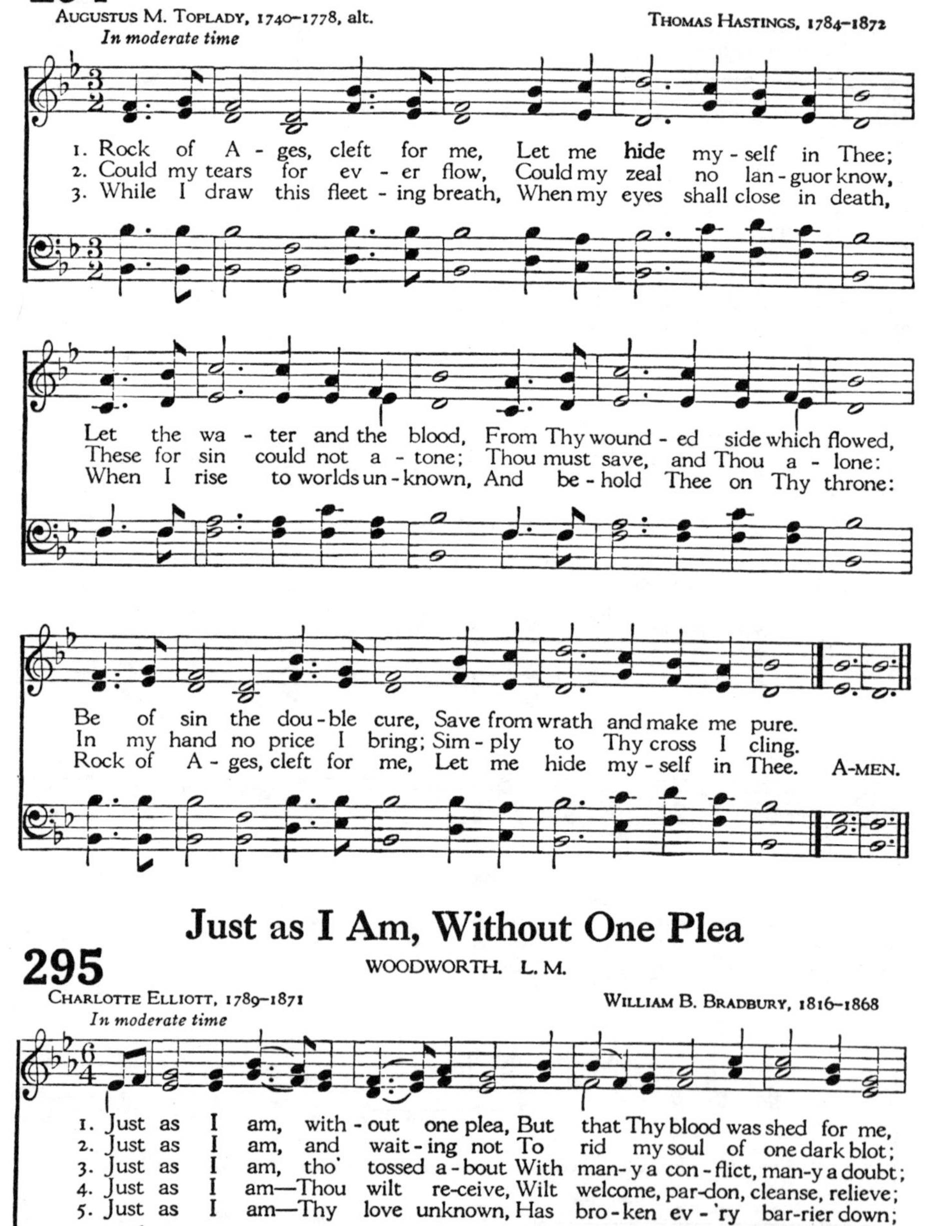
In moderate time
1. Rock of A - ges, cleft for me, Let me hide my - self in Thee;
2. Could my tears for ev - er flow, Could my zeal no lan - guor know,
3. While I draw this fleet - ing breath, When my eyes shall close in death,
Let the wa - ter and the blood, From Thy wound - ed side which flowed,
These for sin could not a - tone; Thou must save, and Thou a - lone:
When I rise to worlds un - known, And be - hold Thee on Thy throne:
Be of sin the dou - ble cure, Save from wrath and make me pure.
In my hand no price I bring; Sim - ply to Thy cross I cling.
Rock of A - ges, cleft for me, Let me hide my - self in Thee.
A-MEN.
In moderate time
1. Just as I am, with - out one plea, But that Thy blood was shed for me,
2. Just as I am, and wait - ing not To rid my soul of one dark blot;
3. Just as I am, tho' tossed a - bout With man - y a con - flict, man - y a doubt;
4. Just as I am—Thou wilt re - ceive, Wilt welcome, par - don, cleanse, relieve;
5. Just as I am—Thy love unknown, Has bro - ken ev - 'ry bar - rier down;

295 Just as I Am, Without One Plea

WOODWORTH. L. M.

CHARLOTTE ELLIOTT, 1789–1871 — WILLIAM B. BRADBURY, 1816–1868

And that Thou bid'st me come to Thee, O Lamb of God, I come, I come!
To Thee, whose blood can cleanse each spot, O Lamb of God, I come, I come!
With fears with-in, and foes with-out, O Lamb of God, I come, I come!
Be-cause Thy prom-ise I be-lieve, O Lamb of God, I come, I come!
Now, to be Thine, yea, Thine a-lone, O Lamb of God, I come, I come! A - MEN.
Take my Life, and Let It Be
HENDON. 7. 7. 7. 7. 7.
296
FRANCES R. HAVERGAL, 1836–1879
H. A. CESAR MALAN, 1787–1864
In moderate time
1. Take my life, and let it be Con - se - crat - ed, Lord, to Thee, Take my mo - ments and my days; Let them flow in cease - less praise, Let them flow in cease - less praise.
2. Take my hands, and let them move At the im - pulse of Thy love. Take my feet, and let them be Swift and beau - ti - ful for Thee, Swift and beau - ti - ful for Thee.
3. Take my voice, and let me sing, Al - ways, on - ly, for my King. Take my in - tel - lect, and use Ev - ery power as Thou shalt choose, Ev - ery power as Thou shalt choose.
4. Take my will, and make it Thine; It shall be no lon - ger mine. Take my heart, it is Thine own; It shall be Thy roy - al throne, It shall be Thy roy - al throne.
5. Take my love; my Lord, I pour At Thy feet its treas - ure - store. Take my self, and I will be Ev - er, on - ly, all for Thee, Ev - er, on - ly, all for Thee. A - MEN.

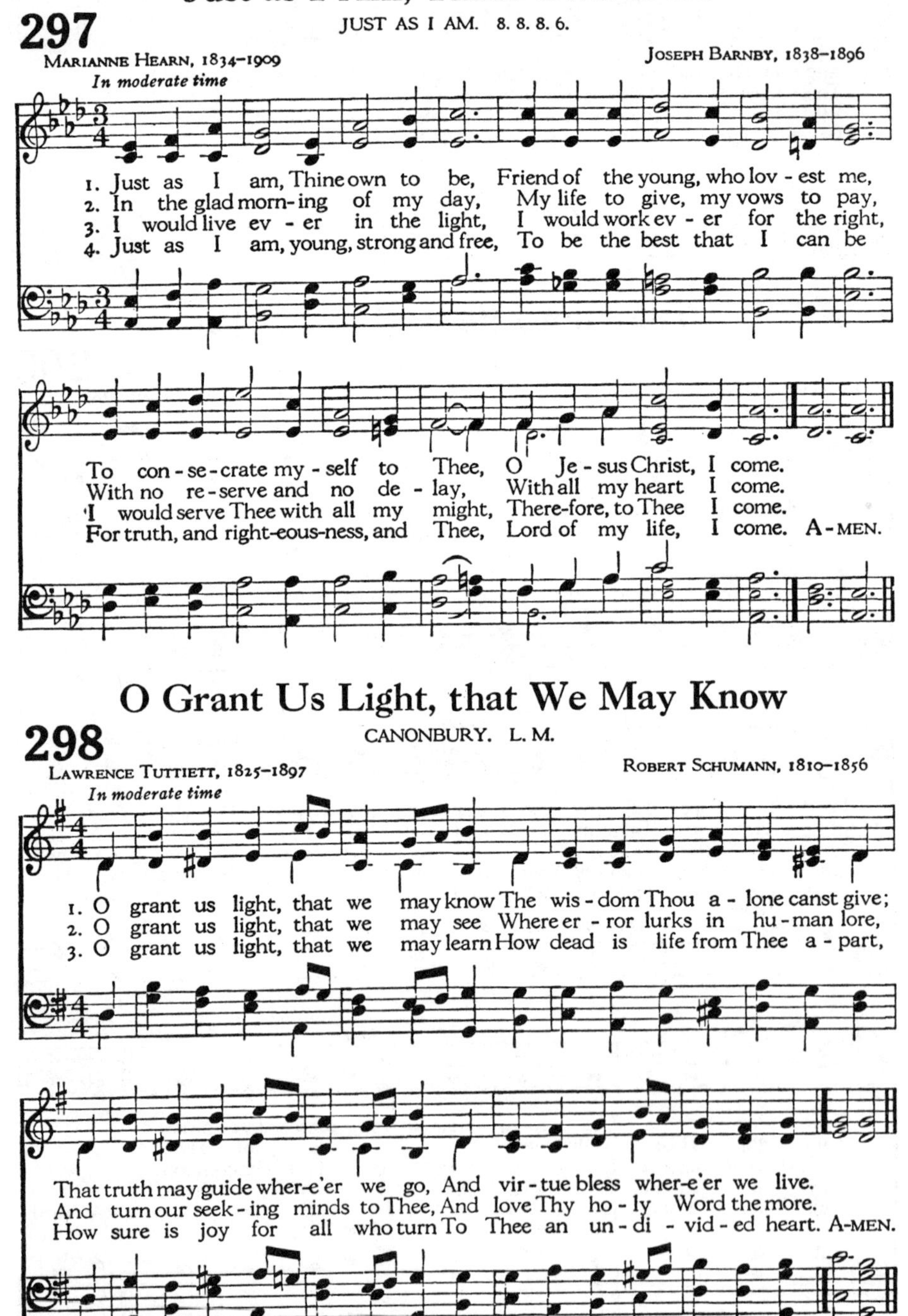
Just as I Am, Thine Own to Be
297
JUST AS I AM. 8. 8. 8. 6.
MARIANNE HEARN, 1834–1909
JOSEPH BARNBY, 1838–1896
In moderate time
1. Just as I am, Thine own to be, Friend of the young, who lov - est me,
2. In the glad morn-ing of my day, My life to give, my vows to pay,
3. I would live ev - er in the light, I would work ev - er for the right,
4. Just as I am, young, strong and free, To be the best that I can be
To con-se-crate my-self to Thee, O Je-sus Christ, I come.
With no re-serve and no de - lay, With all my heart I come.
I would serve Thee with all my might, There-fore, to Thee I come.
For truth, and right-eous-ness, and Thee, Lord of my life, I come. A-MEN.
O Grant Us Light, that We May Know
298
CANONBURY. L. M.
LAWRENCE TUTTIETT, 1825–1897
ROBERT SCHUMANN, 1810–1856
In moderate time
1. O grant us light, that we may know The wis - dom Thou a - lone canst give;
2. O grant us light, that we may see Where er - ror lurks in hu - man lore,
3. O grant us light, that we may learn How dead is life from Thee a - part,
That truth may guide wher-e'er we go, And vir - tue bless wher-e'er we live.
And turn our seek - ing minds to Thee, And love Thy ho - ly Word the more.
How sure is joy for all who turn To Thee an un - di - vid - ed heart. A-MEN.

I Feel the Winds of God Today

KINGSFOLD. C. M. D.

301

JESSIE ADAMS, 1863–

Arr. from an English traditional melody

In moderate time

1. I feel the winds of God to - day; To - day my sail I lift,
2. It is the wind of God that dries My vain re - gret-ful tears,
3. If ev - er I for - get thy love And how that love was shown,

Tho' hea - vy oft with drench-ing spray, And torn with ma-ny a rift;
Un - til with brav-er thoughts shall rise The pur - er, bright-er years;
Lift high the blood-red flag a - bove; It bears thy Name a - lone.

If hope but light the wa - ter's crest, And Christ my bark will use,
If cast on shores of self - ish ease Or pleas-ure I should be,
Great Pi - lot of my on - ward way, Thou wilt not let me drift;

I'll seek the seas at his be - hest, And brave an - oth - er cruise.
Lord, let me feel thy fresh -'ning breeze, And I'll put back to sea.
I feel the winds of God to - day, To - day my sail I lift. A-MEN.

I Bind my Heart this Tide

302

FEALTY. 6. 7. 7. 7. 6. 7. 7. 7.

LAUCHLAN MACLEAN WATT, 1867-

GRACE WILBUR CONANT

In moderate time
1. I bind my heart this tide To the Gal - i - le - an's side,
2. I bind my heart in thrall To the God, the Lord of All,
To the wounds of Cal - va - ry,— To the Christ who died for me.
To the God, the poor man's Friend, And the Christ whom he did send.
I bind my soul this day To the broth - er far a - way,
I bind my - self to peace, To make strife and en - vy cease,
And the broth-er near at hand, In this town, and in this land.
God! knit thou sure the cord Of my thral- dom to my Lord. A - MEN.

Master, No Offering Costly and Sweet

LOVE'S OFFERING. 6. 4. 6. 4. 6. 6. 4. 4.

303

EDWIN P. PARKER, 1836–1925 — EDWIN P. PARKER, 1836–1925

In moderate time
1. Mas - ter, no of - fer - ing Cost - ly and sweet
2. Dai - ly our lives would show Weak - ness made strong,
3. Some word of hope for hearts Bur - dened with fears,
4. Thus in Thy serv - ice, Lord, Till e - ven - tide
May we, like Mag - da - lene, Lay at Thy feet;
Toil - some and gloom - y ways Bright - ened with song;
Some balm of peace for eyes Blind - ed with tears,
Clos - es the day of life, May we a - bide.
Yet may love's in - cense rise, Sweet - er than sac - ri - fice,
Some deeds of kind - ness done, Some souls by pa - tience won,
Some dews of mer - cy shed, Some way - ward foot - steps led,
And when earth's la - bors cease, Let us de - part in peace,
Dear Lord, to Thee, Dear Lord, to Thee. A - MEN.

Living for Jesus a Life That Is True

304

LIVING FOR JESUS. 10. 10. 10. 10. with Refrain.

THOMAS O. CHISHOLM, 1866–
C. HAROLD LOWDEN, 1883–
Not fast, and in a reverent manner
1. Liv-ing for Je-sus a life that is true, Striv-ing to please Him in all that I do; Yield-ing al-le-giance, glad-heart-ed and free, This is the path-way of bless-ing for me.
2. Liv-ing for Je-sus who died in my place, Bear-ing on Cal-vary my sin and dis-grace; Such love con-strains me to an-swer His call, Fol-low His lead-ing and give Him my all.
3. Liv-ing for Je-sus wher-ev-er I am, Do-ing each du-ty in His ho-ly name; Will-ing to suf-fer af-flic-tion and loss, Deem-ing each tri-al a part of my cross.
4. Liv-ing for Je-sus through earth's lit-tle while, My dear-est treas-ure, the light of His smile; Seek-ing the lost ones He died to re-deem, Bring-ing the wea-ry to find rest in Him.
CHORUS Unison. Slower
O Je-sus, Lord and Sav-iour, I give my-self to Thee, For Thou, in Thy a-tone-ment, Didst give Thy-self for me; I own no oth-er Mas-ter, My heart shall be Thy

throne, My life I give, hence-forth to live, O Christ, for Thee a - lone. A-MEN.

No Longer of Him Be It Said

SHELTERING WING. L. M.

305

JOYCE KILMER, 1886–1918 — JOSEPH BARNBY, 1838–1896

In moderate time

1. No lon - ger of Him be it said, "He hath no place
2. There is no strange and dis - tant place That is not glad -
3. Im - pris - oned for His love of me He makes my spir -

to lay His head"; In eve - ry land a con - stant
dened by His face; And eve - ry na - tion kneels to
it great - ly free; And through my lips that ut - tered

lamp Flames by His small and might - y camp.
hail The Splen - dor shin - ing through its veil.
sin The King of Glo - ry en - ters in. A - MEN.

O Master, Let Me Walk with Thee

306

SAXBY. L. M.

WASHINGTON GLADDEN, 1836–1918 (*First Tune*) TIMOTHY R. MATTHEWS, 1826–1910

In moderate time

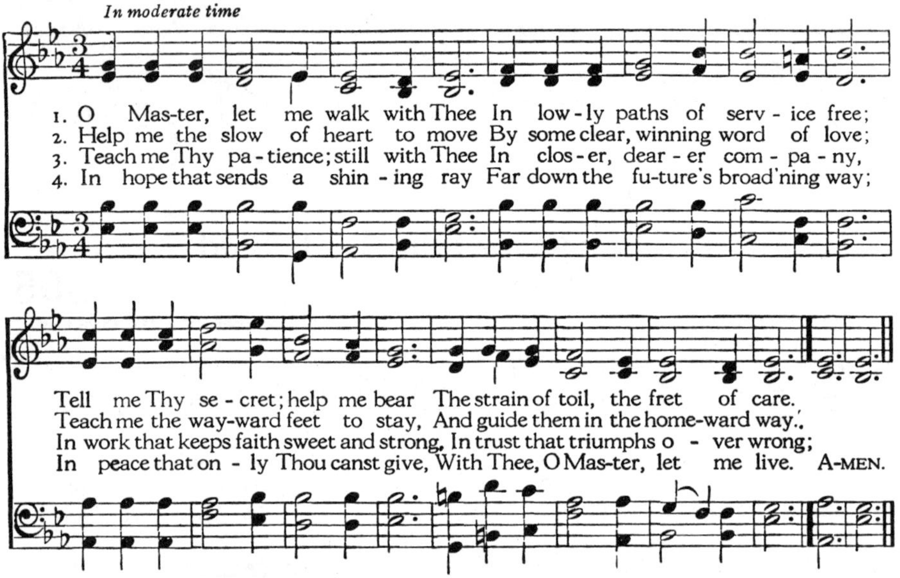

1. O Mas-ter, let me walk with Thee In low-ly paths of serv-ice free;
Tell me Thy se-cret; help me bear The strain of toil, the fret of care.
2. Help me the slow of heart to move By some clear, winning word of love;
Teach me the way-ward feet to stay, And guide them in the home-ward way.
3. Teach me Thy pa-tience; still with Thee In clos-er, dear-er com-pa-ny,
In work that keeps faith sweet and strong, In trust that triumphs o-ver wrong;
4. In hope that sends a shin-ing ray Far down the fu-ture's broad'ning way;
In peace that on-ly Thou canst give, With Thee, O Mas-ter, let me live. A-MEN.

O Master, Let Me Walk with Thee

307

MARYTON. L. M.

WASHINGTON GLADDEN, 1836–1918 (*Second Tune*) H. PERCY SMITH, 1825–1898

In moderate time

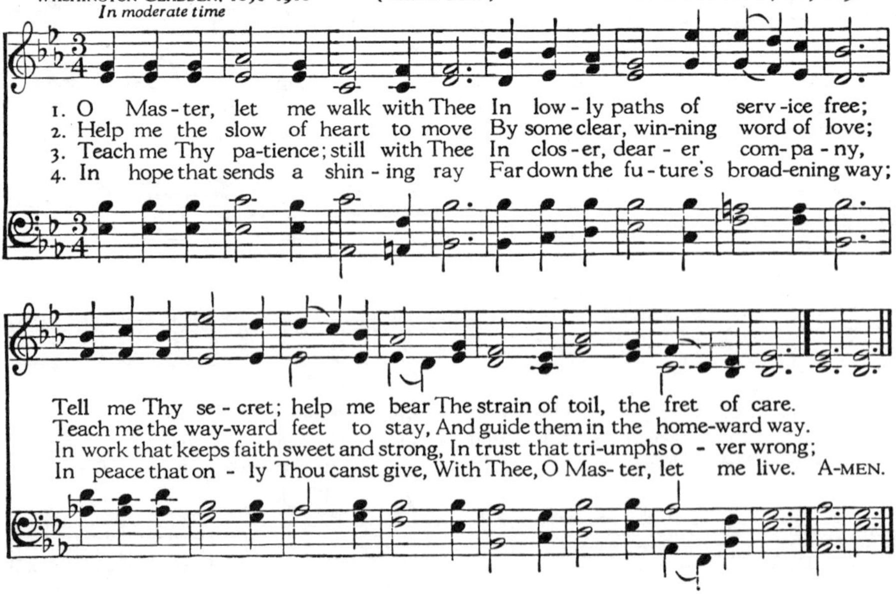

1. O Mas-ter, let me walk with Thee In low-ly paths of serv-ice free;
Tell me Thy se-cret; help me bear The strain of toil, the fret of care.
2. Help me the slow of heart to move By some clear, win-ning word of love;
Teach me the way-ward feet to stay, And guide them in the home-ward way.
3. Teach me Thy pa-tience; still with Thee In clos-er, dear-er com-pa-ny,
In work that keeps faith sweet and strong, In trust that tri-umphs o-ver wrong;
4. In hope that sends a shin-ing ray Far down the fu-ture's broad-ening way;
In peace that on-ly Thou canst give, With Thee, O Mas-ter, let me live. A-MEN.

O Jesus, I Have Promised

ANGEL'S STORY. 7. 6. 7. 6. D.

308

JOHN E. BODE, 1816–1874
ARTHUR H. MANN, 1850–1929
In moderate time
1. O Je - sus, I have prom - ised To serve Thee to the end;
2. O let me feel Thee near me! The world is ev - er near;
3. O let me hear Thee speak - ing, In ac - cents clear and still,
4. O Je - sus, Thou hast prom - ised To all who fol - low Thee
Be Thou for ev - er near me, My Mas - ter and my Friend:
I see the sights that daz - zle, The tempt - ing sounds I hear;
A - bove the storms of pas - sion, The mur - murs of self - will;
That where Thou art in glo - ry There shall Thy ser - vant be;
I shall not fear the bat - tle If Thou art by my side,
My foes are ev - er near me, A - round me and with - in;
O speak to re - as - sure me, To has - ten or con - trol;
And, Je - sus, I have prom - ised To serve Thee to the end;
Nor wan - der from the path - way If Thou wilt be my guide.
But, Je - sus, draw Thou near - er, And shield my soul from sin.
O speak, and make me lis - ten, Thou guard - ian of my soul.
O give me grace to fol - low, My Mas - ter and my Friend.
A - MEN.

309 Thou, Lord of Life, our Saving Health

ST. POLYCARP. L. M.

SAMUEL LONGFELLOW, 1819–1892 — IGNACE PLEYEL, 1757–1831

In moderate time

1. Thou, Lord of Life, our sav - ing Health, Who mak'st thy
2. As on the riv - er's ris - ing tide Flow strength and
3. To heal the wound, to still the pain, And strength to
4. Bless thou the gifts our hands have brought! Bless thou the

suf - f'ring ones our care, Our gifts are still our tru - est
cool - ness from the sea, So thro' the ways our hands pro -
fail - ing puls - es bring, Till the lame feet shall leap a -
work our hearts have planned; Ours is the faith, the will, the

wealth, To serve thee our sin - cer - est prayer.
vide, May quick - 'ning life flow in from thee;—
gain, And the parched lips with glad - ness sing.
thought— The rest, O God, is in thy hand. A - MEN.

310 O for a Closer Walk with God

NAOMI. C. M.

WILLIAM COWPER, 1731–1800 — HANS G. NAEGELI, 1768–1836; Arr. by LOWELL MASON, 1792–1872

In moderate time

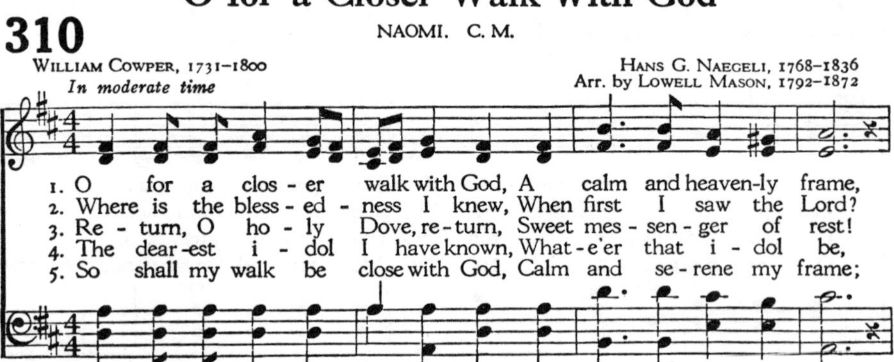
1. O for a clos - er walk with God, A calm and heaven-ly frame,
2. Where is the bless - ed - ness I knew, When first I saw the Lord?
3. Re - turn, O ho - ly Dove, re - turn, Sweet mes - sen - ger of rest!
4. The dear-est i - dol I have known, What - e'er that i - dol be,
5. So shall my walk be close with God, Calm and se - rene my frame;

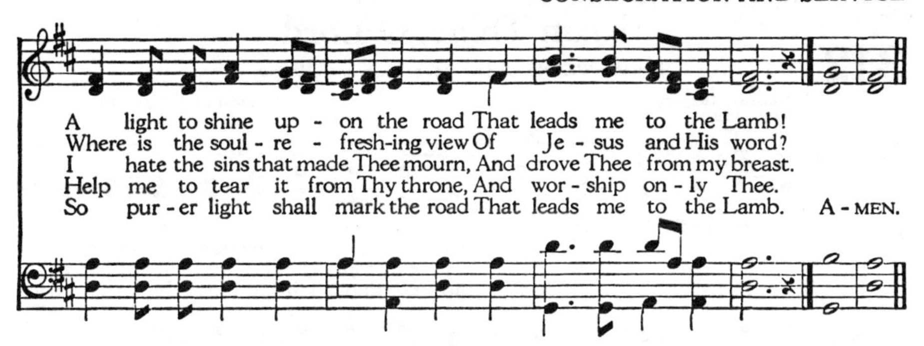
A light to shine up - on the road That leads me to the Lamb!
Where is the soul - re - fresh-ing view Of Je - sus and His word?
I hate the sins that made Thee mourn, And drove Thee from my breast.
Help me to tear it from Thy throne, And wor - ship on - ly Thee.
So pur - er light shall mark the road That leads me to the Lamb. A - MEN.

God of the Strong, God of the Weak

GODWIN. L. M.

311

RICHARD W. GILDER, 1844–1909

WILLIAM G. BLANCHARD, 1905–

In moderate time
1. God of the strong, God of the weak, Lord of all
2. In suf - fering Thou hast made us one, In might - y
3. Teach us, great Teach - er of man - kind, The sac - ri -
4. Teach Thou, and we shall know in - deed The truth di -
lands and our own land, Light of all souls: from Thee we seek
bur - dens one are we: Teach us that low - liest du - ty done
fice that brings Thy balm: The love, the work that bless and bind;
vine that mak - eth free; And know - ing, we may sow the seed
Light from Thy light, strength from Thy hand.
Is high - est serv - ice un - to Thee.
Teach us Thy maj - es - ty, Thy calm.
That blos - soms through e - ter - ni - ty. A - MEN.

I Am Thine, O Lord

312

DRAW ME NEARER. 10. 7. 10. 7. with Refrain

FANNY J. CROSBY, 1823–1915 — WILLIAM H. DOANE, 1831–1915

In moderate time
1. I am Thine, O Lord, I have heard Thy voice, And it told Thy love to
2. Con - se - crate me now to Thy serv - ice, Lord, By the pow'r of grace di -
3. O the pure de - light of a sin - gle hour That be - fore Thy throne I
4. There are depths of love that I can - not know Till I cross the nar - row
me; But I long to rise in the arms of faith, And be
vine; Let my soul look up with a stead - fast hope, And my
spend, When I kneel in prayer, and with Thee, my God, I com -
sea; There are heights of joy that I may not reach Till I
REFRAIN
clos - er drawn to Thee. Draw me near - er, near - er, bless - ed Lord,
will be lost in Thine.
mune as friend with friend!
rest in peace with Thee.
near - er, near - er,
To the cross where Thou hast died; Draw me near - er, near - er,
near - er, bless - ed Lord, To Thy pre - cious, bleed - ing side. A-MEN.

Brightly Beams our Father's Mercy

LOWER LIGHTS. 8. 7. 8. 7. with Refrain

313

PHILIP P. BLISS, 1838–1876 PHILIP P. BLISS, 1838–1876

In moderate time

1. Bright-ly beams our Fa-ther's mer-cy From His light-house ev-er-more;
2. Dark the night of sin has set-tled, Loud the an-gry bil-lows roar:
3. Trim your fee-ble lamp, my broth-er! Some poor sea-man, tem-pest-tossed,
But to us He gives the keep-ing Of the lights a-long the shore.
Ea-ger eyes are watch-ing, long-ing, For the lights a-long the shore.
Try-ing now to make the har-bor, In the dark-ness may be lost.
REFRAIN
Let the low-er lights be burn-ing! Send a gleam a-cross the wave!
Some poor faint-ing, strug-gling sea-man You may res-cue, you may save.
A-MEN.

Jesus, I Live to Thee

314

LAKE ENON. S. M.

HENRY HARBAUGH, 1817–1867 ISAAC B. WOODBURY, 1819–1858

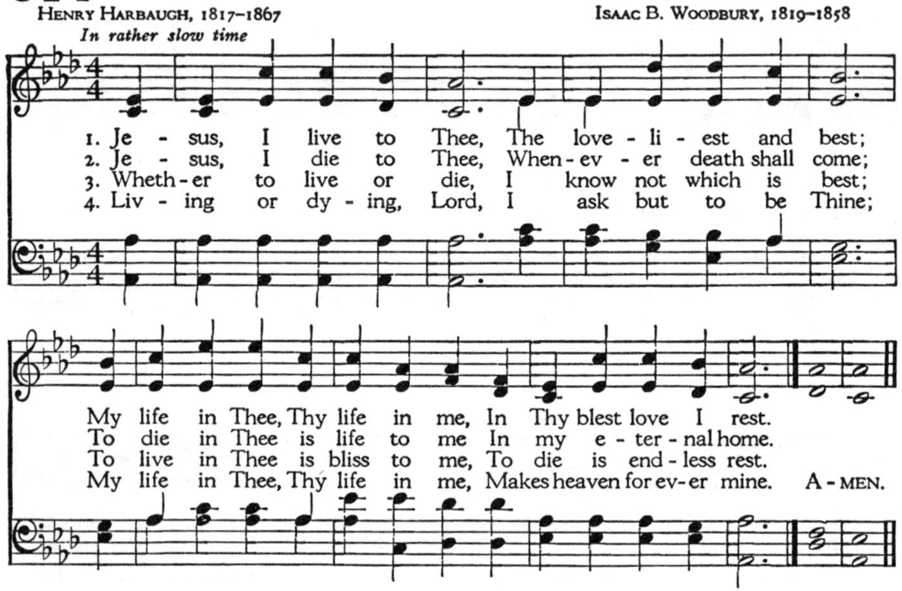
In rather slow time
1. Je - sus, I live to Thee, The love - li - est and best;
2. Je - sus, I die to Thee, When - ev - er death shall come;
3. Wheth - er to live or die, I know not which is best;
4. Liv - ing or dy - ing, Lord, I ask but to be Thine;
My life in Thee, Thy life in me, In Thy blest love I rest.
To die in Thee is life to me In my e - ter - nal home.
To live in Thee is bliss to me, To die is end - less rest.
My life in Thee, Thy life in me, Makes heaven for ev - er mine. A - MEN.

God, Who Touchest Earth with Beauty

315

GENEVA. 8. 5. 8. 5.

MARY S. EDGAR C. HAROLD LOWDEN, 1883–

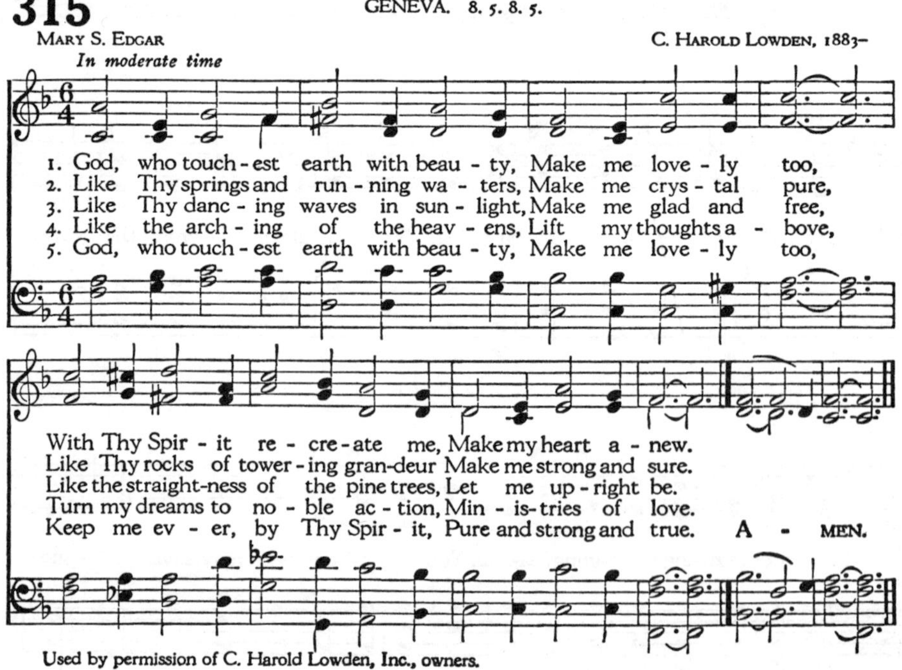
In moderate time
1. God, who touch - est earth with beau - ty, Make me love - ly too,
2. Like Thy springs and run - ning wa - ters, Make me crys - tal pure,
3. Like Thy danc - ing waves in sun - light, Make me glad and free,
4. Like the arch - ing of the heav - ens, Lift my thoughts a - bove,
5. God, who touch - est earth with beau - ty, Make me love - ly too,
With Thy Spir - it re - cre - ate me, Make my heart a - new.
Like Thy rocks of tower - ing gran - deur Make me strong and sure.
Like the straight - ness of the pine trees, Let me up - right be.
Turn my dreams to no - ble ac - tion, Min - is - tries of love.
Keep me ev - er, by Thy Spir - it, Pure and strong and true. A - MEN.

The Wise May Bring Their Learning

FOREST GREEN. C. M. D.

316

ANONYMOUS
From THE BOOK OF PRAISE FOR CHILDREN, 1881
English traditional melody
Arr. by R. VAUGHAN WILLIAMS, 1872-
Joyfully, with flowing rhythm
1. The wise may bring their learn - ing, The rich may bring their wealth,
2. We'll bring Him hearts that love him; We'll bring Him thank-ful praise,
3. We'll bring the lit - tle du - ties We'll have to do each day;
And some may bring their great - ness, And some bring strength and health;
And young souls meek - ly striv - ing To walk in ho - ly ways:
We'll try our best to please Him, At home, at school, at play:
We, too, would bring our treas - ures To of - fer to the King;
And these shall be the treas - ures We of - fer to the King,
And bet - ter are these treas - ures To of - fer to our King
We have no wealth or learn - ing: What shall we chil - dren bring?
And these are gifts that ev - en The poor - est child may bring.
Than rich - est gifts with - out them; Yet these a child may bring.
A-MEN.

From "The English Hymnal." Permission Oxford University Press.

Great Master, Touch Us

317

CONISBOROUGH. 10. 10. 10. 10.

Horatius Bonar, 1808–1889 — Wilfrid Sanderson

In moderate time
1. Great Mas-ter, touch us with thy skill-ful hands; Let not the mu-sic that is in us die: Great Sculp-tor, hew and pol-ish us, nor let, Hid-den and lost, thy form with-in us lie.
2. Spare not the stroke; do with us what thou wilt; Let there be naught un-fin-ished, bro-ken, marred; Com-plete thy pur-pose that we may be-come Thy per-fect im-age—thou our God and Lord.
A-men.

Used by permission of the Wesleyan Methodist Publishing Co.

Dear Master, in Whose Life I See

318

HURSLEY. L. M.

John Hunter, 1848–1917 — Katholisches Gesangbuch, 1774

In moderate time

1. Dear Mas-ter, in whose life I see All that I
2. Though what I dream and what I do In my weak

would, but fail to be; Let Thy clear light for
days are al - ways two, Help me, op - pressed by
ev - er shine, To shame and guide this life of mine.
things un - done, O Thou, whose deeds and dreams were one! A - MEN.

Words used by permission of Canon L. S. Hunter, Bishop of Sheffield.

Go Forth to Life, O Child of Earth

MENDON. L. M.

319

Samuel Longfellow, 1819–1892

German melody.
Arr. by Samuel Dyer, 1785–1835

In moderate time

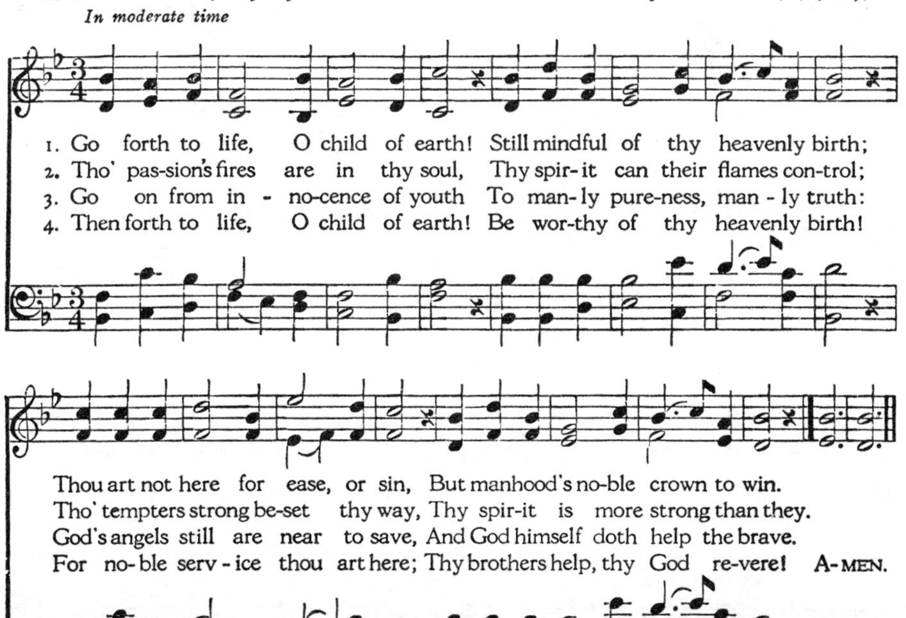
1. Go forth to life, O child of earth! Still mindful of thy heavenly birth;
2. Tho' pas-sion's fires are in thy soul, Thy spir-it can their flames con-trol;
3. Go on from in - no-cence of youth To man-ly pure-ness, man - ly truth:
4. Then forth to life, O child of earth! Be wor-thy of thy heavenly birth!
Thou art not here for ease, or sin, But manhood's no-ble crown to win.
Tho' tempters strong be-set thy way, Thy spir-it is more strong than they.
God's angels still are near to save, And God himself doth help the brave.
For no-ble serv - ice thou art here; Thy brothers help, thy God re-vere! A-MEN.

Light of the World, How Long the Quest

320
QUEST. L. M.
EDWIN MCNEILL POTEAT, 1892–
EDWIN MCNEILL POTEAT, 1892–
In moderate time
1. Light of the world, how long the quest
2. Cring - ing be - fore the riv - en oak,
3. Yet all the while, though hearts were dark,
4. In Thee, O Christ, we hail the dawn,
down wea - ry years to learn thy name!
man fain the light - ning would ap - pease;
soft glints of light were en - ter - ing;
with un - cre - a - ted light a - flame;
From sa - cred fire, on mount - ain crest; or
In fear the flam - ing dawn in - voke; or
Each gleam of truth a glow - ing spark of
Be - fore Thee ter - ror is with - drawn; Thou
tem - ple al - tar's lam - bent flame.
greet the morn - ing on his knees.
Thy di - vine il - lu - min - ing.
light of all times and hearts the same.
A - MEN.

Used by permission of Edwin McNeill Poteat.

Be Thou My Vision, O Lord of My Heart

SLANE. 10. 10. 10. 10.
Ancient Irish; tr. by MARY BYRNE
Versified by ELEANOR HULL
Ancient Irish traditional melody
Harmonized by DAVID EVANS, 1874–
Unison. Moderately slow, with great dignity
1. Be Thou my Vi - sion, O Lord of my heart;
2. Be Thou my Wis - dom, and Thou my true Word;
3. Rich - es I heed not, nor man's emp - ty praise,
4. High King of heav - en, my vic - to - ry won,
Naught be all else to me, save that Thou art—
I ev - er with Thee and Thou with me, Lord;
Thou mine in - her - it - ance, now and al - ways:
May I reach heav - en's joys, O bright heaven's Sun!
Thou my best thought, by day or by night,
Thou my great Fa - ther, I Thy true son;
Thou and Thou on - ly, first in my heart,
Heart of my own heart, what - ev - er be - fall,
Wak - ing or sleep - ing, Thy pres - ence my light.
Thou in me dwell - ing, and I with Thee one.
High King of heav - en, my treas - ure Thou art.
Still be my Vi - sion, O Rul - er of all.
A - MEN.

Words from the "Poem Book of the Gael," by Eleanor Hull. Used by permission of Chatto and Windus, London, England.
Tune copyright Educational Company of Ireland—used by permission.
Harmony from "The Church Hymnary," Revised. Used by permission of the Oxford University Press.

Marching With the Heroes

322

ROSMORE. 6. 5. 6. 5. D. with Refrain.

WILLIAM G. TARRANT, 1853–1928

HENRY G. TREMBATH, 1844–1908

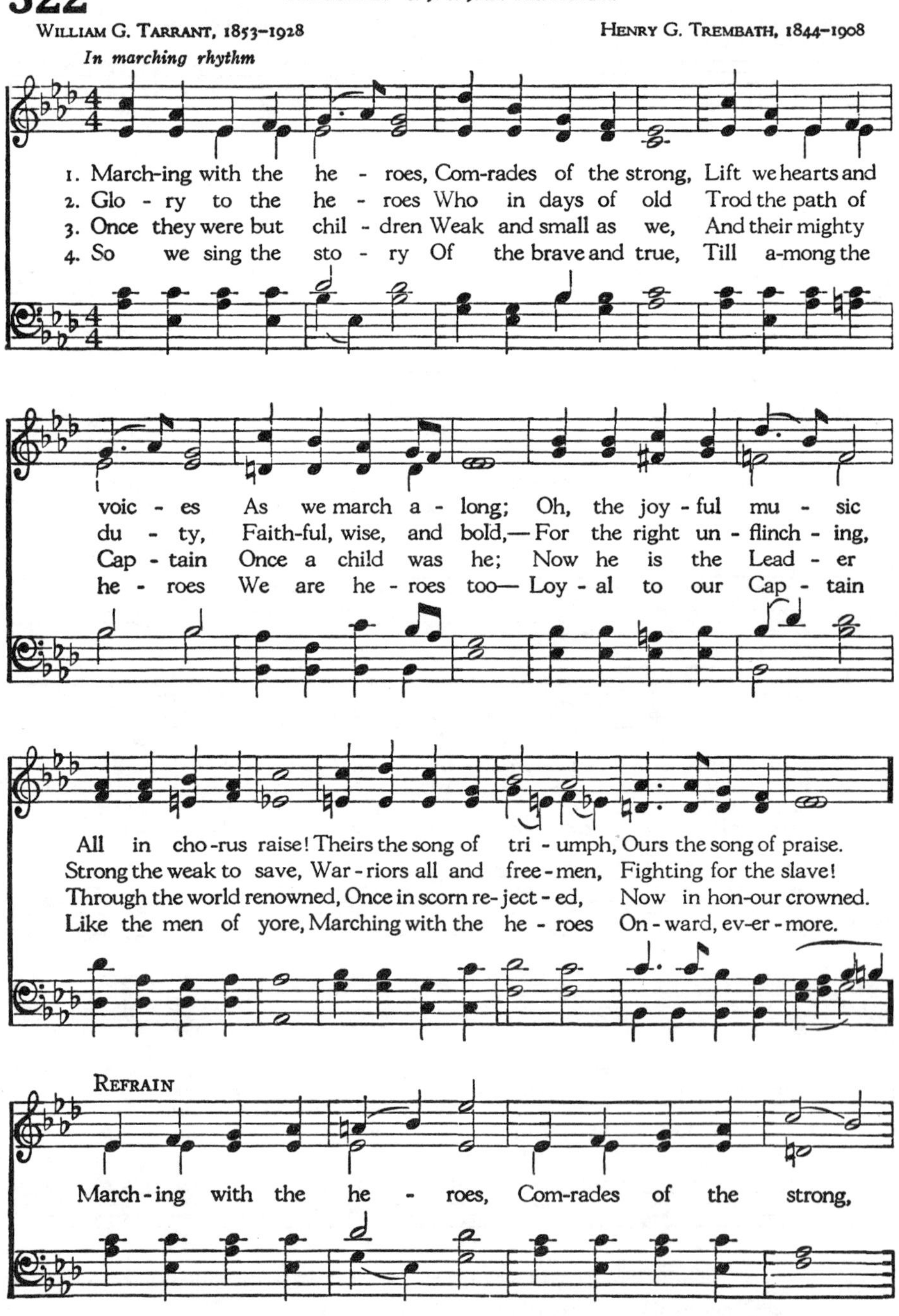
In marching rhythm
1. March-ing with the he - roes, Com-rades of the strong, Lift we hearts and
2. Glo - ry to the he - roes Who in days of old Trod the path of
3. Once they were but chil - dren Weak and small as we, And their mighty
4. So we sing the sto - ry Of the brave and true, Till a-mong the
voic - es As we march a - long; Oh, the joy - ful mu - sic
du - ty, Faith-ful, wise, and bold,— For the right un - flinch - ing,
Cap - tain Once a child was he; Now he is the Lead - er
he - roes We are he - roes too— Loy - al to our Cap - tain
All in cho-rus raise! Theirs the song of tri - umph, Ours the song of praise.
Strong the weak to save, War - riors all and free - men, Fighting for the slave!
Through the world renowned, Once in scorn re- ject - ed, Now in hon-our crowned.
Like the men of yore, Marching with the he - roes On - ward, ev-er - more.
REFRAIN
March - ing with the he - roes, Com-rades of the strong,

Lift we hearts and voic - es As we march a - long. A-MEN.

Awake, Awake to Love and Work

SHELTERED DALE. 8. 6. 8. 6. 8. 6.

323

GEOFFREY A. STUDDERT-KENNEDY, 1883–1929

German traditional melody

Joyfully
1. A - wake, a - wake to love and work, The lark is in the sky,
2. Come, let thy voice be one with theirs, Shout with their shout of praise;
3. To give and give, and give a - gain, What God hath giv - en thee;
The fields are wet with dia - mond dew, The worlds a - wake to cry
See how the gi - ant sun soars up, Great lord of years and days!
To spend thy - self nor count the cost, To serve right glo - rious - ly
Their bless-ings on the Lord of Life, As He goes meek-ly by.
So let the love of Je - sus come And set thy soul a - blaze:
The God who gave all worlds that are, And all that are to be. A - MEN.

Have Thine Own Way, Lord!

324

ADELAIDE. 5. 4. 5. 4. D.

ADELAIDE A. POLLARD, 1860–1934

GEORGE C. STEBBINS, 1846–

In moderate time, and like a prayer

1. Have Thine own way, Lord! Have Thine own way! Thou art the
2. Have Thine own way, Lord! Have Thine own way! Search me and
3. Have Thine own way, Lord! Have Thine own way! Wound-ed and
4. Have Thine own way, Lord! Have Thine own way! Hold o'er my
Pot - ter; I am the clay. Mould me and make me After - er Thy
try me, Mas-ter, to - day! Whit - er than snow, Lord, Wash me just
wea - ry, Help me, I pray! Pow - er— all pow - er— Sure - ly is
be - ing Ab - so - lute sway! Fill with Thy Spir - it Till all shall
will, While I am wait - ing, Yield - ed and still.
now, As in Thy pres - ence Hum - bly I bow.
Thine! Touch me and heal me, Sav - iour di - vine!
see Christ on - ly, al - ways, Liv - ing in me!
A - MEN.

Father, Loving Father

325

LIVERMORE. 6. 5. 6. 5.

JEAN MILNE GOWER, 1867–

JEAN MILNE GOWER, 1867–

In moderate time, like a prayer

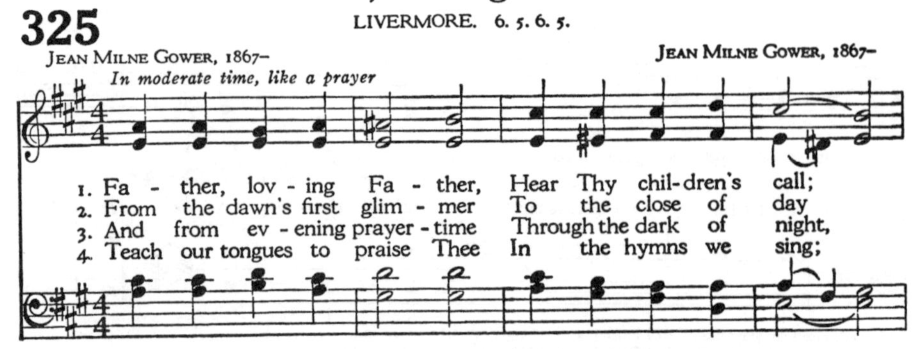
1. Fa - ther, lov - ing Fa - ther, Hear Thy chil-dren's call;
2. From the dawn's first glim - mer To the close of day
3. And from ev - ening prayer - time Through the dark of night,
4. Teach our tongues to praise Thee In the hymns we sing;

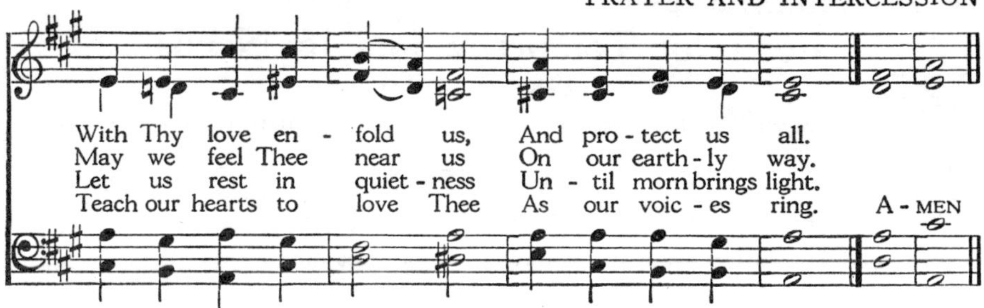
With Thy love en - fold us, And pro - tect us all.
May we feel Thee near us On our earth - ly way.
Let us rest in quiet - ness Un - til morn brings light.
Teach our hearts to love Thee As our voic - es ring. A - MEN

Used by permission of Mrs. John H. Gower.

Lord, As to Thy Dear Cross We Flee

326

ST. COLUMBA (Irish). C. M.

JOHN H. GURNEY, 1802–1862 — Old Irish melody; from DR. PETRIE'S Collection

In moderate time, with flowing rhythm

1. Lord, as to Thy dear cross we flee, And plead to be for - given, So let Thy life our pat - tern be, And form our souls for heaven.
2. Help us through good re - port and ill Our dai - ly cross to bear, Like Thee to do our Fa - ther's will, Our breth - ren's griefs to share.
3. Let grace our self - ish - ness ex - pel, Our earth - li - ness re - fine, And kind - ness in our bos - oms dwell, As free and true as Thine.
4. If joy shall at Thy bid - ding fly, And grief's dark day come on, We in our turn would meek - ly cry "Fa - ther, Thy will be done."
5. Kept peace - ful in the midst of strife, For - giv - ing and for - given, O may we lead the pilg - rim's life, And fol - low Thee to heaven. A - MEN.

Tune used by permission of Messrs. Stainer and Bell, Ltd., London.

Lord, for Tomorrow and Its Needs

327

VINCENT. 8. 4. 8. 4. D.

SYBIL F. PARTRIDGE (Sister Mary Xavier) — HORATIO R. PALMER, 1834–1907

In moderate time

1. Lord, for to-mor - row and its needs I do not pray; Keep me, my God, from
2. Let me be slow to do my will, Prompt to o - bey; Help me to sac - ri -
3. Let me in sea - son, Lord, be grave, In sea - son gay; Let me be faith-ful

stain of sin Just for to-day. Help me to la - bor ear - nest- ly,
fice my-self, Fa - ther, to-day. Let me no wrong or i - dle word
to Thy grace, Fa - ther, to-day. Lord, for to - mor-row and its needs

And du - ly pray; Let me be kind in word and deed, Fa - ther, to-day.
Un-think-ing say; Set Thou a seal up-on my lips Thro' all to-day.
I do not pray; Still keep me, guide me, love me, Lord, Thro' each to-day. A-MEN.

Jesus, Kneel Beside Me

328

EUDOXIA. 6. 5. 6. 5.

ALLEN EASTMAN CROSS, 1864– — SABINE BARING-GOULD, 1834–1924

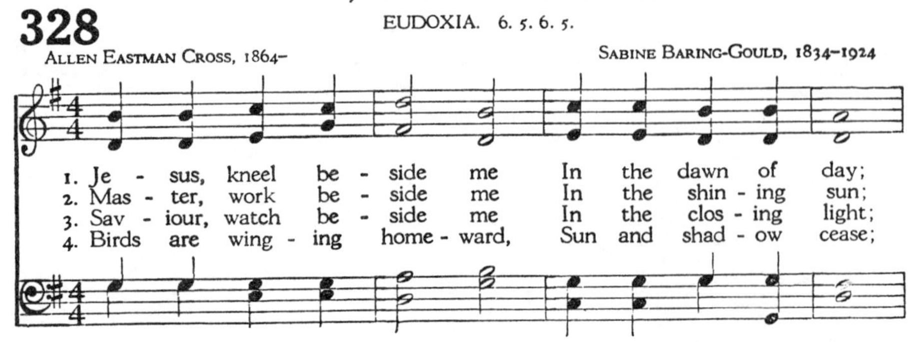
1. Je - sus, kneel be - side me In the dawn of day;
2. Mas - ter, work be - side me In the shin - ing sun;
3. Sav - iour, watch be - side me In the clos - ing light;
4. Birds are wing - ing home - ward, Sun and shad - ow cease;

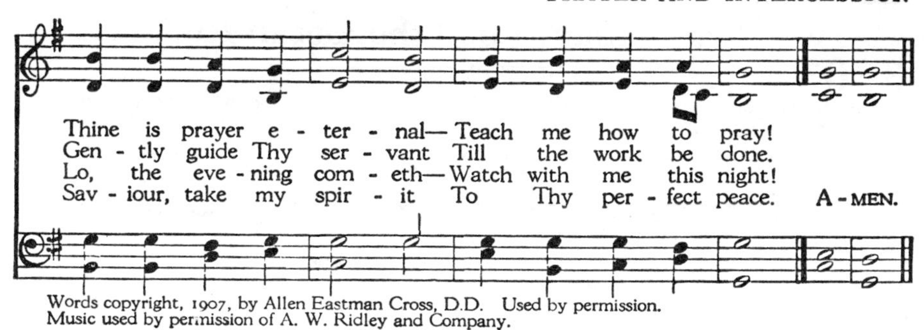
Thine is prayer e - ter - nal— Teach me how to pray!
Gen - tly guide Thy ser - vant Till the work be done.
Lo, the eve - ning com - eth— Watch with me this night!
Sav - iour, take my spir - it To Thy per - fect peace. A - MEN.

Nearer, My God, To Thee

BETHANY. 6. 4. 6. 4. 6. 6. 6. 4.

329

SARAH F. ADAMS, 1805–1848

LOWELL MASON, 1792–1872

In moderate time

1. Near - er, my God, to Thee, Near - er to Thee! E'en though it be a cross
2. Though like the wan - der - er, The sun gone down, Dark-ness be o - ver me,
3. There let the way ap - pear, Steps un - to heaven; All that Thou send-est me,
4. Then, with my wak-ing thoughts Bright with Thy praise, Out of my ston - y griefs
5. Or if, on joy - ful wing Cleav - ing the sky, Sun, moon, and stars for-got,
That rais - eth me; Still all my song shall be, Near - er, my
My rest a stone; Yet in my dreams I'd be Near - er, my
In mer - cy given; An - gels to beck - on me Near - er, my
Beth - el I'll raise; So by my woes to be Near - er, my
Up - ward I fly, Still all my song shall be, Near - er, my
God, to Thee, Near - er, my God, to Thee, Near - er to Thee!
God, to Thee, Near - er, my God, to Thee, Near - er to Thee!
God, to Thee, Near - er, my God, to Thee, Near - er to Thee!
God, to Thee, Near - er, my God, to Thee, Near - er to Thee!
God, to Thee, Near - er, my God, to Thee, Near - er to Thee! A - MEN.

Dear Father, Loud the Ocean Rolls

330
PETITION. 8. 4. 8. 4. D.
Jean Milne Gower, 1867–
John H. Gower, 1855–1922
In moderate time
1. Dear Fa - ther, loud the o - cean rolls O - ver our souls;
2. When skies are dark, or when at night Un - ho - ly light
3. Should treas - ures van - ish from our life A - mid the strife,
4. Dear heaven - ly Fa - ther, hear our prayer; Calm our de - spair.
Life seems a seeth - ing waste of doubt With - in, with - out.
Casts on the dear place where we dwell Its e - vil spell;
Come, Thou who know - est what we need, And help us heed
Give to all anx - ious hearts re - lease And bless - ed peace.
Help us to know Thou keep - est still A lov - ing will
Be Thou, O Fa - ther, near to bring Us com - fort - ing,
The high - er things which ev - ery day Il - lume our way;
Show dy - ing men Thy shin - ing face In ev - ery place;
To teach Thy ques-tioning chil - dren love Be - low, a - bove.
And sur - e - ty that we shall be Up - held by Thee.
And may we for Thy boun - ty give Thanks while we live.
That those who walk the ways of fear May know Thee near.
A - MEN.

What a Friend We Have in Jesus

ERIE. 8. 7. 8. 7. D.

331

JOSEPH SCRIVEN, 1820–1886

CHARLES C. CONVERSE, 1832–1918

In moderate time

1. What a friend we have in Je - sus, All our sins and griefs to bear;
2. Have we tri - als and temp-ta - tions? Is there trou-ble an - y-where?
3. Are we weak and heav - y - la - den, Cum-bered with a load of care?
What a priv - i - lege to car - ry Ev - ery-thing to God in prayer!
We should nev - er be dis - cour - aged; Take it to the Lord in prayer.
Pre - cious Sav - iour, still our ref - uge; Take it to the Lord in prayer.
O what peace we oft - en for - feit, O what need-less pain we bear,
Can we find a friend so faith - ful, Who will all our sor-rows share?
Do thy friends des-pise, for - sake thee? Take it to the Lord in prayer;
All be-cause we do not car - ry Ev - ery-thing to God in prayer.
Je - sus knows our ev - ery weak-ness; Take it to the Lord in prayer.
In His arms He'll take and shield thee, Thou wilt find a sol-ace there.
A-MEN.

'Tis the Blessed Hour of Prayer

332

DOANE. 13. 12. 13. 13. with Refrain.

FANNY J. CROSBY, 1823–1915

WILLIAM H. DOANE, 1831–1915

In moderate time

1. 'Tis the bless-ed hour of pray'r, when our hearts low-ly bend, And we gath-er to Je-sus, our Sav-iour and Friend; If we come to Him in faith, His pro-tec-tion to share, What a balm for the wea-ry! O how
2. 'Tis the bless-ed hour of pray'r, when the Sav-iour draws near, With a ten-der com-pas-sion, His chil-dren to hear; When He tells us we may cast at His feet ev-'ry care, What a balm for the wea-ry! O how
3. 'Tis the bless-ed hour of pray'r, when the temp-ted and tried To the Sav-iour who loves them their sor-rows con-fide; With a sym-pa-thiz-ing heart He re-moves ev-'ry care; What a balm for the wea-ry! O how
4. 'Tis the bless-ed hour of pray'r; trust-ing Him, we be-lieve That the bless-ing we're need-ing we'll sure-ly re-ceive; In the ful-ness of this trust we shall lose ev-'ry care; What a balm for the wea-ry! O how

sweet to be there!

REFRAIN

Bless-ed hour of pray'r, bless-ed hour of pray'r;

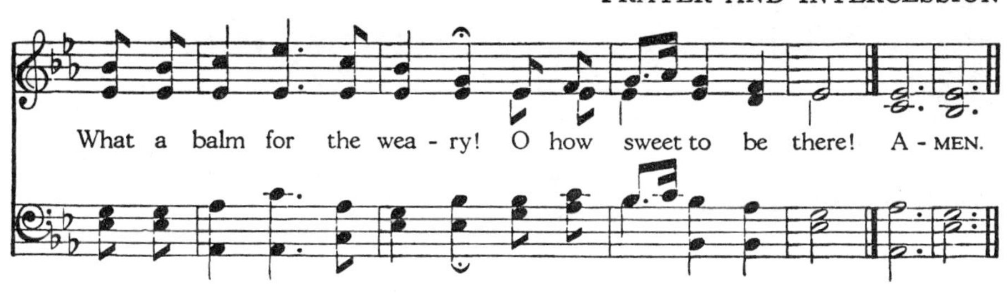
What a balm for the wea - ry! O how sweet to be there! A - MEN.

In the Hour of Trial

PENITENCE. 6. 5. 6. 5. D.

333

JAMES MONTGOMERY, 1771–1854
Alt. by FRANCES A. HUTTON, 1811–1877

SPENCER LANE, 1843–1903

In moderate time

1. In the hour of tri - al, Je - sus, plead for me; Lest by base de - ni - al,
2. With for - bid-den pleas-ures Would this vain world charm, Or its sor-did treas-ures
3. Should Thy mer - cy send me Sor - row, toil, and woe, Or should pain at-tend me
4. When my last hour com-eth, Fraught with strife and pain, When my dust re-turn - eth

I de-part from Thee. When Thou see'st me wa - ver, With a look re - call,
Spread to work me harm; Bring to my re-mem-brance Sad Geth-sem-a - ne,
On my path be - low, Grant that I may nev - er Fail Thy hand to see:
To the dust a - gain; On Thy truth re - ly - ing, Thro' that mor-tal strife:

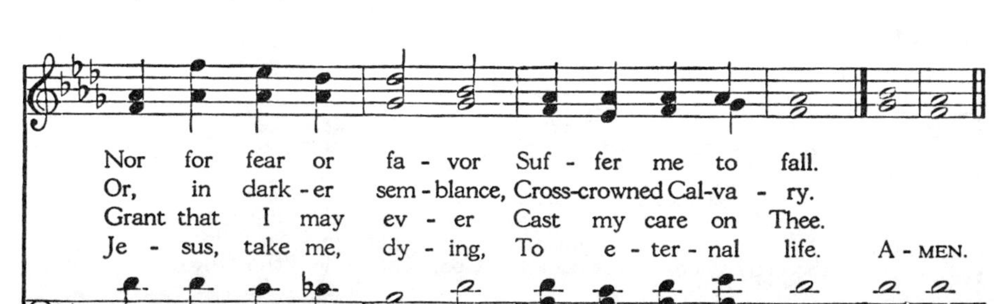
Nor for fear or fa - vor Suf - fer me to fall.
Or, in dark - er sem - blance, Cross-crowned Cal-va - ry.
Grant that I may ev - er Cast my care on Thee.
Je - sus, take me, dy - ing, To e - ter - nal life. A - MEN.

While Thee I Seek, Protecting Power

334

BEATITUDO. C. M.

HELEN M. WILLIAMS, 1762–1827

JOHN B. DYKES, 1823–1876

In moderate time

1. While thee I seek, pro - tect - ing Power, Be my vain
2. Thy love the powers of thought be-stowed; To thee my
3. In each e - vent of life, how clear Thy rul - ing
4. In ev - ery joy that crowns my days, In ev - 'ry
wish - es stilled; And may this con - se - crat - ed
thoughts would soar: Thy mer - cy o'er my life has
hand I see; Each bless - ing to my soul more
pain I bear, My heart shall find de - light in
hour With bet - ter hopes be filled.
flowed; That mer - cy I a - dore.
dear Be - cause con - ferred by thee.
praise, Or seek re - lief in prayer. A - MEN.

Prayer Is the Soul's Sincere Desire

335

NAOMI. C.M.

HANS G. NAEGELI, 1768–1836
Arr. by LOWELL MASON, 1792–1872

JAMES MONTGOMERY, 1771–1854

In moderate time

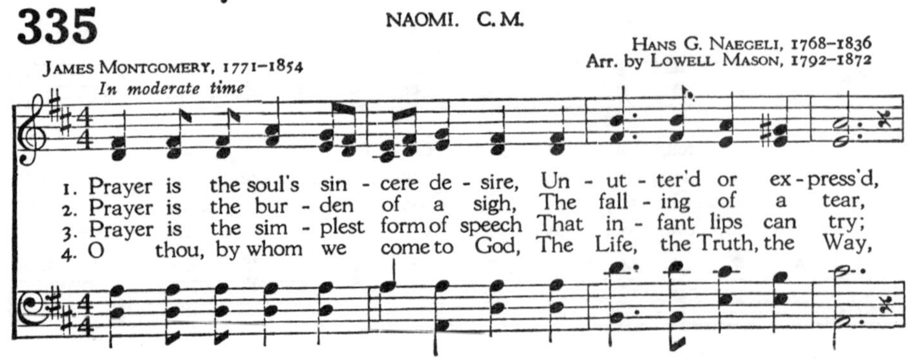
1. Prayer is the soul's sin - cere de - sire, Un - ut - ter'd or ex - press'd,
2. Prayer is the bur - den of a sigh, The fall - ing of a tear,
3. Prayer is the sim - plest form of speech That in - fant lips can try;
4. O thou, by whom we come to God, The Life, the Truth, the Way,

The mo-tion of a hid-den fire That trem-bles in the breast.
The up-ward glanc-ing of an eye When none but God is near.
Pray'r the sub-lim - est strains that reach The Ma - jes - ty on high.
The path of prayer thy - self hast trod; Lord, teach us how to pray. A - MEN.

Hear Us, Our Father!

CURFEW. 11. 10. 11. 10.

336

Anonymous

FREDERICK C. MAKER, 1844–1927

In moderate time, with flowing rhythm

1. Hear us, our Fa - ther! we know thou wilt hear us; Nor need our voic - es as - cend far a - way; Thou art a - round us, be - side us, with - in us: Thou wilt at - tend when we ear - nest - ly pray.
2. Love us, our Fa - ther! we know thou wilt love us; We are thy chil-dren, we turn un - to thee; For all a - round us, with - in us, a - bove us, Proofs of thine in - fin - ite kind - ness we see.
3. Aid us, our Fa - ther! we know thou wilt aid us; We are so fee - ble, and thou art so strong; Al - might - y Pow - er that made us and keeps us, Thou wilt pro - tect us from dan - ger and wrong.
4. Hear us, our Fa - ther! and help us and love us, Till more and more of thy - self we shall know; Wheth-er we go to the bright world a - bove us, Or stay to serve thee in homes here be - low. A - MEN.

Sweet Hour of Prayer, Sweet Hour of Prayer

337 WALFORD. L. M. D.

William W. Walford — William B. Bradbury, 1816–1868

In moderate time

1. Sweet hour of prayer! sweet hour of prayer! That calls me from a world of care,
2. Sweet hour of prayer! sweet hour of prayer! The joys I feel, the bliss I share,
3. Sweet hour of prayer! sweet hour of prayer! Thy wings shall my pe - ti - tion bear
And bids me at my Fa-ther's throne Make all my wants and wish-es known;
Of those whose anx-ious spir - its burn With strong de-sires for thy re - turn!
To Him whose truth and faith-ful - ness En-gage the wait -ing soul to bless;
In sea - sons of dis-tress and grief, My soul has oft - en found re - lief;
With such I has - ten to the place Where God my Sav - iour shows His face,
And since He bids me seek His face, Be - lieve His Word and trust His grace,
And oft es-caped the tempt-er's snare, By thy re - turn, sweet hour of prayer!
And glad - ly take my sta - tion there, And wait for thee, sweet hour of prayer!
I'll cast on Him my ev - ery care, And wait for thee, sweet hour of prayer! A-MEN.

O Gracious Father of Mankind

ST. LEONARD (HILES). C. M. D.

338

HENRY HALLAM TWEEDY, 1868– HENRY HILES, 1826–1904

In moderate time
1. O gra-cious Fa-ther of man-kind, Our spir-its' un-seen Friend,
2. Thou hear-est these—the good and ill—Deep bur-ied in each breast;
3. Our best is but Thy-self in us, Our high-est tho't Thy will;
4. Thou seek-est us in love and truth More than our minds seek Thee;
High heav-en's Lord, our hearts' dear Guest, To Thee our pray'rs as-cend.
The se-cret tho't, the hid-den plan, Wro't out or un-ex-pressed.
To hear Thy voice we need but love And lis-ten, and be still.
Thro' o-pen gates Thy pow'r flows in Like flood-tides from the sea.
Thou dost not wait till hu-man speech Thy gifts di-vine im-plore;
O, cleanse our pray'rs from hu-man dross! At-tune our lives to Thee,
We would not bend Thy will to ours, But blend our wills with Thine;
No more we seek Thee from a-far, Nor ask Thee for a sign,
Our dreams, our aims, our work, our lives Are pray'rs Thou lov-est more.
Un-til we la-bor for those gifts We ask on bend-ed knee.
Not beat with cries on heav-en's doors, But live Thy life di-vine.
Con-tent to pray in life and love And toil, till all are Thine.
A-MEN.

Jesus, Keep Me Near the Cross

339

NEAR THE CROSS. 7. 6. 7. 6. with Refrain

FANNY J. CROSBY, 1823–1915 — WILLIAM H. DOANE, 1831–1915

In moderate time

1. Je - sus, keep me near the cross: There a pre-cious foun-tain, Free to all, a healing stream, Flows from Calv'ry's mountain.
2. Near the cross, a trembling soul, Love and mer - cy found me; There the bright and Morn - ing Star Sheds its beams a-round me.
3. Near the cross! O Lamb of God, Bring its scenes be - fore me; Help me walk from day to day, With its shad-ow o'er me.
REFRAIN
In the cross, in the cross, Be my glo - ry ev - er, Till my raptured soul shall find Rest beyond the riv - er. A - MEN.

I Do Not Ask, O Lord, That Life May Be

340

SUBMISSION. 10. 4. 10. 4.

ADELAIDE A. PROCTOR, 1825–1864 — ALBERT L. PEACE, 1844–1912

In moderate time

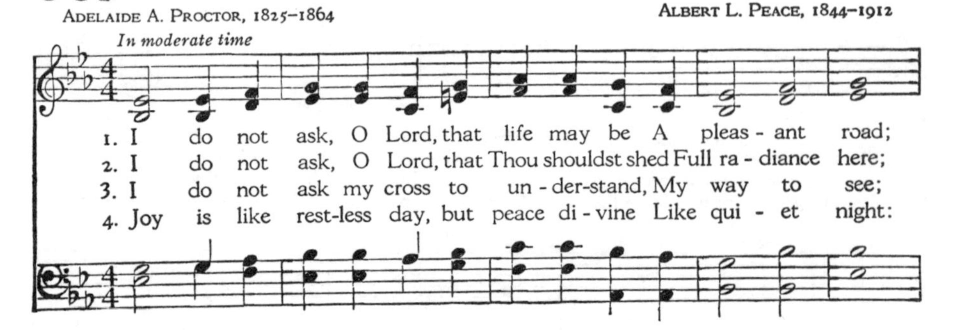
1. I do not ask, O Lord, that life may be A pleas - ant road;
2. I do not ask, O Lord, that Thou shouldst shed Full ra - diance here;
3. I do not ask my cross to un - der-stand, My way to see;
4. Joy is like rest-less day, but peace di - vine Like qui - et night:

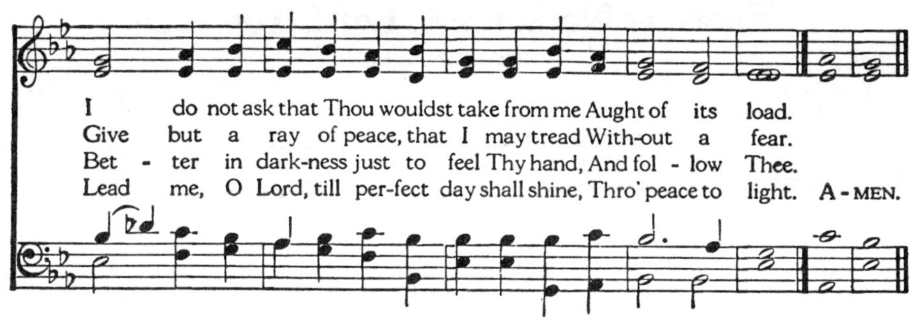

I do not ask that Thou wouldst take from me Aught of its load.
Give but a ray of peace, that I may tread With-out a fear.
Bet - ter in dark-ness just to feel Thy hand, And fol - low Thee.
Lead me, O Lord, till per-fect day shall shine, Thro' peace to light. A - MEN.

I Need Thee Every Hour

I NEED THEE. 6. 4. 6. 4. with Refrain

341

ANNIE S. HAWKES, 1835–1918

ROBERT LOWRY, 1826–1899

In moderate time
1. I need Thee ev - ery hour, Most gra - cious Lord; No ten-der voice like Thine
2. I need Thee ev - ery hour; Stay Thou near by; Temp-ta-tions lose their power
3. I need Thee ev - ery hour, In joy or pain; Come quick-ly and a - bide,
4. I need Thee ev - ery hour; Teach me Thy will; And Thy rich prom-is - es
REFRAIN
Can peace af - ford. I need Thee, O I need Thee, Ev - ery hour I
When Thou art nigh.
Or life is vain.
In me ful - fill.
need Thee; O bless me now, my Sav-iour, I come to Thee! A - MEN.

There Is No Sorrow, Lord, Too Light

342
WIGTOWN. C. M.
JANE CREWDSON, 1809–1863
SCOTTISH PSALTER, 1635
Moderately slow
1. There is no sor - row, Lord, too light To bring in prayer to Thee;
2. Thou, who hast trod the thorn-y road, Wilt share each small dis - tress;
3. There is no se - cret sigh we breathe But meets Thine ear di - vine;
4. Life's ills with - out, sin's strife with - in, The heart would o - ver - flow,
There is no anx - ious care too slight To wake Thy sym - pa - thy.
The love which bore the great - er load Will not re - fuse the less.
And ev - ery cross grows light be - neath The shad - ow, Lord, of Thine.
But for that love which died for sin, That love which wept with woe.
A-MEN.
Purer in Heart, O God
343
PURER IN HEART. 6. 4. 6. 4. 6. 6. 4. 4.
MRS. ANNA L. DAVISON
JAMES H. FILLMORE, 1849-1941
In moderate time
1. Pur - er in heart, O God, Help me to be; May I de - vote my life Whol - ly to Thee. Watch Thou my way - ward feet,
2. Pur - er in heart, O God, Help me to be; Teach me to do Thy will Most lov - ing - ly. Be Thou my Friend and Guide,
3. Pur - er in heart, O God, Help me to be; That I Thy ho - ly face One day may see. Keep me from se - cret sin,

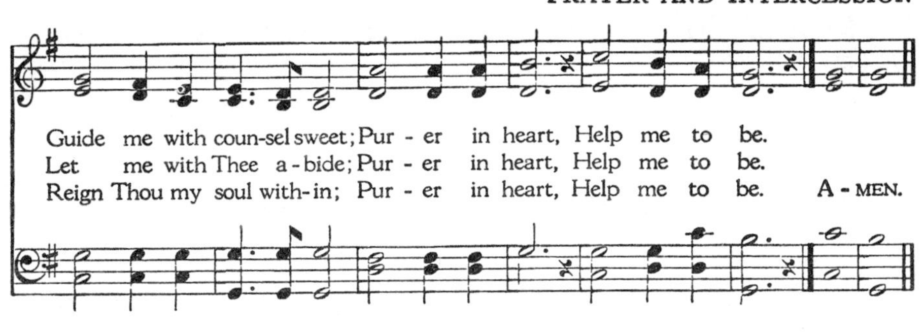
Guide me with coun-sel sweet; Pur - er in heart, Help me to be.
Let me with Thee a - bide; Pur - er in heart, Help me to be.
Reign Thou my soul with-in; Pur - er in heart, Help me to be. A - MEN.

Father Almighty, Bless Us With Thy Blessing

FLEMMING. 11. 11. 11. 5.

344

BERWICK HYMNAL, 1886

FRIEDRICH F. FLEMMING, 1778–1813

In moderate time

1. Fa - ther Al-might - y, bless us with Thy bless - ing, An - swer in
2. Shep - herd of souls, who bring - est all who seek thee To pas - tures
3. Fa - ther of mer - cy, from thy watch and keep - ing No place can
love thy chil - dren's sup - pli - ca - tion; Hear thou our prayer, the
green be - side the peace - ful wa - ters; Ten - der - est guide, in
part, nor hour of time re - move us; Give us thy good, and
spo - ken and un - spo - ken; Hear us, our Fa - ther.
ways of cheer - ful du - ty, Lead us, good Shep - herd.
save us from our e - vil, In - fi - nite Spir - it. A - MEN.

Father, in Thy Mysterious Presence Kneeling

345

HENLEY. 11. 10. 11. 10.

SAMUEL JOHNSON, 1822–1882 | LOWELL MASON, 1792–1872

In moderate time

1. Fa - ther, in Thy mys - te - rious pres - ence kneel - ing,
2. Lord, we have wan - dered forth through doubt and sor - row,
3. Now, Fa - ther, now in Thy dear pres - ence kneel - ing,

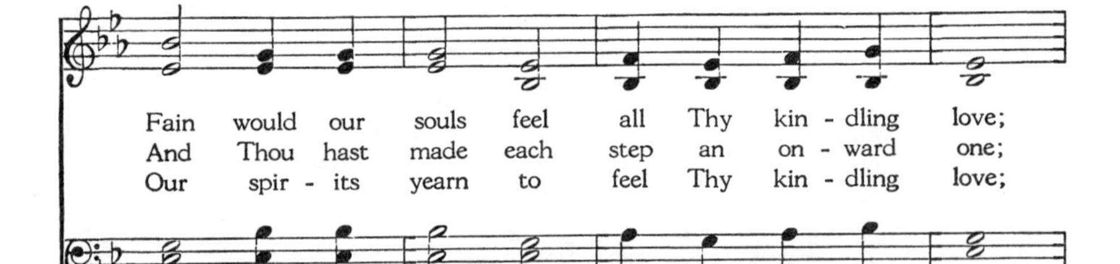
Fain would our souls feel all Thy kin - dling love;
And Thou hast made each step an on - ward one;
Our spir - its yearn to feel Thy kin - dling love;

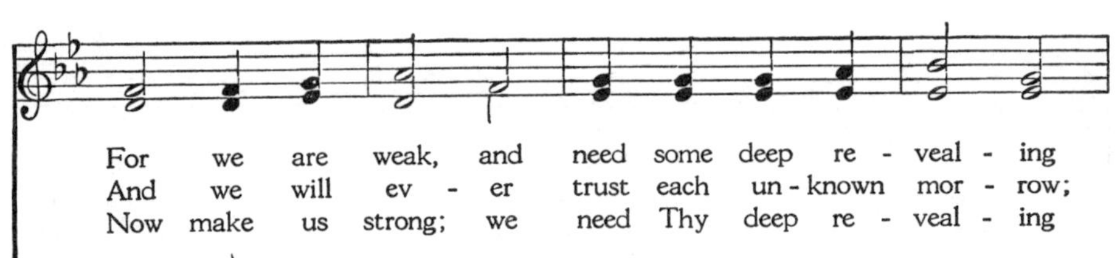
For we are weak, and need some deep re - veal - ing
And we will ev - er trust each un - known mor - row;
Now make us strong; we need Thy deep re - veal - ing

Of trust and strength and calm - ness from a - bove.
Thou wilt sus - tain us till its work is done.
Of trust and strength and calm - ness from a - bove. A - MEN.

Take Time to Be Holy

HOLINESS. 6. 5. 6. 5. D.

346

W. D. LONGSTAFF, 1822–1894

GEORGE C. STEBBINS, 1846–

In moderate time

1. Take time to be ho - ly, Speak oft with thy Lord;
2. Take time to be ho - ly, The world rush - es on;
3. Take time to be ho - ly, Let Him be thy Guide,
4. Take time to be ho - ly, Be calm in thy soul;
A - bide in Him al - ways, And feed on His word.
Spend much time in se - cret With Je - sus a - lone.
And run not be - fore Him, What - ev - er be - tide;
Each thought and each mo - tive Be - neath His con - trol;
Make friends of God's chil - dren; Help those who are weak;
By look - ing to Je - sus, Like Him thou shalt be;
In joy or in sor - row, Still fol - low thy Lord,
Thus led by His Spir - it To foun - tains of love,
For - get - ting in noth - ing His bless - ing to seek.
Thy friends in thy con - duct His like - ness shall see.
And, look - ing to Je - sus, Still trust in His word.
Thou soon shalt be fit - ted For serv - ice a - bove.
A - MEN.

O Thou Great Friend to All the Sons of Men

347
LANGRAN. 10. 10. 10. 10.
THEODORE PARKER, 1810–1860
JAMES LANGRAN, 1835–1909
In moderate time
1. O Thou great Friend to all the sons of men,
2. Thee would I sing: Thy truth is still the light
3. Yes, Thou art still the Life; Thou art the Way
Who once ap - pear'dst in hum - blest guise be - low,
Which guides the na - tions grop - ing on their way,
The ho - liest know— Light, Life, and Way of heaven;
Sin to re - buke, to break the cap - tive's chain,
Stum - bling and fall - ing in dis - as - trous night,
And they who dear - est hope and deep - est pray
To call Thy breth - ren forth from want and woe,
Yet hop - ing ev - er for the per - fect day.
Toil by the truth, life, way that Thou hast given.
A - MEN.

Faith of Our Fathers! Living Still

ST. CATHERINE. 8. 8. 8. 8. 8. 8.

348

FREDERICK W. FABER, 1814–1863
In moderate time
HENRY F. HEMY, 1818–1888
and JAMES G. WALTON, 1821–1905
1. Faith of our fa - thers! liv - ing still In spite of dun - geon, fire, and sword, O how our hearts beat high with joy When-e'er we hear that glo - rious word! Faith of our fa - thers, ho - ly faith! We will be true to thee till death.
2. Faith of our fa - thers! we will strive To win all na - tions un - to thee, And through the truth that comes from God Man-kind shall then be tru - ly free. Faith of our fa - thers, ho - ly faith! We will be true to thee till death.
3. Faith of our fa - thers! we will love Both friend and foe in all our strife, And preach thee, too, as love knows how By kind - ly words and vir - tuous life: Faith of our fa - thers, ho - ly faith! We will be true to thee till death.
A-MEN.

349 Strong Son of God, Immortal Love

ST. CRISPIN. L. M.

ALFRED TENNYSON, 1809–1892 — GEORGE J. ELVEY, 1816–1893

In moderate time

1. Strong Son of God, im - mor - tal Love, Whom we, that have not
2. Thou seem - est hu - man and di - vine, The high - est, ho - liest
3. Our lit - tle sys - tems have their day; They have their day and
4. We have but faith, we can - not know, For knowl-edge is of
5. Let knowl-edge grow from more to more, But more of rev - erence

seen Thy face, By faith, and faith a - lone, em -
man - hood, Thou; Our wills are ours, we know not
cease to be; They are but bro - ken lights of
things we see; And yet we trust it comes from
in us dwell; That mind and soul, ac - cord - ing

brace, Be - liev - ing where we can - not prove.
how; Our wills are ours, to make them Thine.
Thee, And Thou, O Lord, art more than they.
Thee, A beam in dark - ness: let it grow.
well, May make one mu - sic as be - fore. A - MEN.

350 O Holy Saviour, Friend Unseen

FLEMMING. 8. 8. 8. 6.

CHARLOTTE ELLIOTT, 1789–1871 — FRIEDRICH F. FLEMMING, 1778–1813

Moderately slow

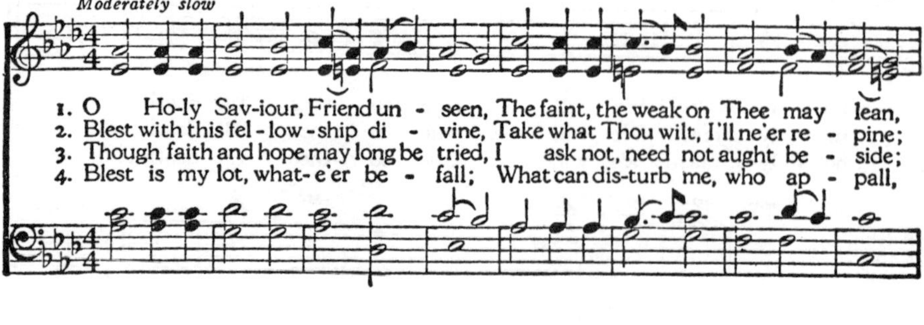

1. O Ho-ly Sav-iour, Friend un - seen, The faint, the weak on Thee may lean,
2. Blest with this fel - low - ship di - vine, Take what Thou wilt, I'll ne'er re - pine;
3. Though faith and hope may long be tried, I ask not, need not aught be - side;
4. Blest is my lot, what- e'er be - fall; What can dis-turb me, who ap - pall,

Help me, throughout life's vary-ing scene, By faith to cling to Thee.
E'en as the branch-es to the vine, My soul would cling to Thee.
How safe, how calm, how sat - is - fied, The souls that cling to Thee!
While as my Strength, my Rock, my All, Sav - iour, I cling to Thee? A-MEN.

Our Faith Is in the Christ Who Walks

WAREHAM. L. M.

351

THOMAS CURTIS CLARK, 1877–

WILLIAM KNAPP, 1698–1768

In moderate time

1. Our faith is in the Christ who walks With men to - day, in street and mart; The con - stant Friend who thinks and talks With those who seek Him with the heart.
2. His Gos - pel calls for liv - ing men, With sing - ing blood and minds a - lert; Strong men, who fall to rise a - gain, Who strive and bleed, with cour - age girt.
3. We serve no God whose work is done, Who rests with - in His firm - a - ment; Our God, His la - bors but be - gun, Toils ev - er - more, with power un - spent.
4. God was and is and e'er shall be; Christ lived and loved and loves us still; And man goes for - ward, proud and free, God's pres - ent pur - pose to ful - fill. A - MEN.

Words used by permission of Thomas Curtis Clark. From "One Thousand Quotable Poems."

Jesus, These Eyes Have Never Seen

352

SAWLEY. C. M.
RAY PALMER, 1808–1887
JAMES WALCH, 1837–1901
Rather slow
1. Je - sus, these eyes have nev - er seen That ra - diant form of Thine;
2. I see Thee not, I hear Thee not, Yet art Thou oft with me;
3. Yet, though I have not seen, and still Must rest in faith a - lone,
4. When death these mor-tal eyes shall seal, And still this throb-bing heart,
The veil of sense hangs dark be-tween Thy bless-ed face and mine.
And earth hath ne'er so dear a spot As where I meet with Thee.
I love Thee, dear - est Lord,—and will, Un-seen, but not un-known.
The rend-ing veil shall Thee re - veal, All glo-rious as Thou art! A - MEN.
O Love Divine, That Stooped to Share
353
QUEBEC (HESPERUS). L. M.
OLIVER W. HOLMES, 1809–1894
HENRY BAKER, 1835–1910
In moderate time
1. O Love di - vine, that stooped to share Our sharp-est pang, our bit - t'rest tear!
2. Though long the wea - ry way we tread, And sor - row crown each lingering year,
3. When drooping pleas-ure turns to grief, And trem-bling faith is changed to fear,
4. On Thee we fling our bur-dening woe, O Love di - vine, for - ev - er dear!
On Thee we cast each earth-born care; We smile at pain while Thou art near.
No path we shun, no dark-ness dread, Our hearts still whis-p'ring, "Thou art near!"
The murmuring wind, the quivering leaf, Shall soft-ly tell us Thou art near!
Con-tent to suf - fer while we know, Liv-ing and dy - ing, Thou art near! A - MEN.

All My Hope on God Is Founded

354

NEANDER. 8. 7. 8. 7. 6. 7.

JOACHIM NEANDER, 1650–1680
From Chorale UNSER HERRSCHER, by JOACHIM NEANDER, 1650–1680
In moderate time, with dignity
1. All my hope on God is founded; He doth still my trust renew. Me thro' change and chance he guideth, Only good and only true. God unknown, he alone Calls my heart to be his own.
2. Pride of man and earthly glory, Sword and crown betray his trust; What with care and toil he buildeth, Tow'r and temple fall to dust. But God's pow'r, hour by hour, Is my temple and my tow'r.
3. God's great goodness aye endureth, Deep his wisdom, passing thought; Splendor, light and life attend him, Beauty springeth out of nought. Evermore, from his store New-born worlds rise and adore.
A-MEN.

355 My Faith Looks Up to Thee

OLIVET. 6. 6. 4. 6. 6. 6. 4.

RAY PALMER, 1808–1887 LOWELL MASON, 1792–1872

In moderate time

1. My faith looks up to Thee, Thou Lamb of Cal - va - ry,
2. May Thy rich grace im - part Strength to my faint - ing heart,
3. While life's dark maze I tread, And griefs a - round me spread,
4. When ends life's tran - sient dream, When death's cold, sul - len stream

Sav - iour di - vine! Now hear me while I pray, Take all my
My zeal in - spire; As Thou hast died for me, O may my
Be Thou my guide; Bid dark - ness turn to day, Wipe sor - row's
Shall o'er me roll; Blest Sav - iour, then, in love, Fear and dis -

guilt a - way, O let me from this day Be whol - ly Thine!
love to Thee Pure, warm, and change-less be, A liv - ing fire!
tears a - way, Nor let me ev - er stray From Thee a - side.
trust re-move; O bear me safe a-bove, A ran - somed soul! A-MEN.

356 When Courage Fails and Faith Burns Low

ST. PETER. C. M.

FREDERICK L. HOSMER, 1840–1928 ALEXANDER R. REINAGLE, 1799–1877

In moderate time

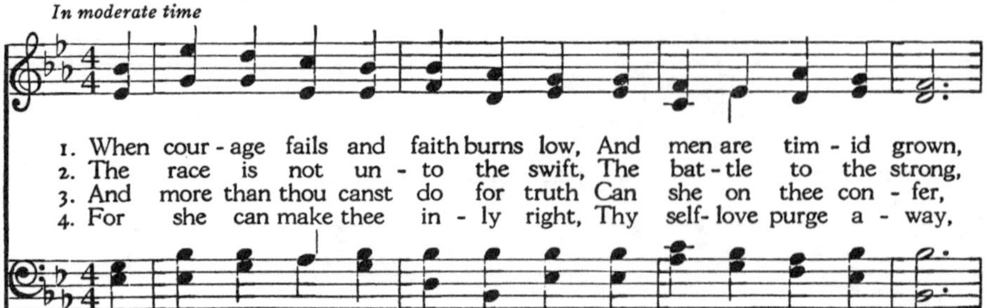

1. When cour - age fails and faith burns low, And men are tim - id grown,
2. The race is not un - to the swift, The bat - tle to the strong,
3. And more than thou canst do for truth Can she on thee con - fer,
4. For she can make thee in - ly right, Thy self- love purge a - way,

Hold fast thy loy-al-ty and know That truth still mov-eth on.
When dawn her judgment-days that sift The claims of right and wrong.
If thou, O heart, but give thy youth And man-hood un-to her;
And lead thee in the path whose light Shines to the per-fect day. A-MEN.
Jesus, Still Lead On
ST. HUBERT. 5. 5. 8. 8. 5. 5.
357
N. L. VON ZINZENDORF, 1700–1760
L. DARWALL, 1813–?
In moderate time
1. Je-sus, still lead on, Till our rest be won, And, al-though the way be cheer-less, We will fol-low, calm and fear-less Guide us by Thy hand, To our Fa-ther-land.
2. If the way be drear, If the foe be near, Let not faith-less fears o'er-take us, Let not faith and hope for-sake us; For, through ma-ny a foe To our home we go.
3. When we seek re-lief For a long-felt grief, When temp-ta-tions come al-lur-ing, Make us pa-tient and en-dur-ing; Show us that bright shore Where we weep no more.
4. Je-sus, still lead on, Till our rest be won: Heaven-ly Lead-er, still di-rect us, Still sup-port, con-sole, pro-tect us, Till we safe-ly stand In our Fa-ther-land. A-MEN.

The Son of God Goes Forth to War

358

ALL SAINTS. C. M. D.

REGINALD HEBER, 1783–1826 | HENRY S. CUTLER, 1824–1902

In martial rhythm

1. The Son of God goes forth to war, A king - ly crown to gain;
2. The mar - tyr first, whose ea - gle eye Could pierce be - yond the grave,
3. A glo - rious band, the cho - sen few On whom the Spir - it came,

His blood - red ban - ner streams a - far: Who fol - lows in His train?
Who saw his Mas - ter in the sky, And called on Him to save:
Twelve val - iant saints, their hope they knew, And mocked the cross and flame;

Who best can drink his cup of woe, Tri - umph-ant o - ver pain,
Like Him, with par - don on His tongue, In midst of mor - tal pain,
They climbed the steep as - cent of heav'n Thro' per - il, toil, and pain:

Who pa - tient bears his cross be - low, He fol - lows in His train.
He prayed for them that did the wrong: Who fol - lows in His train?
O God, to us may grace be given To fol - low in their train! A - MEN.

March On, O Soul, With Strength

ARTHUR'S SEAT. 6. 6. 6. 6. 8. 8.

359

George T. Coster, 1835–1912

Arr. from John Goss, 1800–1880

In march rhythm

1. March on, O soul, with strength! Like those strong men of old
2. The sons of fa - thers we By whom our faith is taught
3. March on, O soul, with strength, As strong the bat - tle rolls!
4. Not long the con - flict: soon The ho - ly war shall cease,
Who 'gainst en - thron - ed wrong Stood con - fi - dent and bold;
To fear no ill, to fight The ho - ly fight they fought:
'Gainst lies and lusts and wrongs, Let cour - age rule our souls:
Faith's war - fare end - ed, won The home of end - less peace!
Who, thrust in prison or cast to flame,
He - ro - ic war - riors, ne'er from Christ
In keen - est strife, Lord, may we stand,
Look up! the vic - tor's crown at length!
Still made their glo - - - ry in Thy name.
By an - y lure or guile en - ticed.
Up - held and strength - ened by Thy hand.
March on, O soul, march on, with strength!
A - MEN.

"Are Ye Able," Said the Master

360

BEACON HILL. Irregular

EARL MARLATT, 1892–

HARRY S. MASON, 1881–

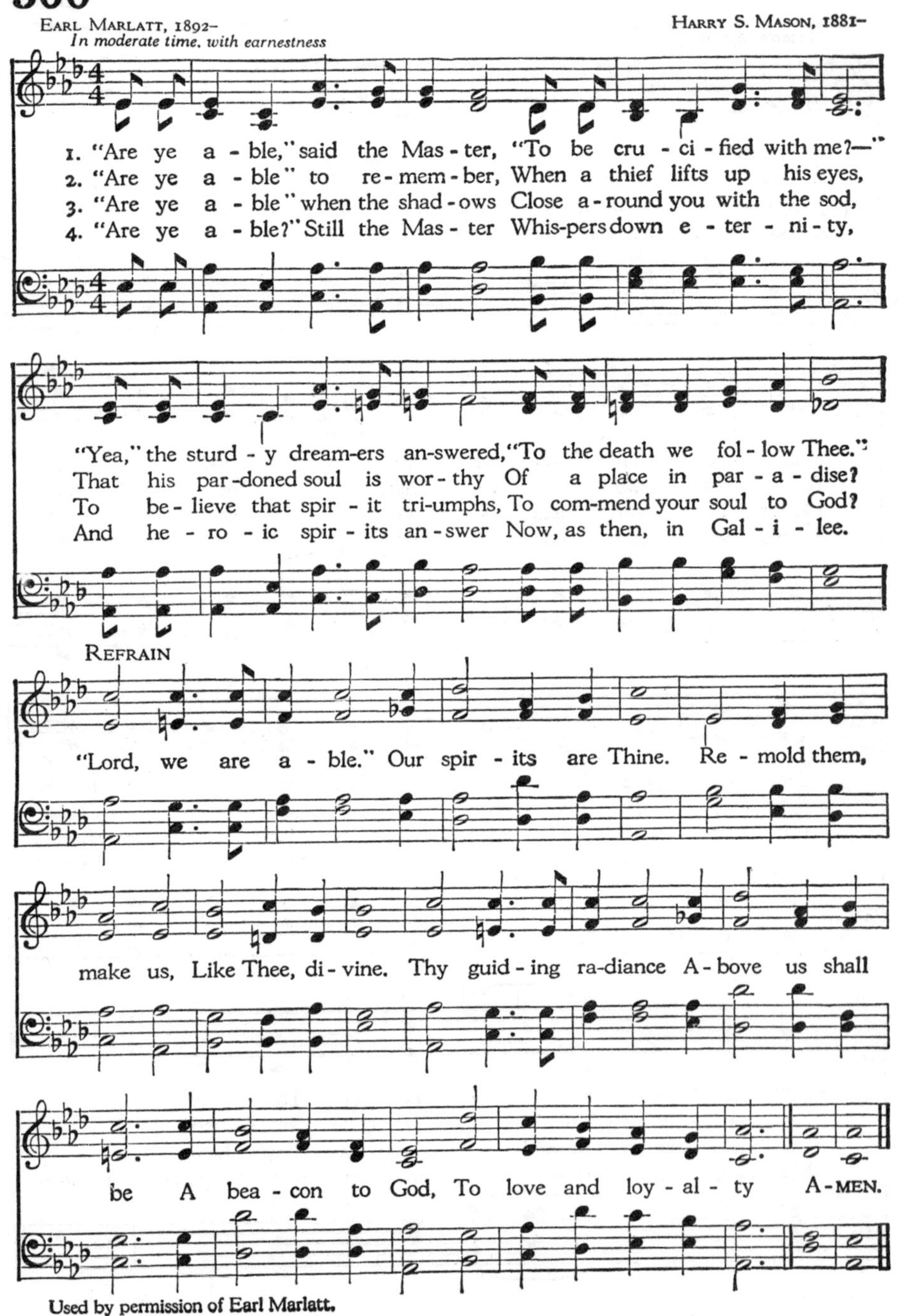
In moderate time, with earnestness
1. "Are ye a - ble," said the Mas - ter, "To be cru - ci - fied with me?—"
2. "Are ye a - ble" to re - mem - ber, When a thief lifts up his eyes,
3. "Are ye a - ble" when the shad - ows Close a - round you with the sod,
4. "Are ye a - ble?" Still the Mas - ter Whis-pers down e - ter - ni - ty,
"Yea," the sturd - y dream-ers an-swered, "To the death we fol - low Thee."
That his par-doned soul is wor - thy Of a place in par - a - dise?
To be - lieve that spir - it tri-umphs, To com-mend your soul to God?
And he - ro - ic spir - its an - swer Now, as then, in Gal - i - lee.
REFRAIN
"Lord, we are a - ble." Our spir - its are Thine. Re - mold them,
make us, Like Thee, di - vine. Thy guid - ing ra-diance A - bove us shall
be A bea - con to God, To love and loy - al - ty A - MEN.

Used by permission of Earl Marlatt.

I Would Be True

PEEK. 11. 10. 11. 10.

361

HOWARD ARNOLD WALTER, 1883–1918
JOSEPH YATES PEEK
In moderate time
1. I would be true, for there are those who trust me; I would be pure, for there are those who care; I would be strong, for there is much to suffer; I would be brave, for there is much to dare, I would be brave, for there is much to dare.
2. I would be friend of all— the foe, the friend-less; I would be giv-ing, and for-get the gift; I would be hum-ble, for I know my weak-ness; I would look up, and laugh, and love, and lift, I would look up, and laugh, and love, and lift.
3. I would be learn-ing, day by day, the les-sons My heaven-ly Fa-ther gives me in his Word; I would be quick to hear his light-est whis-per, And prompt and glad to do the things I've heard, And prompt and glad to do the things I've heard.
A-MEN.

O Young and Fearless Prophet

362

BLAIRGOWRIE (Dykes). 13. 13. 13. 13.

S. RALPH HARLOW, 1885– JOHN B. DYKES, 1823–1876

In moderate time

1. O young and fear - less Proph - et of an - cient Gal - i - lee:
2. We mar - vel at the pur - pose that held Thee to Thy course
3. O help us stand un - swerv - ing a - gainst war's blood - y way,
4. Cre - ate in us the splen - dor that dawns when hearts are kind,
5. O young and fear - less Proph - et, we need Thy pres - ence here,

Thy life is still a sum - mons to serve hu - man - i - ty,
While ev - er on the hill - top be - fore Thee loomed the cross;
Where hate and lust and false - hood hold back Christ's ho - ly sway;
That knows not race nor sta - tion as boun - daries of the mind;
A - mid our pride and glo - ry to see Thy face ap - pear;

To make our thoughts and ac - tions less prone to please the crowd,
Thy stead - fast face set for - ward where love and du - ty shone,
For - bid false love of coun - try, that blinds us to His call
That learns to val - ue beau - ty, in heart, or brain, or soul,
Once more to hear Thy chal - lenge a - bove our noi - sy day,

To stand with hum - ble cour - age for Truth with hearts un - cowed.
While we be - tray so quick - ly and leave Thee there a - lone.
Who lifts a - bove the na - tion the broth - er - hood of all.
And longs to bind God's chil - dren in - to one per - fect whole.
A - gain to lead us for - ward a - long God's ho - ly way. A-MEN.

Lead On, O King Eternal

LANCASHIRE. 7. 6. 7. 6. D.

363

ERNEST W. SHURTLEFF, 1862–1917

HENRY SMART, 1813–1879

With martial rhythm

1. Lead on, O King E - ter - nal, The day of march has come;
2. Lead on, O King E - ter - nal, Till sin's fierce war shall cease,
3. Lead on, O King E - ter - nal: We fol - low, not with fears,
Hence-forth in fields of con - quest Thy tents shall be our home:
And Ho - li - ness shall whis - per The sweet A - men of peace;
For glad-ness breaks like morn - ing Wher-e'er Thy face ap - pears;
Thro' days of prep - a - ra - tion Thy grace has made us strong,
For not with swords loud clash - ing, Nor roll of stir - ring drums;
Thy cross is lift - ed o'er us; We jour - ney in its light:
And now, O King E - ter - nal, We lift our bat - tle song.
With deeds of love and mer - cy, The heav'n-ly king-dom comes.
The crown a - waits the con - quest; Lead on, O God of might.
A-MEN.

He Who Would Valiant Be

364

ST. DUNSTAN'S. 6. 5. 6. 5. 6. 6. 6. 5.

JOHN BUNYAN, 1628–1688, alt. WINFRED DOUGLAS, 1867–

In moderate time, with great dignity
1. He who would val - iant be 'Gainst all dis - as - ter,
2. Who so be - set him round With dis - mal sto - ries,
3. Since, Lord, thou dost de - fend Us with thy Spir - it,
Let him in con - stan - cy Fol - low the Mas - ter.
Do but them - selves con - found, His strength the more is.
We know we at the end Shall life in - her - it.
There's no dis - cour - age-ment Shall make him once re - lent His
No foes shall stay his might, Tho' he with gi - ants fight; He
Then fan - cies, flee a - way! I'll fear not what men say, I'll
first a - vow'd in - tent To be a pil - grim.
will make good his right To be a pil - grim.
la - bor night and day To be a pil - grim. A - MEN.

O God of Truth, Whose Living Word

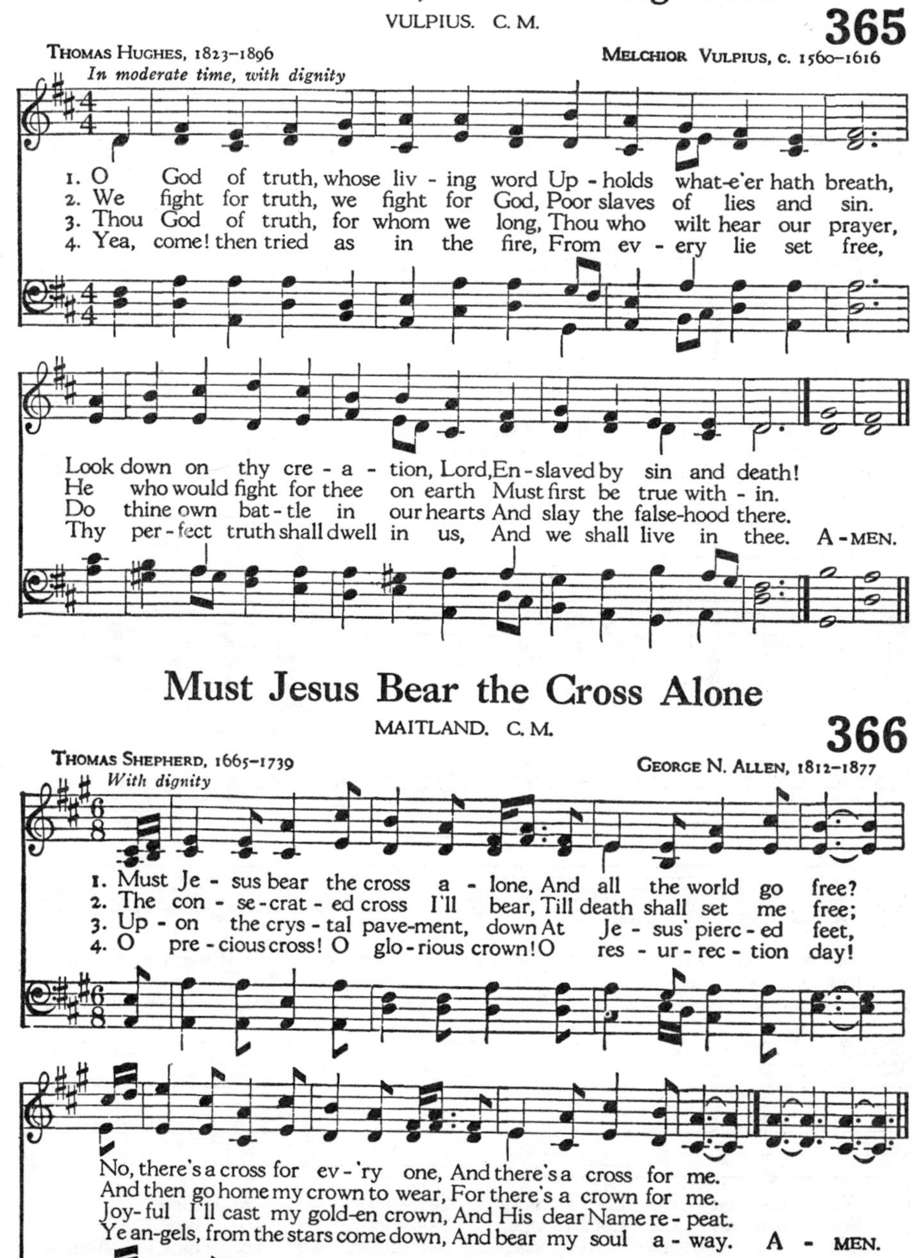
VULPIUS. C. M.
365
Thomas Hughes, 1823–1896
Melchior Vulpius, c. 1560–1616
In moderate time, with dignity
1. O God of truth, whose liv - ing word Up - holds what-e'er hath breath,
2. We fight for truth, we fight for God, Poor slaves of lies and sin.
3. Thou God of truth, for whom we long, Thou who wilt hear our prayer,
4. Yea, come! then tried as in the fire, From ev - ery lie set free,
Look down on thy cre - a - tion, Lord, En - slaved by sin and death!
He who would fight for thee on earth Must first be true with - in.
Do thine own bat - tle in our hearts And slay the false-hood there.
Thy per - fect truth shall dwell in us, And we shall live in thee. A - men.
Must Jesus Bear the Cross Alone
MAITLAND. C. M.
366
Thomas Shepherd, 1665–1739
George N. Allen, 1812–1877
With dignity
1. Must Je - sus bear the cross a - lone, And all the world go free?
2. The con - se - crat - ed cross I'll bear, Till death shall set me free;
3. Up - on the crys - tal pave-ment, down At Je - sus' pierc - ed feet,
4. O pre - cious cross! O glo - rious crown! O res - ur - rec - tion day!
No, there's a cross for ev - 'ry one, And there's a cross for me.
And then go home my crown to wear, For there's a crown for me.
Joy - ful I'll cast my gold-en crown, And His dear Name re - peat.
Ye an-gels, from the stars come down, And bear my soul a - way. A - men.

Who Is on The Lord's Side?

367
ARMAGEDDON. 6. 5. 6. 5. 12 L
FRANCES R. HAVERGAL, 1836–1879
JOHN GOSS, 1800–1880
In stately rhythm
1. Who is on the Lord's side? Who will serve the King?
2. Not for weight of glo - ry, Not for crown and palm,
3. Fierce may be the con - flict, Strong may be the foe,
Who will be His help - ers, Oth - er lives to bring? Who will leave the
En - ter we the ar - my, Raise the war - rior psalm; But for Love that
But the King's own ar - my None can o - ver - throw: Round His stand - ard
world's side? Who will face the foe? Who is on the Lord's side?
claim - eth Lives for whom He died: He whom Je - sus nam - eth
rang - ing, Vic - tory is se - cure; For His truth un - chang - ing
Who for Him will go? By Thy call of mer - cy, By Thy grace di - vine,
Must be on His side. By Thy love con - strain - ing, By Thy grace di - vine,
Makes the tri - umph sure. Joy - ful - ly en - list - ing By Thy grace di - vine,
We are on the Lord's side, Sav - iour, we are Thine.
We are on the Lord's side, Sav - iour, we are Thine.
We are on the Lord's side, Sav - iour, we are Thine. A-MEN.

Not in Dumb Resignation

SAVOY CHAPEL. 7. 6. 8. 6. D.

368

John Hay, 1838–1905, alt.
John B. Calkin, 1827–1905
In moderate time
1. Not in dumb res - ig - na - tion We lift our hands on high;
2. When ty - rant feet are tram - pling Up - on the com - mon weal,
3. Thy will! It strength-ens weak - ness, It bids the strong be just;
Not like the nerve-less fa - tal - ist Con - tent to trust and die:
Thou dost not bid us bend and writhe Be - neath the i - ron heel.
No lip to fawn, no hand to beg, No brow to seek the dust.
Our faith springs like the ea - gle, Who soars to meet the sun,
In thy name we as - sert our right By sword or tongue or pen,
Wher - ev - er man op - press - es man Be - neath thy lib - 'ral sun,
And cries ex - ult - ing un - to thee, O Lord, thy will be done!
And oft a peo-ple's wrath may flash Thy mes - sage un - to men.
O Lord, be there thine arm made bare, Thy right-eous will be done!
A-men.

Awake, My Soul, Stretch Every Nerve

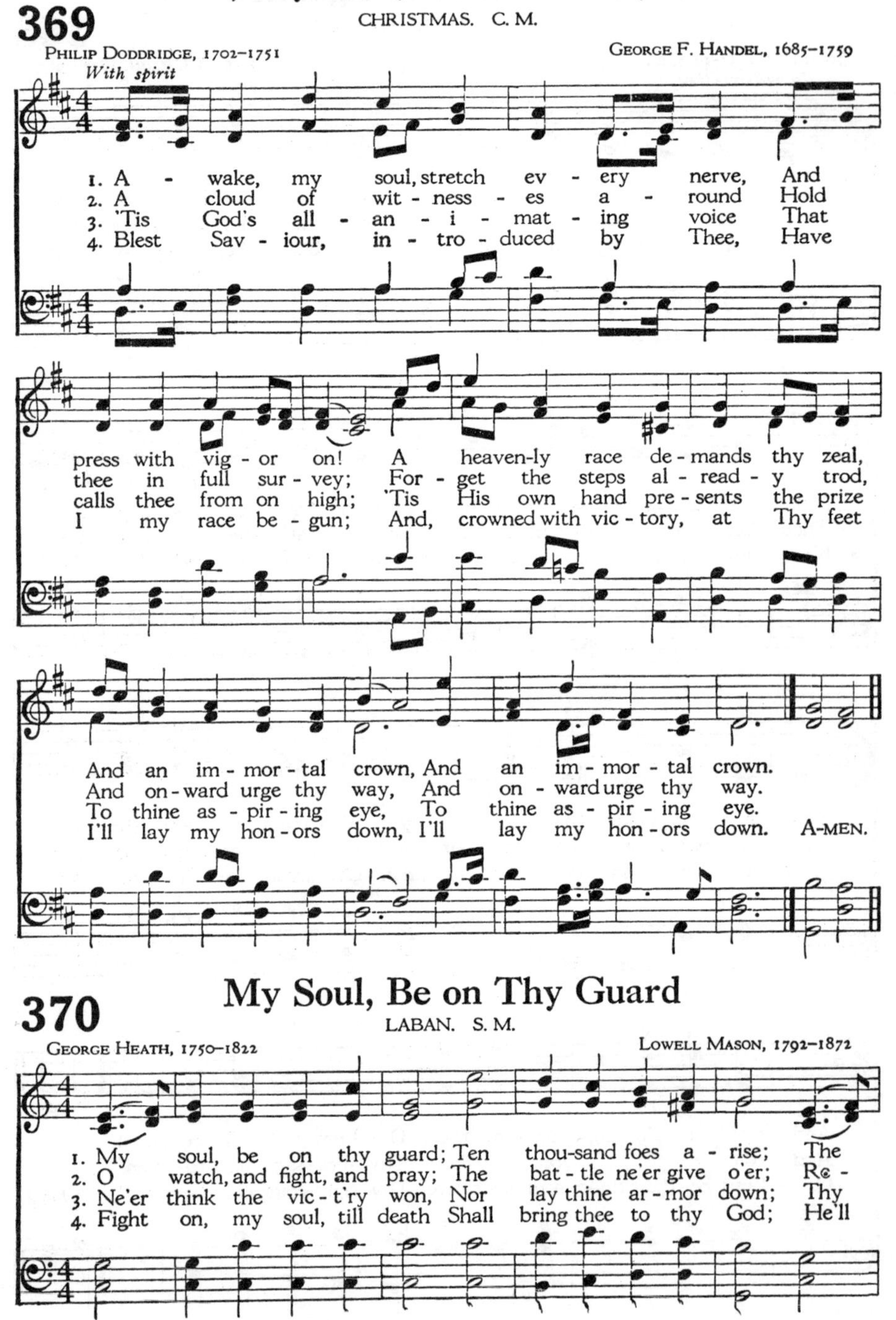
369
CHRISTMAS. C. M.
Philip Doddridge, 1702–1751
George F. Handel, 1685–1759
With spirit
1. A - wake, my soul, stretch ev - ery nerve, And
2. A cloud of wit - ness - es a - round Hold
3. 'Tis God's all - an - i - mat - ing voice That
4. Blest Sav - iour, in - tro - duced by Thee, Have
press with vig - or on! A heaven-ly race de - mands thy zeal,
thee in full sur - vey; For - get the steps al - read - y trod,
calls thee from on high; 'Tis His own hand pre - sents the prize
I my race be - gun; And, crowned with vic - tory, at Thy feet
And an im - mor - tal crown, And an im - mor - tal crown.
And on - ward urge thy way, And on - ward urge thy way.
To thine as - pir - ing eye, To thine as - pir - ing eye.
I'll lay my hon - ors down, I'll lay my hon - ors down. A-men.
370
My Soul, Be on Thy Guard
LABAN. S. M.
George Heath, 1750–1822
Lowell Mason, 1792–1872
1. My soul, be on thy guard; Ten thou-sand foes a - rise; The
2. O watch, and fight, and pray; The bat - tle ne'er give o'er; Re -
3. Ne'er think the vic - t'ry won, Nor lay thine ar - mor down; Thy
4. Fight on, my soul, till death Shall bring thee to thy God; He'll

CONFLICT AND COURAGE
hosts of sin are press - ing hard To draw thee from the skies.
new it bold - ly ev - 'ry day, And help di - vine im - plore.
ar - duous work will not be done Till thou ob - tain thy crown.
take thee, at thy part - ing breath, To His di - vine a - bode. A - MEN.
Stand Up, Stand Up for Jesus
371
WEBB. 7. 6. 7. 6. D.
GEORGE DUFFIELD, 1818–1888
GEORGE J. WEBB, 1803–1887
In moderate march time
1. Stand up, stand up for Je - sus, Ye sol - diers of the cross;
2. Stand up, stand up for Je - sus, The trum - pet call o - bey;
3. Stand up, stand up for Je - sus, Stand in His strength a - lone;
4. Stand up, stand up for Je - sus, The strife will not be long;
Lift high His roy - al ban - ner, It must not suf - fer loss:
Forth to the might - y con - flict, In this His glo - rious day:
The arm of flesh will fail you; Ye dare not trust your own:
This day the noise of bat - tle, The next the vic - tor's song:
From vic - t'ry un - to vic - t'ry His ar - my shall He lead,
"Ye that are men, now serve Him," A - gainst un - num - bered foes;
Put on the gos - pel ar - mor, And, watch - ing un - to pray'r,
To him that o - ver - com - eth, A crown of life shall be;
Till ev - 'ry foe is vanquished, And Christ is Lord in - deed.
Let cour - age rise with dan - ger, And strength to strength oppose.
Where du - ty calls, or dan - ger, Be nev - er want - ing there.
He with the King of glo - ry Shall reign e - ter - nal - ly. A - MEN.

372 Lift Up Your Hearts!

OLD 124TH. 10. 10. 10. 10.

H. MONTAGU BUTLER, 1833–1918

GENEVAN PSALTER, 1551

With great dignity

1. "Lift up your hearts!" We lift them, Lord, to thee;
Here at thy feet none other may we see:
"Lift up your hearts!" E'en so, with one accord,
We lift them up, we lift them to the Lord.

2. Above the level of the former years,
The mire of sin, the slough of guilty fears,
The mist of doubt, the blight of love's decay,
O Lord of Light, lift all our hearts today!

3. Above the swamps of subterfuge and shame,
The deeds, the thoughts that honor may not name,
The halting tongue that dare not tell the whole,
O Lord of Truth, lift every Christian soul!

4. Lift every gift that thou thyself hast given;
Low lies the best till lifted up to heaven
Low lie the bounding heart, the teeming brain,
Till, sent from God, they mount to God again.

5. Then, as the trumpet-call, in after years,
"Lift up your hearts!" rings pealing in our ears,
Still shall those hearts respond, with full accord,
"We lift them up, we lift them to the Lord!"

A-MEN.

A Charge to Keep I Have

BOYLSTON. S. M.
373
Charles Wesley, 1707–1788
Lowell Mason, 1792–1872
In moderate time
1. A charge to keep I have, A God to glo - ri - fy;
2. To serve the pres - ent age, My call - ing to ful - fil,—
3. Arm me with jeal - ous care, As in Thy sight to live;
4. Help me to watch and pray, And on Thy - self re - ly,
A nev - er - dy - ing soul to save, And fit it for the sky.
O may it all my pow'rs en-gage, To do my Mas-ter's will.
And O, Thy serv - ant, Lord, pre-pare A strict ac-count to give.
As - sured, if I my trust be-tray, I shall for - ev - er die.
A - MEN.
Rise Up, O Men of God!
FESTAL SONG. S. M.
374
William P. Merrill, 1867–
William H. Walter, 1825–1893
With spirit
1. Rise up, O men of God! Have done with less - er things
2. Rise up, O men of God! His king-dom tar - ries long;
3. Rise up, O men of God! The Church for you doth wait,
4. Lift high the cross of Christ! Tread where His feet have trod;
Give heart and mind and soul and strength To serve the King of kings.
Bring in the day of broth - er - hood And end the night of wrong.
Her strength un - e - qual to her task; Rise up, and make her great!
As broth - ers of the Son of man, Rise up, O men of God!
A - MEN.

Words used by permission of "The Presbyterian Tribune," 70 Fifth Avenue, New York.

Jesus, I My Cross Have Taken

375

ELLESDIE. 8. 7. 8. 7. D.

Henry F. Lyte, 1793–1847

Arranged from W. A. Mozart by Hubert P. Main, 1839–1926

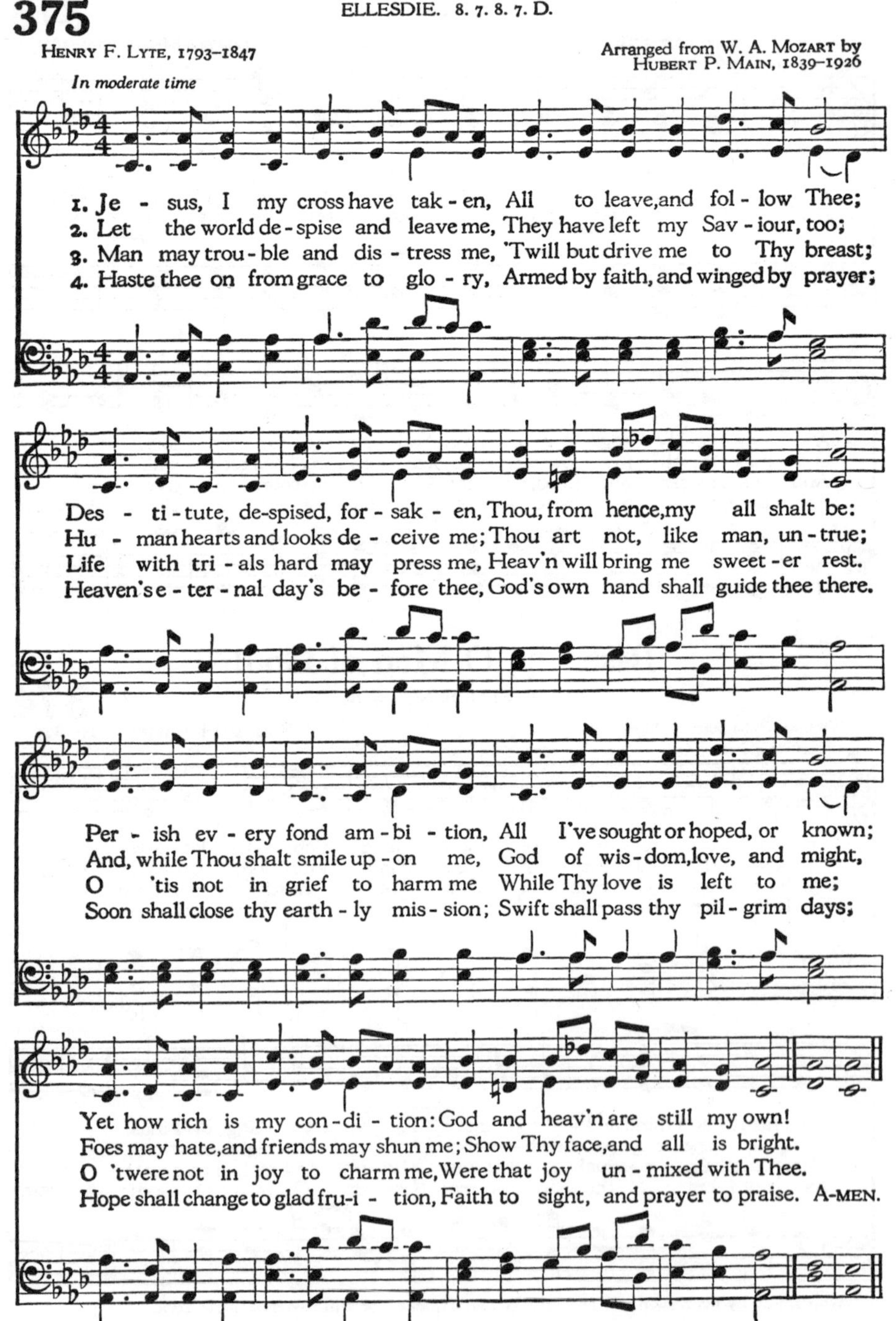
In moderate time
1. Je - sus, I my cross have tak - en, All to leave, and fol - low Thee;
2. Let the world de - spise and leave me, They have left my Sav - iour, too;
3. Man may trou - ble and dis - tress me, 'Twill but drive me to Thy breast;
4. Haste thee on from grace to glo - ry, Armed by faith, and winged by prayer;
Des - ti - tute, de-spised, for - sak - en, Thou, from hence, my all shalt be:
Hu - man hearts and looks de - ceive me; Thou art not, like man, un - true;
Life with tri - als hard may press me, Heav'n will bring me sweet - er rest.
Heaven's e - ter - nal day's be - fore thee, God's own hand shall guide thee there.
Per - ish ev - ery fond am - bi - tion, All I've sought or hoped, or known;
And, while Thou shalt smile up - on me, God of wis - dom, love, and might,
O 'tis not in grief to harm me While Thy love is left to me;
Soon shall close thy earth - ly mis - sion; Swift shall pass thy pil - grim days;
Yet how rich is my con - di - tion: God and heav'n are still my own!
Foes may hate, and friends may shun me; Show Thy face, and all is bright.
O 'twere not in joy to charm me, Were that joy un - mixed with Thee.
Hope shall change to glad fru - i - tion, Faith to sight, and prayer to praise. A-MEN.

Fight the Good Fight With All Thy Might

ZELOTES (MOZART). L. M.
376
JOHN S. B. MONSELL, 1811–1875
Adapted from MOZART, 1756–1791
In moderate time
1. Fight the good fight with all thy might; Christ is thy strength, and Christ thy light:
2. Run the straight race thro' God's good grace, Lift up thine eyes, and seek His face:
3. Cast care a - side; up - on thy Guide Lean, and His mer - cy will pro-vide;
Lay hold on life, and it shall be Thy joy and crown e - ter - nal - ly.
Life with its way be-fore us lies, Christ is the path, and Christ the prize.
Lean, and the trust - ing soul shall prove Christ is its life, and Christ its love. A-MEN.
God Send Us Men Whose Aim 'Twill Be
MELROSE. L. M.
377
FREDERICK J. GILLMAN, 1866– Alt.
FREDERICK C. MAKER, 1844–1927
In moderate time
1. God send us men whose aim 'twill be, Not to de - fend some an - cient creed,
2. God send us men a - lert and quick His loft - y pre-cepts to trans - late,
3. God send us men of stead - fast will, Pa - tient, cou - ra-geous, strong and true;
4. God send us men with hearts a - blaze All truth to love, all wrong to hate;
But to live out the laws of Christ In ev - 'ry tho't and word and deed.
Un - til the laws of Christ be - come The laws and hab - its of the State.
With vi-sion clear and mind e - quipped, His will to learn, His work to do.
These are the pa - triots na - tions need, These are the bul-warks of the State. A-MEN.

God of Grace and God of Glory

378

REGENT SQUARE. 8. 7. 8. 7. 8. 7.

HARRY EMERSON FOSDICK, 1878–

HENRY SMART, 1813–1879

In moderate time, with earnestness

1. God of grace and God of glo - ry, On Thy peo - ple pour Thy power;
Crown Thine an - cient church's sto - ry; Bring her bud to glo - rious flower.
Grant us wis - dom, Grant us cour - age, For the fac - ing of this hour.

2. Lo! the hosts of e - vil round us Scorn Thy Christ, as - sail His ways!
From the fears that long have bound us Free our hearts to faith and praise:
Grant us wis - dom, Grant us cour - age, For the liv - ing of these days.

3. Cure Thy chil - dren's war - ring mad - ness, Bend our pride to Thy con - trol;
Shame our wan - ton, self - ish glad - ness, Rich in things and poor in soul.
Grant us wis - dom, Grant us cour - age, Lest we miss Thy king-dom's goal.

4. Set our feet on loft - y pla - ces; Gird our lives that they may be
Ar - mored with all Christ - like grac - es In the fight to set men free.
Grant us wis - dom, Grant us cour - age, That we fail not man nor Thee!

5. Save us from weak res - ig - na - tion To the e - vils we de - plore;
Let the search for Thy sal - va - tion Be our glo - ry ev - er - more.
Grant us wis - dom, Grant us cour - age, Serv - ing Thee whom we a - dore.

A - MEN.

Love Divine, All Love Excelling

BEECHER. 8. 7. 8. 7. D.

379

CHARLES WESLEY, 1707-1788
JOHN ZUNDELL, 1815-1882
In moderate time
1. Love di - vine, all love ex - cell - ing, Joy of heaven, to earth come down;
2. Breathe, O breathe Thy lov - ing Spir - it In - to ev - ery trou - bled breast!
3. Come, Al-might - y to de - liv - er, Let us all Thy grace re - ceive;
4. Fin - ish, then, Thy new cre - a - tion; Pure and spot - less let us be;
Fix in us Thy hum - ble dwell - ing, All Thy faith - ful mer - cies crown!
Let us all in Thee in - her - it, Let us find the prom - ised rest;
Sud - den - ly re - turn, and nev - er, Nev - er more Thy tem - ples leave.
Let us see Thy great sal - va - tion Per - fect - ly re - stored in Thee:
Je - sus, Thou art all com - pas - sion, Pure, un - bound - ed love Thou art;
Take a - way our bent to sin - ning; Al - pha and O - me - ga be;
Thee we would be al - ways bless - ing, Serve Thee as Thy hosts a - bove,
Changed from glo - ry in - to glo - ry, Till in heaven we take our place,
Vis - it us with Thy sal - va - tion, En - ter ev - ery trem - bling heart.
End of faith, as its be - gin - ning, Set our hearts at lib - er - ty.
Pray, and praise Thee with - out ceas - ing, Glo - ry in Thy per - fect love.
Till we cast our crowns be - fore Thee, Lost in won - der, love, and praise. A - MEN.

Jesus, Thy Boundless Love to Me

380

ST. CATHERINE. 8. 8. 8. 8. 8. 8.

PAUL GERHARDT, 1607–1676
Tr. by JOHN WESLEY, 1703–1791

HENRY F. HEMY, 1818–1888 and
JAMES G. WALTON, 1821–1905

In moderate time

1. Je - sus, Thy bound-less love to me No thought can reach, no tongue de - clare;
2. O grant that noth-ing in my soul May dwell, but Thy pure love a - lone;
3. O love, how cheer-ing is Thy ray! All pain be - fore Thy pres - ence flies;

O knit my thank-ful heart to Thee, And reign with - out a ri - val there:
O may Thy love pos - sess me whole, My joy, my treas-ure, and my crown.
Care, an-guish, sor - row, melt a - way, Where-e'er Thy heal - ing beams a - rise.

Thine whol - ly, Thine a - lone, I am; Be Thou a - lone my con-stant Flame.
Strange fires far from my soul re-move; My ev - ery act, word, thought, be love.
O Je - sus, noth - ing may I see, Noth-ing de - sire, or seek, but Thee! A-MEN.

Majestic Sweetness Sits Enthroned

381

ORTONVILLE. C. M.

SAMUEL STENNETT, 1728–1795

THOMAS HASTINGS, 1784–1872

With dignity

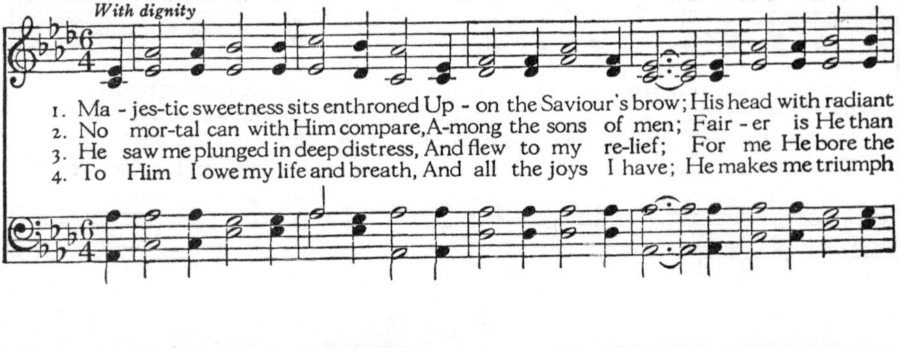

1. Ma - jes-tic sweetness sits enthroned Up - on the Saviour's brow; His head with radiant
2. No mor-tal can with Him compare, A-mong the sons of men; Fair - er is He than
3. He saw me plunged in deep distress, And flew to my re-lief; For me He bore the
4. To Him I owe my life and breath, And all the joys I have; He makes me triumph

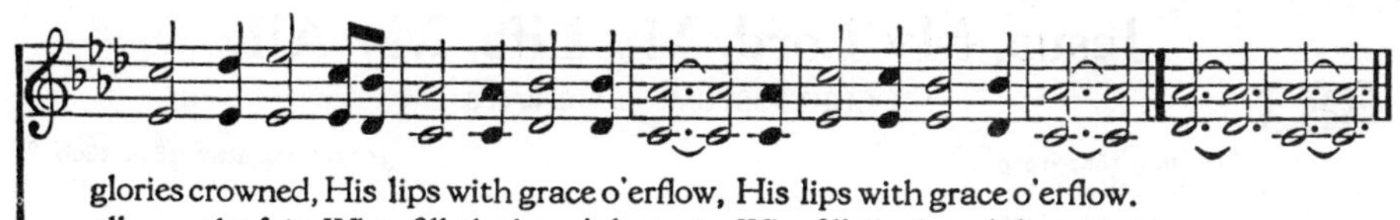

glories crowned, His lips with grace o'erflow, His lips with grace o'erflow.
all the fair Who fill the heav'nly train, Who fill the heav'nly train.
shame-ful cross, And car-ried all my grief, And car-ried all my grief.'
o - ver death, And saves me from the grave, And saves me from the grave. A - MEN.

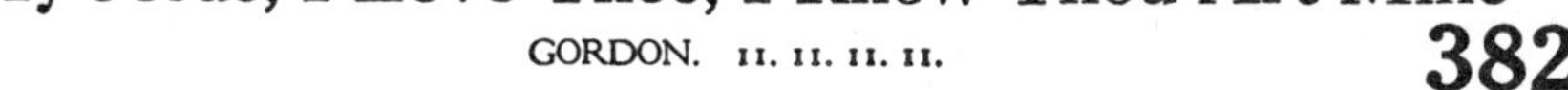

My Jesus, I Love Thee, I Know Thou Art Mine

GORDON. 11. 11. 11. 11.

382

Anonymous

ADONIRAM J. GORDON, 1836–1895

With feeling
1. My Je - sus, I love Thee, I know Thou art mine; For Thee all the fol - lies
2. I love Thee, be - cause Thou hast first lov-ed me, And purchased my par - don
3. I will love Thee in life, I will love Thee in death; And praise Thee as long as
4. In man-sions of glo - ry and end-less de-light, I'll ev - er a - dore Thee
of sin I re - sign; My gra - cious Re - deem-er, my Sav - iour art Thou;
on Cal - va - ry's tree; I love Thee for wear-ing the thorns on Thy brow;
Thou lend-est me breath; And say, when the death-dew lies cold on my brow,
in heav - en so bright; I'll sing with the glit - ter - ing crown on my brow,
If ev - er I loved Thee, my Je - sus, 'tis now. A - MEN.

Jesus, My Lord, My Life, My All

383

ST. CHRYSOSTOM. 8. 8. 8. 8. 8. 8.

HENRY COLLINS, 1827–1919
Stanza 1, line 1, alt.

JOSEPH BARNBY, 1838–1896

In moderate time

1. Jesus, my Lord, my Life, my All,
Hear me, blest Saviour, when I call;
Hear me, and from Thy dwelling place
Pour down the riches of Thy grace.
Jesus, my Lord, I Thee adore;
O make me love Thee more and more.

2. Jesus, too late I Thee have sought;
How can I love Thee as I ought?
And how extol Thy matchless fame,
The glorious beauty of Thy name?
Jesus, my Lord, I Thee adore;
O make me love Thee more and more.

3. Jesus, what didst Thou find in me,
That Thou hast dealt so lovingly?
How great the joy that Thou hast brought,
So far exceeding hope or thought.
Jesus, my Lord, I Thee adore;
O make me love Thee more and more.

4. Jesus, of Thee shall be my song,
To Thee my heart and soul belong;
All that I have or am is Thine,
And Thou, blest Saviour, Thou art mine.
Jesus, my Lord, I Thee adore;
O make me love Thee more and more.

Slower (at "Jesus, my Lord, I Thee adore")

AMEN.

In Heavenly Love Abiding

SEASONS. 7. 6. 7. 6. D.

ANNA L. WARING, 1820–1910

FELIX MENDELSSOHN, 1809–1847

In moderate time
1. In heav'n-ly love a-bid-ing, No change my heart shall fear;
2. Wher-ev-er He may guide me, No want shall turn me back;
3. Green pas-tures are be-fore me, Which yet I have not seen;
And safe is such con-fid-ing, For noth-ing chang-es here.
My Shep-herd is be-side me, And noth-ing can I lack.
Bright skies will soon be o'er me, Where the dark clouds have been.
The storm may roar with-out me, My heart may low be laid,
His wis-dom ev-er wak-eth, His sight is nev-er dim;
My hope I can-not meas-ure, My path to life is free;
But God is round a-bout me, And can I be dis-mayed?
He knows the way He tak-eth, And I will walk with Him.
My Sav-iour has my treas-ure, And He will walk with me.
A-MEN.

I Sought His Love in Sun and Stars

385
HARVARD. 8. 6. 8. 6. 8. 8.
Thomas Curtis Clark, 1877–
Arthur Berridge, 1855–
In moderate time
1. I sought his love in sun and stars, And where the wild seas roll,
2. I sought his love in lore of books, In charts of sci-ence's skill;
I found it not. As mute I stood, Fear o-ver-whelmed my soul; But when I
They left me or-phaned as be-fore—His love e-lud-ed still; Then in de-
gave to one in need, I found the Lord of Love in-deed.
spair I breathed a prayer; The Lord of Love was stand-ing there! A-MEN.
From "Love Off to The War And Other Poems." Used by permission.
Love Is Kind and Suffers Long
386
CAPETOWN. 7. 7. 7. 5.
Christopher Wordsworth, 1807–1885
Friedrich Filitz, 1804–1876
In moderate time
1. Love is kind and suf-fers long; Love is meek and thinks no wrong;
2. Proph-e-cy will fade a-way, Melt-ing in the light of day;
3. Faith will van-ish in-to sight; Hope be emp-tied in de-light;
4. Faith and hope and love we see, Join-ing hand in hand, a-gree;

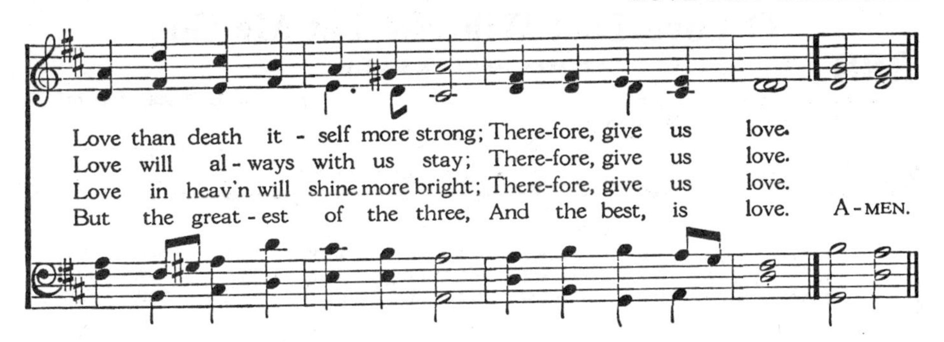
Love than death it - self more strong; There-fore, give us love.
Love will al - ways with us stay; There-fore, give us love.
Love in heav'n will shine more bright; There-fore, give us love.
But the great - est of the three, And the best, is love. A - MEN.

Saviour, Thy Dying Love

387

SOMETHING FOR JESUS. 6. 4. 6. 4. 6. 6. 6. 4.

Sylvanus D. Phelps, 1816–1895

Robert Lowry, 1826–1899

In moderate time
1. Sav - iour, Thy dy - ing love Thou gav - est me; Nor should I
2. O'er the blest mer - cy - seat, Plead - ing for me, My fee - ble
3. Give me a faith - ful heart— Like - ness to Thee— That each de -
aught with-hold, Dear Lord, from Thee: In love my soul would bow, My heart ful -
faith looks up, Je - sus, to Thee; Help me the cross to bear, Thy wondrous
part - ing day Henceforth may see Some work of love be-gun, Some deed of
fil its vow, Some of - f'ring bring Thee now, Some-thing for Thee.
love de- clare, Some song to raise, or pray'r, Some-thing for Thee.
kind-ness done, Some wan-d'rer sought and won, Some-thing for Thee. A - MEN.

O Love That Wilt Not Let Me Go

388

ST. MARGARET. 8. 8. 8. 8. 6.

GEORGE MATHESON, 1842–1906 | ALBERT L. PEACE, 1844–1912

Moderately slow; with exaltation

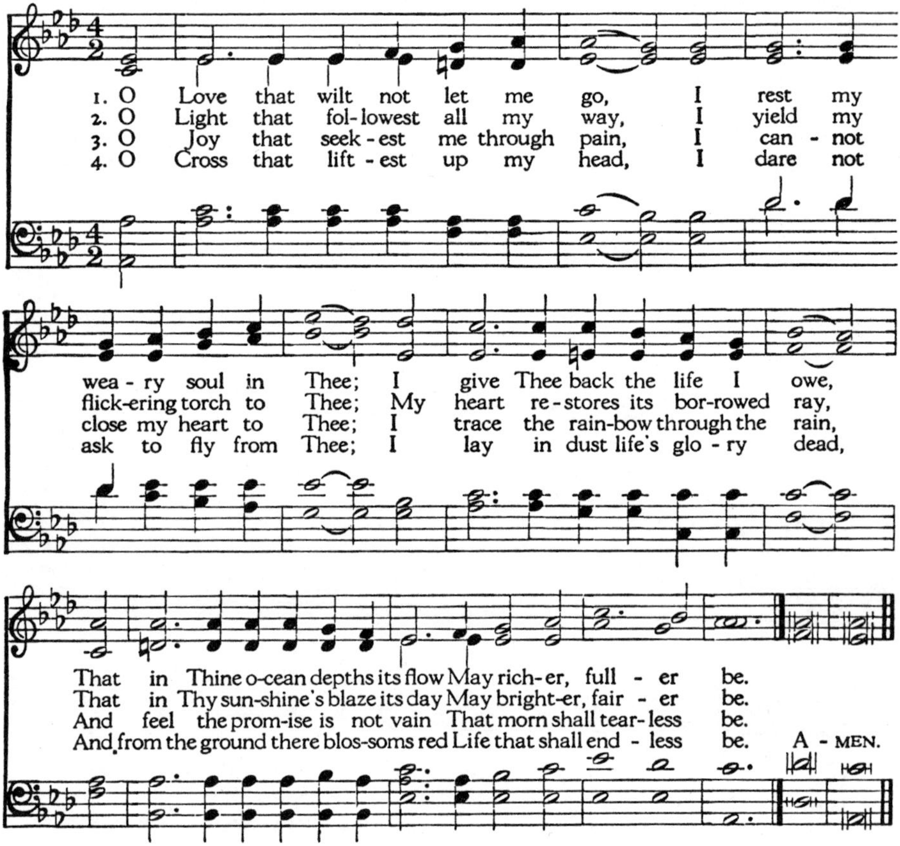

1. O Love that wilt not let me go, I rest my wea-ry soul in Thee; I give Thee back the life I owe, That in Thine o-cean depths its flow May rich-er, full-er be.
2. O Light that fol-lowest all my way, I yield my flick-ering torch to Thee; My heart re-stores its bor-rowed ray, That in Thy sun-shine's blaze its day May bright-er, fair-er be.
3. O Joy that seek-est me through pain, I can-not close my heart to Thee; I trace the rain-bow through the rain, And feel the prom-ise is not vain That morn shall tear-less be.
4. O Cross that lift-est up my head, I dare not ask to fly from Thee; I lay in dust life's glo-ry dead, And from the ground there blos-soms red Life that shall end-less be. A-MEN.

Saviour, Teach Me, Day By Day

389

SEYMOUR. 7. 7. 7. 7.

JANE E. LEESON, 1807–1882 | CARL M. VON WEBER, 1786–1826

In moderate time

1. Sav-iour, teach me, day by day, Love's sweet les-son to o-bey:
2. With a child-like heart of love, At Thy bid-ding may I move;
3. Teach me all Thy steps to trace, Strong to fol-low in Thy grace;
4. Love in lov-ing finds em-ploy, In o-be-dience all her joy;

Sweet - er les - son can - not be— Lov - ing Him who first loved me.
Prompt to serve and fol - low Thee—Lov - ing Him who first loved me.
Learn - ing how to love from Thee—Lov - ing Him who first loved me.
Ev - er new that joy will be— Lov - ing Him who first loved me. A - MEN.

More Love to Thee, O Christ

MORE LOVE TO THEE. 6. 4. 6. 4. 6. 6. 4. 4.

390

MRS. ELIZABETH P. PRENTISS, 1818–1878

WILLIAM H. DOANE, 1832–1915

In moderate time; with devotion

1. More love to Thee, O Christ, More love to Thee! Hear Thou the pray'r I make, On bend - ed knee; This is my ear - nest plea,
2. Once earth - ly joy I craved, Sought peace and rest; Now Thee a - lone I seek, Give what is best; This all my pray'r shall be,
3. Let sor - row do its work, Send grief and pain; Sweet are Thy mes - sen-gers, Sweet their re - frain, When they can sing with me.
4. Then shall my la - test breath Whis - per Thy praise; This be the part - ing cry My heart shall raise, This still its pray'r shall be.
More love, O Christ, to Thee, More love to Thee, More love to Thee. A - MEN.

In His Love Abiding, Wait On the Lord

391

IN HIS LOVE ABIDING. Irregular.

Paul Wengel, 1892- | I. I. Räder alt.

In moderate time

1. In His love a - bid - ing, Wait on the Lord;
2. In His love a - bid - ing, Wait on the Lord;

All in Him con - fid - ing, Trust thou in His word:
All in Him con - fid - ing, Trust thou in His word:

Hope is not gone; Morn - ing soon will dawn,
Thou wilt con - cede, God is true in - deed,

And an - oth - er spring - time Sure - ly come a - long;
Great - er than our Help - er Ne'er has been a need;

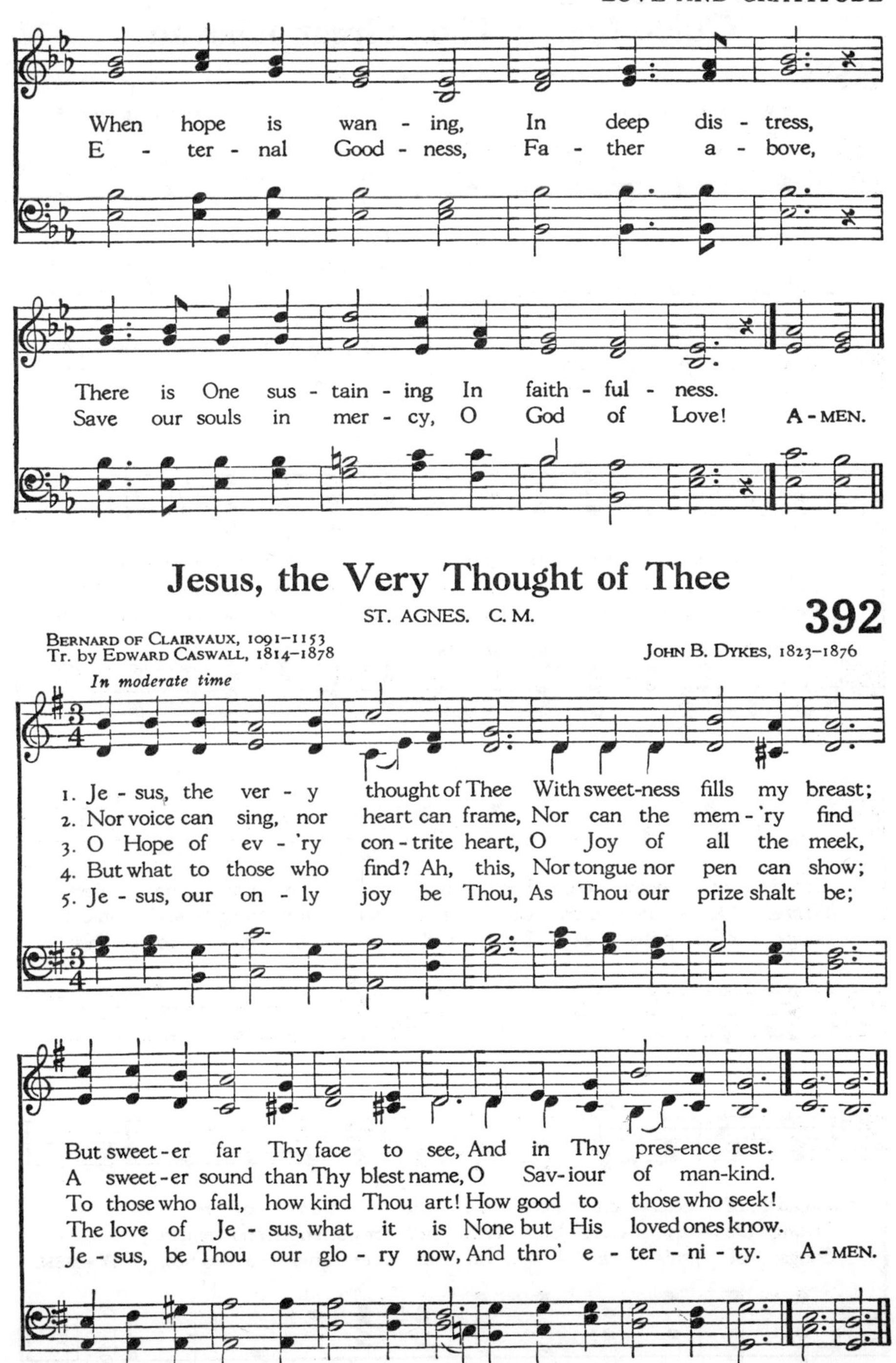
When hope is wan - ing, In deep dis - tress,
E - ter - nal Good - ness, Fa - ther a - bove,
There is One sus - tain - ing In faith - ful - ness.
Save our souls in mer - cy, O God of Love! A - MEN.
Jesus, the Very Thought of Thee
ST. AGNES. C. M.
392
BERNARD OF CLAIRVAUX, 1091–1153
Tr. by EDWARD CASWALL, 1814–1878
JOHN B. DYKES, 1823–1876
In moderate time
1. Je - sus, the ver - y thought of Thee With sweet-ness fills my breast;
2. Nor voice can sing, nor heart can frame, Nor can the mem - 'ry find
3. O Hope of ev - 'ry con - trite heart, O Joy of all the meek,
4. But what to those who find? Ah, this, Nor tongue nor pen can show;
5. Je - sus, our on - ly joy be Thou, As Thou our prize shalt be;
But sweet - er far Thy face to see, And in Thy pres-ence rest.
A sweet - er sound than Thy blest name, O Sav - iour of man-kind.
To those who fall, how kind Thou art! How good to those who seek!
The love of Je - sus, what it is None but His loved ones know.
Je - sus, be Thou our glo - ry now, And thro' e - ter - ni - ty. A - MEN.

Guide Me, O Thou Great Jehovah

393

ZION. 8. 7. 8. 7. 4. 7. 4. 7.

William Williams, 1717–1791 — Thomas Hastings, 1784–1872

With spirit

1. Guide me, O Thou great Je - ho - vah, Pil - grim through this bar - ren land;
2. O - pen now the crys - tal foun - tain, Whence the heal - ing wa - ters flow;
3. When I tread the verge of Jor - dan, Bid my anx - ious fears sub - side;

I am weak, but Thou are might - y, Hold me with Thy power - ful hand;
Let the fier - y, cloud - y pil - lar Lead me all my jour - ney through;
Bear me through the swell - ing cur - rent; Land me safe on Ca - naan's side;

Bread of heav - en, Feed me till I want no more;
Strong De - liv - erer, Be Thou still my strength and shield;
Songs of prais - es I will ev - er give to Thee;

Bread of heav - en, Feed me till I want no more.
Strong De - liv - erer, Be Thou still my strength and shield.
Songs of prais - es I will ev - er give to Thee. A - MEN.

From Every Stormy Wind That Blows

RETREAT. L. M.

394

HUGH STOWELL, 1799–1865

THOMAS HASTINGS, 1784–1872

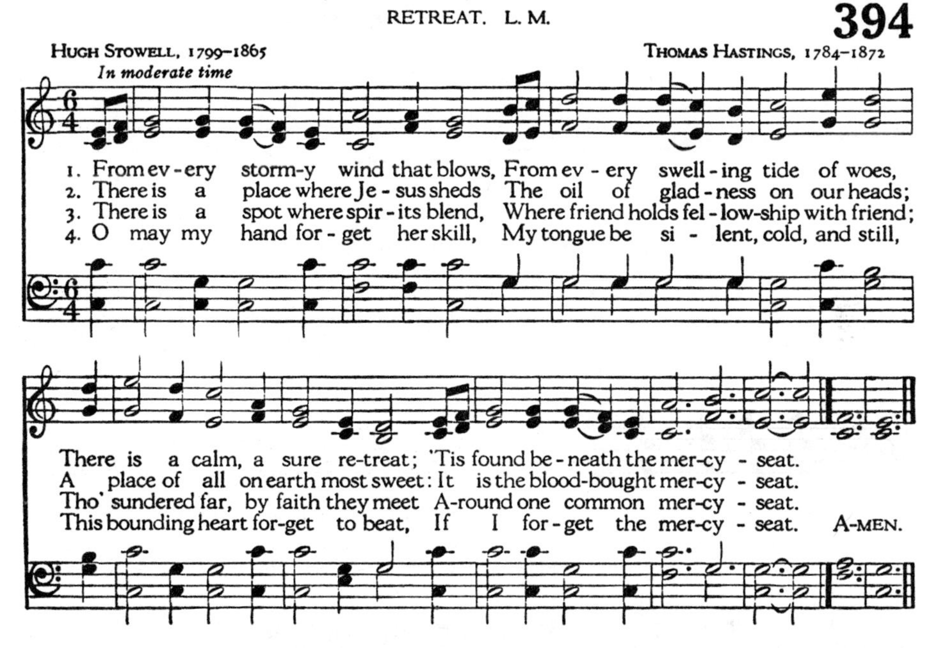
In moderate time
1. From ev - ery storm-y wind that blows, From ev - ery swell - ing tide of woes,
2. There is a place where Je - sus sheds The oil of glad - ness on our heads;
3. There is a spot where spir - its blend, Where friend holds fel - low-ship with friend;
4. O may my hand for - get her skill, My tongue be si - lent, cold, and still,
There is a calm, a sure re-treat; 'Tis found be - neath the mer-cy - seat.
A place of all on earth most sweet: It is the blood-bought mer-cy - seat.
Tho' sundered far, by faith they meet A-round one common mer-cy - seat.
This bounding heart for-get to beat, If I for-get the mer-cy - seat. A-MEN.

My Times Are in Thy Hand

FERGUSON. S. M.

395

WILLIAM F. LLOYD, 1791–1853

GEORGE KINGSLEY, 1811–1884

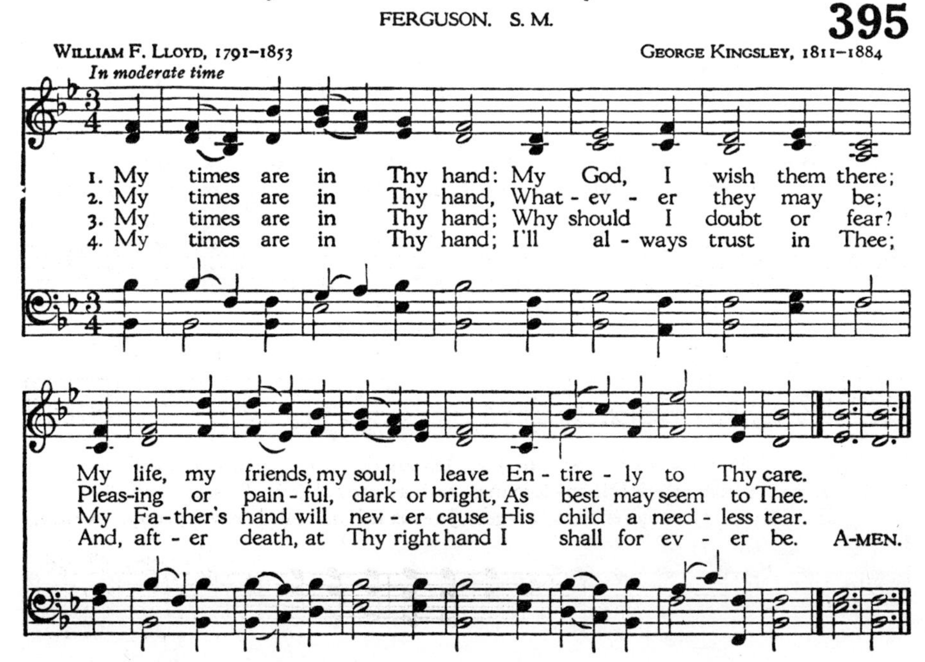
In moderate time
1. My times are in Thy hand: My God, I wish them there;
2. My times are in Thy hand, What - ev - er they may be;
3. My times are in Thy hand; Why should I doubt or fear?
4. My times are in Thy hand; I'll al - ways trust in Thee;
My life, my friends, my soul, I leave En - tire - ly to Thy care.
Pleas-ing or pain - ful, dark or bright, As best may seem to Thee.
My Fa - ther's hand will nev - er cause His child a need - less tear.
And, aft - er death, at Thy right hand I shall for ev - er be. A-MEN.

All the Way My Saviour Leads Me

396

ALL THE WAY. 8. 7. 8. 7. D. with Repeat

FANNY J. CROSBY, 1823–1915 — ROBERT LOWRY, 1826–1899

In moderate time

1. All the way my Sav-iour leads me; What have I to ask be-side?
2. All the way my Sav-iour leads me, Cheers each wind-ing path I tread,
3. All the way my Sav-iour leads me; Oh, the full-ness of His love!
Can I doubt His ten-der mer-cy, Who through life has been my Guide?
Gives me grace for ev-ery tri-al, Feeds me with the liv-ing bread.
Per-fect rest to me is prom-ised In my Fa-ther's house a-bove.
Heaven-ly peace, di-vin-est com-fort, Here by faith in Him to dwell!
Though my wea-ry steps may fal-ter, And my soul a-thirst may be,
When my spir-it, clothed im-mor-tal, Wings its flight to realms of day,
For I know, what-e'er be-fall me, Je-sus do-eth all things well; well.
Gush-ing from the Rock be-fore me, Lo! a spring of joy I see; see.
This my song through endless a-ges: Je-sus led me all the way; way. A-MEN.
1
2

Saviour, More Than Life to Me

EVERY DAY AND HOUR. 7. 9. 7. 9. with Refrain

397

FANNY J. CROSBY, 1823–1915
WILLIAM H. DOANE, 1831–1915
In moderate time
1. Sav - iour, more than life to me, I am cling-ing, cling-ing close to Thee;
2. Thro' this chang-ing world be - low, Lead me gen - tly, gen - tly as I go;
3. Let me love Thee more and more, Till this fleet - ing, fleet-ing life is o'er;
Let Thy pre - cious blood ap-plied, Keep me ev - er, ev - er near Thy side.
Trust-ing Thee, I can - not stray, I can nev - er, nev - er lose my way.
Till my soul is lost in love, In a bright-er, bright-er world a - bove.
REFRAIN
Ev - ery day, ev - ery hour, Let me feel Thy cleans-ing
Ev - ery day and hour, ev - ery day and hour,
power; May Thy ten-der love to me Bind me clos-er, clos-er, Lord, to Thee. A - MEN.

Come, Ye Disconsolate

398
CONSOLATOR. 11. 10. 11. 10.
Thomas Moore, 1779–1852
and Thomas Hastings, 1784–1872
Samuel Webbe, 1740–1816
Moderately fast
1. Come, ye dis - con - so - late, wher - e'er ye lan - guish, Come to the mer - cy seat, fer - vent - ly kneel! Here bring your wound - ed hearts, here tell your an - guish: Earth has no sor - row that heaven can - not heal.
2. Joy of the des - o - late, Light of the stray - ing, Hope of the pen - i - tent, fade - less and pure! Here speaks the Com - fort - er, ten - der - ly say - ing, "Earth has no sor - row that heaven can - not cure.
3. Here see the Bread of Life; see wa - ters flow - ing Forth from the throne of God, pure from a - bove: Come to the feast of love; come, ev - er know - ing Earth has no sor - row but heaven can re - move.
AMEN.
How Gentle God's Commands
399
DENNIS. S. M.
Arr. from Hans G. Naegeli, 1768–1836
By Lowell Mason, 1792–1872
Philip Doddridge, 1702–1751
In moderate time
1. How gen - tle God's com - mands! How kind His pre - cepts are!
2. While Prov - i - dence sup - ports, Let saints se - cure - ly dwell;
3. Why should this anx - ious load Press down your wea - ry mind?
4. His good - ness stands ap - proved, Down to the pres - ent day;

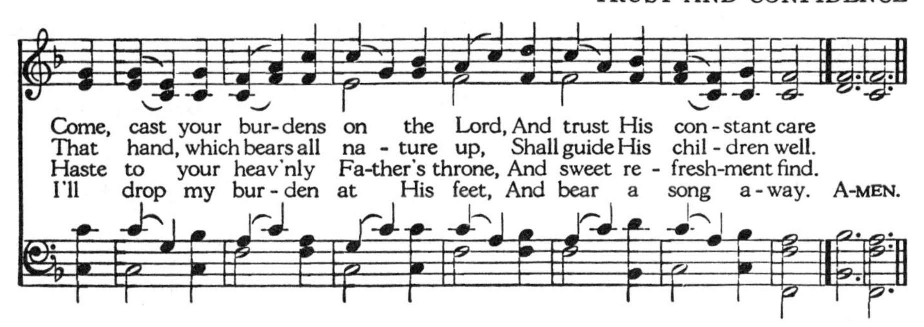
Come, cast your bur-dens on the Lord, And trust His con-stant care
That hand, which bears all na - ture up, Shall guide His chil - dren well.
Haste to your heav'nly Fa-ther's throne, And sweet re - fresh-ment find.
I'll drop my bur - den at His feet, And bear a song a - way. A-MEN.

We Would See Jesus - for the Shadows Lengthen

CONSOLATION. 11. 10. 11. 10.

400

ANNA B. WARNER, 1820–1915 — FELIX MENDELSSOHN, 1809–1847

In moderate time—not too slow

1. We would see Je - sus— for the shad-ows length - en A - cross this lit - tle landscape of our life; We would see Je - sus, our weak faith to strength-en, For the last wea - ri - ness, the fi - nal strife.
2. We would see Je - sus— the great Rock Foun-da - tion Where-on our feet were set with sov-'reign grace; Not life, nor death, with all their ag - i - ta - tion, Can thence re - move us, if we see His face.
3. We would see Je - sus—oth - er lights are pal - ing, Which for long years we have re-joiced to see: The bless-ings of our pil-grim-age are fail - ing, We would not mourn them, for we go to Thee.
4. We would see Je - sus—this is all we're need - ing; Strength, joy, and will - ing-ness come with the sight; We would see Je - sus, dy - ing, ris - en, plead - ing, Then wel-come day, and fare-well mor - tal night. A - MEN.

Saviour, Like a Shepherd Lead Us

401

BRADBURY. 8. 7. 8. 7. D.

Dorothy A. Thrupp, 1779–1847
William B. Bradbury, 1816–1868
In moderate time
1. Sav - iour, like a shep - herd lead us, Much we need Thy ten - der care;
2. We are Thine, do Thou be - friend us, Be the guard-ian of our way;
3. Thou hast prom-ised to re - ceive us, Poor and sin - ful tho' we be;
4. Ear - ly let us seek Thy fa - vor, Ear - ly let us do Thy will;
In Thy pleas-ant pas-tures feed us, For our use Thy folds pre - pare:
Keep Thy flock, from sin de - fend us, Seek us when we go a - stray:
Thou hast mer - cy to re - lieve us, Grace to cleanse, and power to free:
Bless - ed Lord and on - ly Sav - iour, With Thy love our bos - oms fill:
Bless - ed Je - sus, Bless-ed Je - sus! Thou hast bought us, Thine we are,
Bless - ed Je - sus, Bless-ed Je - sus! Hear, O hear us, when we pray,
Bless - ed Je - sus, Bless-ed Je - sus! We will ear - ly turn to Thee,
Bless - ed Je - sus, Bless-ed Je - sus! Thou hast loved us, love us still,
Bless - ed Je - sus, Bless-ed Je - sus! Thou hast bought us, Thine we are.
Bless - ed Je - sus, Bless-ed Je - sus! Hear, O hear us, when we pray.
Bless - ed Je - sus, Bless-ed Je - sus! We will ear - ly turn to Thee.
Bless - ed Je - sus, Bless-ed Je - sus! Thou hast loved us, love us still.
A-men.

Give to the Winds Thy Fears

DIADEMATA. S. M. D.

402

PAUL GERHARDT, 1607–1676
Tr. by JOHN WESLEY, 1703–1791
GEORGE J. ELVEY, 1816–1893
With spirit
1. Give to the winds thy fears, Hope, and be un-dis-mayed; God hears thy sighs, and counts thy tears, God shall lift up thy head, Thro waves and clouds and storms He gent-ly clears the way; Wait thou his time, so shall the night Soon end in joy-ous day.
2. Still heav-y is thy heart? Still sink thy spir-its down? Cast off the weight, let fear de-part, And ev-'ry care be gone. He ev-'ry-where hath sway, And all things serve his mind; His ev-'ry act pure bless-ing is, His path un-sul-lied light.
3. Far, far a-bove thy thought His coun-sel shall ap-pear, When full-y he the work hath wro't That caused thy need-less fear. Leave to his sov-'reign will To choose and to com-mand: With won-der filled, thou then shalt own How wise, how strong his hand.
A-MEN.

403 I Sought the Lord, and Afterward I Knew

KERR. 10. 10. 10. 6.

Anonymous, c. 1904 — Calvin W. Laufer, 1874–1938

May be sung in unison. Moderately slow

1. I sought the Lord, and aft - er - ward I knew
2. Thou didst reach forth Thy hand and mine en - fold;
3. I find, I walk, I love, but O the whole
He moved my soul to seek Him, seek - ing me;
I walked and sank not on the storm - vexed sea;
Of love is but my an - swer, Lord, to Thee!
It was not I that found, O Sav - iour true;
'Twas not so much that I on Thee took hold
For Thou wert long be - fore - hand with my soul;
No, I was found of Thee.
As Thou, dear Lord, on me.
Al - ways Thou lov - edst me.
A - MEN.

If Thou But Suffer God to Guide Thee

NEUMARK. 9. 8. 9. 8. 8. 8.

404

Georg Neumark, 1621–1681
Tr. by Catherine Winkworth, 1829–1878

Georg Neumark, 1621–1681

In moderate time, with assurance

1. If thou but suf - fer God to guide thee, And hope in
2. On - ly be still, and wait His lei - sure In cheer - ful
3. Sing, pray, and swerve not from His ways, But do thine

Him through all thy ways, He'll give thee strength, what-e'er be - tide thee,
hope, with heart con - tent To take what - e'er thy Fa-ther's pleas-ure
own part faith - ful - ly; Trust His rich prom - is - es of grace,

And bear thee through the e - vil days; Who trusts in God's un -
And all - dis - cern - ing love hath sent; Nor doubt our in - most
So shall they be ful - filled in thee; God nev - er yet for -

chang - ing love Builds on the rock that naught can move.
wants are known To Him who chose us for His own.
sook at need The soul that trust - ed Him in - deed. A - men.

He Leadeth Me: O Blessed Thought

405

HE LEADETH ME. L. M. with Refrain

JOSEPH H. GILMORE, 1834–1918

WILLIAM B. BRADBURY, 1816–1868

Not too fast

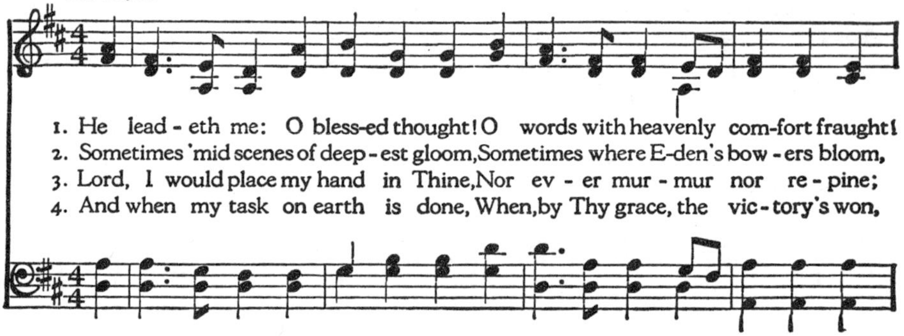

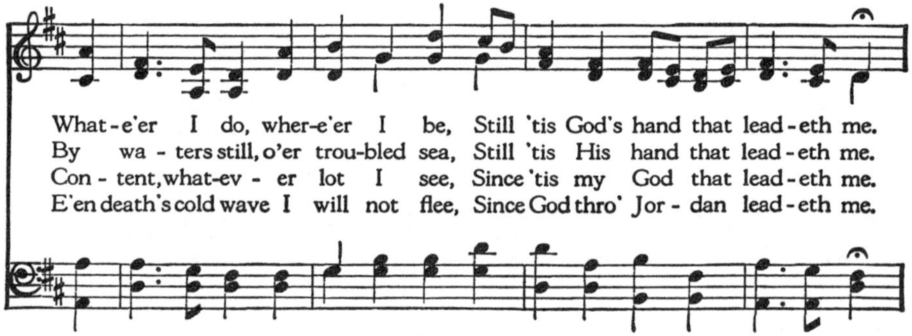

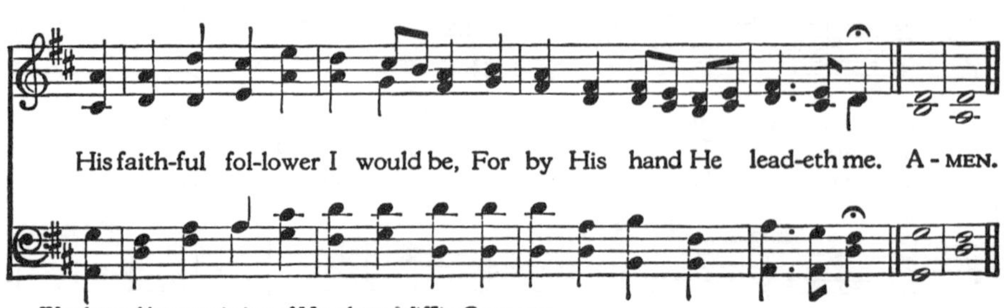

1. He lead - eth me: O bless-ed thought! O words with heavenly com-fort fraught!
What - e'er I do, wher-e'er I be, Still 'tis God's hand that lead - eth me.

2. Sometimes 'mid scenes of deep - est gloom, Sometimes where E-den's bow - ers bloom,
By wa - ters still, o'er trou-bled sea, Still 'tis His hand that lead - eth me.

3. Lord, I would place my hand in Thine, Nor ev - er mur - mur nor re - pine;
Con - tent, what-ev - er lot I see, Since 'tis my God that lead - eth me.

4. And when my task on earth is done, When, by Thy grace, the vic - tory's won,
E'en death's cold wave I will not flee, Since God thro' Jor - dan lead - eth me.

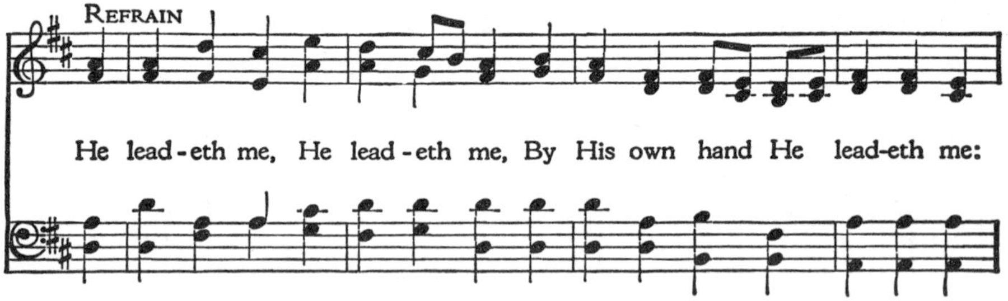

REFRAIN

He lead - eth me, He lead - eth me, By His own hand He lead-eth me:
His faith-ful fol-lower I would be, For by His hand He lead-eth me. A - MEN.

How Firm a Foundation, Ye Saints of the Lord

FOUNDATION. 11. 11. 11. 11.

406

"K" in John Rippon's Selection, 1787

Early American melody

In moderate time, with spirit
1. How firm a foun - da - tion, ye saints of the Lord,
2. "Fear not, I am with thee, O be not dis - mayed,
3. "When through the deep wa - ters I call thee to go,
4. "When through fier - y tri - als thy path - way shall lie,
5. "The soul that on Je - sus hath leaned for re - pose,
Is laid for your faith in His ex - cel - lent word!
For I am thy God, and will still give thee aid;
The riv - ers of sor - row shall not o - ver - flow;
My grace, all - suf - fi - cient, shall be thy sup - ply;
I will not, I will not de - sert to his foes;
What more can He say than to you He hath said,
I'll strength - en thee, help thee, and cause thee to stand,
For I will be with thee, thy trou - bles to bless,
The flame shall not hurt thee; I on - ly de - sign
That soul, though all hell should en - deav - or to shake,
To you who for ref - uge to Je - sus have fled.
Up - held by My right - eous, om - nip - o - tent hand.
And sanc - ti - fy to thee thy deep - est dis - tress.
Thy dross to con - sume, and thy gold to re - fine.
I'll nev - er, no nev - er, no nev - er for - sake!" A - MEN.

Mighty Rock, Whose Towering Form

407

MIGHTY ROCK. 7. 7. 7. 7. with Refrain

FANNY J. CROSBY, 1823–1915

TULLIUS C. O'KANE, 1830–?

In moderate time, with dignity

1. Might - y Rock, whose tow - 'ring form Looks a - bove the frown - ing storm,
2. Of the springs that from Thee burst, Let me drink and quench my thirst;
3. When I near the stream of death, When I feel its chill - y breath,

Rock a - mid the des - ert waste, To Thy shad - ow now I haste.
Wea - ry, faint - ing, toil - op-pressed, In Thy shad - ow let me rest.
Rock where all my hopes a - bide, In Thy shad - ow let me hide.

REFRAIN

Un - to Thee, un - to Thee, Pre - cious Sav - iour, now I flee;

"Rock of A - ges, cleft for me,. Let me hide my-self in Thee." A-MEN.

My Jesus, As Thou Wilt!

JEWETT. 6. 6. 6. 6. D.

408

Benjamin Schmolck, 1672–1737
Tr. by Jane Borthwick, 1813–1897

Arr. from Carl M. von Weber, 1786–1826, by
Joseph P. Holbrook, 1822–1888

In moderate time
1. My Je - sus, as Thou wilt! O may Thy will be mine!
2. My Je - sus, as Thou wilt! Tho' seen thro' many a tear,
3. My Je - sus, as Thou wilt! All shall be well for me;
In - to Thy hand of love I would my all re - sign.
Let not my star of hope Grow dim or dis - ap - pear.
Each chang - ing fu - ture scene I glad - ly trust with Thee.
Through sor - row or thro' joy, Con - duct me as Thine own;
Since Thou on earth hast wept And sor - rowed oft a - lone,
Straight to my home a - bove I trav - el calm - ly on,
And help me still to say, "My Lord, Thy will be done."
If I must weep with Thee, My Lord, Thy will be done.
And sing, in life or death, "My Lord, Thy will be done."
A - men.

Jesus, Saviour, Pilot Me
409
PILOT. 7. 7. 7. 7. 7. 7.
EDWARD HOPPER, 1818–1888
JOHN E. GOULD, 1822–1875
In moderate time
1. Je - sus, Sav - iour, pi - lot me O - ver life's tem-pest-uous sea;
2. As a moth - er stills her child, Thou canst hush the o - cean wild;
3. When at last I near the shore, And the fear - ful break-ers roar
Un-known waves be - fore me roll, Hid - ing rock and treach-erous shoal;
Bois-terous waves o - bey Thy will When Thou sayest to them 'Be still.'
'Twixt me and the peace-ful rest, Then, while lean - ing on Thy breast,
Chart and com - pass came from Thee: Je - sus, Sav - iour, pi - lot me.
Won-drous Sov-ereign of the sea, Je - sus, Sav - iour, pi - lot me.
May I hear Thee say to me, 'Fear not, I will pi - lot thee.' A-MEN.
O Christ, the Way, the Truth, the Life
410
BEATITUDO. C. M.
GEORGE L. SQUIER
JOHN B. DYKES, 1823–1876
In moderate time
1. O Christ, the Way, the Truth, the Life, Show me the liv - ing way,
2. Teach me Thy Truth, O Christ, my Light, The Truth that makes me free,
3. The Life that Thou a - lone canst give, Im - part in love to me,

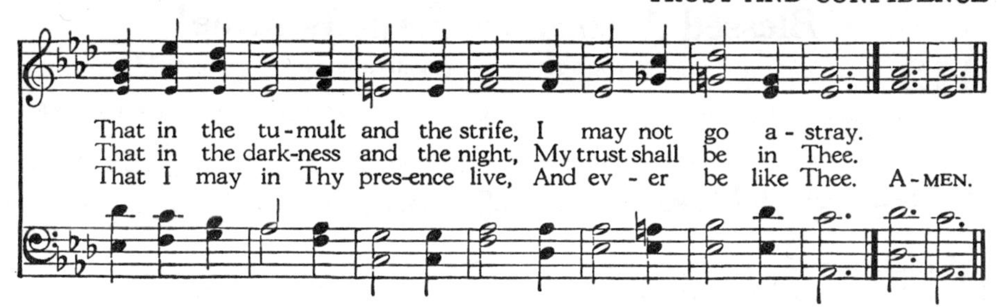
That in the tu-mult and the strife, I may not go a-stray.
That in the dark-ness and the night, My trust shall be in Thee.
That I may in Thy pres-ence live, And ev-er be like Thee. A-MEN.

Dear Lord and Father of Mankind

WHITTIER. 8. 6. 8. 8. 6.

411

JOHN G. WHITTIER, 1807–1892

FREDERICK C. MAKER, 1844–1927

In moderate time
1. Dear Lord and Fa-ther of man-kind, For-give our fool-ish ways;
2. In sim-ple trust like theirs who heard, Be-side the Syr-ian sea,
3. O Sab-bath rest by Gal-i-lee! O calm of hills a-bove!
4. Drop Thy still dews of qui-et-ness, Till all our striv-ings cease;
5. Breathe through the heats of our de-sire Thy cool-ness and Thy balm;
Re-clothe us in our right-ful mind; In pur-er lives Thy
The gra-cious call-ing of the Lord, Let us, like them, with-
Where Je-sus knelt to share with Thee The si-lence of e-
Take from our souls the strain and stress, And let our or-dered
Let sense be dumb, let flesh re-tire; Speak through the earth-quake,
ser-vice find, In deep-er rev-erence, praise.
out a word, Rise up and fol-low Thee.
ter-ni-ty, In-ter-pret-ed by love.
lives con-fess The beau-ty of Thy peace.
wind, and fire, O still small voice of calm! A-MEN.

Blessed Assurance, Jesus Is Mine!

412

ASSURANCE. 9. 10. 9. 9. with Refrain

FANNY J. CROSBY, 1823–1915

MRS. JOSEPH F. KNAPP, 1839–1908

Joyously

1. Bless-ed as-sur-ance, Je-sus is mine! O what a fore-taste of glo-ry di-vine! Heir of sal-va-tion, pur-chase of God, Born of His Spir-it, washed in His blood.
2. Per-fect sub-mis-sion, per-fect de-light, Vi-sions of rap-ture now burst on my sight; An-gels de-scend-ing, bring from a-bove, Ech-oes of mer-cy, whis-pers of love.
3. Per-fect sub-mis-sion, all is at rest, I in my Sav-iour am hap-py and blest, Watch-ing and wait-ing, look-ing a-bove, Filled with His good-ness, lost in His love.

REFRAIN

This is my sto-ry, this is my song, Prais-ing my Sav-iour all the day long; This is my sto-ry, this is my song, Praising my Sav-iour all the day long. A-MEN.

Thou My Everlasting Portion

CLOSE TO THEE. 8. 7. 8. 7. with Refrain

413

FANNY J. CROSBY, 1823–1915
SILAS J. VAIL, 1818-1884
In moderate time
1. Thou my ev - er - last - ing por - tion, More than friend or life to me,
2. Not for ease or world - ly pleas - ure, Nor for fame my prayer shall be;
3. Lead me through the vale of shad - ows, Bear me o'er life's fit - ful sea;
All a - long my pil - grim jour - ney, Sav - iour, let me walk with Thee.
Glad - ly will I toil and suf - fer, On - ly let me walk with Thee.
Then the gate of life e - ter - nal, May I en - ter, Lord, with Thee.
REFRAIN
Close to Thee, close to Thee, Close to Thee, close to Thee; All a -
Close to Thee, close to Thee, Close to Thee, close to Thee; Glad - ly
Close to Thee, close to Thee, Close to Thee, close to Thee; Then the
long my pil - grim jour - ney, Sav - iour, let me walk with Thee.
will I toil and suf - fer, On - ly let me walk with Thee.
gate of life e - ter - nal, May I en - ter, Lord, with Thee. A - MEN.

Jesus, Lover of My Soul

414

MARTYN. 7. 7. 7. 7. D.
(*First Tune*)

Charles Wesley, 1707–1788 — Simeon B. Marsh, 1798–1875

In moderate time

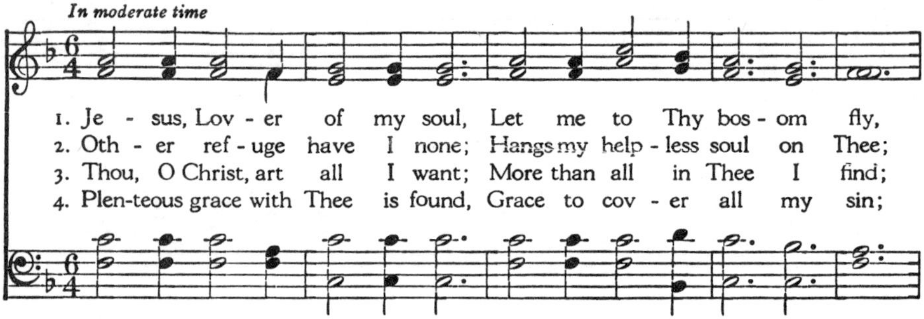

1. Je - sus, Lov - er of my soul, Let me to Thy bos - om fly,
2. Oth - er ref - uge have I none; Hangs my help - less soul on Thee;
3. Thou, O Christ, art all I want; More than all in Thee I find;
4. Plen-teous grace with Thee is found, Grace to cov - er all my sin;

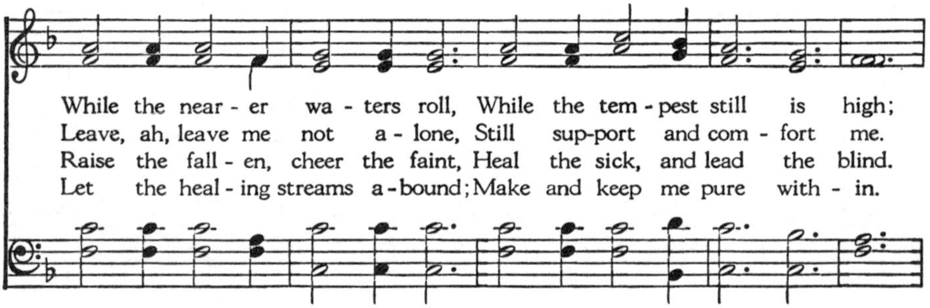

While the near - er wa - ters roll, While the tem - pest still is high;
Leave, ah, leave me not a - lone, Still sup-port and com - fort me.
Raise the fall - en, cheer the faint, Heal the sick, and lead the blind.
Let the heal - ing streams a - bound; Make and keep me pure with - in.

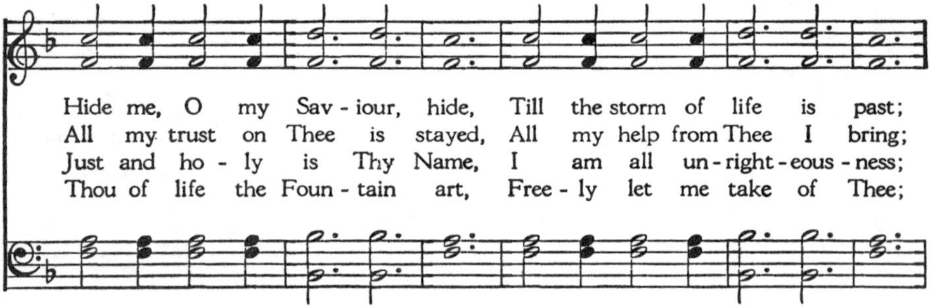

Hide me, O my Sav - iour, hide, Till the storm of life is past;
All my trust on Thee is stayed, All my help from Thee I bring;
Just and ho - ly is Thy Name, I am all un - right - eous - ness;
Thou of life the Foun - tain art, Free - ly let me take of Thee;

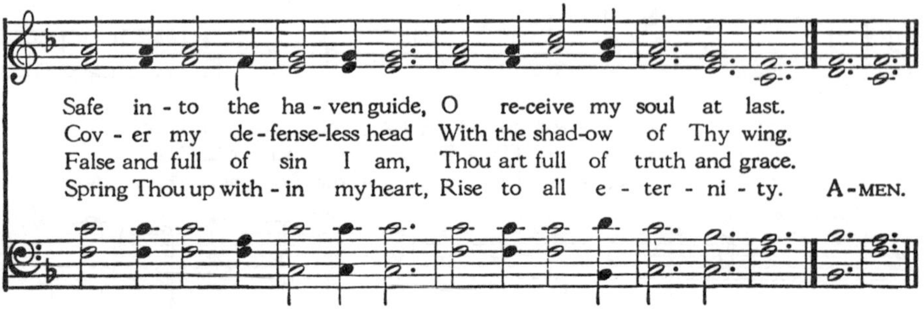

Safe in - to the ha - ven guide, O re-ceive my soul at last.
Cov - er my de - fense-less head With the shad-ow of Thy wing.
False and full of sin I am, Thou art full of truth and grace.
Spring Thou up with - in my heart, Rise to all e - ter - ni - ty. A - MEN.

Jesus, Lover of My Soul

ABERYSTWYTH. 7. 7. 7. 7. D.
(*Second Tune*)

415

CHARLES WESLEY, 1707–1788 — JOSEPH PARRY, 1841–1903

In moderate time

1. Je - sus, Lov - er of my soul, Let me to Thy bos - om fly,
2. Oth - er ref - uge have I none; Hangs my help - less soul on Thee;
3. Thou, O Christ, art all I want; More than all in Thee I find:
4. Plen - teous grace with Thee is found, Grace to cov - er all my sin;
While the near - er wa - ters roll, While the tem - pest still is high:
Leave, ah! leave me not a - lone, Still sup - port and com - fort me:
Raise the fall - en, cheer the faint, Heal the sick, and lead the blind.
Let the heal - ing streams a - bound; Make and keep me pure with - in.
Hide me, O my Sav - iour, hide, Till the storm of life is past;
All my trust on Thee is stayed, All my help from Thee I bring;
Just and ho - ly is Thy Name, I am all un - right - eous-ness;
Thou of life the Foun - tain art, Free - ly let me take of Thee:
Safe in - to the ha - ven guide; O re - ceive my soul at last!
Cov - er my de - fense-less head With the shad - ow of Thy wing.
False and full of sin I am, Thou art full of truth and grace.
Spring Thou up with - in my heart, Rise to all e - ter - ni - ty. A - MEN.

Sowing in the Morning, Sowing Seeds of Kindness

416 BRINGING IN THE SHEAVES. 12. 11. 12. 11. with Refrain

KNOWLES SHAW, 1834-1878 GEORGE A. MINOR

Joyfully

1. Sow-ing in the morn-ing, sow-ing seeds of kind-ness, Sow-ing in the noon-tide
2. Sow-ing in the sun-shine, sow-ing in the shad-ows, Fearing neith-er clouds nor
3. Go, then, e - ven weep-ing, sow-ing for the Mas - ter, Tho' the loss sustained our

and the dew - y eves; Wait-ing for the har-vest, and the time of reap - ing,
win-ter's chill-ing breeze; By and by, the har-vest and the la - bor end - ed,
spir - it oft - en grieves; When our weeping's o - ver, He will bid us wel-come,

We shall come re - joic - ing, bring-ing in the sheaves.
We shall come re - joic - ing, bring-ing in the sheaves. Bringing in the sheaves, Bringing
We shall come re - joic - ing, bring-ing in the sheaves.

REFRAIN

in the sheaves, We shall come re-joic - ing, bring-ing in the sheaves, Bring-ing in the sheaves,

Bring-ing in the sheaves, We shall come re - joic - ing, bring-ing in the sheaves. A - MEN.

On Our Way Rejoicing

ST. ALBAN. 6. 5. 6. 5. D. with Refrain

JOHN S. B. MONSELL, 1811–1875
FRANZ JOSEPH HAYDN, 1732–1809
In moderate time, with joy
1. On our way re - joic - ing As we home-ward move, Hearken to our prais - es,
2. If with hon-est-heart - ed Love for God and man, Day by day Thou find us
3. On our way re - joic - ing Glad-ly let us go; Vic - tor is our Lead - er,
4. Un - to God the Fa - ther Joy - ful songs we sing; Un - to God the Sav - iour
O Thou God of love! Is there grief or sad-ness? Thine it can-not be;
Do - ing all we can, Thou who giv'st the seed-time Wilt give large in - crease,
Van-quished is the foe; Christ with-out, our safe - ty; Christ with-in, our joy;
Thank-ful hearts we bring; Un - to God the Spir - it Bow we and a - dore;
REFRAIN
Is our sky be-cloud-ed? Clouds are not from Thee.
Crown the head with bless-ings, Fill the heart with peace. On our way re - joic - ing,
Who, if we be faith-ful, Can our hope de - stroy?
On our way re - joic - ing Now and ev - er - more.
As we home-ward move, Heark-en to our prais- es, O Thou God of love! A-MEN.

Rejoice, Ye Pure in Heart

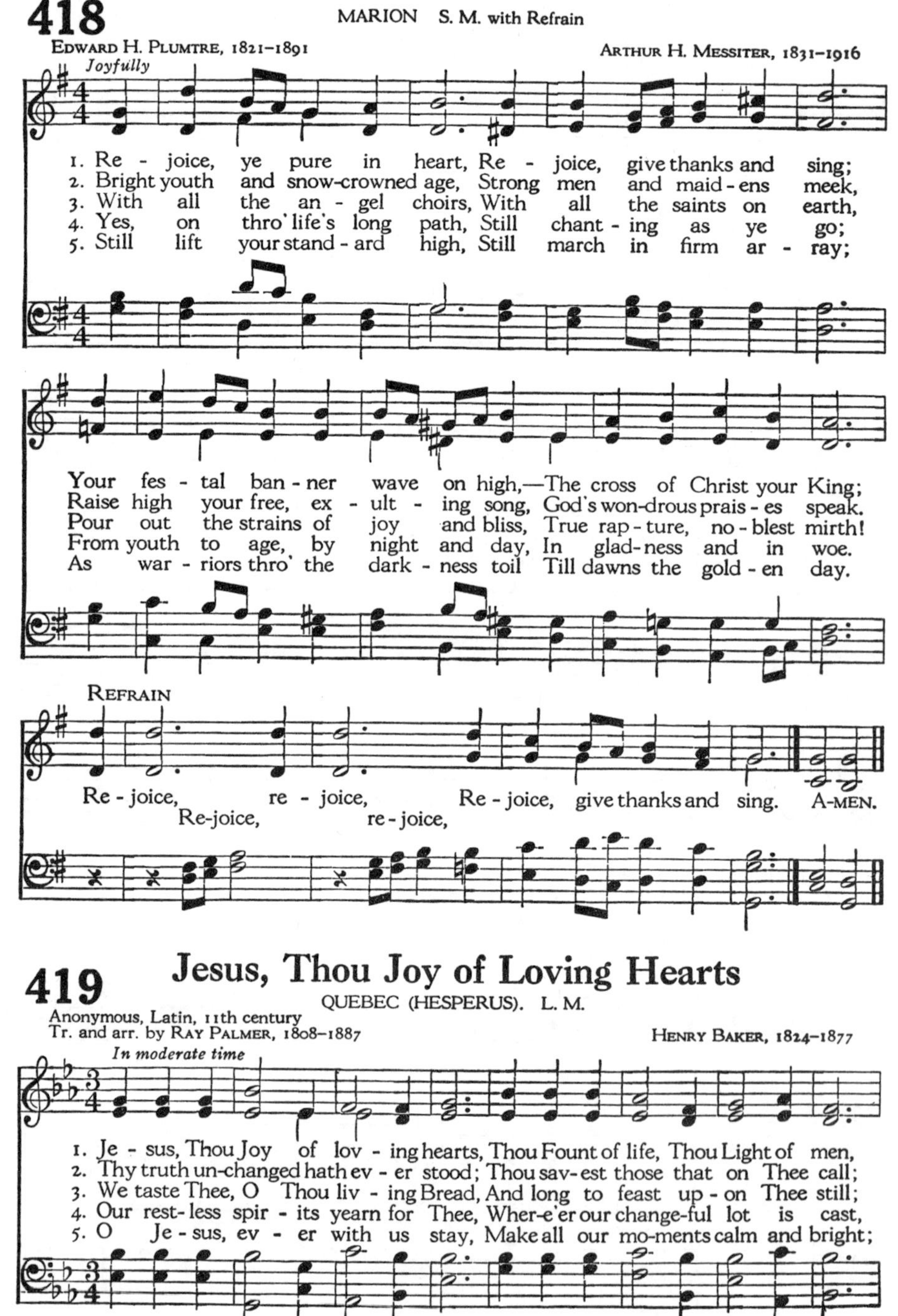
418
MARION S. M. with Refrain
Edward H. Plumtre, 1821–1891
Arthur H. Messiter, 1831–1916
Joyfully
1. Re - joice, ye pure in heart, Re - joice, give thanks and sing; Your fes - tal ban - ner wave on high,—The cross of Christ your King;
2. Bright youth and snow-crowned age, Strong men and maid - ens meek, Raise high your free, ex - ult - ing song, God's won-drous prais - es speak.
3. With all the an - gel choirs, With all the saints on earth, Pour out the strains of joy and bliss, True rap - ture, no - blest mirth!
4. Yes, on thro' life's long path, Still chant - ing as ye go; From youth to age, by night and day, In glad - ness and in woe.
5. Still lift your stand - ard high, Still march in firm ar - ray; As war - riors thro' the dark - ness toil Till dawns the gold - en day.
Refrain
Re - joice, re - joice, Re - joice, give thanks and sing. A-men.
Re-joice, re - joice,
419
Jesus, Thou Joy of Loving Hearts
QUEBEC (HESPERUS). L. M.
Anonymous, Latin, 11th century
Tr. and arr. by Ray Palmer, 1808–1887
Henry Baker, 1824–1877
In moderate time
1. Je - sus, Thou Joy of lov - ing hearts, Thou Fount of life, Thou Light of men,
2. Thy truth un-changed hath ev - er stood; Thou sav - est those that on Thee call;
3. We taste Thee, O Thou liv - ing Bread, And long to feast up - on Thee still;
4. Our rest - less spir - its yearn for Thee, Wher-e'er our change-ful lot is cast,
5. O Je - sus, ev - er with us stay, Make all our mo-ments calm and bright;

From the best bliss that earth im-parts We turn un - filled to Thee a - gain.
To them that seek Thee Thou art good, To them that find Thee All in all.
We drink of Thee, the Foun-tain-head, And thirst our souls from Thee to fill.
Glad when Thy gra-cious smile we see, Blest when our faith can hold Thee fast.
Chase the dark night of sin a - way, Shed o'er the world Thy ho - ly light. A-MEN.

Where Winds the Road O'er Hill and Dale

GERMANY. L. M.

420

HOWARD E. MATHER

In moderate time

Adapted from SACRED MELODIES, WILLIAM GARDINER, 1770–1853

1. Where winds the road o'er hill and dale, Where field and for - est mark the land, In all that Thou dost man en - tail, We see the im - print of Thy hand.
2. On fur - row long, in vil - lage street, By sing - ing brook, or cot - tage door, In friend - ly word where neigh - bors meet, We come to feel Thee more and more.
3. In win - ter's snow, in sum - mer's sun, The joy of spring, the hush of fall, In all the course the sea - sons run, We praise Thee as the Lord of all.
4. Thou Christ who lov - est field and wood, E'er sought new strength in qui - et glen, Help us to stand where Thou has stood, Come now and walk the fields a - gain;
5. Till men in all Thy coun - try - side, Shall cease from wan - ton greed and strife, Shall learn in Thy way to a - bide, The joy of more a - bun - dant life. A-MEN.

The Bounties, Gracious Lord

421

FERGUSON. S. M.

ELIZABETH SCOTT — GEORGE KINGSLEY, 1811–1884

In moderate time

1. Thy boun-ties, gra-cious Lord, With grat-i-tude we own;
2. With joy the peo-ple bring Their of-f'rings round Thy throne;
3. O may this sac-ri-fice To Thee, the Lord, as-cend,
We bless Thy prov-i-den-tial grace, Which show'rs its bless-ings down.
With thank-ful souls, be-hold, we pay A trib-ute of Thine own.
An o-dor of a sweet per-fume, Pres-ent-ed by His hand. A-MEN.

We Give Thee But Thine Own

422

SCHUMANN. S. M.

WILLIAM W. HOW, 1823–1897 — MASON AND WEBB'S CANTICA LAUDIS. Boston, 1850

In moderate time

1. We give Thee but Thine own, What-e'er the gift may be:
All that we have is Thine a-lone, A trust, O Lord, from Thee.

2. May we Thy boun-ties thus As stew-ards true re-ceive,
And glad-ly, as Thou bless-est us, To Thee our first fruits give. A-MEN.

The Church's One Foundation

AURELIA. 7. 6. 7. 6. D.

423

Samuel J. Stone, 1839-1900
Samuel S. Wesley, 1810-1876
In moderate time, with dignity
1. The Church's one foundation Is Jesus Christ her Lord;
2. Elect from every nation, Yet one o'er all the earth,
3. 'Mid toil and tribulation, And tumult of her war,
4. Yet she on earth hath union With God the Three in One,
She is His new creation By water and the word:
Her charter of salvation, One Lord, one faith, one birth;
She waits the consummation Of peace for evermore;
And mystic sweet communion With those whose rest is won:
From heaven He came and sought her To be His holy bride;
One holy Name she blesses, Partakes one holy food,
Till, with the vision glorious, Her longing eyes are blest,
O happy ones and holy! Lord, give us grace that we,
With His own blood He bought her, And for her life He died.
And to one hope she presses, With every grace endued.
And the great Church victorious Shall be the Church at rest.
Like them, the meek and lowly, On high may dwell with Thee.
A-men.

One Holy Church of God Appears

424

ST. JAMES. C. M.

SAMUEL LONGFELLOW, 1819–1892 — RAPHAEL COURTEVILLE, d. 1772

In moderate time

1. One ho - ly Church of God ap - pears Through ev - ery age and race,
Un - wast - ed by the lapse of years, Un-changed by chang-ing place.
2. From old - est time, on far-thest shores, Be - neath the pine or palm,
One un - seen Pres-ence she a - dores, With si - lence, or with psalm.
3. The truth is her pro - phet - ic gift, The soul her sa - cred page;
And feet on mer - cy's er - rands swift Do make her pil - grim - age.
4. O liv - ing Church, thine er - rand speed, Ful - fill thy task sub - lime;
With Bread of life earth's hun-gers feed; Re - deem the e - vil time! A-MEN.

Our Church Proclaims God's Love and Care

425

TRURO. L. M.

MABEL NIEDERMEYER, 1899– — T. WILLIAMS PSALMODIA EVANGELICA, 1789

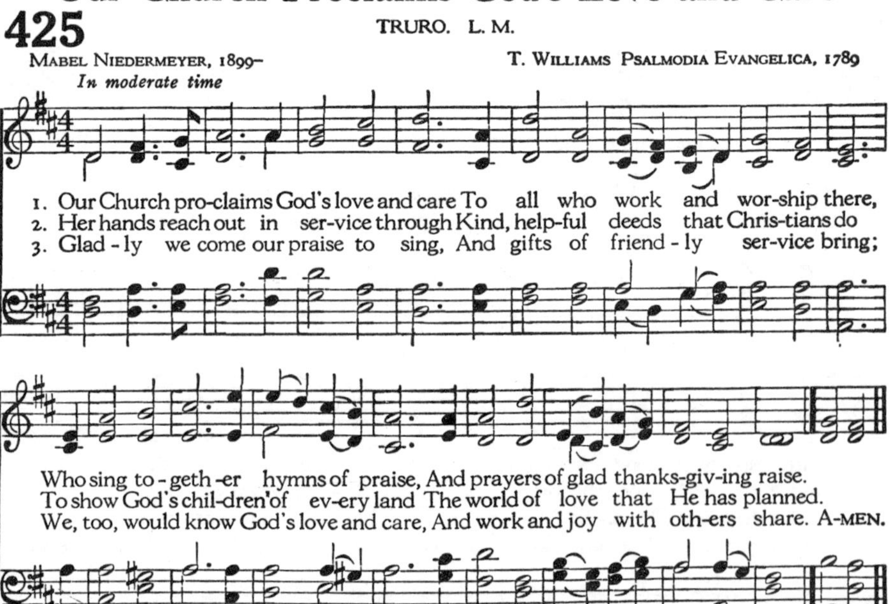
In moderate time
1. Our Church pro-claims God's love and care To all who work and wor-ship there,
2. Her hands reach out in ser-vice through Kind, help-ful deeds that Chris-tians do
3. Glad - ly we come our praise to sing, And gifts of friend - ly ser-vice bring;
Who sing to - geth - er hymns of praise, And prayers of glad thanks-giv-ing raise.
To show God's chil-dren of ev-ery land The world of love that He has planned.
We, too, would know God's love and care, And work and joy with oth-ers share. A-MEN.

City of God, How Broad and Far

NOX PRAECESSIT. C. M.

426

Samuel Johnson, 1822–1882
John B. Calkin, 1827–1905
In moderate time
1. Cit - y of God, how broad and far Out-spread thy walls sub - lime!
2. How pure - ly hath thy speech come down From man's pri - me - val youth!
3. How gleam thy watch-fires thro' the night With nev - er - faint - ing ray!
4. In vain the sur - ge's an - gry shock, In vain the drift - ing sands:
The true thy char-tered free-men are Of ev - ry age and clime.
How grand - ly hath thine em - pire grown Of free - dom, love and truth!
How rise thy tow'rs, se - rene and bright, To meet the dawn - ing day!
Un-harmed up - on th' e - ter-nal Rock Th' e-ter - nal cit - y stands. A - MEN.
O Where Are Kings and Empires Now
ST. ANNE. C. M.
427
A. Cleveland Coxe, 1818–1896
William Croft, 1868–1727
Majestically
1. O where are kings and em - pires now Of old that went and came?
2. We mark her good - ly bat - tle - ments, And her foun - da - tions strong;
3. For not like king-doms of the world Thy ho - ly Church, O God;
4. Un - shak - en as e - ter - nal hills, Im - mov - a - ble she stands,

But, Lord, Thy Church is pray-ing yet, A thou-sand years the same.
We hear with - in the sol - emn voice Of her un - end - ing song.
Tho' earthquake shocks are threat'ning her, And tem - pests are a - broad.
A moun - tain that shall fill the earth, A house not made by hands. A - MEN.

I Love Thy Kingdom, Lord

428

BEALOTH. S. M. D.

TIMOTHY DWIGHT, 1752–1817 — (*First Tune*) — From MASON'S SACRED HARP, 1843

With stateliness, in moderate time

1. I love Thy kingdom, Lord, The house of Thine a - bode, The Church our blest Re -
2. For her my tears shall fall, For her my pray'rs as - cend; To her my cares and
3. Je - sus, Thou Friend divine, Our Sav-iour and our King! Thy hand from ev - 'ry

deem-er saved With His own pre-cious blood. I love Thy Church, O God! Her walls be -
toils be giv'n, Till toils and cares shall end. Be-yond my high-est joy I prize her
snare and foe Shall great de-liv-'rance bring. Sure as Thy truth shall last, To Zi - on

fore Thee stand Dear as the ap-ple of Thine eye, And grav-en on Thy hand.
heav'n-ly ways, Her sweet communion, solemn vows, Her hymns of love and praise.
shall be giv'n The brightest glories earth can yield, And brighter bliss of heav'n. A-MEN.

I Love Thy Kingdom, Lord

429
ST. THOMAS. S. M.
TIMOTHY DWIGHT, 1752–1817
(Second Tune)
WILLIAMS' PSALMODY, 1770
In moderate time
1. I love Thy king - dom, Lord, The house of Thine a - bode,
2. I love Thy Church, O God! Her walls be - fore Thee stand,
3. For her my tears shall fall, For her my prayers as - cend,
4. Be - yond my high - est joy I prize her heavenly ways,
5. Je - sus, Thou Friend di - vine, Our Sav - iour and our King!
6. Sure as Thy truth shall last, To Zi - on shall be given

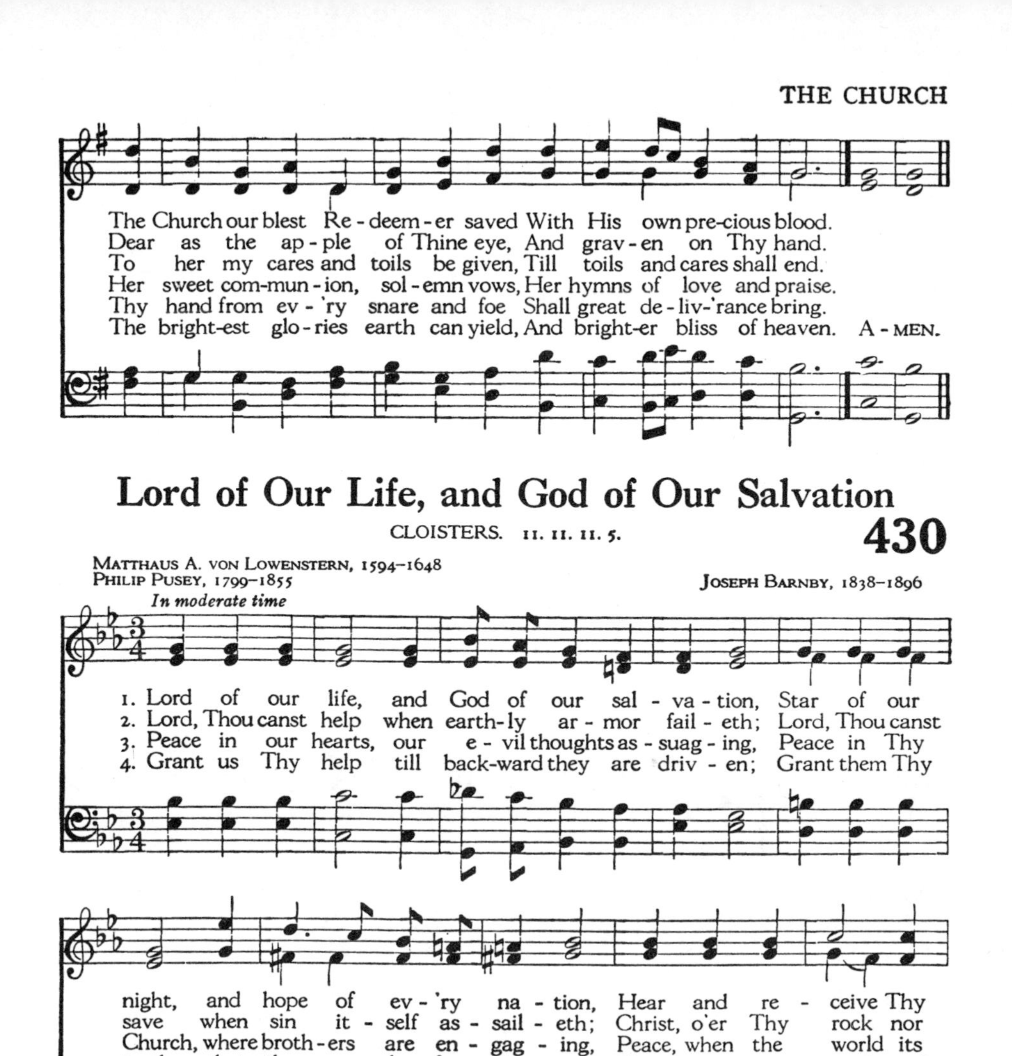
The Church our blest Re-deem-er saved With His own pre-cious blood.
Dear as the ap-ple of Thine eye, And grav-en on Thy hand.
To her my cares and toils be given, Till toils and cares shall end.
Her sweet com-mun-ion, sol-emn vows, Her hymns of love and praise.
Thy hand from ev-'ry snare and foe Shall great de-liv-'rance bring.
The bright-est glo-ries earth can yield, And bright-er bliss of heaven. A-MEN.

Lord of Our Life, and God of Our Salvation

CLOISTERS. 11. 11. 11. 5.

430

MATTHAUS A. VON LOWENSTERN, 1594–1648
PHILIP PUSEY, 1799–1855

JOSEPH BARNBY, 1838–1896

In moderate time

1. Lord of our life, and God of our sal-va-tion, Star of our night, and hope of ev-'ry na-tion, Hear and re-ceive Thy Church's sup-pli-ca-tion, Lord God Al-might-y!
2. Lord, Thou canst help when earth-ly ar-mor fail-eth; Lord, Thou canst save when sin it-self as-sail-eth; Christ, o'er Thy rock nor death nor hell pre-vail-eth; Grant us Thy peace, Lord.
3. Peace in our hearts, our e-vil thoughts as-suag-ing, Peace in Thy Church, where broth-ers are en-gag-ing, Peace, when the world its bus-y war is wag-ing; Calm Thy foes' rag-ing.
4. Grant us Thy help till back-ward they are driv-en; Grant them Thy truth, that they may be for-giv-en; Grant peace on earth, and af-ter we have striv-en, Peace in Thy heav-en. A-MEN.

Glorious Things of Thee Are Spoken

431

AUSTRIAN HYMN. 8. 7. 8. 7. D.

JOHN NEWTON, 1725–1807

FRANZ JOSEPH HAYDN, 1732–1809

Majestically, in moderate time

1. Glo-rious things of thee are spo-ken, Zi-on, cit-y of our God;
2. See, the streams of liv-ing wa-ters, Spring-ing from e-ter-nal Love,
3. Round each hab-i-ta-tion hov-ering, See the cloud and fire ap-pear
He, whose word can-not be bro-ken, Formed thee for His own a-bode:
Well sup-ply thy sons and daugh-ters, And all fear of want re-move:
For a glo-ry and a cov-ering, Show-ing that the Lord is near!
On the Rock of A-ges found-ed, What can shake thy sure re-pose?
Who can faint, while such a riv-er Ev-er flows their thirst t'as-suage?
Glo-rious things of thee are spo-ken, Zi-on, cit-y of our God;
With sal-va-tion's walls sur-round-ed, Thou may'st smile at all thy foes.
Grace which, like the Lord, the Giv-er, Nev-er fails from age to age.
He, whose word can-not be bro-ken, Formed thee for His own a-bode. A-MEN.

O Church of God, Our Solitude Forsaking

FINLANDIA. 11. 10. 11. 10. 11. 9.

432

ROLLAND W. SCHLOERB, 1893–

JEAN SIBELIUS, 1865–

In moderate time

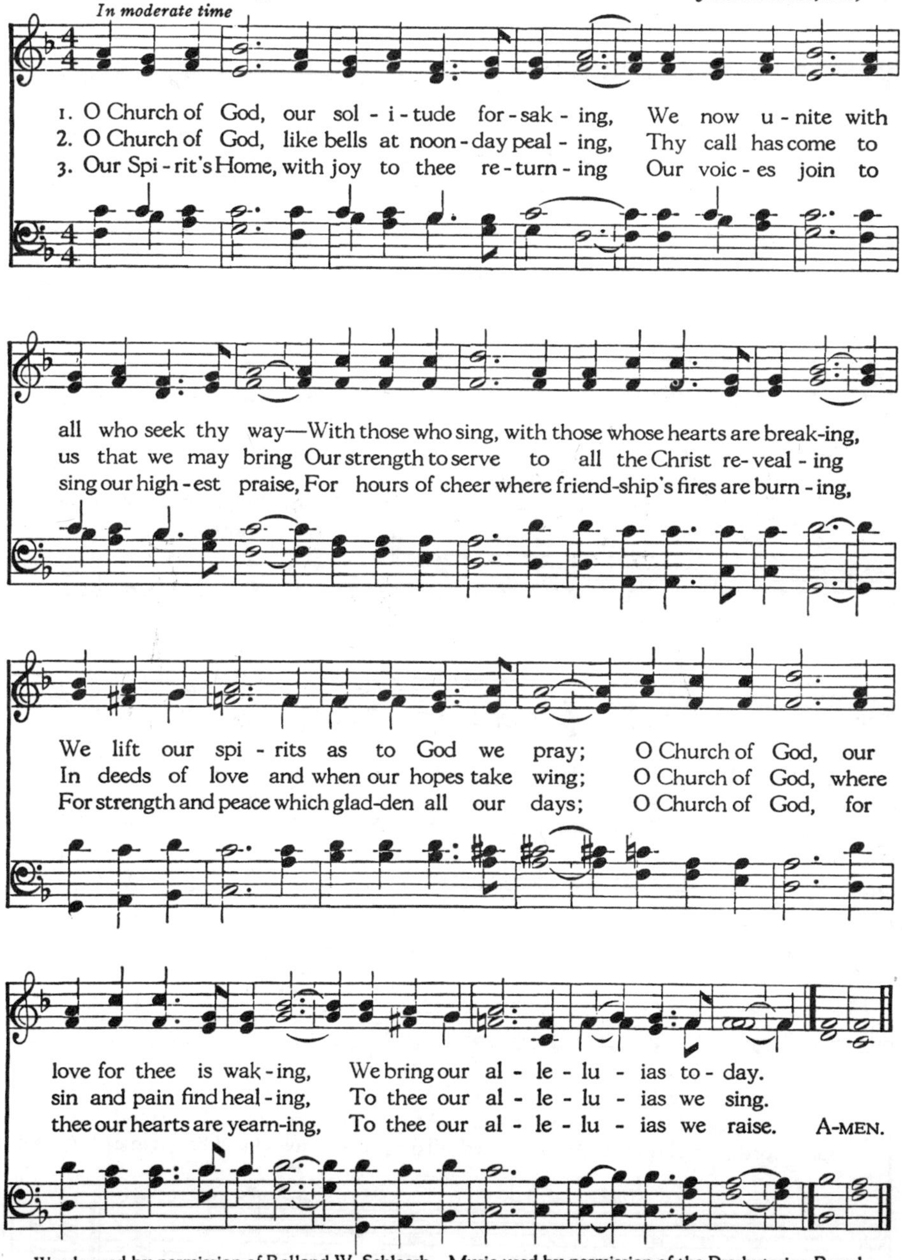

1. O Church of God, our sol - i - tude for - sak - ing, We now u - nite with all who seek thy way—With those who sing, with those whose hearts are break-ing, We lift our spi - rits as to God we pray; O Church of God, our love for thee is wak - ing, We bring our al - le - lu - ias to - day.

2. O Church of God, like bells at noon - day peal - ing, Thy call has come to us that we may bring Our strength to serve to all the Christ re - veal - ing In deeds of love and when our hopes take wing; O Church of God, where sin and pain find heal - ing, To thee our al - le - lu - ias we sing.

3. Our Spi - rit's Home, with joy to thee re - turn - ing Our voic - es join to sing our high - est praise, For hours of cheer where friend-ship's fires are burn - ing, For strength and peace which glad-den all our days; O Church of God, for thee our hearts are yearn-ing, To thee our al - le - lu - ias we raise. A-MEN.

O Church of God, Divided

433

ROTTERDAM. 7. 6. 7. 6. D.

MARION FRANKLIN HAM, 1867–

BERTHOLD TOURS, 1838-1897

In moderate time, with spirit

1. O Church of God, di - vid - ed And rent by end - less strife!
2. The sub - tle powers of dark - ness, Like foe - men in the night,
3. Dis - perse thy war - ring fac - tions, And bid their con - flicts cease;
Thy war - ring sects ob - scur - ing The way, the truth, the life;
Ad - vance up - on the strong-holds Of jus - tice, truth and right;
Lift high the fall - en stan - dard Of Christ, the Prince of Peace;
A strick - en world, de - spair - ing, Is call - ing un - to thee;
The might - y sway of e - vil Pre - vails in ev - ery land;
One Lord, one faith, one spi - rit, One God of all pro - claim;
O Church of Christ's e - van - gel, What shall thine an - swer be?
O Church of God's a - noint - ing, A - rise, and take thy stand!
Go forth, O Church, u - ni - ted, To con - quer in His name! A-MEN.

O Word of God Incarnate

MUNICH. 7. 6. 7. 6. D.

434

William W. How, 1823-1897
With joyous feeling
"Neuvermehrtes Meiningisches Gesangbuch," 1693
1. O Word of God In - car - nate, O Wis - dom from on high,
2. The Church from Thee, her Mas - ter, Re - ceived the gift di - vine,
3. It float - eth like a ban - ner Be - fore God's host un - furled;
4. O make Thy Church, dear Sav - iour, A lamp of pur - est gold,
O Truth un - changed, un - chang - ing, O Light of our dark sky:
And still that light she lift - eth O'er all the earth to shine.
It shin - eth like a bea - con A - bove the dark - ling world.
To bear be - fore the na - tions Thy true light as of old.
We praise Thee for the ra - diance That from the hal - lowed page,
It is the sa - cred cas - ket, Where gems of truth are stored;
It is the chart and com - pass That o'er life's surg - ing sea,
O teach Thy wan-dering pil - grims By this their path to trace,
A lan - tern to our foot - steps, Shines on from age to age.
It is the heaven-drawn pic - ture Of Thee, the liv - ing Word.
'Mid mists and rocks and quick-sands, Still guides, O Christ, to Thee.
Till, clouds and dark - ness end - ed, They see Thee face to face. A - MEN.

There Is a Book That All May Read

435
ARLINGTON. C. M.
JOHN KEBLE, 1792–1866
THOMAS A. ARNE, 1710–1778
In moderate time
1. There is a Book that all may read, Which heav'n-ly truth im - parts,
2. The works of God a - bove, be - low, With - in us and a - round,
3. The glo - rious sky, em - brac - ing all, Is like the Mak-er's love,
4. The dew of heav'n is like Thy grace, It steals in si - lence down;
5. Thou, who hast giv'n me eyes to see, And love this sight so fair,
And all the lore its schol - ars need, Pure eyes and Chris - tian hearts.
Are pa - ges in that Book, to show How God Him - self is found.
Wherewith en-compassed, great and small In peace and or - der move.
But where it lights, the fa-vored place By rich - est fruits is known.
Give me a heart to find out Thee, And read Thee ev - 'ry-where.
A - MEN.
Lamp of Our Feet, Whereby We Trace
436
LAMBETH. C. M.
BERNARD D. BARTON, 1784–1849
WILLIAM A. F. SCHULTHES, 1816–1879
In moderate time
1. Lamp of our feet, where-by we trace Our path, when wont to stray;
2. Bread of our souls, where-on we feed, True man - na from on high;
3. Pil - lar of fire, through watch-es dark, Or ra-diant cloud by day;
4. Word of the ev - er liv - ing God, Will of His glo - rious Son;
Stream from the fount of heaven - ly grace, Brook by the trav-eler's way.
Our guide and chart, where-in we read Of realms be - yond the sky.
When waves would 'whelm our tossing bark Our an - chor and our stay.
With - out thee how could earth be trod, Or heaven it - self be won?
A - MEN.

The Spirit of the Lord Revealed

OLD 137TH. 8. 6. 8. 6. 6. 8. 8. 6.

437

GEORGE W. BRIGGS, 1875–

DAY'S PSALTER, 1563

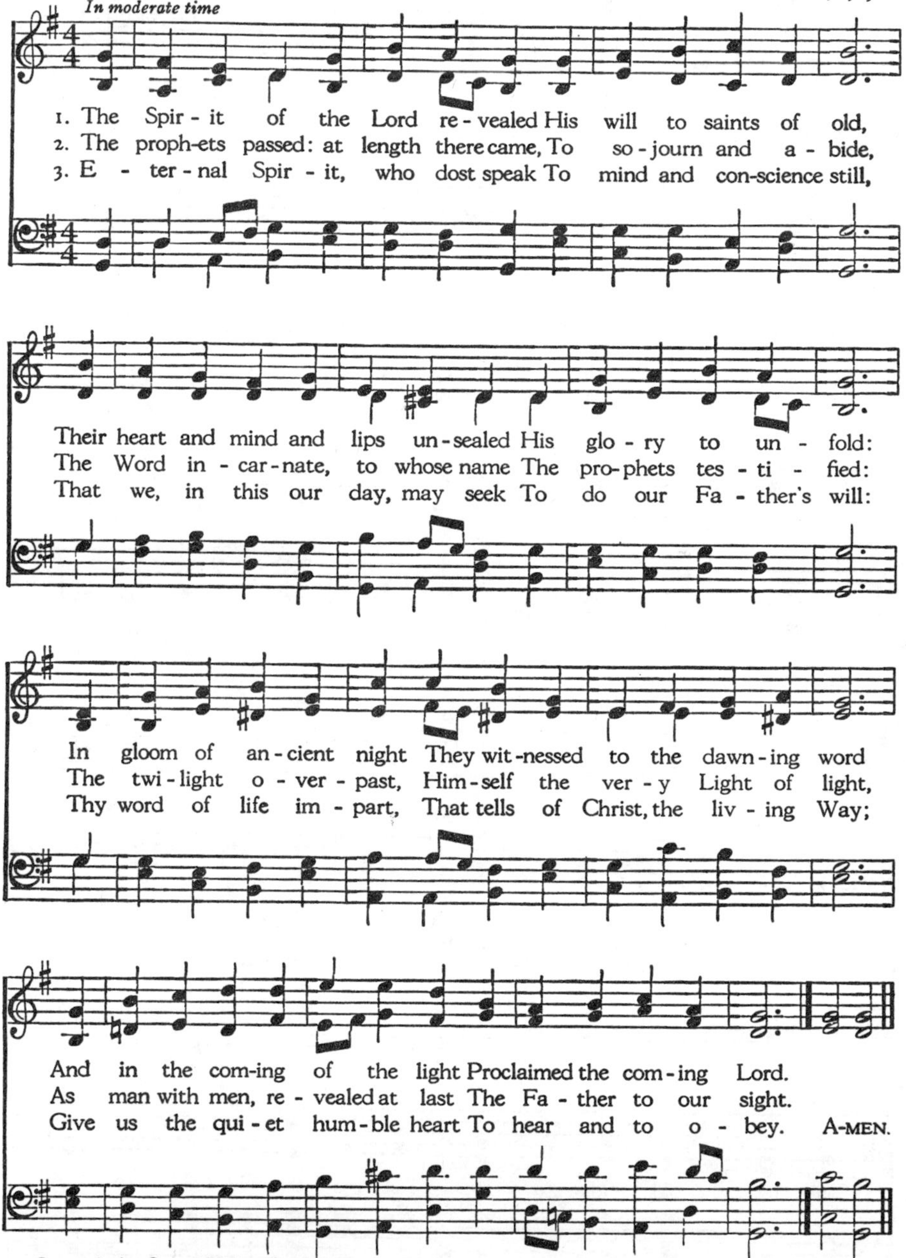

In moderate time

1. The Spir-it of the Lord re-vealed His will to saints of old,
Their heart and mind and lips un-sealed His glo-ry to un-fold:
In gloom of an-cient night They wit-nessed to the dawn-ing word
And in the com-ing of the light Proclaimed the com-ing Lord.

2. The proph-ets passed: at length there came, To so-journ and a-bide,
The Word in-car-nate, to whose name The pro-phets tes-ti-fied:
The twi-light o-ver-past, Him-self the ver-y Light of light,
As man with men, re-vealed at last The Fa-ther to our sight.

3. E-ter-nal Spir-it, who dost speak To mind and con-science still,
That we, in this our day, may seek To do our Fa-ther's will:
Thy word of life im-part, That tells of Christ, the liv-ing Way;
Give us the qui-et hum-ble heart To hear and to o-bey. A-MEN.

Tell Me the Old, Old Story

438

OLD, OLD STORY. 7. 6. 7. 6. D. with Refrain.

KATHERINE HANKEY, 1834-1911

WILLIAM H. DOANE, 1831-1915

In moderate time
1. Tell me the old, old story Of unseen things above,
2. Tell me the story slowly, That I may take it in—
3. Tell me the story softly, With earnest tones, and grave;
Of Jesus and His glory, Of Jesus and His love.
The wonderful redemption, God's remedy for sin.
Remember, I'm the sinner Whom Jesus came to save.
Tell me the story simply, As to a little child;
Tell me the story often, For I forget so soon;
Tell me that story always, If you would really be,
For I am weak and weary, And helpless and defiled.
The early dew of morning Has passed away at noon.
In any time of trouble, A comforter to me.
REFRAIN
Tell me the old, old story, Tell me the old, old story.

Tell me the old, old sto - ry Of Je - sus and His love. A-MEN.

Book of Grace and Book of Glory

STAR OF PEACE. 8. 7. 8. 4. 8. 4.

439

THOMAS MACKELLAR, 1812–?

LOWELL MASON, 1792–1872

In moderate time, with reverence
1. Book of grace and book of glo - ry, Gift of God to age and youth,
2. Book of love in ac - cents ten - der, Speak - ing un - to such as we;
Won - drous is thy sa - cred sto - ry, Bright, bright with truth;
May it lead us, Lord, to ren - der All, all to Thee;
Won - drous is thy sa - cred sto - ry, Bright, bright with truth.
May it lead us, Lord, to ren - der All, all to Thee. A-MEN.

Father of Mercies, in Thy Word
440
SAWLEY. C. M.
ANNE STEELE, 1716–1778
JAMES WALCH, 1836–1901
In moderate time
1. Fa - ther of mer - cies, in Thy word What end - less glo - ry shines;
2. Here the Re - deem - er's wel - come voice Spreads heaven - ly peace a - round;
3. O may these heaven - ly pag - es be My ev - er dear de - light,
4. Di - vine In - struc - tor, gra - cious Lord, Be Thou for - ev - er near;
For - ev - er be Thy name a - dored For these ce - les - tial lines.
And life and ev - er - last - ing joys At - tend the bliss - ful sound.
And still new beau - ties may I see, And still in - creas - ing light.
Teach me to love Thy sa - cred word, And view my Sav - iour there. A - MEN.
The Heavens Declare Thy Glory, Lord
441
UXBRIDGE. L. M.
ISAAC WATTS, 1674–1748
LOWELL MASON, 1792–1872
Majestically
1. The heavens de - clare Thy glo - ry, Lord; In ev - ery star Thy wis - dom shines;
2. The roll - ing sun, the chang - ing light, And night and day, Thy power con - fess;
3. Sun, moon, and stars con - vey Thy praise Round the whole earth, and nev - er stand;
4. Nor shall Thy spreading gos - pel rest Till through the world Thy truth has run;
But when our eyes be - hold Thy Word, We read Thy Name in fair - er lines.
But the blest volume Thou hast writ Re - veals Thy jus - tice and Thy grace.
So when Thy truth be - gan its race, It touched and glanced on every land.
Till Christ has all the na - tions blest That see the light, or feel the sun. A - MEN.

Sing Them Over Again to Me

WONDERFUL WORDS OF LIFE. 8. 6. 8. 6. 6. 6. with Refrain

442

PHILIP P. BLISS, 1838–1876 PHILIP P. BLISS, 1838–1876

Joyfully
1. Sing them o - ver a - gain to me, Won-der - ful words of Life;
2. Christ, the bless - ed One, gives to all, Won-der - ful words of Life;
3. Sweet - ly ech - o the gos - pel call, Won-der - ful words of Life;
Let me more of their beau - ty see, Won - der - ful words of Life.
Sin - ner, list to the lov - ing call, Won - der - ful words of Life.
Of - fer par-don and peace to all, Won - der - ful words of Life.
Words of life and beau - ty, Teach me faith and du - ty;
All so free - ly giv - en, Woo - ing us to heav - en;
Je - sus, on - ly Sav - iour, Sanc - ti - fy for - ev - er;
REFRAIN
Beau - ti - ful words, won - der - ful words, Won-der - ful words of Life, . . .
Beau -ti - ful words, won-der -ful words, Won-der- ful words of Life.
A-MEN.

O Day of Rest and Gladness

443

MENDEBRAS. 7. 6. 7. 6. D.

CHRISTOPHER WORDSWORTH, 1807–1885, alt. — LOWELL MASON, 1792–1872

Joyfully

1. O day of rest and glad-ness, O day of joy and light:
2. This day, on hun - gry na - tions, The heav'n-ly man - na falls;
3. New gra - ces ev - er gain - ing From this sweet day of rest,

A balm for care and sad - ness, Most beau - ti - ful and bright!
To ho - ly con - vo - ca - tions The gos - pel mes - sage calls;
Type of the rest re - main - ing For spir - its of the blest,

This day the meek and low - ly, Bowed down be - fore the throne,
The light from heav'n is glow - ing With pure and ra - diant beams,
There we shall share the glo - ry With all the saints a - bove,

Sing, ho - ly, ho - ly, ho - ly, Is the E - ter - nal One.
And liv - ing wa - ters flow - ing In soul - re - fresh - ing streams.
And sing the won-drous sto - ry Of Je - sus' dy - ing love. A - MEN.

Welcome, Delightful Morn

LISCHER. 6. 6. 6. 6. 8. 8. 8.

444

THOMAS HAYWARD in JOHN DOBELL'S COLLECTION, 1806 — FRIEDRICH SCHNEIDER, 1786–1853

In moderate time, joyfully

1. Wel-come, de-light-ful morn, Thou day of sa-cred rest!
2. Now may the King de-scend, And fill His throne with grace;
3. De-scend, ce-les-tial Dove, With all Thy quick-ening powers;

I hail thy kind re-turn; Lord, make these mo-ments blest:
Thy scep-ter, Lord, ex-tend, While saints ad-dress Thy face:
Dis-close a Sav-iour's love, And bless the sa-cred hours:

From the low plane of mor-tal toys I soar to reach im-
Let sin-ners feel Thy quick-ening word, And learn to know and
Then shall my soul new life ob-tain, Nor wor-ship be en-

mor-tal joys I soar to reach im-mor-tal joys.
fear the Lord, And learn to know and fear the Lord.
joyed in vain, Nor wor-ship be en-joyed in vain. A-MEN.

Light of Light, Enlighten Me

445

HINCHMAN. 7. 8. 7. 8. 7. 7.

BENJAMIN SCHMOLCK, 1672–1737
Trs. by CATHERINE WINKWORTH, 1829–1878

UZZIAH C. BURNAP, 1834–1900

In moderate time, with dignity

1. Light of Light, en - light-en me, Now a - new the day is dawn - ing;
2. Fount of all our joy and peace, To Thy liv - ing wa - ters lead me;
3. Kin - dle Thou the sac - ri - fice That up - on my lips is ly - ing,
4. Let me, with my heart to - day, Ho - ly, ho - ly, ho - ly, sing - ing,
Sun of grace, the shad-ows flee; Bright-en Thou my Lord's Day morn - ing;
Thou from earth my soul re - lease, And with grace and mer - cy feed me;
Clear the shad-ows from my eyes, That, from ev - ery er - ror fly - ing,
Rapt a - while from earth a - way, All my soul to Thee up-spring - ing,
With Thy joy - ous sun-shine blest, Hap - py is my day of rest.
Bless Thy word, that it may prove Rich in fruits that Thou dost love.
No strange fire may in me glow That Thine al - tar doth not know.
Have a fore-taste in - ly given How they wor - ship Thee in heaven. A - MEN.

This Is the Day of Light

446

STATE STREET. S. M.

JOHN ELLERTON, 1826–1893

JOHNATHAN C. WOODMAN, 1813–1894

In moderate time

1. This is the day of light: Let there be light to - day;
2. This is the day of rest: Our fail - ing strength re - new;
3. This is the day of peace: Thy peace our spir - its fill;
4. This is the day of prayer: Let earth to heaven draw near;
5. This is the first of days: Send forth Thy quicken - ing breath,

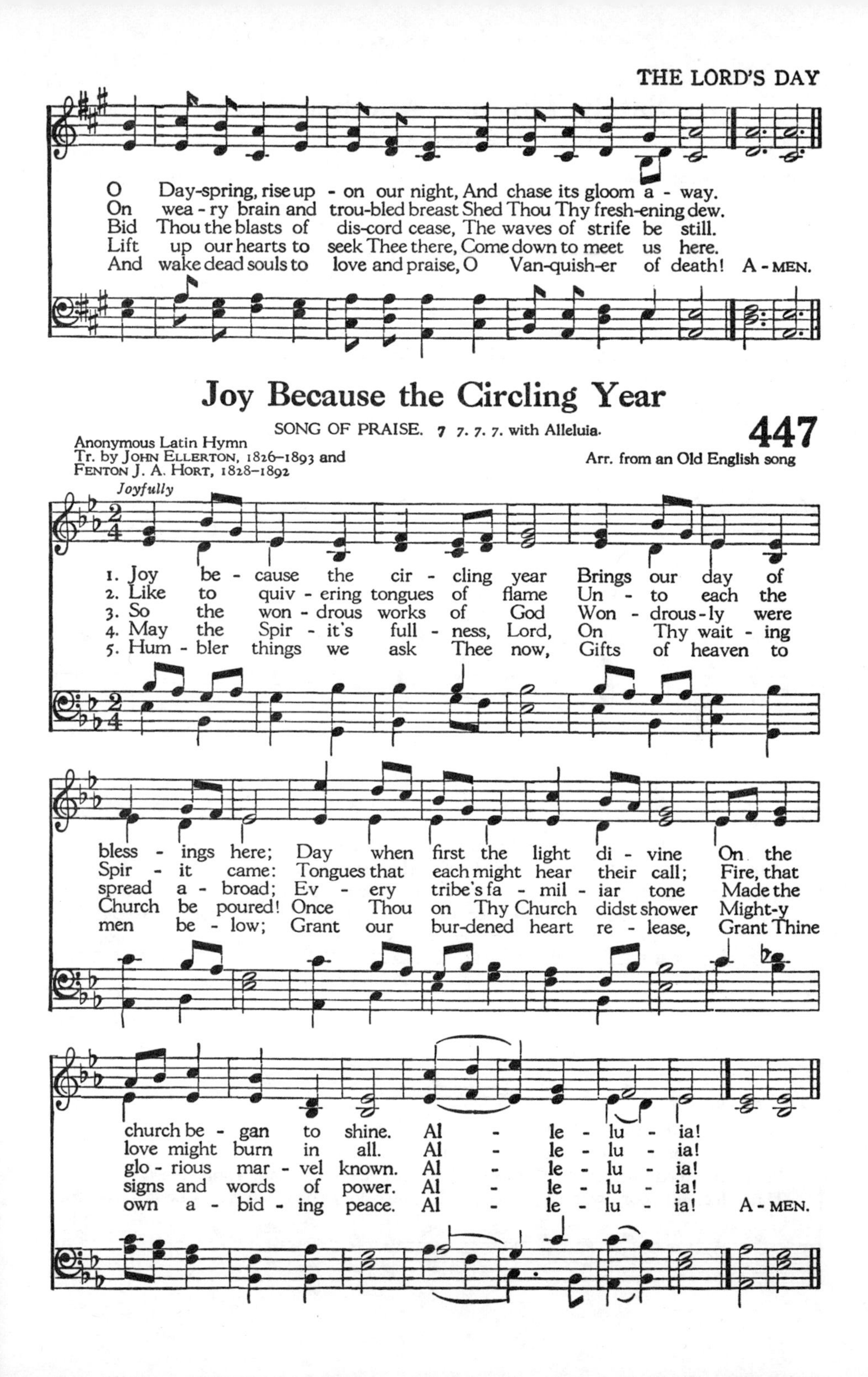
THE LORD'S DAY
O Day-spring, rise up - on our night, And chase its gloom a - way.
On wea - ry brain and trou-bled breast Shed Thou Thy fresh-ening dew.
Bid Thou the blasts of dis-cord cease, The waves of strife be still.
Lift up our hearts to seek Thee there, Come down to meet us here.
And wake dead souls to love and praise, O Van-quish-er of death! A - MEN.
Joy Because the Circling Year
SONG OF PRAISE. 7 7. 7. 7. with Alleluia.
447
Anonymous Latin Hymn
Tr. by JOHN ELLERTON, 1826–1893 and
FENTON J. A. HORT, 1828–1892
Arr. from an Old English song
Joyfully
1. Joy be - cause the cir - cling year Brings our day of bless - ings here; Day when first the light di - vine On the church be - gan to shine. Al - le - lu - ia!
2. Like to quiv - ering tongues of flame Un - to each the Spir - it came: Tongues that each might hear their call; Fire, that love might burn in all. Al - le - lu - ia!
3. So the won - drous works of God Won - drous - ly were spread a - broad; Ev - ery tribe's fa - mil - iar tone Made the glo - rious mar - vel known. Al - le - lu - ia!
4. May the Spir - it's full - ness, Lord, On Thy wait - ing Church be poured! Once Thou on Thy Church didst shower Might-y signs and words of power. Al - le - lu - ia!
5. Hum - bler things we ask Thee now, Gifts of heaven to men be - low; Grant our bur-dened heart re - lease, Grant Thine own a - bid - ing peace. Al - le - lu - ia! A - MEN.

Safely Through Another Week

448

SABBATH. 7. 7. 7. 7. D.

JOHN NEWTON, 1725–1807
LOWELL MASON, 1792–1872
In moderate time
1. Safe - ly through an - oth - er week God has brought us on our way;
2. While we pray for par-doning grace, Thro' the dear Re-deem-er's Name,
3. Here we come Thy Name to praise; May we feel Thy pres-ence near:
4. May Thy gos - pel's joy - ful sound Con - quer sin - ners, com - fort saints;
Let us now a bless - ing seek, Wait - ing in His courts to - day:
Show Thy rec - on - cil - ed face, Take a - way our sin and shame;
May Thy glo - ry meet our eyes, While we in Thy house ap - pear:
Make the fruits of grace a - bound, Bring re - lief for all com-plaints:
Day of all the week the best, Em - blem of e - ter - nal rest;
From our world - ly cares set free, May we rest this day in Thee;
Here af - ford us, Lord, a taste Of our ev - er - last - ing feast;
Thus let all our wor-ship prove, Till we join the Church a - bove;
Day of all the week the best, Em - blem of e - ter - nal rest.
From our world - ly cares set free, May we rest this day in Thee.
Here af - ford us, Lord, a taste Of our ev - er - last - ing feast.
Thus let all our wor-ship prove, Till we join the Church a - bove. A-MEN.

O God, Thy Summons Still Is Heard

SERENITY. C. M.

449

ROLLAND W. SCHLOERB, 1893–

WILLIAM V. WALLACE, 1814–1865

In moderate time

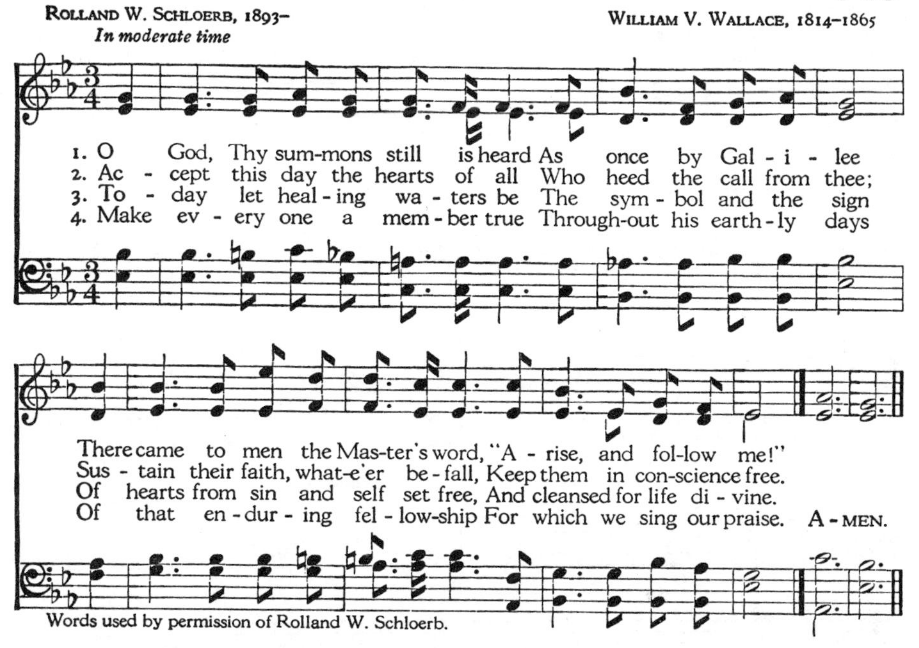
1. O God, Thy sum-mons still is heard As once by Gal - i - lee
2. Ac - cept this day the hearts of all Who heed the call from thee;
3. To - day let heal-ing wa - ters be The sym - bol and the sign
4. Make ev - ery one a mem - ber true Through-out his earth-ly days
There came to men the Mas-ter's word, "A - rise, and fol-low me!"
Sus - tain their faith, what-e'er be-fall, Keep them in con-science free.
Of hearts from sin and self set free, And cleansed for life di - vine.
Of that en-dur - ing fel - low-ship For which we sing our praise. A - MEN.

Words used by permission of Rolland W. Schloerb.

Here, Saviour, We Would Come

TRENTHAM. S. M.

450

Anonymous
From ALEXANDER CAMPBELL'S CHRISTIAN HYMN BOOK.

ROBERT JACKSON, 1842–1914

In moderate time

1. Here, Sav-iour, we would come, In Thine ap-point - ed way; O - be-dient
2. O bless this sa - cred rite, To bring us near to Thee; And may we
to thy high com-mands, Our sol - emn vows we pay.
find that as our day, Our strength shall al - so be. A - MEN.

Here at Thy Table, Lord

451

BREAD OF LIFE. 6. 4. 6. 4. D.

MAY P. HOYT — WILLIAM F. SHERWIN, 1826–1888

In moderate time

1. Here at Thy ta - ble, Lord, This sa - cred hour, O let us
2. Sit at the feast, dear Lord, Break Thou the bread; Fill Thou the
3. So shall our life of faith Be full, be sweet; And we shall
4. Come then, O ho - ly Christ, Feed us, we pray; Touch with Thy

feel Thee near, In lov - ing pow'r; Call - ing our thoughts a - way
cup that brings Life to the dead; That we may find in Thee,
find our strength For each day meet; Fed by Thy liv - ing bread,
pierc-ed hand Each com - mon day; Mak - ing this earth - ly life

From self and sin, As to Thy ban-quet hall We en - ter in.
Par - don and peace; And from all bond-age win A full re - lease.
All hun - ger past, We shall be sat - is-fied, And saved at last.
Full of Thy grace, Till in the home of heav'n We find our place. A-MEN.

O God, Unseen, Yet Ever Near

452

BELMONT. C. M.

Anonymous — Adapted from SACRED MELODIES, WILLIAM GARDINER, 1770-1853

In moderate time

1. O God, un-seen, yet ev - er near, Re - veal Thy pres-ence now,
2. Here may o - be-dient spir - its find The bless-ings of Thy love—
3. A - while be-side the fount we stay And eat this bread of Thine;

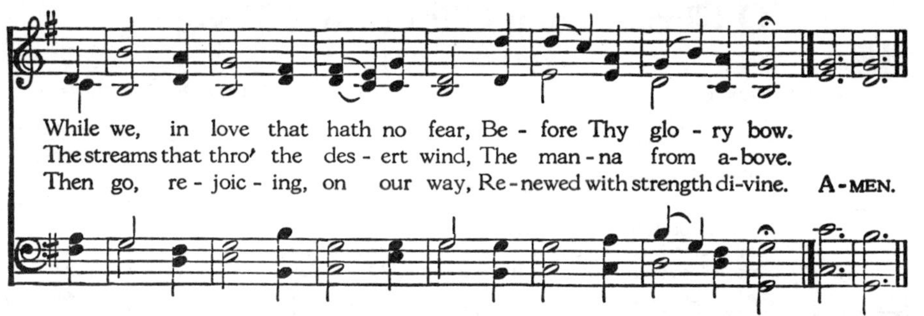
While we, in love that hath no fear, Be - fore Thy glo - ry bow.
The streams that thro' the des - ert wind, The man - na from a - bove.
Then go, re - joic - ing, on our way, Re - newed with strength di - vine. A - MEN.

Bread of the World in Mercy Broken

EUCHARISTIC HYMN. 9. 8. 9. 8.

453

REGINALD HEBER, 1783–1826

JOHN S. B. HODGES, 1830–1915

Slowly and reverently

1. Bread of the world in mer - cy bro - ken, Wine of the
2. Look on the heart by sor - row bro - ken, Look on the
soul in mer - cy shed, By whom the words of
tears by sin - ners shed; And be Thy feast to
life were spo-ken, And in whose death our sins are dead;
us the to-ken That by Thy grace our souls are fed. A - MEN.

O Christ, Thou Gift of Love Divine!

454

MEMORY. C. M.

CHARLES H. HARMER, 1865-. CHARLES H. HARMER, 1865-

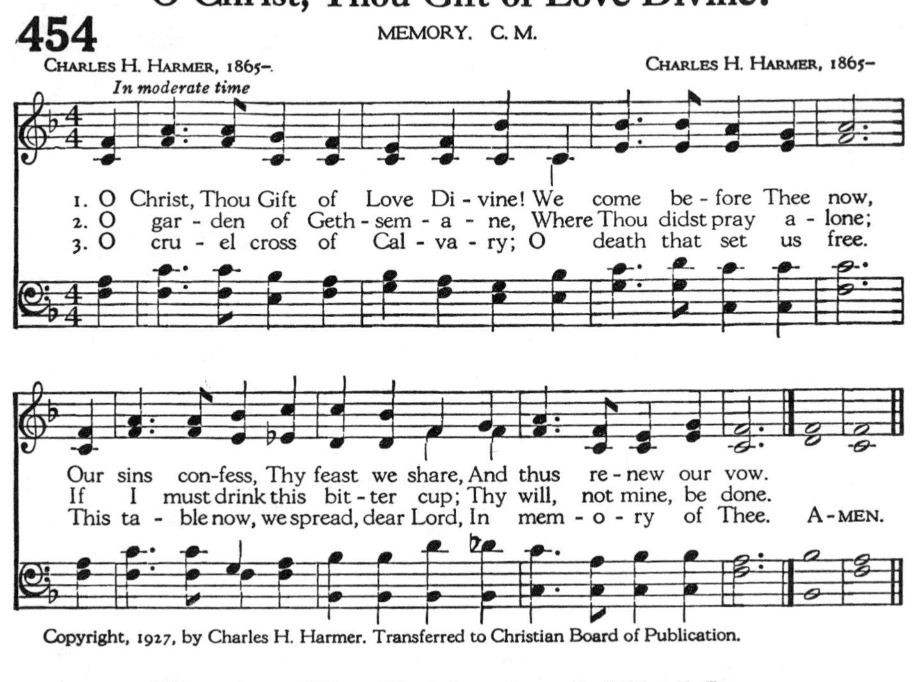
In moderate time
1. O Christ, Thou Gift of Love Di - vine! We come be - fore Thee now,
2. O gar - den of Geth - sem - a - ne, Where Thou didst pray a - lone;
3. O cru - el cross of Cal - va - ry; O death that set us free.
Our sins con-fess, Thy feast we share, And thus re - new our vow.
If I must drink this bit - ter cup; Thy will, not mine, be done.
This ta - ble now, we spread, dear Lord, In mem - o - ry of Thee. A - MEN.

Here at Thy Table, Lord, We Meet

455

AVON (MARTYRDOM). C. M.

SAMUEL STENNETT, 1728-1795 HUGH WILSON, 1766-1824

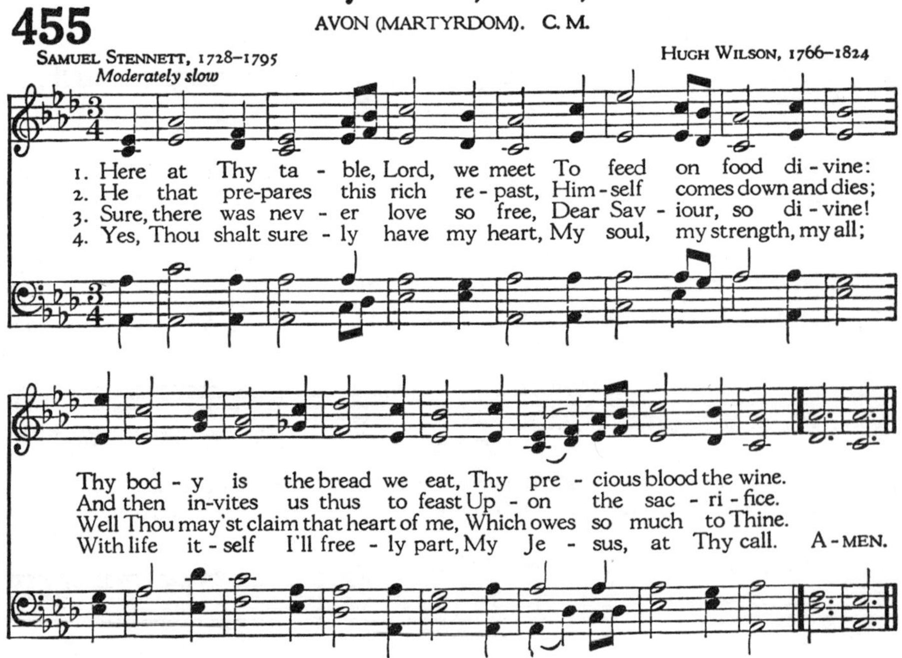
Moderately slow
1. Here at Thy ta - ble, Lord, we meet To feed on food di - vine:
2. He that pre-pares this rich re - past, Him - self comes down and dies;
3. Sure, there was nev - er love so free, Dear Sav - iour, so di - vine!
4. Yes, Thou shalt sure - ly have my heart, My soul, my strength, my all;
Thy bod - y is the bread we eat, Thy pre - cious blood the wine.
And then in - vites us thus to feast Up - on the sac - ri - fice.
Well Thou may'st claim that heart of me, Which owes so much to Thine.
With life it - self I'll free - ly part, My Je - sus, at Thy call. A - MEN.

According to Thy Gracious Word
456
BEATITUDO. C. M.
JAMES MONTGOMERY, 1771–1854
In moderate time
JOHN B. DYKES, 1823–1876
1. Ac - cord-ing to Thy gra - cious word, In meek hu - mil - i - ty,
2. Thy bod - y, bro - ken for my sake, My bread from heav'n shall be;
3. When to the cross I turn mine eyes, And rest on Cal - va - ry,
4. Re - mem - ber Thee, and all Thy pains, And all Thy love to me;
5. And when these fail - ing lips grow dumb, And mind and mem - 'ry flee,
This will I do, my dy - ing Lord, I will re - mem - ber Thee.
Thy tes - ta - ment - al cup I take, And thus re - mem - ber Thee.
O Lamb of God, my sac - ri - fice, I must re - mem - ber Thee.
Yea, while a breath, a pulse re - mains, Will I re - mem - ber Thee.
When Thou shalt in Thy king-dom come, Je - sus, re - mem - ber me.
A - MEN.
Blest Feast of Love Divine
457
THATCHER. S. M.
EDWARD DENNY, 1796–1889
GEORGE F. HANDEL, 1685–1759
In moderate time
1. Blest feast of love di - vine! 'Tis grace that makes us free
2. That blood which flowed for sin, In sym - bol here we see,
3. O if this glimpse of love Be so di - vine - ly sweet,
4. To see Thee face to face, Thy per - fect like - ness wear,
To feed up - on this bread and wine, In mem-'ry, Lord, of Thee!
And feel the bless - ed pledge with - in, That we are loved of Thee.
What will it be, O Lord, a - bove, Thy gladd'ning smile to meet!
And all Thy ways of won - drous grace Thro' end - less years de - clare!
A - MEN.

458 Here, O My Lord, I See Thee Face to Face

CONSOLATION. 10. 10. 10. 10.

HORATIUS BONAR, 1808–1889 — FELIX MENDELSSOHN, 1809–1847

Rather slowly, with deep reverence

1. Here, O my Lord, I see thee face to face;
Here would I touch and handle things unseen;
Here grasp with firmer hand th'eternal grace,
And all my weariness upon thee lean.

2. Here would I feed upon the bread of God;
Here drink with thee the royal wine of heav'n;
Here would I lay aside each earthly load;
Here taste afresh the calm of sin forgiv'n.

3. Too soon we rise; the symbols disappear;
The feast, tho' not the love, is past and gone;
The bread and wine remove, but thou art here—
Nearer than ever— still my Shield and Sun.

4. Feast after feast thus comes and passes by;
Yet, passing, points to the glad feast above—
Giving sweet foretaste of the festal joy,
The Lamb's great bridal feast of bliss and love.

A-MEN.

Beneath the Forms of Outward Rite

BELMONT. C. M.

459

JAMES A. BLAISDELL, 1867–

In moderate time

Adapted from SACRED MELODIES
WILLIAM GARDINER, 1770-1853

1. Be-neath the forms of out-ward rite Thy sup-per, Lord, is spread
In ev-'ry qui-et up-per room Where faint-ing souls are fed.

2. The bread is al-ways con-se-crate Which men di-vide with men;
And ev-'ry act of broth-er-hood Re-peats Thy feast a-gain.

3. The bless-ed cup is on-ly passed True mem-o-ry of Thee,
When life a-new pours out its wine With rich suf-fi-cien-cy.

4. O Mas-ter, through these sym-bols shared, Thine own dear self im-part,
That in our dai-ly life may flame The pas-sion of Thy heart. A-MEN.

While in Sweet Communion Feeding

KNOWSLEY. 8. 7. 8. 7.

460

EDWARD DENNY, 1796–1889

In moderate time

EDWARD J. HOPKINS, 1818–1901

1. While in sweet com-mun-ion feed-ing On this earth-ly bread and wine,
Sav-iour, may we see Thee bleed-ing On the cross, to make us Thine.

2. Though un-seen, now be Thou near us; With the still small voice of love,
Whisp'ring words of peace to cheer us, Ev-ry doubt and fear re-move.

3. Bring be-fore us all the sto-ry Of Thy life and death of woe;
And, with hopes of end-less glo-ry, Wean our hearts from all be-low. A-MEN.

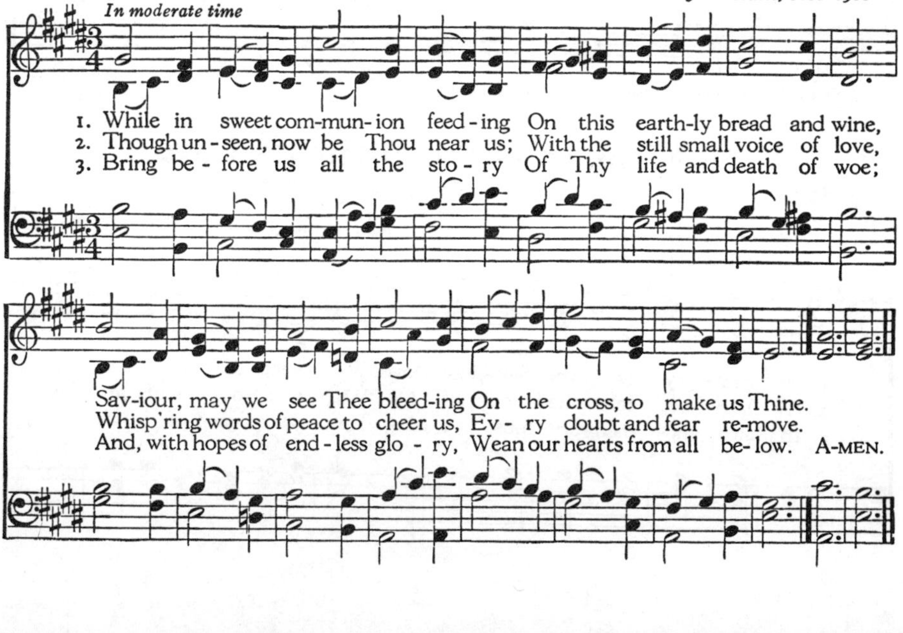

Break Thou the Bread of Life

461

BREAD OF LIFE. 6. 4. 6. 4. D.

MARY A. LATHBURY, 1841–1913

WILLIAM F. SHERWIN, 1826–1888

In moderate time, with flowing rhythm
1. Break Thou the bread of life, Dear Lord, to me, As Thou didst break the loaves Beside the sea; Beyond the sacred page I seek Thee, Lord; My spirit pants for Thee, O living Word!
2. Bless Thou the truth, dear Lord, To me—to me, As Thou didst bless the bread By Galilee; Then shall all bondage cease, All fetters fall; And I shall find my peace, My All-in-All. A-MEN.

Courtesy Chautauqua Institution, Chautauqua, N. Y.

In Memory of the Saviour's Love

462

SALZBURG. C. M.

THOMAS COTTERILL, 1779–1823

Adapted from JOHANN M. HAYDN, 1737–1806

In moderate time

1. In memory of the Saviour's love, We keep the sacred feast,
2. By faith we take the bread of life With which our souls are fed,
3. In faith and memory thus we sing The wonders of His love,

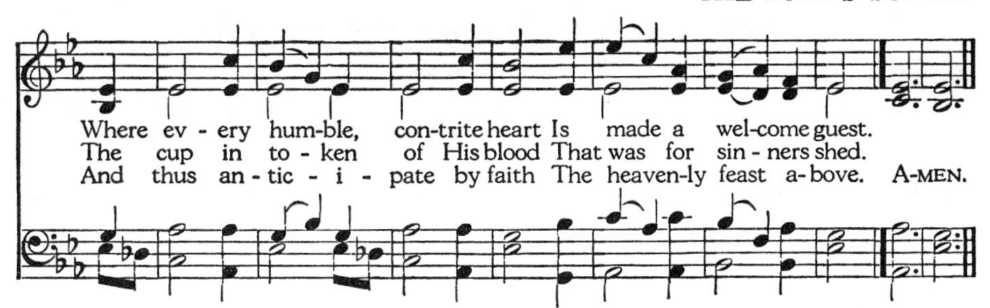
Where ev - ery hum-ble, con-trite heart Is made a wel-come guest.
The cup in to - ken of His blood That was for sin - ners shed.
And thus an - tic - i - pate by faith The heaven-ly feast a - bove. A-MEN.

For the Bread, Which Thou Hast Broken

AGAPÉ. 8. 7. 8. 7.

463

LOUIS F. BENSON, 1855–1930

CHARLES J. DICKINSON, 1822–1883

In moderate time
1. For the bread, which Thou hast bro - ken; For the wine, which Thou hast poured; For the words, which Thou hast spo - ken; Now we give Thee thanks, O Lord.
2. By this pledge that Thou dost love us, By Thy gift of peace re - stored, By Thy call to heaven a - bove us, Hal - low all our lives, O Lord.
3. With our saint - ed ones in glo - ry Seat - ed at our Fa - ther's board, May the Church that wait - eth for Thee Keep love's tie un - bro - ken, Lord.
4. In Thy serv - ice, Lord, de - fend us; In our hearts keep watch and ward; In the world where Thou dost send us Let Thy King - dom come, O Lord. A - MEN.

Words used by permission of Mrs. Robert F. Jefferys.

Lord, at Thy Table We Behold

464

CHIMES. C. M.

JOSEPH STENNETT, 1663–1713 — LOWELL MASON, 1792–1872

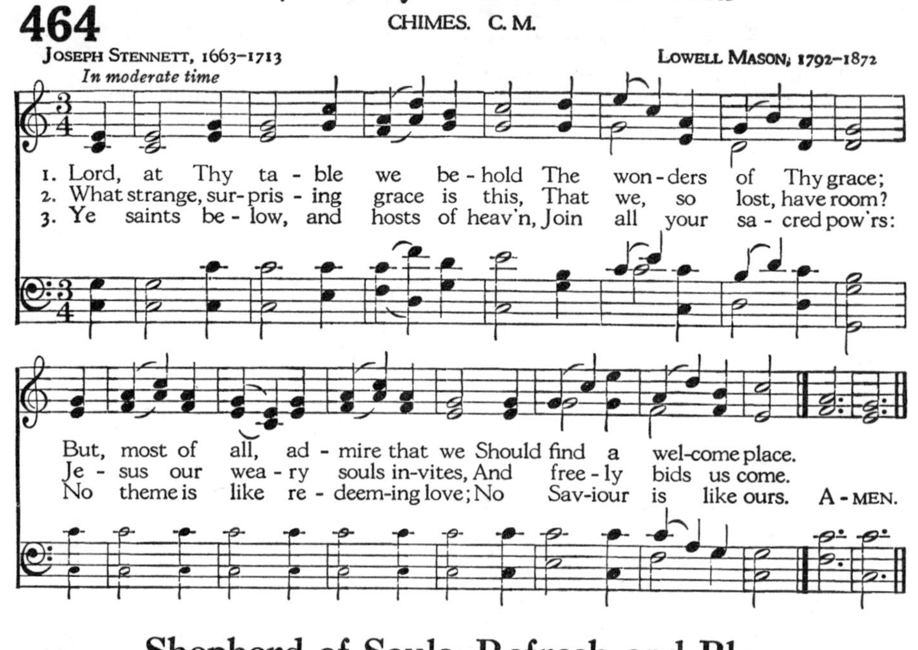
In moderate time
1. Lord, at Thy ta - ble we be - hold The won - ders of Thy grace;
2. What strange, sur - pris - ing grace is this, That we, so lost, have room?
3. Ye saints be - low, and hosts of heav'n, Join all your sa - cred pow'rs:
But, most of all, ad - mire that we Should find a wel-come place.
Je - sus our wea - ry souls in - vites, And free - ly bids us come.
No theme is like re - deem - ing love; No Sav - iour is like ours.
A - MEN.

Shepherd of Souls, Refresh and Bless

465

ST. AGNES. C. M.

JAMES MONTGOMERY, 1771–1854 — JOHN B. DYKES, 1823–1876

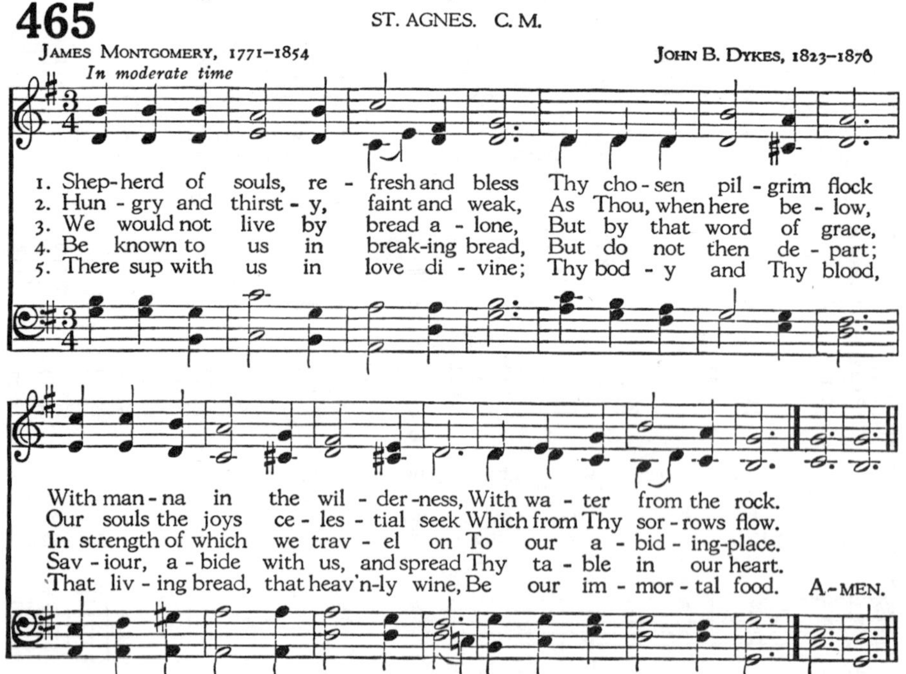
In moderate time
1. Shep - herd of souls, re - fresh and bless Thy cho - sen pil - grim flock
2. Hun - gry and thirst - y, faint and weak, As Thou, when here be - low,
3. We would not live by bread a - lone, But by that word of grace,
4. Be known to us in break - ing bread, But do not then de - part;
5. There sup with us in love di - vine; Thy bod - y and Thy blood,
With man - na in the wil - der - ness, With wa - ter from the rock.
Our souls the joys ce - les - tial seek Which from Thy sor - rows flow.
In strength of which we trav - el on To our a - bid - ing - place.
Sav - iour, a - bide with us, and spread Thy ta - ble in our heart.
That liv - ing bread, that heav'n - ly wine, Be our im - mor - tal food.
A - MEN.

Lord of Our Highest Love!

FRANCONIA. S. M.

466

G. Y. TICKLE, 1819–1888

W. H. HAVERGAL, 1793–1870
(Founded on a melody by J. B. KÖNIG)

In a reverent manner, in moderate time
1. Lord of our high - est love! Let now Thy peace be given;
2. Then, dear - est Lord, draw near, Whilst we Thy ta - ble spread;
3. And when the loaf we break, Thine own rich bless - ing give,
4. Dear Lord! what mem - ories crowd A - round the sa - cred cup!
5. O scenes of suf - fering love, E - nough our souls to win—
Fix all our thoughts on things a - bove, Our hearts on Thee in heaven.
And crown the feast with heaven-ly cheer, Thy - self the liv - ing Bread.
May all with lov - ing hearts par-take And all new strength re-ceive.
The up - per room! Geth-sem - a - ne! Thy foes! Thy lift - ing up!
E - nough to melt our hearts and prove The an - ti - dote of sin.
A - MEN.

Words from "The Christian Hymnary."

A Holy Air Is Breathing Round

NAOMI. C. M.

467

ABIEL ABBOT LIVERMORE, 1811–?

HANS G. NAEGELI, 1768–1836
Arr. by LOWELL MASON, 1792–1872

In moderate time
1. A ho - ly air is breathing round, A fra-grance from a - bove:
2. O God, u - nite us heart to heart, In sym - pa - thy di - vine,
3. But by the cross of Je - sus taught, And all his gra - cious word,
Be ev - 'ry soul from sense unbound, Be ev - 'ry spir-it love.
That we be nev - er drawn a-part, To love not thee nor thine.
Be near - er to each oth - er bro't, And near - er thee, O Lord.
A - MEN.

From the Table Now Retiring

468
DORRNANCE. 8. 7. 8. 7.
John Rowe, 1764–1833
Isaac B. Woodbury, 1819–1858
In moderate time
1. From the table now re-tir-ing Which for us the Lord hath spread,
May our souls, re-freshment find-ing, Grow in all things like our Head.
2. His ex-am-ple while be-hold-ing, May our lives His im-age bear;
Him our Lord and Mas-ter call-ing, His commands may we re-vere.
3. Love to God and man dis-play-ing, Walk-ing stead-fast in His way,
Joy at-tend us in be-liev-ing, Peace from God thro' endless day. A-men.
A Parting Hymn We Sing
469
BOYLSTON. S. M.
Aaron R. Wolfe, 1831–1902
Lowell Mason, 1792–1872
In moderate time
1. A part-ing hymn we sing A-round Thy ta-ble, Lord;
A-gain our grate-ful trib-ute bring, Our sol-emn vows re-cord.
2. Here have we seen Thy face, And felt Thy pres-ence here;
So may the sav-or of Thy grace In word and life ap-pear.
3. In self-for-get-ting love Be our com-mun-ion shown,
Un-til we join the church a-bove, And know as we are known. A-men.

Lord, Speak to Me, That I May Speak

HOLLEY. L. M.

470

FRANCES R. HAVERGAL, 1836–1879

GEORGE HEWS, 1806–1873

In moderate time

1. Lord, speak to me, that I may speak In living echoes of Thy tone; As Thou hast sought, so let me seek, Thy erring children lost and lone.
2. O strengthen me, that while I stand Firm on the Rock, and strong in Thee, I may stretch out a loving hand To wrestlers with the troubled sea.
3. O teach me, Lord, that I may teach The precious things Thou dost impart; And wing my words, that they may reach The hidden depths of many a heart.
4. O fill me with Thy fulness, Lord, Until my very heart o'erflow In kindling tho't and glowing word, Thy love to tell, Thy praise to show.
5. O use me, Lord, use even me, Just as Thou wilt, and when, and where; Until Thy blessed face I see, Thy rest, Thy joy, Thy glory share. Amen.

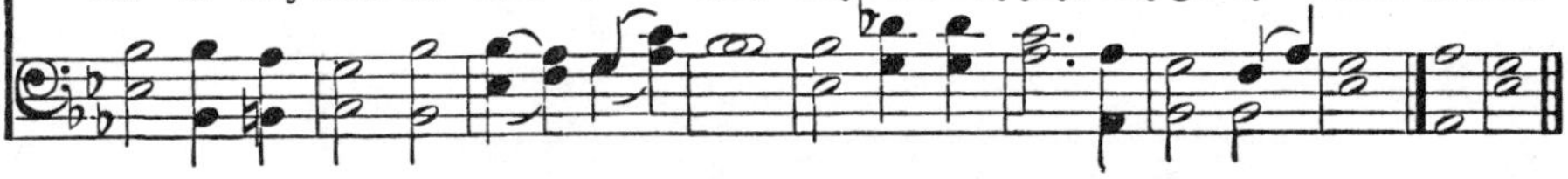

O Men of God, Go Forth to Win

WINCHESTER, NEW. L. M.

471

THOMAS TIPLADY, 1882–

MUSIKALISCHES HANDBUCH, 1690

In moderate time, with earnestness

1. O men of God, go forth to win The world for Jesus Christ your Lord; With faith that glows, and love that burns, Proclaim to all His gracious Word.
2. To North and South, to East and West, Go forth in Christ's most holy Name; On every hill a beacon light, And set the world with truth aflame.
3. Let nothing daunt your ardor pure, Nor turn you from your purpose great; To save a world Christ sends you out, And for your message millions wait.
4. On Calvary the Saviour died For every man of every race; 'Tis yours to make the good news known, And be the channels of His grace. Amen.

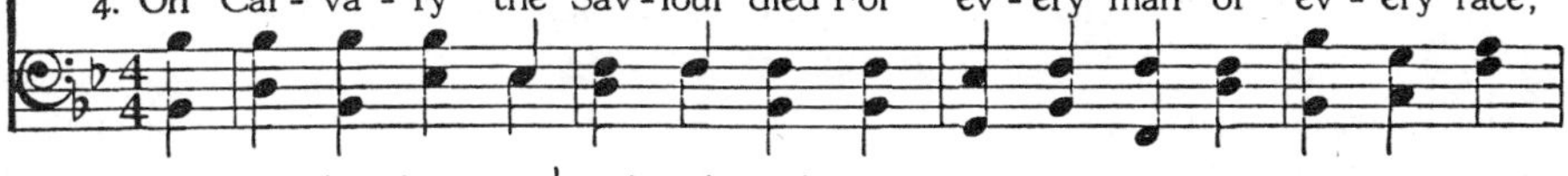

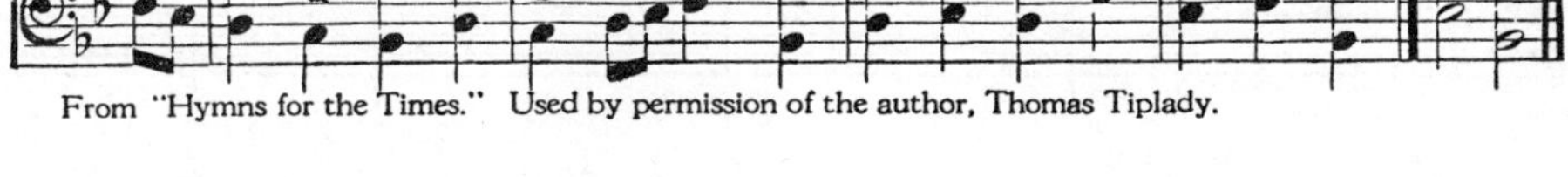

God of the Prophets! Bless the Prophets' Sons

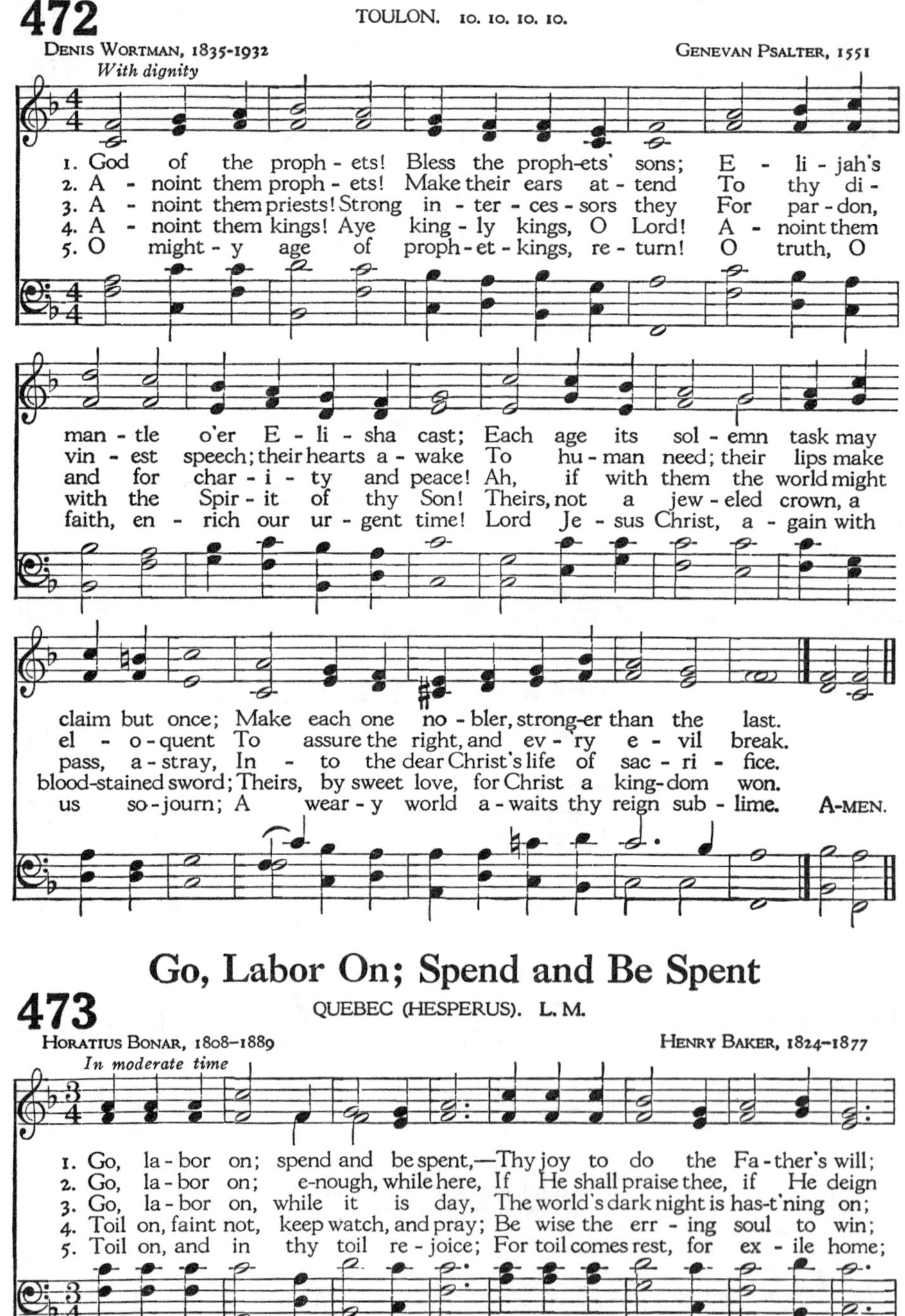
472
TOULON. 10. 10. 10. 10.
Denis Wortman, 1835-1932
Genevan Psalter, 1551
With dignity
1. God of the proph - ets! Bless the proph-ets' sons; E - li - jah's
2. A - noint them proph - ets! Make their ears at - tend To thy di -
3. A - noint them priests! Strong in - ter - ces - sors they For par - don,
4. A - noint them kings! Aye king - ly kings, O Lord! A - noint them
5. O might - y age of proph - et - kings, re - turn! O truth, O
man - tle o'er E - li - sha cast; Each age its sol - emn task may
vin - est speech; their hearts a - wake To hu - man need; their lips make
and for char - i - ty and peace! Ah, if with them the world might
with the Spir - it of thy Son! Theirs, not a jew - eled crown, a
faith, en - rich our ur - gent time! Lord Je - sus Christ, a - gain with
claim but once; Make each one no - bler, strong-er than the last.
el - o - quent To assure the right, and ev - 'ry e - vil break.
pass, a - stray, In - to the dear Christ's life of sac - ri - fice.
blood-stained sword; Theirs, by sweet love, for Christ a king - dom won.
us so - journ; A wear - y world a - waits thy reign sub - lime.
A-men.
Go, Labor On; Spend and Be Spent
473
QUEBEC (HESPERUS). L. M.
Horatius Bonar, 1808–1889
Henry Baker, 1824–1877
In moderate time
1. Go, la - bor on; spend and be spent,—Thy joy to do the Fa - ther's will;
2. Go, la - bor on; e - nough, while here, If He shall praise thee, if He deign
3. Go, la - bor on, while it is day, The world's dark night is has-t'ning on;
4. Toil on, faint not, keep watch, and pray; Be wise the err - ing soul to win;
5. Toil on, and in thy toil re - joice; For toil comes rest, for ex - ile home;

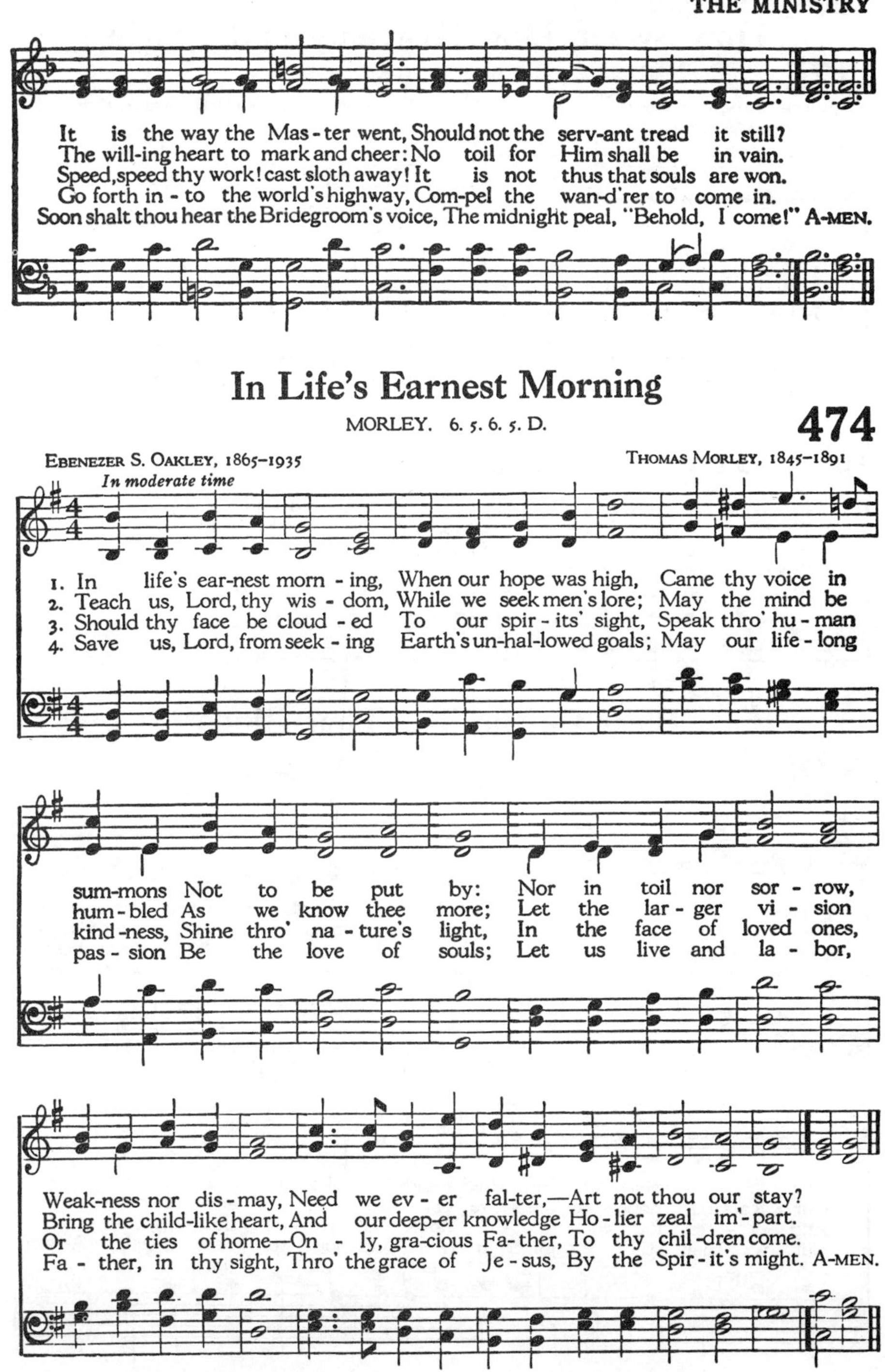
It is the way the Mas-ter went, Should not the serv-ant tread it still?
The will-ing heart to mark and cheer: No toil for Him shall be in vain.
Speed, speed thy work! cast sloth away! It is not thus that souls are won.
Go forth in-to the world's highway, Com-pel the wan-d'rer to come in.
Soon shalt thou hear the Bridegroom's voice, The midnight peal, "Behold, I come!" A-MEN.
In Life's Earnest Morning
MORLEY. 6. 5. 6. 5. D.
474
EBENEZER S. OAKLEY, 1865–1935
THOMAS MORLEY, 1845–1891
In moderate time
1. In life's ear-nest morn-ing, When our hope was high, Came thy voice in sum-mons Not to be put by: Nor in toil nor sor-row, Weak-ness nor dis-may, Need we ev-er fal-ter,—Art not thou our stay?
2. Teach us, Lord, thy wis-dom, While we seek men's lore; May the mind be hum-bled As we know thee more; Let the lar-ger vi-sion Bring the child-like heart, And our deep-er knowledge Ho-lier zeal im-part.
3. Should thy face be cloud-ed To our spir-its' sight, Speak thro' hu-man kind-ness, Shine thro' na-ture's light, In the face of loved ones, Or the ties of home—On-ly, gra-cious Fa-ther, To thy chil-dren come.
4. Save us, Lord, from seek-ing Earth's un-hal-lowed goals; May our life-long pas-sion Be the love of souls; Let us live and la-bor, Fa-ther, in thy sight, Thro' the grace of Je-sus, By the Spir-it's might. A-MEN.

How Sweet, How Heavenly Is the Sight

475

BROWN. C. M.

JOSEPH SWAIN, 1761–1796

WILLIAM B. BRADBURY, 1816–1868

In moderate time

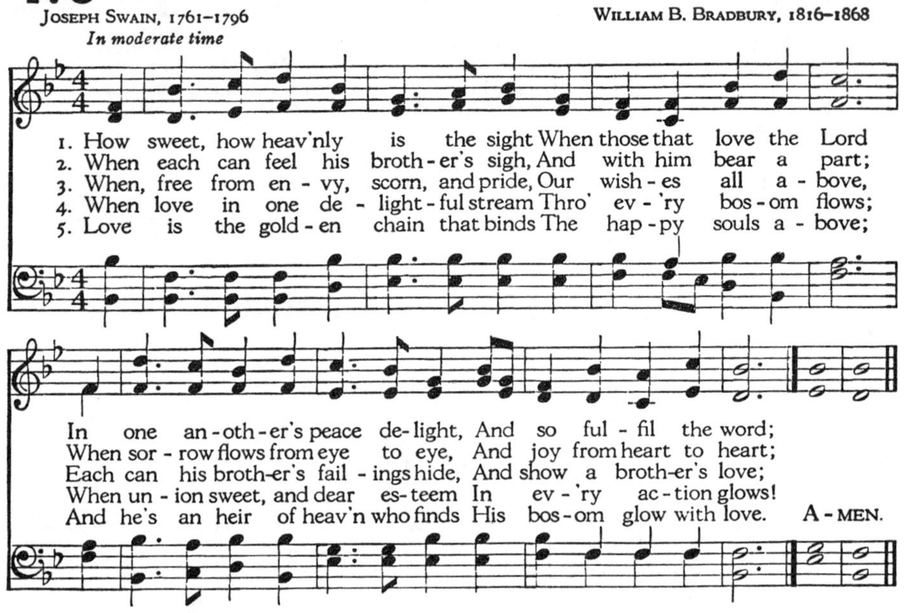
1. How sweet, how heav'nly is the sight When those that love the Lord
2. When each can feel his broth-er's sigh, And with him bear a part;
3. When, free from en-vy, scorn, and pride, Our wish-es all a-bove,
4. When love in one de-light-ful stream Thro' ev-'ry bos-om flows;
5. Love is the gold-en chain that binds The hap-py souls a-bove;
In one an-oth-er's peace de-light, And so ful-fil the word;
When sor-row flows from eye to eye, And joy from heart to heart;
Each can his broth-er's fail-ings hide, And show a broth-er's love;
When un-ion sweet, and dear es-teem In ev-'ry ac-tion glows!
And he's an heir of heav'n who finds His bos-om glow with love. A-MEN.

Blest Be the Tie That Binds

476

DENNIS. S. M.

JOHN FAWCETT, 1740–1817

Arr. from HANS G. NAEGELI, 1768–1836
by LOWELL MASON, 1792–1872

In moderate time

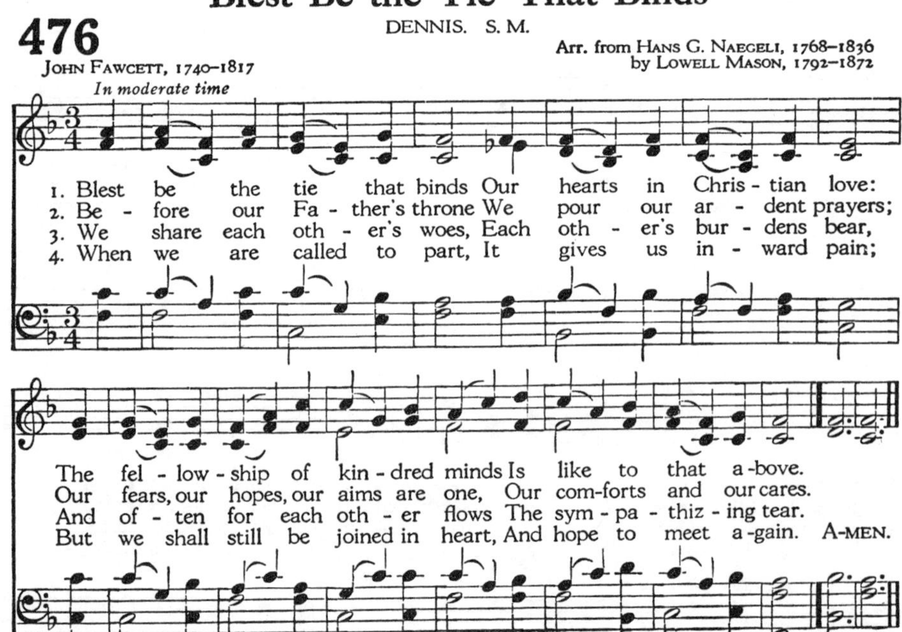
1. Blest be the tie that binds Our hearts in Chris-tian love:
2. Be-fore our Fa-ther's throne We pour our ar-dent prayers;
3. We share each oth-er's woes, Each oth-er's bur-dens bear,
4. When we are called to part, It gives us in-ward pain;
The fel-low-ship of kin-dred minds Is like to that a-bove.
Our fears, our hopes, our aims are one, Our com-forts and our cares.
And of-ten for each oth-er flows The sym-pa-thiz-ing tear.
But we shall still be joined in heart, And hope to meet a-gain. A-MEN.

Rise, Crowned With Light, Imperial Salem, Rise!

RUSSIAN HYMN. 10. 10. 10. 10. **477**

ALEXANDER POPE, 1688–1744, alt.
ALEXIS T. LWOFF, 1799–1870
In stately rhythm
1. Rise, crowned with light, im - pe - rial Sa - lem, rise!
2. See a long race thy spa - cious courts a - dorn:
3. See bar - b'rous na - tions at thy gates at - tend,
4. The seas shall waste, the skies to smoke de - cay,
Ex - alt thy tow'r - ing head and lift thine eyes!
See fu - ture sons, and daugh - ters yet un - born,
Walk in thy light, and in thy tem - ple bend:
Rocks fall to dust, and moun - tains melt a - way;
See heav'n its spark - ling por - tals wide dis - play,
In crowd - ing ranks on ev - 'ry side a - rise,
See thy bright al - tars thronged with pros - trate kings,
But fixed his word, his sav - ing pow'r re - mains;
And break up - on thee in a flood of day.
De - mand - ing life, im - pa - tient for the skies.
While ev - 'ry land its joy - ous trib - ute brings.
Thy realms shall last, thine own Mes - si - ah reigns. A-MEN.

O Thou Not Made With Hands

478

OLD 120TH. 6. 6. 6. 6. 6. 6.

FRANCIS TURNER PALGRAVE, 1824–1897 — Melody from ESTE'S PSALTER, 1592

With dignity, in moderate time

With dignity, in moderate time
1. O thou not made with hands, Not throned a - bove the skies,
2. Wher - e'er the gen - tle heart Finds cour - age from a - bove,
3. Where in life's com - mon ways With cheer - ful feet we go,
4. Not throned a - bove the skies, Nor gold - en - walled a - far,
Nor walled with shin - ing walls, Nor framed with stones of price,
Wher - e'er the heart for - sook Warms with the breath of love,
When in his steps we tread Who trod the way of woe;
But where Christ's two or three In his name gath - ered are;
More bright than gold or gem, God's own Je - ru - sa - lem!
Where faith bids fear de - part; Cit - y of God! thou art.
Where he is in the heart, Cit - y of God! thou art.
Be in the midst of them, God's own Je - ru - sa - lem! A-MEN.

Walk in the Light! So Shalt Thou Know

479

MANOAH. C. M.

BERNARD D. BARTON, 1784–1849 — From HENRY W. GREATOREX'S COLLECTION, 1851

In moderate time

In moderate time
1. Walk in the light! so shalt thou know That
2. Walk in the light! and thou shalt find Thy
3. Walk in the light! and thou shalt own Thy
4. Walk in the light! and thine shall be A

fel - low - ship of love His Spir - it on - ly
heart made tru - ly His, Who dwells in cloud - less
dark - ness passed a - way, Be - cause that light hath
path, though thorn - y, bright: For God, by grace, shall
can be - stow, Who reigns in light a - bove.
light en - shrined, In whom no dark - ness is.
on thee shone, In which is per - fect day.
dwell in thee, And God Him - self is light. A - MEN.

In Christ There Is No East or West

ST. PETER. C. M.

480

JOHN OXENHAM, d. 1941 — ALEXANDER R. REINAGLE, 1799-1877

In moderate time

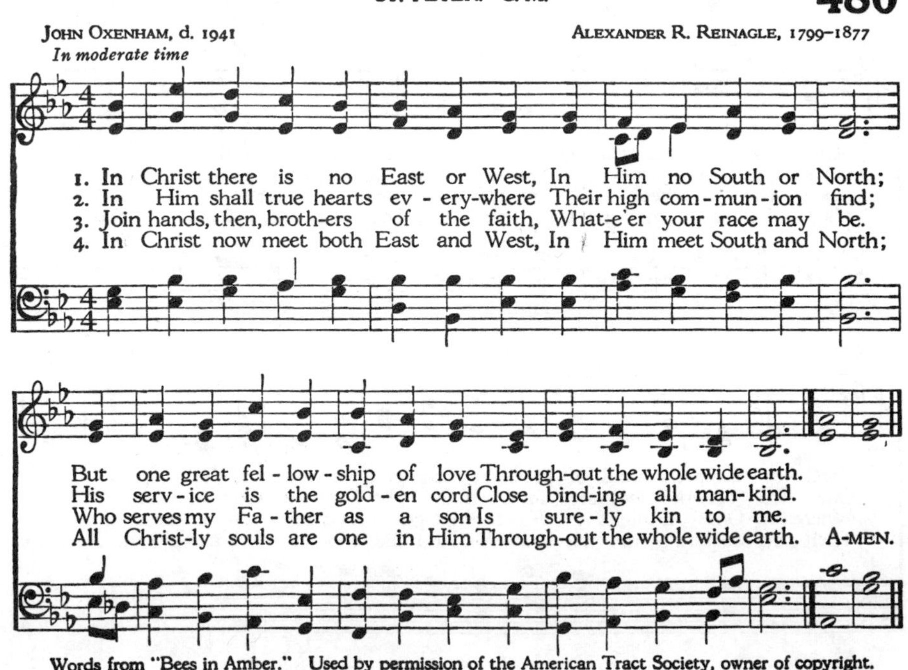
1. In Christ there is no East or West, In Him no South or North;
2. In Him shall true hearts ev - ery-where Their high com - mun - ion find;
3. Join hands, then, broth-ers of the faith, What-e'er your race may be.
4. In Christ now meet both East and West, In Him meet South and North;
But one great fel - low - ship of love Through-out the whole wide earth.
His serv - ice is the gold - en cord Close bind-ing all man - kind.
Who serves my Fa - ther as a son Is sure - ly kin to me.
All Christ-ly souls are one in Him Through-out the whole wide earth. A-MEN.

Through the Night of Doubt and Sorrow

481

ST. ASAPH. 8. 7. 8. 7. D.

BERNHARDT S. INGEMANN, 1789-1862
Tr. by SABINE BARING-GOULD, 1834-1924

WILLIAM S. BAMBRIDGE, 1842-1923

With exultation

1. Through the night of doubt and sor - row On - ward goes the pil - grim band,
2. One the light of God's own pres-ence O'er His ran-somed peo - ple shed,
3. One the strain that lips of thou-sands Lift as from the heart of one,
4. On - ward, there - fore, pil - grim broth-ers, On - ward, with the cross our aid;

Sing - ing songs of ex - pec - ta - tion, March-ing to the prom-ised land:
Chas - ing far the gloom and ter - ror, Bright-ening all the path we tread;
One the con - flict, one the per - il, One the march in God be - gun;
Bear its shame, and fight its bat - tle, Till we rest be - neath its shade;

Clear be - fore us through the dark - ness Gleams and burns the guid - ing light;
One the ob - ject of our jour - ney, One the faith which nev - er tires,
One the glad - ness of re - joic - ing On the far e - ter - nal shore,
Soon shall come the great a - wak - ing, Soon the rend - ing of the tomb,

Broth - er clasps the hand of broth - er, Step-ping fear-less through the night.
One the ear - nest look-ing for-ward, One the hope our God in-spires;
Where the One Al-might -y Fa - ther Reigns in love for - ev - er-more.
Then the scattering of all shad-ows And the end of toil and gloom. A - MEN.

Onward, Christian Soldiers

482

ST. GERTRUDE. 6. 5. 6. 5. D. with Refrain

SABINE BARING-GOULD, 1834–1924 — ARTHUR S. SULLIVAN, 1842–1900

With a martial rhythm
1. On - ward,Chris-tian sol - diers! March-ing as to war, With the cross of
2. Like a might - y arm - y Moves the Church of God; Broth-ers, we are
3. Crowns and thrones may per - ish, King-doms rise and wane, But the Church of
4. On - ward,then, ye peo - ple, Join our hap - py throng,Blend with ours your
Je - sus Go - ing on be - fore. Christ, the roy - al Mas - ter,
tread-ing Where the saints have trod; We are not di - vid - ed,
Je - sus Con - stant will re - main; Gates of hell can nev - er
voic - es In the tri - umph - song; Glo - ry, laud, and hon - or
Leads a - gainst the foe; For-ward in - to bat - tle, See His ban - ners go!
All one bod - y we, One in hope and doc - trine, One in char - i - ty.
'Gainst that Church pre - vail; We have Christ's own prom - ise, And that can - not fail.
Un - to Christ the King; This thro' count - less a - ges Men and an - gels sing.
REFRAIN
On - ward, Chris - tian sol - diers, March - ing as to war,
With the cross of Je - sus Go - ing on be - fore. A - MEN.

Blest Be the Dear, Uniting Love

483

HOLY CROSS. C. M.

CHARLES WESLEY, 1708–1788 Adapted by JAMES C. WADE, 1847– ?

In moderate time

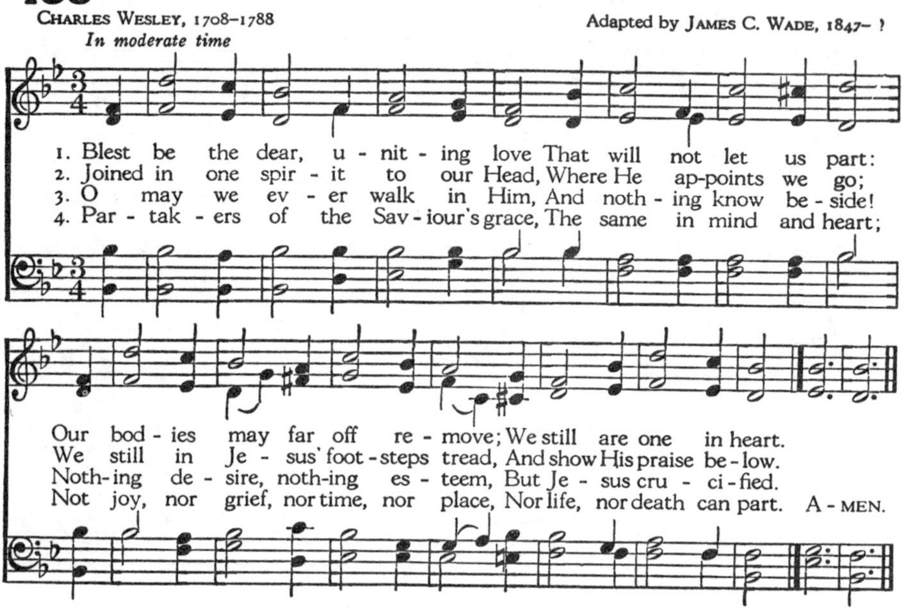
1. Blest be the dear, u-nit-ing love That will not let us part: Our bod-ies may far off re-move; We still are one in heart.
2. Joined in one spir-it to our Head, Where He ap-points we go; We still in Je-sus' foot-steps tread, And show His praise be-low.
3. O may we ev-er walk in Him, And noth-ing know be-side! Noth-ing de-sire, noth-ing es-teem, But Je-sus cru-ci-fied.
4. Par-tak-ers of the Sav-iour's grace, The same in mind and heart; Not joy, nor grief, nor time, nor place, Nor life, nor death can part. A-MEN.

Forgive, O Lord, Our Severing Ways

484

O MENSCH SIEH. 8. 8. 8.

Composite, based on JOHN G. WHITTIER, 1807–1892 BOHEMIAN BRETHREN'S GESANGBUCH, 1566, alt.

In moderate time

1. For-give, O Lord, our sev-ering ways; The ri-val al-tars that we raise, The wran-gling tongues that mar Thy praise.
2. Thy grace im-part; in time to be Shall one great tem-ple rise to Thee— One Church for all hu-man-i-ty.
3. White flowers of love its walls shall climb, Soft bells of peace shall ring its chime, Its days shall all be ho-ly time.
4. A sweet-er song shall then be heard, Con-fess-ing, in a world's ac-cord, The in-ward Christ, the liv-ing Word.
5. That song shall swell from shore to shore, One hope, one faith, one love re-store The seam-less robe that Je-sus wore. A-MEN.

Brightly Gleams Our Banner

ST. ALBAN. 6. 5. 6. 5. D. with Refrain

485

THOMAS J. POTTER, 1827–1873 — FRANZ JOSEPH HAYDN, 1732–1809

In moderate time
1. Brightly gleams our ban - ner, Pointing to the sky, Wav-ing wand'rers on - ward
2. Je - sus, Lord and Mas - ter, At Thy sa-cred feet, Here with hearts re - joi - cing
3. All our days di - rect us In the way we go; Lead us on vic - to - rious
4. Then with saints and an - gels May we join a - bove, Off'ring pray'rs and prais - es
To their home on high. Journeying o'er the des - ert, Glad - ly thus we pray,
See Thy chil-dren meet: Oft - en have we left Thee, Oft - en gone a - stray;
O - ver ev - 'ry foe: Bid Thine an-gels shield us When the storm-clouds low'r,
At Thy throne of love. When the march is o - ver, Then come rest and peace,
REFRAIN
And with hearts u - nit - ed Take our heav'nward way.
Keep us, might-y Sav-iour, In the nar - row way. Brightly gleams our ban - ner,
Par - don Thou and save us, E - ven in this hour.
Je - sus in His beau - ty, Songs that nev - er cease.
Point-ing to the sky, Wav-ing wand'rers on - ward To their home on high. A-MEN.

The Light of God Is Falling

486

GREENLAND. 7. 6. 7. 6. D.

Louis F. Benson, 1855–1930

Arr. from J. Michael Haydn, 1737–1806
In B. Jacob's National Psalmody, 1819

Not too slow
1. The light of God is fall - ing Up - on life's com-mon way;
2. Who shares his life's pure pleas - ures, And walks the hon - est road,
3. Where hu - man lives are throng - ing In toil and pain and sin,
4. Thy ran-somed host in glo - ry, All souls that sin and pray,
The Mas - ter's voice still call - ing, "Come, walk with Me to - day";
Who trades with heap - ing meas - ures, And lifts his broth - er's load,
While clois - tered hearts are long - ing To bring the King-dom in,
Turn toward the cross that bore Thee; "Be - hold the Man!" they say:
No du - ty can seem low - ly To him who lives with Thee,
Who turns the wrong down blunt - ly. And lends the right a hand,
O Christ, the Eld - er Broth - er Of proud and beat - en men,
And while Thy Church is plead - ing For all who would do good,
And all of life grows ho - ly, O Christ of Gal - i - lee!
He dwells in God's own coun - try, He tills the Ho - ly Land.
When they have found each oth - er, Thy King-dom will come then!
We hear Thy true voice lead - ing Our song of broth - er - hood. A-MEN.

Words used by permission of Mrs. Robert F. Jefferys.

Come Forth, Ye Men of Every Race and Nation!

CREATION. Irregular.

487

JAY HOLMES SMITH | FRANZ JOSEPH HAYDN, 1732–1809

With great dignity

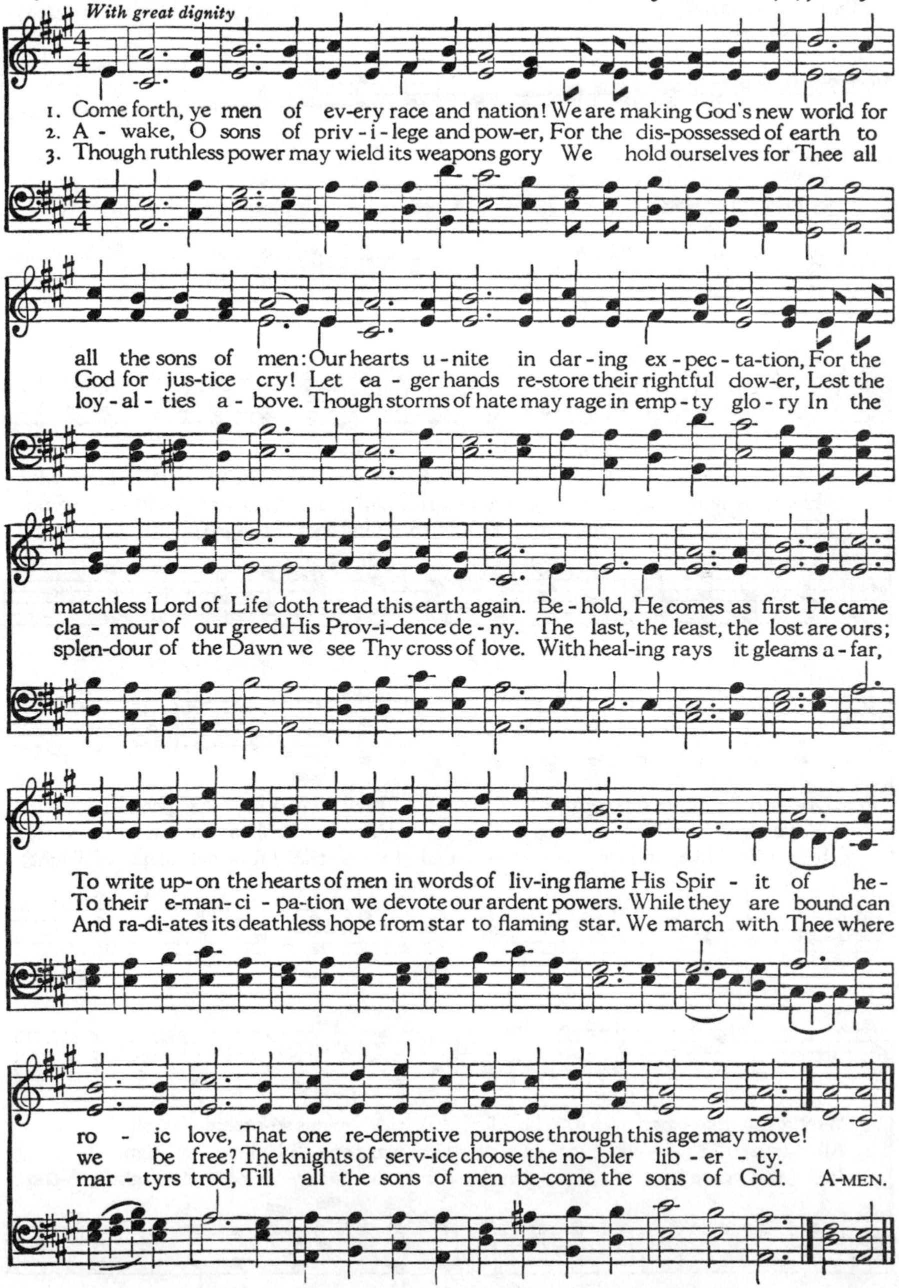

1. Come forth, ye men of ev-ery race and nation! We are making God's new world for
2. A - wake, O sons of priv - i - lege and pow-er, For the dis-possessed of earth to
3. Though ruthless power may wield its weapons gory We hold ourselves for Thee all

all the sons of men: Our hearts u - nite in dar - ing ex - pec - ta-tion, For the
God for jus-tice cry! Let ea - ger hands re-store their rightful dow-er, Lest the
loy - al - ties a - bove. Though storms of hate may rage in emp - ty glo - ry In the

matchless Lord of Life doth tread this earth again. Be - hold, He comes as first He came
cla - mour of our greed His Prov-i-dence de - ny. The last, the least, the lost are ours;
splen-dour of the Dawn we see Thy cross of love. With heal-ing rays it gleams a - far,

To write up-on the hearts of men in words of liv-ing flame His Spir - it of he-
To their e-man-ci - pa-tion we devote our ardent powers. While they are bound can
And ra-di-ates its deathless hope from star to flaming star. We march with Thee where

ro - ic love, That one re-demptive purpose through this age may move!
we be free? The knights of serv-ice choose the no-bler lib - er - ty.
mar - tyrs trod, Till all the sons of men be-come the sons of God. A-MEN.

Hail the Glorious Golden City

488

AUSTRIAN HYMN. 8. 7. 8. 7. D.

FELIX ADLER, 1851–1936
FRANZ JOSEPH HAYDN, 1732–1809
With fervor
1. Hail the glo-rious Gold-en Cit - y, Pic-tured by the seers of old!
2. We are build-ers of that cit - y; All our joys and all our groans
3. And the work that we have build-ed, Oft with bleed-ing hands and tears,
Ev - er-last - ing light shines o'er it, Won-drous tales of it are told:
Help to rear its shin - ing ram-parts; All our lives are build - ing stones:
Oft in er - ror, oft in an - guish, Will not per - ish with our years:
On - ly right-eous men and wom - en Dwell with - in its gleam-ing wall;
Wheth-er hum-ble or ex - alt - ed, All are called to tasks di - vine;
It will live and shine trans-fig - ured In the fi - nal reign of Right;
Wrong is ban-ished from its bor-ders, Jus-tice reigns su-preme o'er all.
All must aid a - like to car - ry For - ward one sub - lime de - sign.
It will pass in - to the splen-dors Of the Cit - y of the Light. A-MEN.

We Would Be Building

FINLANDIA. 10. 10. 10. 10. 10. 10.

489

PURD E. DEITZ

JEAN SIBELIUS, 1865–

In moderate time and flowing rhythm

1. We would be build - ing; tem-ples still un - done O'er crum-bling walls their
2. Teach us to build; up - on the sol - id rock We set the dream that
3. O keep us build - ing, Mas-ter; may our hands Ne'er fal - ter when the

cross - es scarce-ly lift; Wait-ing till love can raise the bro - ken stone,
hard-ens in - to deed, Ribbed with the steel that time and change doth mock,
dream is in our hearts, When to our ears there come di - vine com - mands

And hearts cre - a - tive bridge the hu - man rift; We would be build - ing,
Th' un-fail-ing pur - pose of our no - blest creed; Teach us to build; O
And all the pride of sin - ful will de - parts; We build with Thee, O

Mas - ter, let Thy plan Re-veal the life that God would give to man.
Mas - ter, lend us sight To see the tow - ers gleam-ing in the light.
grant en - dur - ing worth Un - til the heav'n-ly King-dom comes on earth. A-MEN.

The Voice of God Is Calling

490

MEIRIONYDD. 7. 6. 7. 6. D.

JOHN HAYNES HOLMES, 1879-

Welsh hymn melody

In moderate time

1. The voice of God is call - ing Its sum-mons un - to men;
2. I hear my peo - ple cry - ing In cot and mine and slum;
3. We heed, O Lord, Thy sum-mons, And an - swer: Here are we!
4. From ease and plen - ty save us; From pride of place ab - solve;

As once He spake in Zi - on, So now He speaks a - gain.
No field or mart is si - lent, No cit - y street is dumb.
Send us up - on Thine er - rand, Let us Thy serv - ants be.
Purge us of low de - sire; Lift us to high re - solve;

Whom shall I send to suc - cor My peo - ple in their need?
I see my peo - ple fall - ing In dark - ness and de - spair.
Our strength is dust and ash - es, Our years a pass - ing hour;
Take us, and make us ho - ly; Teach us Thy will and way.

Whom shall I send to loos - en The bonds of shame and greed?
Whom shall I send to shat - ter The fet - ters which they bear?
But Thou canst use our weak - ness To mag - ni - fy Thy power.
Speak, and, be - hold! we an - swer; Com - mand, and we o - bey! A-MEN.

O Lord of Life, Thy Kingdom Is at Hand

TOULON. 10. 10. 10. 10.

491

MARION FRANKLIN HAM, 1867–

GENEVAN PSALTER, 1551

In moderate time

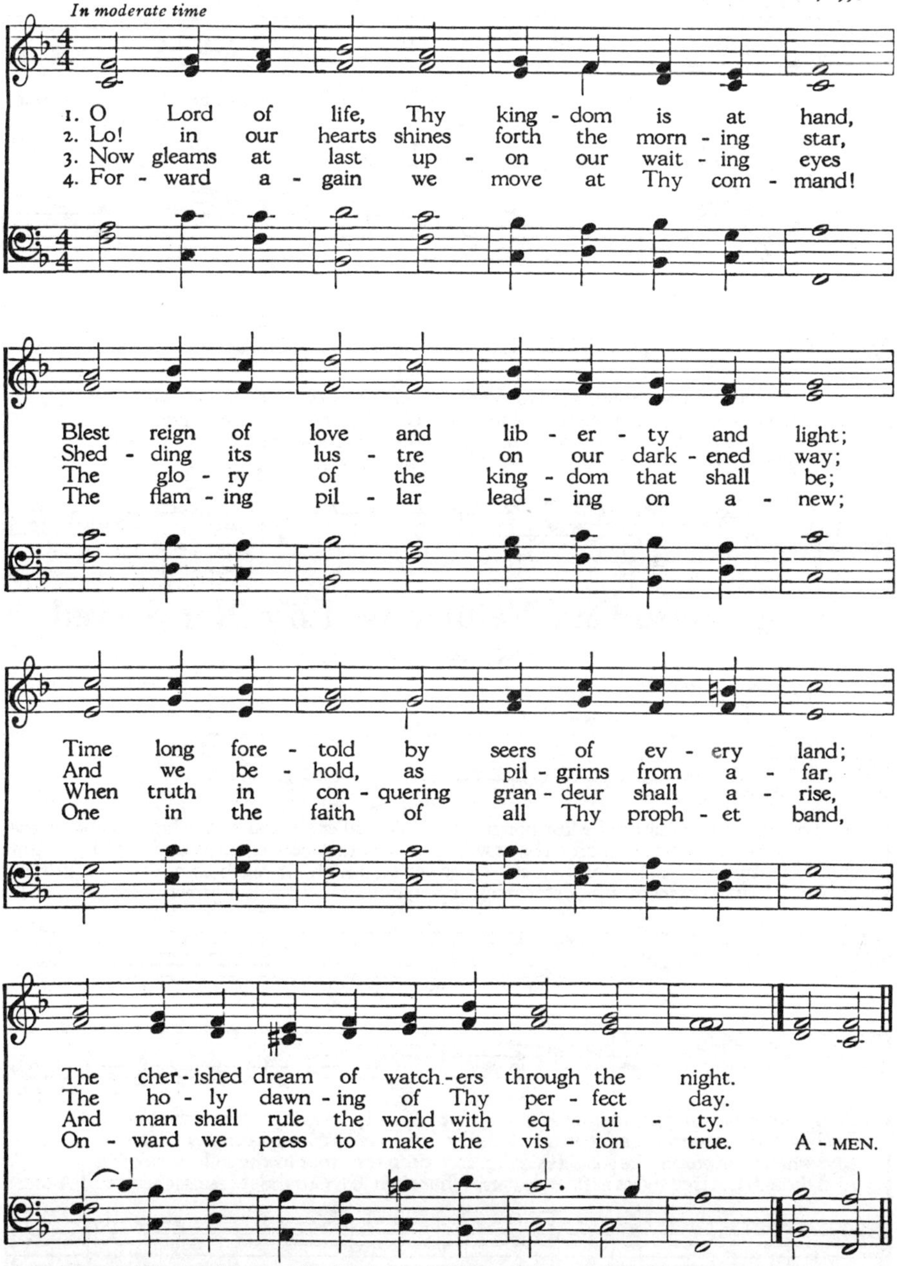

1. O Lord of life, Thy king - dom is at hand,
2. Lo! in our hearts shines forth the morn - ing star,
3. Now gleams at last up - on our wait - ing eyes
4. For - ward a - gain we move at Thy com - mand!

Blest reign of love and lib - er - ty and light;
Shed - ding its lus - tre on our dark - ened way;
The glo - ry of the king - dom that shall be;
The flam - ing pil - lar lead - ing on a - new;

Time long fore - told by seers of ev - ery land;
And we be - hold, as pil - grims from a - far,
When truth in con - quering gran - deur shall a - rise,
One in the faith of all Thy proph - et band,

The cher - ished dream of watch - ers through the night.
The ho - ly dawn - ing of Thy per - fect day.
And man shall rule the world with eq - ui - ty.
On - ward we press to make the vis - ion true. A - MEN.

Creation's Lord, We Give Thee Thanks

492

ROCKINGHAM OLD. L.M.

WILLIAM DEWITT HYDE, 1858–1903

EDWARD MILLER, 1735–1807

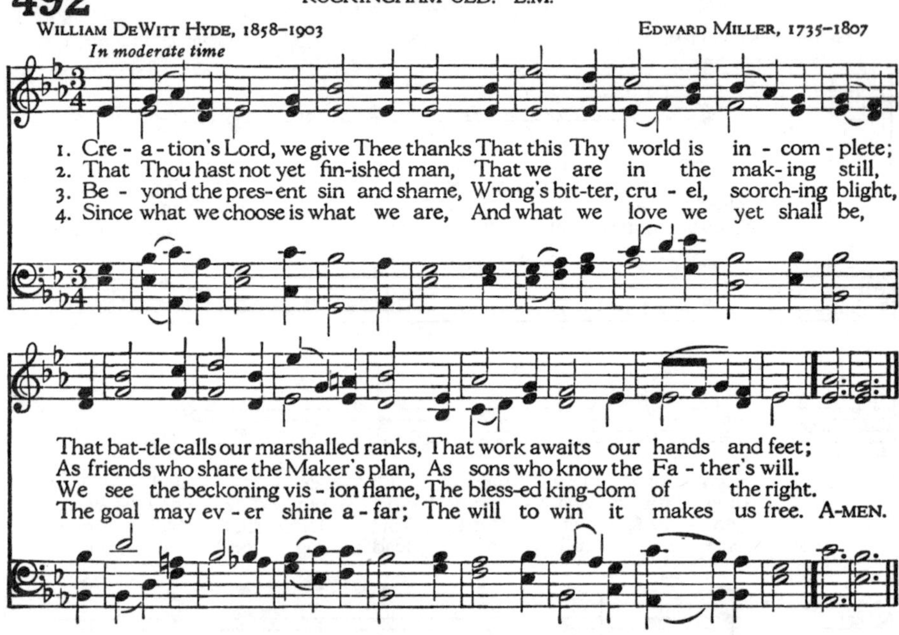
In moderate time
1. Cre - a - tion's Lord, we give Thee thanks That this Thy world is in - com - plete;
2. That Thou hast not yet fin-ished man, That we are in the mak- ing still,
3. Be - yond the pres- ent sin and shame, Wrong's bit-ter, cru - el, scorch-ing blight,
4. Since what we choose is what we are, And what we love we yet shall be,
That bat-tle calls our marshalled ranks, That work awaits our hands and feet;
As friends who share the Maker's plan, As sons who know the Fa - ther's will.
We see the beckoning vis - ion flame, The bless-ed king-dom of the right.
The goal may ev - er shine a - far; The will to win it makes us free. A-MEN.

That Cause Can Neither Be Lost Nor Stayed

493

OSTERGAARD. 9. 9. 10. 10.

CHRISTIAN OSTERGAARD
Tr. by J. A. AABERG

Danish folk tune

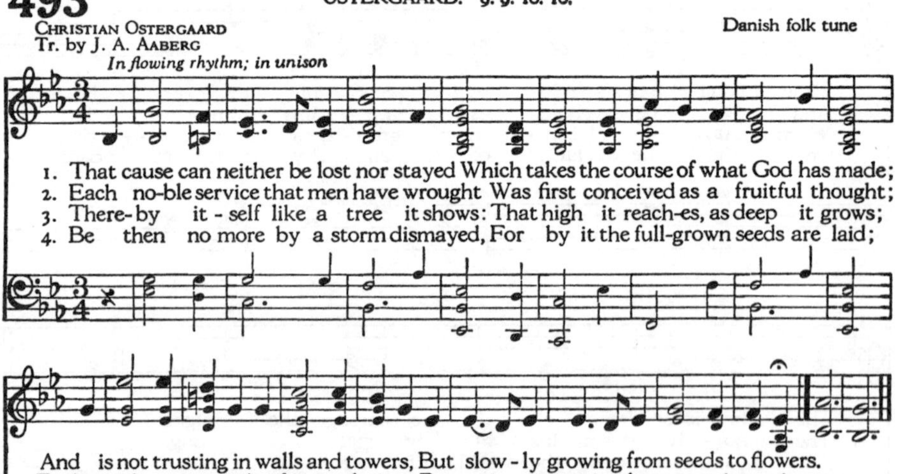
In flowing rhythm; in unison
1. That cause can neither be lost nor stayed Which takes the course of what God has made;
2. Each no-ble service that men have wrought Was first conceived as a fruitful thought;
3. There-by it - self like a tree it shows: That high it reach-es, as deep it grows;
4. Be then no more by a storm dismayed, For by it the full-grown seeds are laid;
And is not trusting in walls and towers, But slow - ly growing from seeds to flowers.
Each worthy cause with a future glorious By qui - et growing becomes vic-to-rious.
And when the storms are its branches shaking, It deep -er root in the soil is tak-ing.
And though the tree by its might it shatters, What then, if thousands of seeds it scatters! A-MEN.

We Are Living, We Are Dwelling

BLAENHAFREN. 8. 7. 8. 7. D.

494

A. Cleveland Coxe, 1818–1896; alt.

Traditional Welsh melody

In unison, with great breadth
1. We are liv - ing, we are dwell-ing In a grand and aw - ful time,
2. Will ye play, then? will ye dal - ly Far be - hind the bat - tle line?
3. Sworn to yield, to wa - ver, nev - er; Con - se - crat - ed, born a - gain;
In an age on a - ges tell - ing; To be liv - ing is sub-lime.
Up! it is Je - ho - vah's ral - ly; God's own arm hath need of thine.
Sworn to be Christ's sol - diers ev - er, O for Christ at least be men!
Hark! the wak - ing up of na-tions, Hosts ad-van - cing to the fray;
Worlds are charg-ing, heaven be-hold-ing; Thou hast but an hour to fight;
O let all the soul with - in you For the truth's sake go a - broad!
Hark! what sound-eth is cre - a - tion's Groan-ing for the lat - ter day.
Now, the bla-zoned cross un - fold - ing, On, right on - ward for the right!
Strike! let ev - ery nerve and sin - ew Tell on a - ges, tell for God. A-MEN.

We Thank Thee, Lord, Thy Paths of Service Lead

495

FIELD. 10. 10. 10. 10.

CALVIN W. LAUFER, 1874–1938 | CALVIN W. LAUFER, 1874–1938

In moderate time

1. We thank Thee, Lord, Thy paths of serv - ice lead
To bla - zoned heights and down the slopes of need;
They reach Thy throne, en - com - pass land and sea,
And he who jour - neys in them walks with Thee.

2. We've sought and found Thee in the se - cret place
And mar - veled at the ra - diance of Thy face;
But of - ten in some far - off Gal - i - lee
Be - held Thee fair - er yet while serv - ing Thee.

3. We've felt Thy touch in sor - row's dark - ened way
A - bound with love and sol - ace for the day;
And, 'neath the bur - dens there, Thy sov - reign - ty
Has held our hearts en-thralled while serv - ing Thee.

4. We've seen Thy glo - ry like a man - tle spread
O'er hill and dale in saf - fron flame and red;
But in the eyes of men, re - deemed and free,
A splen - dor great - er yet while serv - ing Thee.

A - MEN.

They Who Tread the Path of Labour

BITHYNIA (TANTUM ERGO). 8. 7. 8. 7. D.

496

HENRY VAN DYKE, 1852–1933

Melody from S. WEBBE'S MOTETTS OR ANTIPHONS, 1792

In moderate time
1. They who tread the path of la - bour Fol - low where My feet have trod;
2. Where the man - y toil to - geth - er, There am I a - mong My own;
3. Ev - ery task, how - ev - er sim - ple, Sets the soul that does it free;
They who work with - out com-plain-ing Do the ho - ly will of God;
Where the tir - ed work - man sleep-eth, There am I with him a - lone.
Ev - ery deed of love and mer - cy Done to man is done to Me.
Nev - er - more thou need - est seek Me; I am with thee ev - ery-where;
I, the Peace that pass - eth knowledge Dwell a - mid the dai - ly strife;
Nev - er - more thou need - est seek Me; I am with thee ev - ery-where;
Raise the stone, and thou shalt find Me, Cleave the wood and I am there.
I, the Bread of heav'n, am bro - ken In the sac - ra-ment of life.
Raise the stone, and thou shalt find Me, Cleave the wood and I am there. A-MEN.

Lord of Hosts, Whose Purpose, Never Swerving

497

WELWYN. 11. 10. 11. 10.

SHEPHERD KNAPP, 1873–

ALFRED SCOTT-GATTY, 1847–1918

With marked rhythm. May be sung in unison.

1. Lord God of Hosts, whose pur - pose, nev - er swerv - ing,
2. Strong Son of God, whose work was His that sent Thee,
3. O Prince of Peace, Thou bring - er of good ti - dings,
4. Lord God, whose grace has called us to Thy serv - ice,
Leads toward the day of Je - sus Christ Thy Son,
One with the Fa - ther, thought and deed and word,
Teach us to speak Thy word of hope and cheer—
How good Thy thoughts toward us, how great their sum!
Grant us to march a - mong Thy faith - ful le - gions,
One make us all, true com - rades in Thy serv - ice,
Rest for the soul, and strength for all man's striv - ing,
We work with Thee, we go where Thou wilt lead us,
Armed with Thy cour - age, till the world is won.
And make us one in Thee with God the Lord.
Light for the path of life, and God brought near.
Un - til in all the earth Thy King - dom come.
A - MEN.

Forward Through the Ages

498

ST. GERTRUDE. 6. 5. 6. 5. D. with Refrain.
FREDERICK L. HOSMER, 1840–1928
ARTHUR S. SULLIVAN. 1842–1900
With marked rhythm
1. For - ward through the a - ges, In un - bro - ken line,
2. Wid - er grows the king - dom, Reign of love and light;
3. Not a - lone we con - quer, Not a - lone we fall;
Move the faith - ful spir - its At the call di - vine:
For it we must la - bor, Till our faith is sight.
In each loss or tri - umph Lose or tri - umph all.
Gifts in dif-fering meas - ure, Hearts of one ac - cord, Man - i - fold the serv - ice, One the sure re - ward.
Proph-ets have pro - claimed it, Mar - tyrs tes - ti - fied, Po - ets sung its glo - ry, He - roes for it died.
Bound by God's far pur - pose In one liv - ing whole, Move we on to - geth - er To the shin - ing goal!
REFRAIN
For-ward through the a - ges, In un-bro - ken line, Move the faith-ful spir - its At the call di - vine. A - MEN.

I Thank Thee, Lord, for Strength of Arm

499
O JESU. 8. 4. 8. 4. 8. 8.
ROBERT DAVIS, 1881–
Melody in HIRSCHBERG GESANGBUCH, 1741
Not too slowly
1. I thank Thee, Lord, for strength of arm To win my bread, And that, be - yond my need, is meat For friend un - fed: I thank Thee much for bread to live; I thank Thee more for bread to give.
2. I thank Thee, Lord, for snug - thatched roof In cold and storm, And that, be - yond my need, is room For friend for - lorn: I thank Thee much for place to rest, But more for shel - ter for my guest.
3. I thank Thee, Lord, for lav - ish love On me be - stowed, E - nough to share with love - less folk To ease their load: Thy love to me I ill could spare, Yet dear - er is Thy love I share. A - MEN.

My Master Was a Worker

SEASONS. 7. 6. 7. 6. D.

500

William G. Tarrant, 1853–1928
Felix Mendelssohn, 1809–1847
In moderate time
1. My Master was a worker, With daily work to do,
And he who would be like him Must be a worker too;
Then welcome honest labor, And honest labor's fare,
For where there is a worker, The Master's man is there.
2. My Master was a comrade, A trusty friend and true,
And he who would be like him Must be a comrade too;
In happy hours of singing, In silent hours of care,
Where goes a loyal comrade, The Master's man is there.
3. My Master was a helper, The woes of life he knew,
And he who would be like him Must be a helper too;
The burden will grow lighter, If each will take a share,
And where there is a helper The Master's man is there.
4. Then, brothers brave and manly Together let us be,
For he, who is our Master, The Man of men was he;
The men who would be like him Are wanted ev-'ry-where,
And where they love each other The Master's men are there.
A-MEN.

In Homes Where Pride and Splendor

501

CHENIES. 7. 6. 7. 6. D.

BENJAMIN J. RADFORD, 1838–1933 TIMOTHY R. MATTHEWS, 1826–1910

In moderate time

1. In homes where pride and splen - dor Their silk - en ban - ners flare,
2. What tho' our flag in glo - ry Floats o - ver free-dom's land,
3. Shall we, to whom is giv - en For sin the on - ly cure,
4. O God, whilst e - vil low - ers In clouds of sin and shame,

In homes where child - hood ten - der Is crushed by want and care,
While deg - ra - da - tion's sto - ry Is writ on ev - 'ry hand,
Vouch-safed to earth by heav - en, While na - tions shall en - dure;
May these cold hearts of ours Burst in - to liv - ing flame,

Is heard the cry of an - guish From man - y a help - less slave,
While in the marts of la - bor, In lord - ly halls of state,
Shall we, in this her tri - al, For - get our na - tion's weal,
To light and lead our na - tion In this her time of need,

Where Sa - tan's cap - tives lan - guish, And on - ly Christ can save.
The Christ-like love of neigh - bor Is lost in greed and hate?
En - dure no self - de - ni - al, Be want - ing in our zeal?
Un - til in Christ's sal - va - tion She shall be free in - deed. A-MEN.

Son of God, Eternal Saviour

IN BABILONE. 8. 7. 8. 7. D.

502

SOMERSET CORRY LOWRY, 1855–1932

Dutch traditional melody

In moderate time, with dignity

1. Son of God, e - ter - nal Sav - iour, Source of life and truth and grace,
Son of Man, whose birth in - car - nate Hal - lows all our hu - man race;
Thou, our Head, who, throned in glo - ry, For Thine own dost ev - er plead,
Fill us with Thy love and pit - y, Heal our wrongs, and help our need.

2. As Thou, Lord, hast lived for oth - ers, So may we for oth - ers live;
Free - ly have Thy gifts been grant-ed, Free - ly may Thy serv - ants give.
Thine the gold and Thine the sil - ver, Thine the wealth of land and sea,
We but stew-ards of Thy boun-ty, Held in sol - emn trust for Thee.

3. Come, O Christ, and reign a - mong us, King of love and Prince of peace;
Hush the storm of strife and pas - sion, Bid its cru - el dis - cords cease.
Ah, the past is dark be - hind us, Strewn with wrecks and stained with blood!
But be - fore us gleams the vi - sion Of the com - ing broth - er - hood.

4. See the Christ-like host ad - van - cing, High and low - ly, great and small,
Linked in bonds of com - mon serv - ice For the com - mon Lord of all.
Thou who pray-edst, Thou who will - est That Thy peo - ple should be one,
Grant, O grant our hope's fru - i - tion: Here on earth Thy will be done. A-MEN.

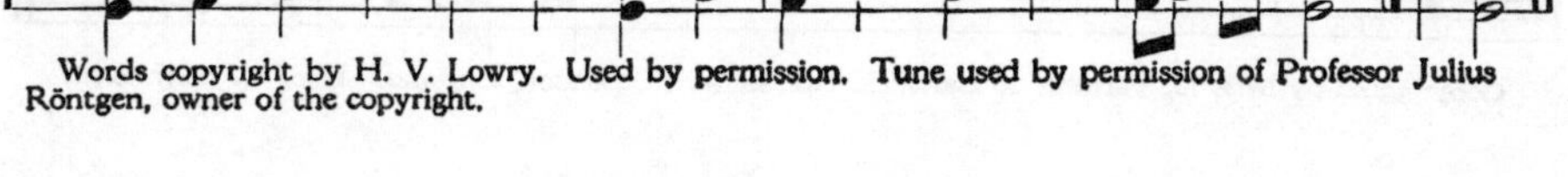

The Fathers Built This City

503

PATMOS. 7. 6. 8. 6. D.

WILLIAM G. TARRANT, 1853–1928 — HENRY J. STORER, 1860–

With steady, flowing rhythm

1. The fa - thers built this cit - y In a - ges long a - go,
2. Yet still the cit - y stand - eth, A hive of toil - ing men,
3. Let all the peo - ple praise Thee, Give all Thy sav - ing health,
4. A com - mon - weal of broth - ers, U - nit - ed, great and small,

And, bus - y in its bus - y streets, They hur - ried to and fro;
And moth - er's love makes hap - py home For chil - dren now as then;
Or vain the la - borer's strong right arm And vain the mer-chant's wealth;
Up - on our ban - ner bla - zoned be The Char - ter, "Each for all!"

The chil - dren played a - round them And sang the songs of yore,
O God of a - ges, help us Such cit - i - zens to be
Send forth Thy light to 'stab - lish The glo - ry of the Word,
Nor let us cease from bat - tle, Nor wea - ry sheathe the sword,

Till, one by one, they fell a - sleep, To work and play no more.
That chil-dren's chil-dren here may sing The songs of lib - er - ty!
Un - til this cit - y is be-come The cit - y of the Lord!
Un - til this cit - y is be-come The cit - y of the Lord. A - MEN.

Lord of Light, Whose Name Outshineth

504

PLEADING SAVIOUR. 8. 7. 8. 7. D.

HOWELL E. LEWIS, 1860–

FROM PLYMOUTH COLLECTION, 1855

In moderate time, with flowing rhythm

1. Lord of light, whose name out-shin - eth All the stars and suns of space,
2. By the toil of low - ly work-ers In some far out - ly - ing field;
3. Grant that know- ledge, still in - creas- ing, At Thy feet may low - ly kneel;
4. By the prayers of faith-ful watch-men, Nev - er si - lent day or night;
Deign to make us Thy co - work- ers In the king - dom of Thy grace;
By the cour - age where the ra-diance Of the Cross is still re - vealed;
With Thy grace our tri-umphs hal - low, With Thy char - i - ty our zeal;
By the Cross of Je - sus bring-ing Peace to men, and heal - ing light;
Use us to ful - fill Thy pur- pose In the gift of Christ Thy Son:
By the vic - to - ries of meek-ness, Through re-proach and suf - fering won,
Lift the na-tions from the shad-ows To the glad-ness of the sun:
By the love that pass - eth know-ledge, Mak- ing all Thy chil - dren one:
Fa - ther, as in high-est heav-en So on earth Thy will be done. A-MEN.

505 O Jesus, Prince of Life and Truth

SERAPH (BETHLEHEM). C. M. D.

ANONYMOUS — GOTTFRIED W. FINK, 1783–1846

In moderate time
1. O Je - sus, Prince of life and truth, Be - neath Thy ban - ner bright,
2. In ser - ried ranks, with fear - less tread, O Cap - tain of us all,
3. O Je - sus, once a Naz - areth boy, And tempt - ed like as we,
We ded - i - cate our strength and youth To bat - tle for the right;
Thy glo - ry on our ban - ners shed, We an - swer to Thy call;
All in - ward foes help us des - troy And spot - less all to be.
We give our lives with glad in - tent To serve the world and Thee,
And where the fierc - est bat - tles press A - gainst the hosts of sin,
We trust Thee for the grace to win The high, vic - to - rious goal,
To die, to suf - fer and be spent To set our broth - ers free.
To res - cue those in dire dis - tress We glad - ly en - ter in.
Where pur - i - ty shall con - quer sin In Christ - like self - con - trol.
A - MEN.

Eternal Ruler of the Ceaseless Round

YORKSHIRE. 10. 10. 10. 10. 10. 10.

506

JOHN W. CHADWICK, 1840–1904

JOHN WAINWRIGHT, 1723–1768

In moderate time

1. E - ter - nal Rul - er of the cease-less round Of cir-cling plan-ets sing-ing on their way, Guide of the na - tions from the night pro - found In - to the glo - ry of the per - fect day, Rule in our hearts that we may ev - er be Guid-ed, and strength-ened, and up-held by Thee.

2. We are of Thee, the chil-dren of Thy love, The broth-ers of Thy well - be - lov - ed Son; De - scend, O Ho - ly Spir - it, like a dove, In - to our hearts that we may be as one—As one with Thee, to whom we ev - er tend, As one with Him, our Broth-er and our Friend.

3. We would be one in ha-tred of all wrong, One in our love of all things sweet and fair, One with the joy that break-eth in - to song, One with the grief that trem-bles in - to prayer, One in the power that makes Thy chil-dren free To fol - low truth, and thus to fol - low Thee. A-MEN.

These Things Shall Be: a Loftier Race

507

TRURO. L. M.

John A. Symonds, 1840–1893 T. Williams' Psalmodia Evangelica, 1789

In moderate time

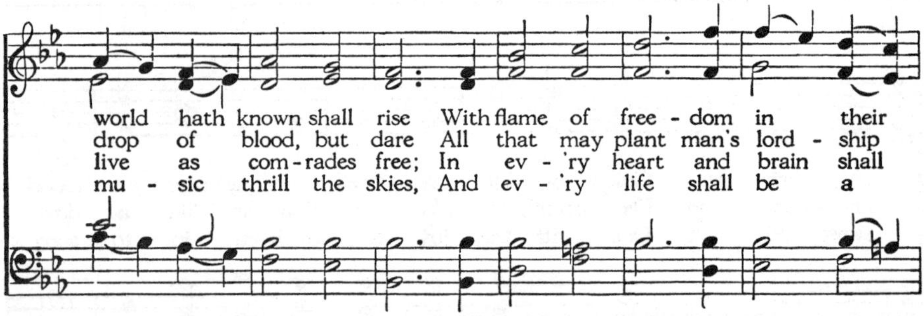

1. These things shall be: a loft - ier race Than e'er the world hath known shall rise With flame of free - dom in their souls, And light of knowl - edge in their eyes;
2. They shall be gen - tle, brave and strong To spill no drop of blood, but dare All that may plant man's lord - ship firm On earth, and fire, and sea, and air.
3. Na - tion with na - tion, land with land, Un - armed shall live as com - rades free; In ev - 'ry heart and brain shall throb The pulse of one fra - ter - ni - ty.
4. New arts shall bloom of loft - ier mould, And might - ier mu - sic thrill the skies, And ev - 'ry life shall be a song, When all the earth is par - a - dise. A - men.

For lower key, see No. 425

When Thy Heart With Joy O'erflowing

508

BULLINGER. 8. 5. 8. 3.

Theodore C. Williams, 1855–1915 Ethelbert W. Bullinger, 1837–1913

In moderate time

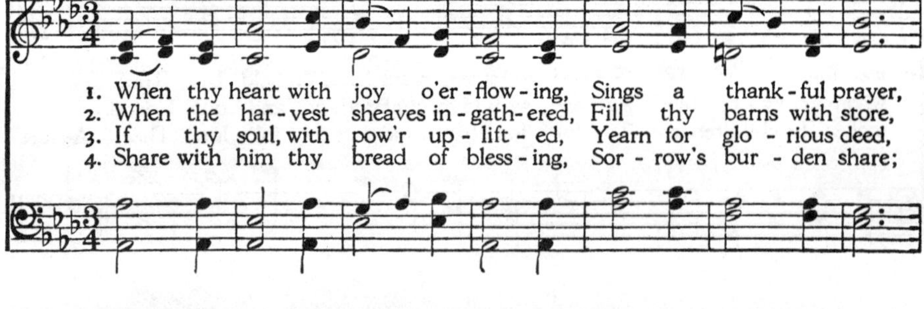

1. When thy heart with joy o'er - flow - ing, Sings a thank - ful prayer,
2. When the har - vest sheaves in - gath - ered, Fill thy barns with store,
3. If thy soul, with pow'r up - lift - ed, Yearn for glo - rious deed,
4. Share with him thy bread of bless - ing, Sor - row's bur - den share;

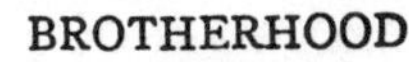

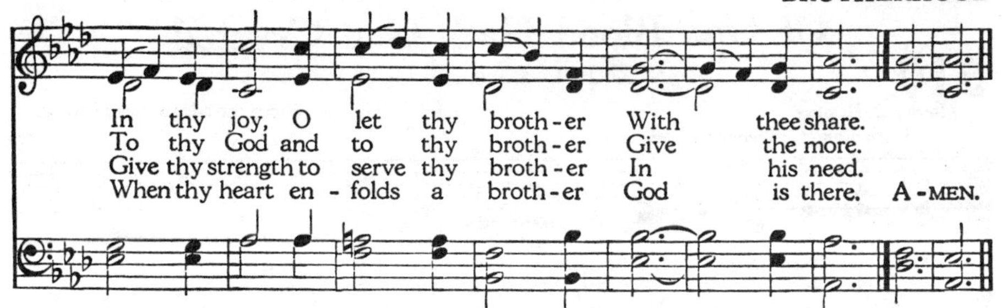
In thy joy, O let thy broth-er With thee share.
To thy God and to thy broth-er Give the more.
Give thy strength to serve thy broth-er In his need.
When thy heart en-folds a broth-er God is there. A-MEN.

We Mix From Many Lands

ST. GERMANS. 6. 6. 6. 6. 6. 5.

509

ALGERNON C. SWINBURNE, 1837–1909

FREDERICK C. MAKER, 1844–1927

In flowing rhythm
1. We mix from man-y lands, We march for ver-y far;
2. It doth not flame and wane With years and spheres that roll;
3. O sor-r'wing hearts of slaves, We heard you beat from far!
4. These have we, these are ours, That no priests give nor kings;
5. Rise, ere the dawn be ris'n, Come, and be all souls fed;
In hearts and lips and hands Our staffs and weap-ons are;
Storms can-not shake nor stain The strength that makes it hold,
We bring the light that saves; We bring the morn-ing star;
The hon-ey of all these flow'rs, The heart of all these springs;
From field and streets and pris'n Come, for the feast is spread.
The light we walk in dark-ens Sun and moon and star.
The fire that moulds and moves Is of the sov-'reign soul.
Free-dom's good things we bring you, Whence all good things are.
Ours, for where free-dom lives not, There live no good things.
Live! for the truth is liv-ing: Wake! for night is dead. A-MEN.

510 Of One Blood Hath God Created

ZÜRICH. 8. 7. 8. 7. 8. 8. 7. 7.

HENRY B. ROBINS

From the MORAVIAN HYMNAL

With dignity, in moderate time

1. Of one blood hath God cre-a-ted Ev-ery kin-dred, tribe and tongue;
2. God of all the war-ring peo-ples, Still art Thou the God of Peace;
3. Keep be-fore us, clear, the vi-sion Of Thy Ho-ly com-mon-wealth;
4. May we, with the Man of Sorrows, Tread the dangerous path of du-ty;
5. Grant to us a sense of presence: Make us all a-ware of Thee;
His is ev-ery fane and al-tar, Though man's em-pire be far-flung;
Love art Thou, but Love in Sor-row, Wound-ed un-til wars shall cease;
Guide us, Thou, in each de-ci-sion; Save us from the sub-tle stealth
Seek-ing not our own, but serving, May we grasp, O Lord, the beauty
May Thy Ho-ly Love u-nite us In the bond that sets men free—
Ev-en though some flout the oth-ers, Un-der-neath are they blood-bro-thers;
Un-til Right shall win, our bur-den Thou, too, bear-est 'tis the guer-don
Which would fill our souls this hour With race-ha-tred, lust of pow-er,
Of Thy Ho-li-ness, where ev-er Flames a Love that fail-eth nev-er,
Free to un-der-stand each oth-er, Free to claim each as his broth-er,
And shall learn, some cru-cial day, How to walk a com-mon way.
Of that daunt-less Sav-iour-hood Which shall rear the com-mon good.
Al-ien-ate our life from Thee And Thy King-dom, yet to be.
Burning out the waste and dross, Sav-ing men from shame and loss.
Free to build in un-i-ty, Free, O God, yet bound to Thee.
A-MEN.

Words used by permission of Henry B. Robins.

At Length There Dawns the Glorious Day

ALL SAINTS. C. M. D.

511

OZORA S. DAVIS, 1866–1931

HENRY S. CUTLER, 1824–1902

In moderate time, with marked rhythm

1. At length there dawns the glo - rious day By pro-phets long fore - told;
2. For what are sun-d'ring strains of blood, Or an-cient caste and creed?
3. One com - mon faith u - nites us all, We seek one com-mon goal,
At length the cho - rus clear - er grows That shep-herds heard of old.
One claim u - nites all men in God To serve each hu - man need.
One ten - der com - fort broods up - on The strug-gling hu - man soul.
The day of dawn - ing Broth - er - hood Breaks on our ea - ger eyes,
Then here to - geth - er broth - er - men We pledge the Lord a - new
To this clear call of Broth - er - hood Our hearts re - spon-sive ring;
And hu - man ha-treds flee be - fore The ra - diant east-ern skies.
Our loy - al love, our stal - wart faith, Our ser - vice strong and true.
We join the glo-rious new cru - sade Of our great Lord and King. A-MEN.

A Noble Life, a Simple Faith

512

HUMMEL. C. M.

A. S. ISAACS, 1851-1920 — CHARLES H. C. ZEUNER, 1797-1857

With dignity, in moderate time
1. A no - ble life, a sim - ple faith, An o - pen heart and hand— These are the love - ly lit - a - nies Which all men un - der - stand.
2. These are the firm - knit bonds of grace, Though hid - den to the view, Which bind in sa - cred broth - er - hood All men the whole world through.
3. The cries of clash - ing creeds are heard, On ev - 'ry side they sound, But no age is de - gen - er - ate In which such lives are found.
4. A no - ble life, a sim - ple faith, An o - pen heart and hand— These are the love - ly lit - a - nies Which all men un - der - stand.
A-MEN.

Let There Be Light, Lord God of Hosts

513

MOZART (ZELOTES). L. M.

WILLIAM M. VORIES, 1880- — Adapted from MOZART, 1756-1791

In moderate time

1. Let there be light, Lord God of Hosts, Let there be wis - dom on the earth
2. With - in our pas - sioned hearts in - still The calm that end - eth strain and strife;
3. Give us the peace of vi - sion clear To see our broth - ers' good our own,
4. Let woe and waste of war - fare cease, That use - ful la - bor yet may build.

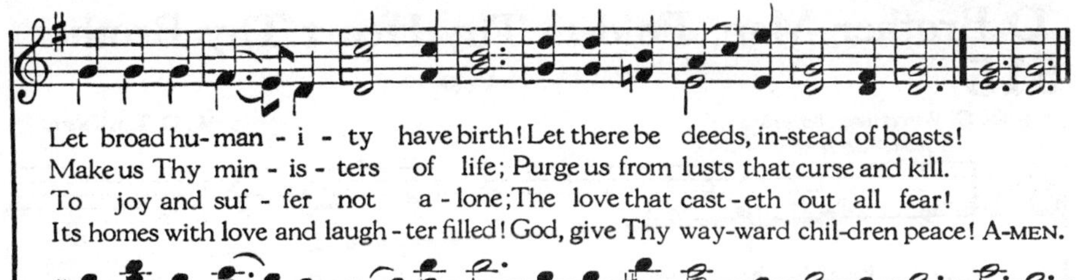
Let broad hu-man - i - ty have birth! Let there be deeds, in-stead of boasts!
Make us Thy min - is - ters of life; Purge us from lusts that curse and kill.
To joy and suf - fer not a - lone; The love that cast - eth out all fear!
Its homes with love and laugh - ter filled! God, give Thy way-ward chil-dren peace! A-MEN.

Words used by permission of the American Peace Society, founded 1828, Washington, D. C.

My Country Is the World

NEW AMERICA. 6. 6. 4. 6. 6. 6. 4.

514

ANONYMOUS — L. B. LONGACRE

In moderate time

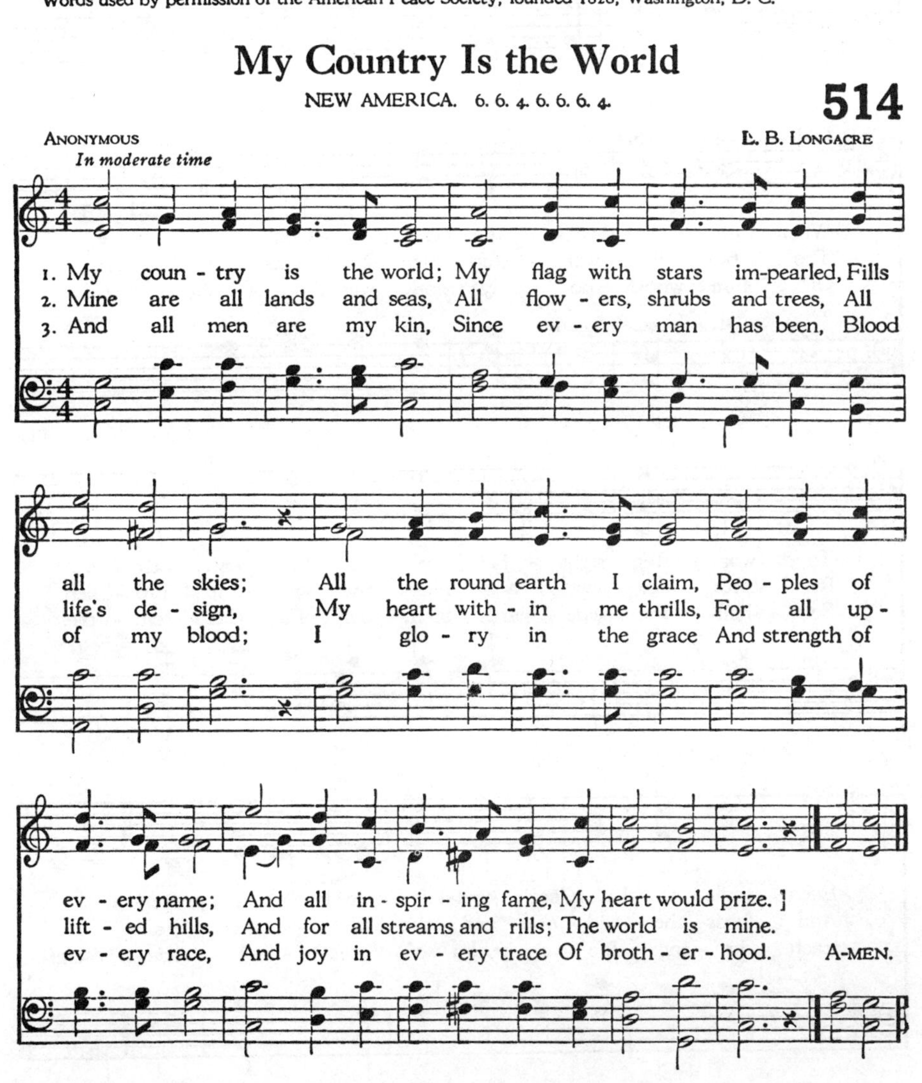
1. My coun - try is the world; My flag with stars im-pearled, Fills all the skies; All the round earth I claim, Peo - ples of ev - ery name; And all in - spir - ing fame, My heart would prize.
2. Mine are all lands and seas, All flow - ers, shrubs and trees, All life's de - sign, My heart with - in me thrills, For all up - lift - ed hills, And for all streams and rills; The world is mine.
3. And all men are my kin, Since ev - ery man has been, Blood of my blood; I glo - ry in the grace And strength of ev - ery race, And joy in ev - ery trace Of broth - er - hood. A-MEN.

O Brother Man, Fold to Thy Heart Thy Brother

515

ACADIA. 11. 10. 11. 10.

John G. Whittier, 1807–1892
W. C. T. Morson
In moderate time
1. O broth - er man, fold to thy heart thy broth - er;
2. For one whom Je - sus loved has tru - ly spo - ken,
3. Fol - low with rev - rent steps the great ex - am - ple
Where pit - y dwells, the peace of God is there;
The ho - lier wor - ship which he deigns to bless
Of him whose ho - ly work was "do - ing good;"
To wor - ship right - ly is to love each oth - er,
Re - stores the lost, and binds the spir - it bro - ken,
So shall the wide earth seem our Fa - ther's tem - ple,
Each smile a hymn, each kind - ly deed a prayer.
And feeds the wid - ow and the fa - ther - less.
Each lov - ing life a psalm of grat - i - tude. A-MEN.

All Hail the Pageant of the Years

O JESU. 8. 6. 8. 6. 8. 8.
JOHN HAYNES HOLMES, 1879–
Melody in the HIRSCHBERG GESANGBUCH, 1741
In moderate time
1. All hail, the pag - eant of the years
2. Be - hind us fade the cen - tu - ries
3. A - round us lies the her - i - tage
4. Be - hold, there looms the mys - te - ry
5. The ae - ons come, the ae - ons go,
That end - less come and go, The brave pro - ces - sion of the spheres
Of man at war with man, The fierce and foul fu - til - i - ties
Of clash - ing sword and shield; The want, the waste, the hate and rage
Of love di - vin - er far, There speaks the stead - fast proph - e - cy
The stars nor pause nor cease; On wings of si - lence, soft as snow,
In Time's re - sist - less flow— A - rise, and crown our
Of bat - tling tribe and clan— A - rise, and crown our
Of man - y a glo - ried field— A - rise, and crown our
Of na - tions freed from war— A - rise, and crown our
Shall come the boon of peace. All hail, our days are
days with good, In glad, ex - ult - ant broth - er - hood.
days with good, In glad, ex - ult - ant broth - er - hood.
days with good, In glad, ex - ult - ant broth - er - hood.
days with good, In glad, ex - ult - ant broth - er - hood.
crowned with good, In glad, ex - ult - ant broth - er - hood. A-MEN.

517 O Jesus, Master, When Today

HUMILITY. L.M.

CHARLES S. NEWHALL, 1842–1935 — SAMUEL P. TUCKERMAN, 1819–1890

In moderate time

1. O Je - sus, Mas - ter, when to - day I meet a - long the crowd - ed way My bur-dened broth - ers— mine and thine— May then through me thy Spir - it shine;
2. To cheer them in their on - ward way, Till eve - ning ends the va - ried day— To kin - dle so a grow - ing light Where else might be but gloom and night.
3. Grant too that they my need may know As side by side we on - ward go— An e - qual need of kind - ly thought, And love like that which thou hast taught.
4. Then give our hands a touch di - vine, And to our voic - es tones like thine, As side by side we on - ward go, Nor need each oth - er's names to know. A - MEN.

518 Christian, Rise and Act Thy Creed

INNOCENTS. 7. 7. 7. 7.

F. A. ROLLO RUSSELL, 1849–1914 — From THE PARISH CHOIR, 1850

With spirit

1. Chris - tian, rise, and act thy creed, Let thy prayer be in thy deed;
2. Hearts a-round thee sink with care; Thou canst help their load to bear,
3. Let thine alms be hope and joy, And thy wor-ship God's em - ploy;
4. Come then, Law di - vine, and reign, Free - st faith as- sailed in vain,

Seek the right, per-form the true, Raise thy work and life a - new.
Thou canst bring in - spir - ing light, Arm their fal-tering wills to fight.
Give Him thanks in hum - ble zeal, Learn - ing all His will to feel.
Per - fect love be - reft of fear, Born in heaven and ra-diant here. A-MEN.

Where Cross the Crowded Ways of Life

GERMANY. L. M.

519

Frank Mason North 1850–1935

Adapted from Sacred Melodies
William Gardiner, 1770–1853

In moderate time
1. Where cross the crowd - ed ways of life, Where sound the
2. In haunts of wretch - ed - ness and need, On shad-owed
3. From ten - der child - hood's help - less - ness, From wo-man's
4. The cup of wa - ter given for Thee Still holds the
5. O Mas - ter, from the moun - tain side, Make haste to
6. Till sons of men shall learn Thy love And fol - low
cries of race and clan, A - bove the noise of
thresh - olds dark with fears, From paths where hide the
grief, man's bur - dened toil, From fam - ished souls, from
fresh - ness of Thy grace; Yet long these mul - ti -
heal these hearts of pain; A - mong these rest - less
where Thy feet have trod; Till, glo - rious from Thy
self - ish strife, We hear Thy voice, O Son of man!
lures of greed, We catch the vi - sion of Thy tears.
sor - row's stress, Thy heart has nev - er known re - coil.
tudes to see The sweet com - pas - sion of Thy face.
throngs a - bide, O tread the ci - ty's streets a - gain,
heaven a - bove, Shall come the ci - ty of our God! A-MEN.

O Blessed Son of God

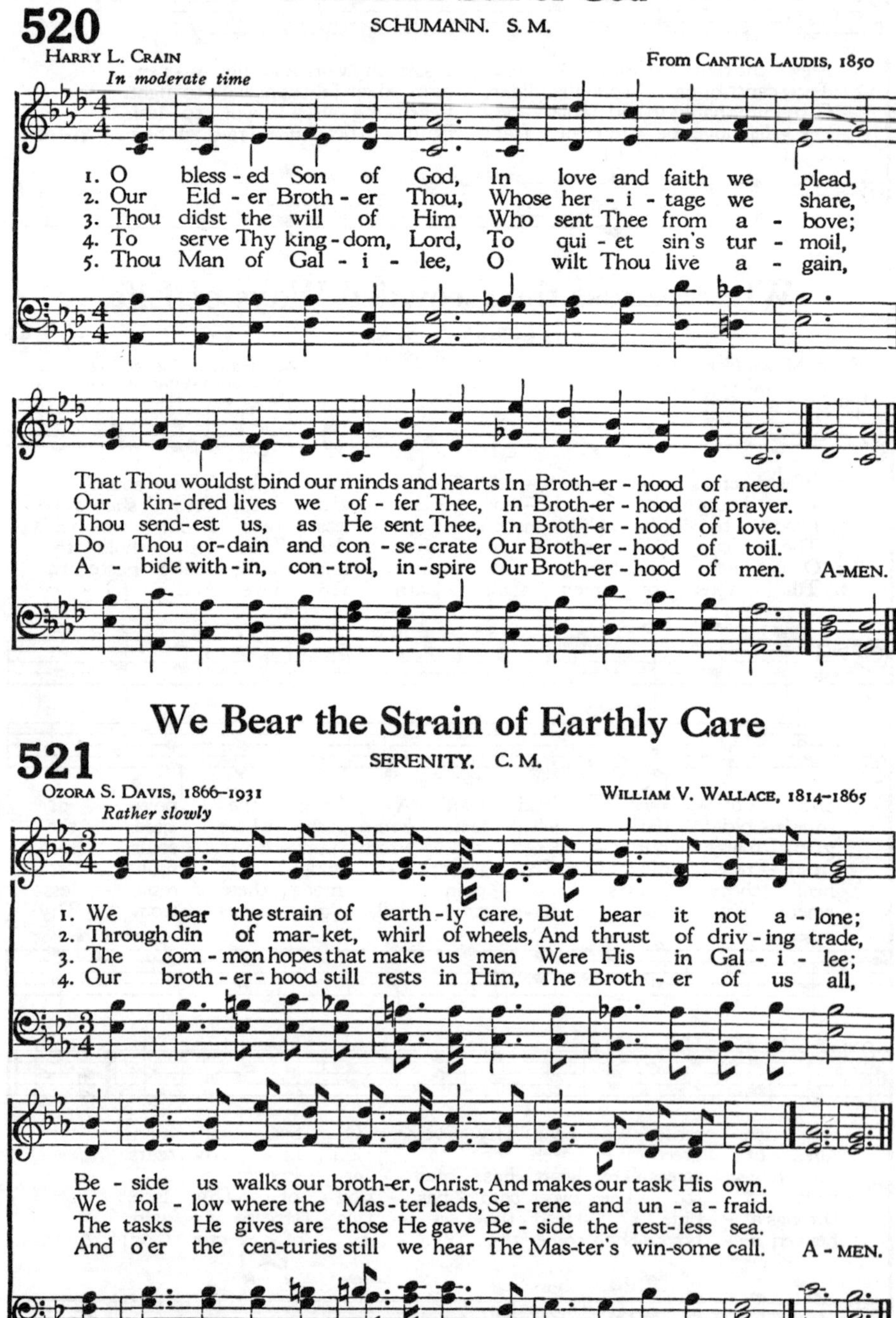
520
SCHUMANN. S. M.
Harry L. Crain
From Cantica Laudis, 1850
In moderate time
1. O blessed Son of God, In love and faith we plead,
That Thou wouldst bind our minds and hearts In Brotherhood of need.
2. Our Elder Brother Thou, Whose heritage we share,
Our kindred lives we offer Thee, In Brotherhood of prayer.
3. Thou didst the will of Him Who sent Thee from above;
Thou sendest us, as He sent Thee, In Brotherhood of love.
4. To serve Thy kingdom, Lord, To quiet sin's turmoil,
Do Thou ordain and consecrate Our Brotherhood of toil.
5. Thou Man of Galilee, O wilt Thou live again,
Abide within, control, inspire Our Brotherhood of men.
A-MEN.
We Bear the Strain of Earthly Care
521
SERENITY. C. M.
Ozora S. Davis, 1866–1931
William V. Wallace, 1814–1865
Rather slowly
1. We bear the strain of earthly care, But bear it not alone;
Beside us walks our brother, Christ, And makes our task His own.
2. Through din of market, whirl of wheels, And thrust of driving trade,
We follow where the Master leads, Serene and unafraid.
3. The common hopes that make us men Were His in Galilee;
The tasks He gives are those He gave Beside the restless sea.
4. Our brotherhood still rests in Him, The Brother of us all,
And o'er the centuries still we hear The Master's winsome call.
A-MEN.

Our Father, Thy Dear Name Doth Show

ELLACOMBE. C. M. D.

522

CHARLES H. RICHARDS, 1839–1925 — GESANGBUCH DER HERZOGL, 1784

In moderate time, with spirit

1. Our Fa - ther, Thy dear name doth show, The great-ness of Thy love;
2. A - like we share Thy ten-der care; We trust one heaven-ly Friend;
3. Bring in, we pray, the glo-rious day When bat - tle cries are stilled;
4. Close knit the warm fra - ter-nal tie That makes the whole world one;

All are Thy chil-dren here be - low, As in Thy heav'n a - bove.
Be - fore one mer - cy - seat in prayer In con - fi - dence we bend;
When bit - ter strife is swept a - way And hearts with love are filled.
Our dis - cords change to har-mo - ny Like an - gel songs be - gun.

One fam - i - ly on earth are we Throughout its wid - est span:
A - like we hear Thy lov - ing call, One heaven-ly vi - sion scan,
O help us ban - ish pride and wrong, Which since the world be - gan
At last, up - on that bright - er shore Com - plete Thy glo - rious plan,

O help us ev - ery-where to see The broth-er - hood of man.
One Lord, one faith, one hope for all, The broth-er - hood of man.
Have marred its peace; help us make strong The broth-er - hood of man.
And heaven shall crown for - ev - er - more The broth-er - hood of man. A - MEN.

Words by Rev. Charles H. Richards, D.D., from "Songs of Christian Life," used by permission of Charles E. Merrill Co.

Hail to the Brightness of Zion's Glad Morning

523

WESLEY. 11. 10. 11. 10.

THOMAS HASTINGS, 1784–1872 — LOWELL MASON, 1792–1872

With spirit

1. Hail to the bright-ness of Zi - on's glad morn - ing,
2. Hail to the bright-ness of Zi - on's glad morn - ing,
3. Lo, in the des - ert rich flow - ers are spring - ing,
4. See, from all lands, from the isles of the o - cean,

Joy to the lands that in dark - ness have lain!
Long by the proph - ets of Is - rael fore - told;
Streams ev - er co - pious are flow - ing a - long;
Praise to the Sav - iour as - cend - ing on high;

Hushed be the ac - cents of sor - row and mourn - ing,
Hail to the mil - lions from bond - age re - turn - ing!
Loud from the moun - tain - tops ech - oes are ring - ing,
Fall - en the wea - pons of war and com - mo - tion,

Zi - on in tri - umph be - gins her mild reign.
Gen - tiles and Jews the blest vi - sion be - hold.
Wastes rise in ver - dure and min - gle in song.
Shouts of sal - va - tion are rend - ing the sky. A - MEN.

The Morning Light Is Breaking

WEBB. 7. 6. 7. 6. D.

524

Samuel F. Smith, 1808–1895 George J. Webb, 1803–1887

Jubilantly

1. The morn - ing light is break - ing, The dark - ness dis - ap - pears;
2. See all the na - tions bend - ing Be - fore the God we love,
3. Blest riv - er of sal - va - tion, Pur - sue thine on - ward way;

The sons of earth are wak - ing To pen - i - ten - tial tears:
And thou - sand hearts as - cend - ing In grat - i - tude a - bove:
Flow thou to ev - ery na - tion, Nor in thy rich - ness stay:

Each breeze that sweeps the o - cean Brings tid - ings from a - far,
While sin - ners, now con - fess - ing, The gos - pel call o - bey,
Stay not till all the low - ly Tri - umph-ant reach their home;

Of na - tions in com - mo - tion, Pre - pared for Zi - on's war.
And seek the Sav-iour's bless - ing, A na - tion in a day.
Stay not till all the ho - ly Pro-claim, "The Lord is come!" A - men.

Whom Oceans Part, O Lord, Unite

525
WAREHAM. L. M.
Howell E. Lewis, 1860–
William Knapp, 1698–1768
In moderate time
1. Whom o - ceans part, O Lord, u - nite To love Thy Name, and seek Thy light: Though from each oth - er far we be, Let none, O Christ, be far from Thee.
2. On man-y a dis - tant is - land shore Still let men see heaven's o - pened door; 'Mid si - lent hills, be - neath fresh skies, Let Beth - el's shin - ing lad - der rise.
3. Our sons and daugh - ters guide in truth; Take for Thy - self the flower of youth; A - far from home, through gain or loss, Keep them true - heart - ed to Thy cross.
4. Whom o - ceans part, O Lord, u - nite— One com - mon - wealth for God and right, A ran - somed peo - ple, strong and free, To bring the whole wide world to Thee! A - men.
Words from "The Christian Hymnary," by permission of Howell Elvet Lewis.
O Christ, Forget Not Them Who Stand
526
MISSIONARY CHANT. L. M.
Margaret E. Sangster, 1838–1912
Charles H. C. Zeuner, 1797–1857
Rather slowly
1. O Christ, for - get not them who stand Thy van-guard in the dis - tant land.
2. Thine is the work they strive to do, Their foes so man - y, they so few.

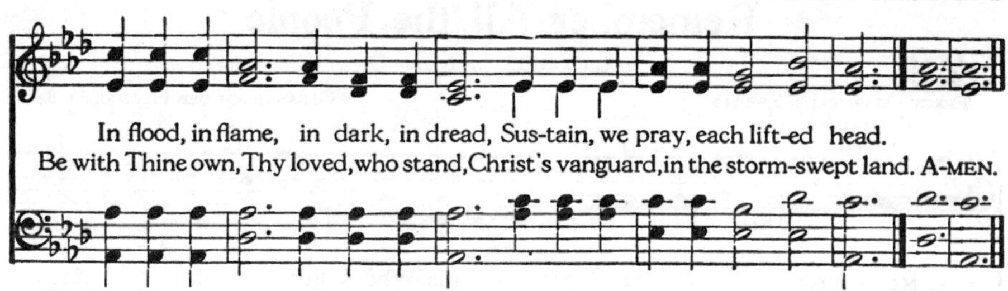
In flood, in flame, in dark, in dread, Sus-tain, we pray, each lift-ed head.
Be with Thine own, Thy loved, who stand, Christ's vanguard, in the storm-swept land. A-MEN.

Words used by permission of Miss Margaret E. Sangster.

Jesus Shall Reign Where'er the Sun

DUKE STREET. L. M.

527

ISAAC WATTS, 1674–1748

JOHN HATTON, ?–1793

With exultation

1. Je - sus shall reign wher - e'er the sun Does his suc - ces - sive jour - neys run; His king - dom spread from shore to shore, Till moons shall wax and wane no more.
2. To Him shall end - less prayer be made, And end - less prais - es crown His head; His name, like sweet per - fume, shall rise With ev - ery morn - ing sac - ri - fice.
3. Peo - ple and realms of ev - ery tongue Dwell on His love with sweet - est song, And in - fant voic - es shall pro - claim Their ear - ly bless - ings on His Name.
4. Let ev - ery crea - ture rise, and bring His grate - ful hon - ors to our King; An - gels de - scend with songs a - gain, And earth re - peat the loud A - men! A - MEN.

Remember All the People

528

ELLACOMBE. 7. 6. 7. 6. D.

PERCY DEARMER, 1867–1936

GESANGBUCH DER HERZOGL., 1784

Fervently

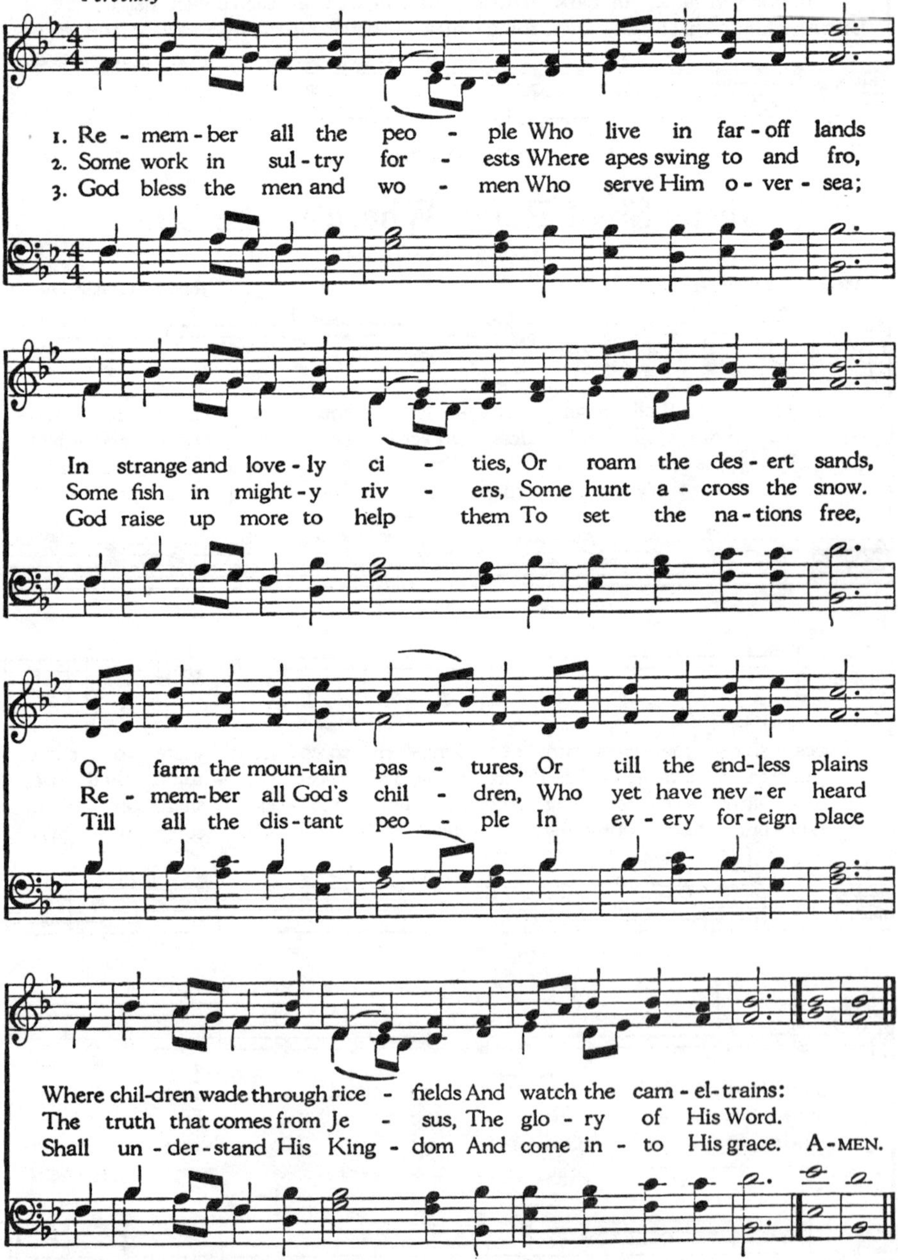

1. Re - mem - ber all the peo - ple Who live in far - off lands
In strange and love - ly ci - ties, Or roam the des - ert sands,
Or farm the moun-tain pas - tures, Or till the end - less plains
Where chil-dren wade through rice - fields And watch the cam - el - trains:

2. Some work in sul - try for - ests Where apes swing to and fro,
Some fish in might - y riv - ers, Some hunt a - cross the snow.
Re - mem - ber all God's chil - dren, Who yet have nev - er heard
The truth that comes from Je - sus, The glo - ry of His Word.

3. God bless the men and wo - men Who serve Him o - ver - sea;
God raise up more to help them To set the na - tions free,
Till all the dis - tant peo - ple In ev - ery for - eign place
Shall un - der - stand His King - dom And come in - to His grace. A - MEN.

O Zion, Haste, Thy Mission High Fulfilling

TIDINGS. 11. 10. 11. 10. with Refrain

529

MARY A. THOMSON, 1834–1923

JAMES WALCH, 1837–1901

With spirit and dignity

1. O Zi - on, haste, thy mis- sion high ful - fill - ing, To tell to all the world that God is Light, That He who made all na - tions is not will - ing One soul should per - ish, lost in shades of night.
2. Pro - claim to ev - ery peo-ple, tongue, and na- tion That God, in whom they live and move, is Love; Tell how He stooped to save His lost cre - a - tion, And died on earth that man might live a - bove.
3. Give of thy sons to bear the mes-sage glo - rious; Give of thy wealth to speed them on their way; Pour out thy soul for them in prayer vic - to - rious; O Zi - on, haste to bring the bright-er day.

REFRAIN

Pub - lish glad tid - ings; Tid - ings of peace; Tid - ings of Je - sus, Re-demption and re-lease. A-MEN.

We've A Story to Tell to the Nations

530

MESSAGE. 10. 8. 8. 7. 7. with Refrain.

COLIN STERNE, 1862–1928 — Adapted from H. ERNEST NICHOL, 1862–1928

With spirit, and well marked rhythm

1. We've a sto - ry to tell to the na - tions That shall
2. We've a song to be sung to the na - tions, That shall
3. We've a mes - sage to give to the na - tions, That the
4. We've a Sav - iour to show to the na - tions, Who the

turn their hearts to the right, A sto - ry of truth and mer - cy,
lift their hearts to the Lord; A song that shall con - quer e - vil
Lord who reign - eth a - bove, Hath sent us His Son to save us,
path of sor - row has trod, That all of the world's great peo - ples

A sto - ry of peace and light, A sto - ry of peace and light.
And shat - ter the spear and sword, And shat - ter the spear and sword.
And show us that God is love, And show us that God is love.
Might come to the truth of God, Might come to the truth of God.

REFRAIN

For the dark-ness shall turn to dawn - ing, And the dawn-ing to noon-day bright,

And Christ's great kingdom shall come on earth, The kingdom of Love and Light. A-MEN.

Let the Song Go Round the Earth

SILKSWORTH. 7. 5. 7. 5. 7. 7.

531

SARAH G. STOCK, 1838–1898

C. J. VINCENT, JR., 1852–

In moderate time

1. Let the song go round the earth: Jesus Christ is Lord; Sound His praises, tell His worth, Be His Name adored; Every clime and every tongue Join the grand, the glorious song.
2. Let the song go round the earth, From the eastern sea, Where the daylight has its birth, Glad, and bright, and free; China's millions join the strains, Waft them on to India's plains.
3. Let the song go round the earth, Where the summer smiles; Let the notes of holy mirth Break from distant isles; Inland forests, dark and dim, Snow-bound coasts give back the hymn.
4. Let the song go round the earth: Jesus Christ is King, With the story of His worth, Let the whole world ring, Him creation all adore Evermore and evermore. A-MEN.

Words from "The Christian Hymnary." Music from "The Christian Hymnary Tune Book."

532 I Love to Tell the Story

HANKEY. 7. 6. 7. 6. D. with Refrain

KATHERINE HANKEY, 1834-1911
Refrain added

WILLIAM G. FISCHER, 1835-1912

Joyously
1. I love to tell the sto - ry Of un - seen things a - bove, Of
2. I love to tell the sto - ry; More won - der - ful it seems Than
3. I love to tell the sto - ry; 'Tis pleas - ant to re - peat What
4. I love to tell the sto - ry, For those who know it best Seem
Je - sus and His glo - ry, Of Je - sus and His love. I love to tell the
all the gold - en fan - cies Of all our gold - en dreams. I love to tell the
seems, each time I tell it, More won - der - ful - ly sweet. I love to tell the
hun - ger - ing and thirst - ing To hear it like the rest. And when, in scenes of
sto - ry, Be - cause I know 'tis true; It sat - is - fies my long - ings
sto - ry, It did so much for me; And that is just the rea - son
sto - ry, For some have nev - er heard The mes - sage of sal - va - tion
glo - ry, I sing the new, new song, 'Twill be the old, old sto - ry
REFRAIN
As noth - ing else can do. I love to tell the sto - ry, 'Twill be my theme in glo - ry,
I tell it now to thee.
From God's own ho - ly Word.
That I have loved so long.
To tell the old, old sto - ry Of Je - sus and His love. A - MEN.

Heralds of Christ, Who Bear the King's Commands

NATIONAL HYMN. 10. 10. 10. 10.

533

LAURA SCHERER COPENHAVER, 1868–

GEORGE W. WARREN, 1828–1902

With martial rhythm
Trumpets, before each stanza
1. Her - alds of Christ, who bear the King's com-mands,
2. Thro' des - ert ways, dark fen, and deep mo - rass,
3. Where once the crook - ed trail in dark-ness wound
4. Lord, give us faith and strength the road to build,
Im - mor - tal ti - dings in your mor - tal hands,
Through jun - gles, slug - gish seas, and moun - tain pass,
Let march - ing feet and joy - ous song re - sound,
To see the prom - ise of the day ful - filled,
Pass on and car - ry swift the news ye bring:
Build ye the road, and fal - ter not, nor stay;
Where burned the funer - al pyres, and cen - sers swing,
When war shall be no more and strife shall cease
Make straight, make straight the high - way of the King.
Pre - pare a - cross the earth the King's high - way.
Make straight, make straight the high - way of the King.
Up - on the high - way of the Prince of Peace.
A - MEN.

An Endless Line of Splendor

534

LANCASHIRE. 7. 6. 7. 6. D.

VACHEL LINDSAY, 1879–1930 HENRY SMART, 1813–1879

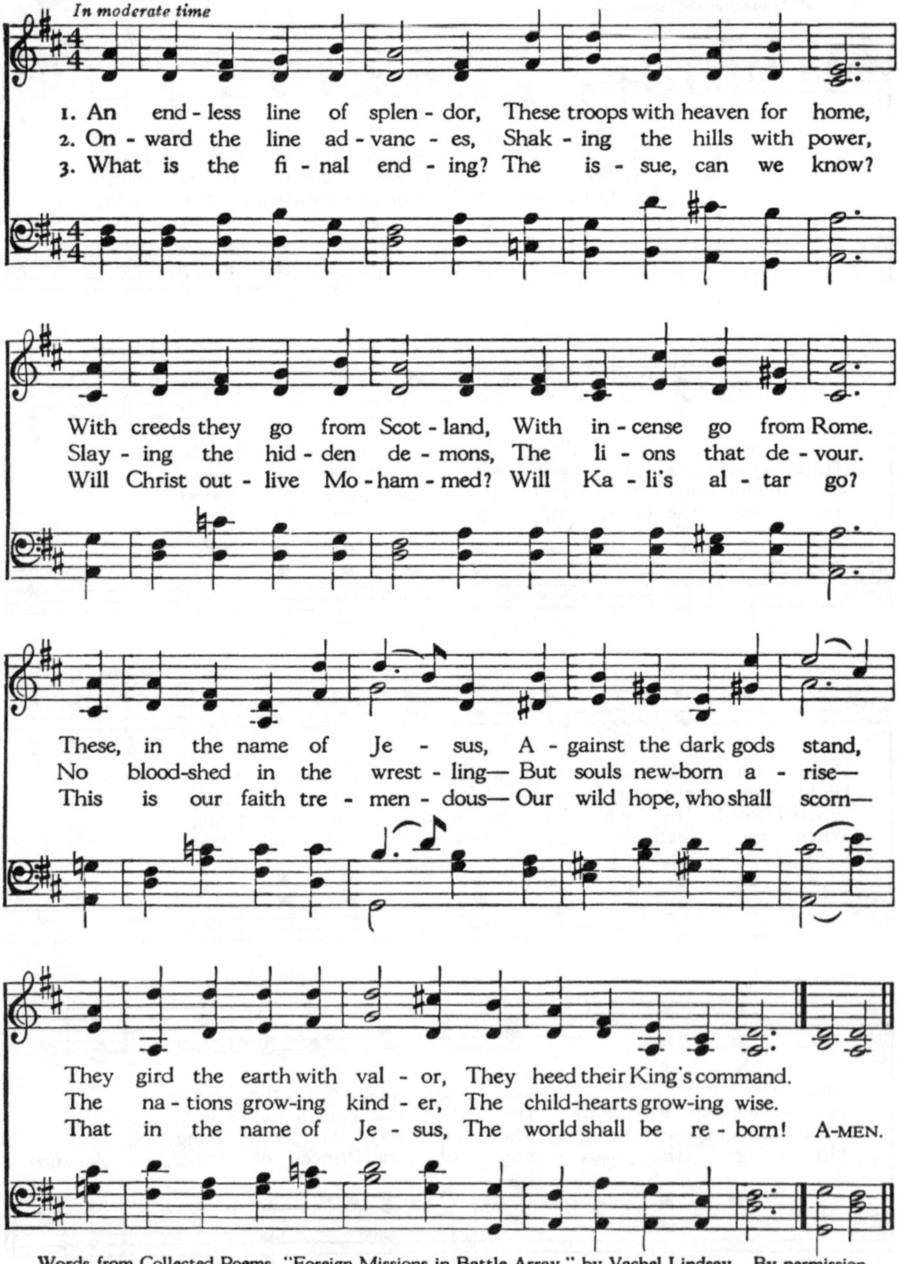

In moderate time

1. An end - less line of splen - dor, These troops with heaven for home,
With creeds they go from Scot - land, With in - cense go from Rome.
These, in the name of Je - sus, A - gainst the dark gods stand,
They gird the earth with val - or, They heed their King's command.

2. On - ward the line ad - vanc - es, Shak - ing the hills with power,
Slay - ing the hid - den de - mons, The li - ons that de - vour.
No blood-shed in the wrest - ling— But souls new-born a - rise—
The na - tions grow-ing kind - er, The child-hearts grow-ing wise.

3. What is the fi - nal end - ing? The is - sue, can we know?
Will Christ out - live Mo - ham - med? Will Ka - li's al - tar go?
This is our faith tre - men - dous— Our wild hope, who shall scorn—
That in the name of Je - sus, The world shall be re - born! A-MEN.

Eternal God, Whose Power Upholds

MATERNA. C. M. D.

Henry Hallam Tweedy, 1868–

Samuel A. Ward, 1847–1903

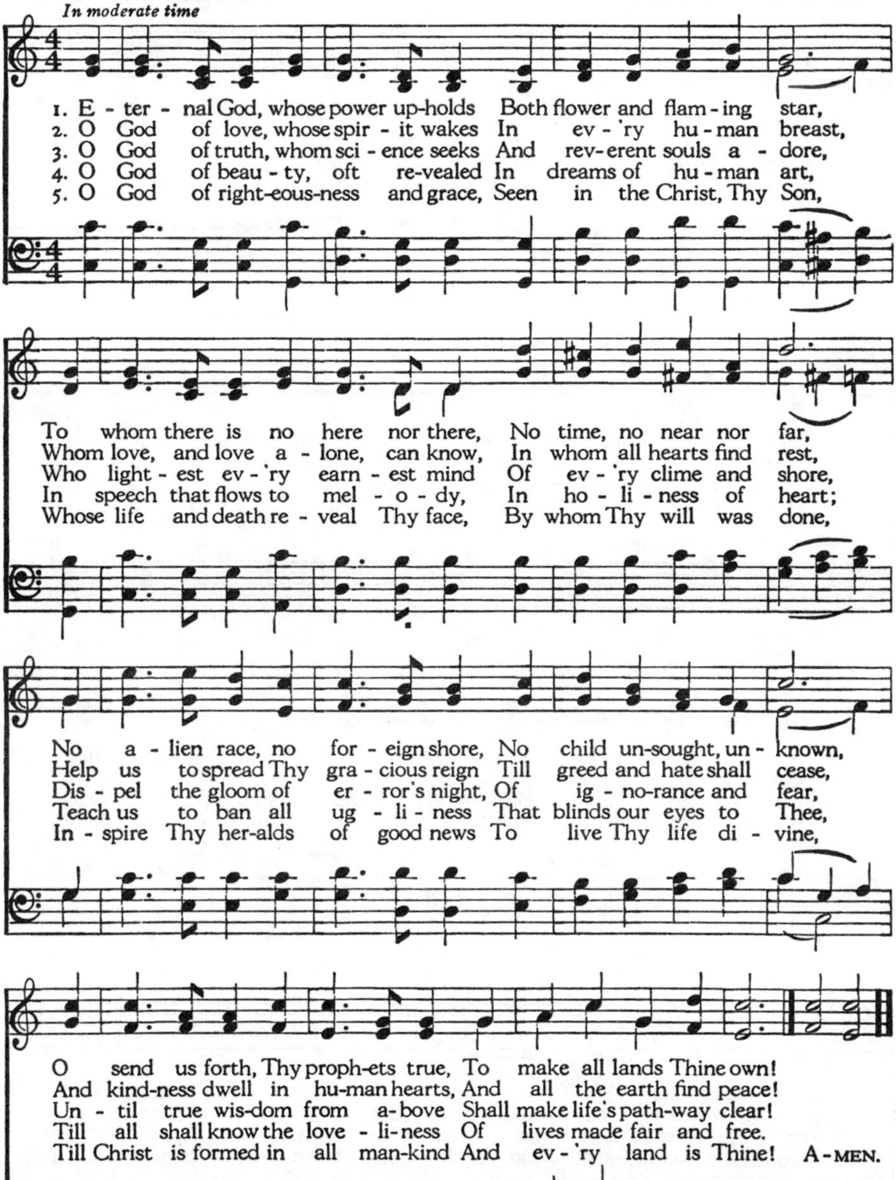

In moderate time

1. Eternal God, whose power upholds Both flower and flaming star,
To whom there is no here nor there, No time, no near nor far,
No alien race, no foreign shore, No child unsought, unknown,
O send us forth, Thy prophets true, To make all lands Thine own!

2. O God of love, whose spirit wakes In every human breast,
Whom love, and love alone, can know, In whom all hearts find rest,
Help us to spread Thy gracious reign Till greed and hate shall cease,
And kindness dwell in human hearts, And all the earth find peace!

3. O God of truth, whom science seeks And reverent souls adore,
Who lightest every earnest mind Of every clime and shore,
Dispel the gloom of error's night, Of ignorance and fear,
Until true wisdom from above Shall make life's pathway clear!

4. O God of beauty, oft revealed In dreams of human art,
In speech that flows to melody, In holiness of heart;
Teach us to ban all ugliness That blinds our eyes to Thee,
Till all shall know the loveliness Of lives made fair and free.

5. O God of righteousness and grace, Seen in the Christ, Thy Son,
Whose life and death reveal Thy face, By whom Thy will was done,
Inspire Thy heralds of good news To live Thy life divine,
Till Christ is formed in all mankind And every land is Thine! Amen.

Thou, Whose Almighty Word

536

FIAT LUX. 6. 6. 4. 6. 6. 6. 4.

JOHN MARRIOTT, 1780–1825 — JOHN B. DYKES, 1823–1876

With dignity
1. Thou, whose al - might - y word Cha - os and
2. Thou, who didst come to bring On Thy re -
3. Spir - it of truth and love, Life - giv - ing,
4. Ho - ly and bless - ed Three, Glo - ri - ous
dark - ness heard, And took their flight, Hear us, we
deem - ing wing Heal - ing and sight, Health to the
ho - ly Dove, Speed forth Thy flight; Move o'er the
Trin - i - ty, Wis - dom, Love, Might! Bound - less as
hum - bly pray; And, where the gos - pel's day
sick in mind, Sight to the in - ly blind,
wa - ters' face, Bear - ing the lamp of grace,
o - cean's tide Roll - ing in full - est pride,
Sheds not its glo - rious ray, Let there be light!
O now to all man - kind Let there be light!
And in earth's dark - est place Let there be light!
Through the world far and wide Let there be light! A - MEN.

We Have Heard a Joyful Sound

JESUS SAVES. 7. 6. 7. 6. 7. 7. 7. 6.

537

PRISCILLA J. OWENS, 1829–?

WILLIAM J. KIRKPATRICK, 1838–1921

Joyfully

1. We have heard a joy - ful sound, Je - sus saves, Je - sus saves;
Spread the glad - ness all a - round, Je - sus saves, Je - sus saves;
Bear the news to ev - 'ry land, Climb the steeps, and cross the waves,
On - ward, 'tis our Lord's com-mand, Je - sus saves, Je - sus saves.

2. Waft it on the roll - ing tide, Je - sus saves, Je - sus saves;
Tell to sin - ners, far and wide, Je - sus saves, Je - sus saves;
Sing, ye is - lands of the sea, Ech - o back, ye o - cean caves,
Earth shall keep her ju - bi - lee, Je - sus saves, Je - sus saves.

3. Sing a - bove the bat - tle's strife, Je - sus saves, Je - sus saves;
By His death and end - less life, Je - sus saves, Je - sus saves;
Sing it soft - ly thro' the gloom, When the heart for mer - cy craves,
Sing in tri - umph o'er the tomb, Je - sus saves, Je - sus saves.

4. Give the winds a might - y voice, Je - sus saves, Je - sus saves;
Let the na - tions now re - joice, Je - sus saves, Je - sus saves;
Shout sal - va - tion, full and free, High - est hills and deep - est caves,
This our song of vic - to - ry, Je - sus saves, Je - sus saves. A - MEN.

Christ for the World We Sing

538
ITALIAN HYMN (TRINITY). 6. 6. 4. 6. 6. 6. 4.
Samuel Wolcott, 1813–1886
Felice de Giardini, 1716–1796
In moderate time, with spirit
1. Christ for the world! we sing; The world to Christ we bring, With lov-ing zeal; The poor and them that mourn, The faint and o-ver-borne, Sin-sick and sor-row-worn, Whom Christ doth heal.
2. Christ for the world! we sing; The world to Christ we bring, With fer-vent prayer; The way-ward and the lost, By rest-less pas-sions tossed, Re-deemed at count-less cost, From dark de-spair.
3. Christ for the world! we sing; The world to Christ we bring, With one ac-cord, With us the work to share, With us re-proach to dare, With us the cross to bear, For Christ our Lord.
4. Christ for the world! we sing; The world to Christ we bring, With joy-ful song; The new-born souls whose days, Re-claimed from er-ror's ways, In-spired with hope and praise, To Christ be-long. A-MEN.
'Thy Kingdom Come,' on Bended Knee
539
CHESTERFIELD. C. M.
Frederick L. Hosmer, 1840–1928
Thomas Haweis, 1733–1820
In moderate time
1. 'Thy Kingdom come,' on bend-ed knee The pass-ing a-ges pray; And faith-ful
2. But the slow watch-es of the night Not less to God be-long; And for the
3. And lo! al-rea-dy on the hills The flags of dawn ap-pear; Gird up your
4. The day in whose clear-shin-ing light All wrong shall stand re-vealed; When jus-tice
5. When know-ledge, hand in hand with peace, Shall walk the earth a-broad; The day of

souls have yearned to see On earth that King-dom's day.
ev - er - last - ing right The si - lent stars are strong.
loins, ye proph - et souls, Pro - claim the day is near:
shall be clothed with might, And ev - ery hurt be healed.
per - fect right - eous - ness, The prom - ised day of God. A - MEN.

Fling Out the Banner! Let It Float

WALTHAM. L. M.

540

George W. Doane, 1799–1859

John B. Calkin, 1827–1905

With spirit
1. Fling out the ban - ner! let it float Sky - ward and sea - ward, high and wide; The sun, that lights its shin - ing folds, The cross, on which the Sav - iour died.
2. Fling out the ban - ner! an - gels bend In anx - ious si - lence o'er the sign, And vain - ly seek to com - pre - hend The won - der of the love di - vine.
3. Fling out the ban - ner! sin - sick souls That sink and per - ish in the strife Shall touch in faith its ra - diant hem, And spring im - mor - tal in - to life.
4. Fling out the ban - ner! let it float Sky - ward and sea - ward, high and wide, Our glo - ry, on - ly in the cross; Our on - ly hope, the Cru - ci - fied! A - MEN.

From Ocean Unto Ocean

541

MISSIONARY HYMN. 7. 6. 7. 6. D.

ROBERT MURRAY, 1832–1910

LOWELL MASON, 1792–1872

In moderate time

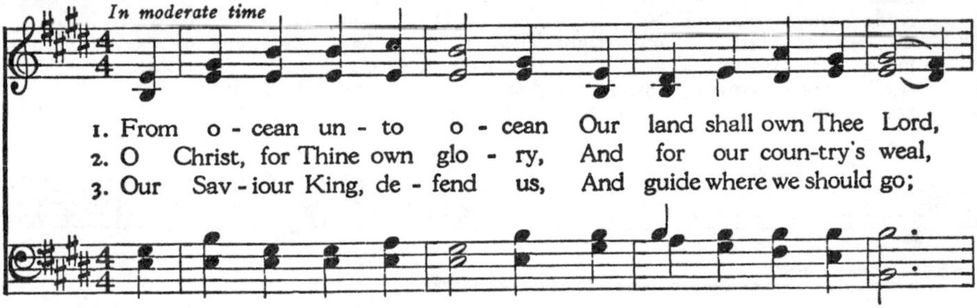

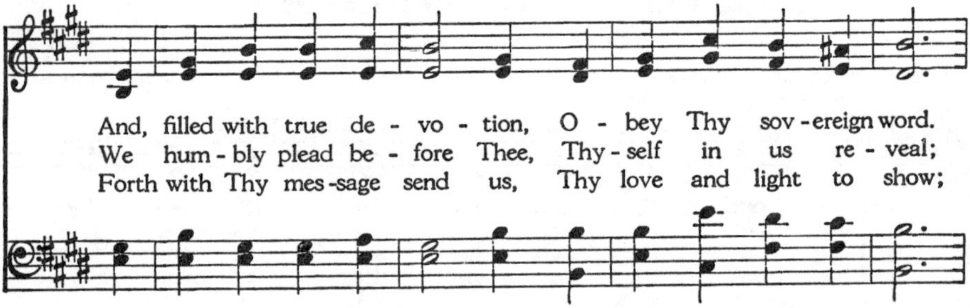

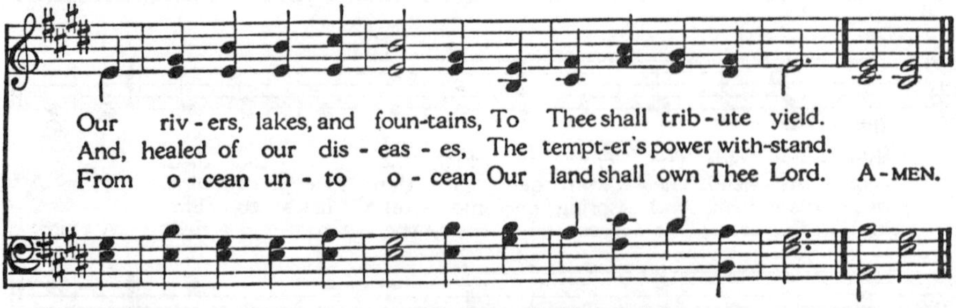

1. From o-cean un-to o-cean Our land shall own Thee Lord,
And, filled with true de-vo-tion, O-bey Thy sov-ereign word.
Our prai-ries and our moun-tains, For-est and fer-tile field,
Our riv-ers, lakes, and foun-tains, To Thee shall trib-ute yield.

2. O Christ, for Thine own glo-ry, And for our coun-try's weal,
We hum-bly plead be-fore Thee, Thy-self in us re-veal;
And may we know, Lord Je-sus, The touch of Thy dear hand;
And, healed of our dis-eas-es, The tempt-er's power with-stand.

3. Our Sav-iour King, de-fend us, And guide where we should go;
Forth with Thy mes-sage send us, Thy love and light to show;
Till, fired with true de-vo-tion, En-kin-dled by Thy Word,
From o-cean un-to o-cean Our land shall own Thee Lord. A-MEN.

O Beautiful, My Country

SALVE DOMINE. 7. 6. 7. 6. D.

542

FREDERICK L. HOSMER, 1840–1928
LAWRENCE W. WATSON, 1860–1927
In moderate time
1. O Beau - ti - ful, my coun - try! Be thine a no - bler care
2. For thee our fa - thers suf-fered,— For thee they toiled and prayed;
3. O Beau - ti - ful, our coun - try! Round thee in love we draw;
Than all thy wealth of com - merce, Thy har - vests wav - ing fair:
Up - on thy ho - ly al - tar Their will - ing lives they laid:
Thine is the grace of free - dom, The ma - jes - ty of law:
Be it thy pride to lift up The man - hood of the poor;
Thou hast no com-mon birth - right, Grand mem - ories on thee shine;
Be right - eous-ness thy scep - ter, Jus - tice thy di - a - dem;
Be thou to the op - press - ed Fair free-dom's o - pen door!
The blood of pil - grim na - tions Com - min-gled flows in thine.
And on thy shin - ing fore - head Be peace the crown-ing gem! A-MEN.

O God, Beneath Thy Guiding Hand

543

DUKE STREET. L. M.

LEONARD BACON, 1802–1881 — JOHN HATTON, ?-1793

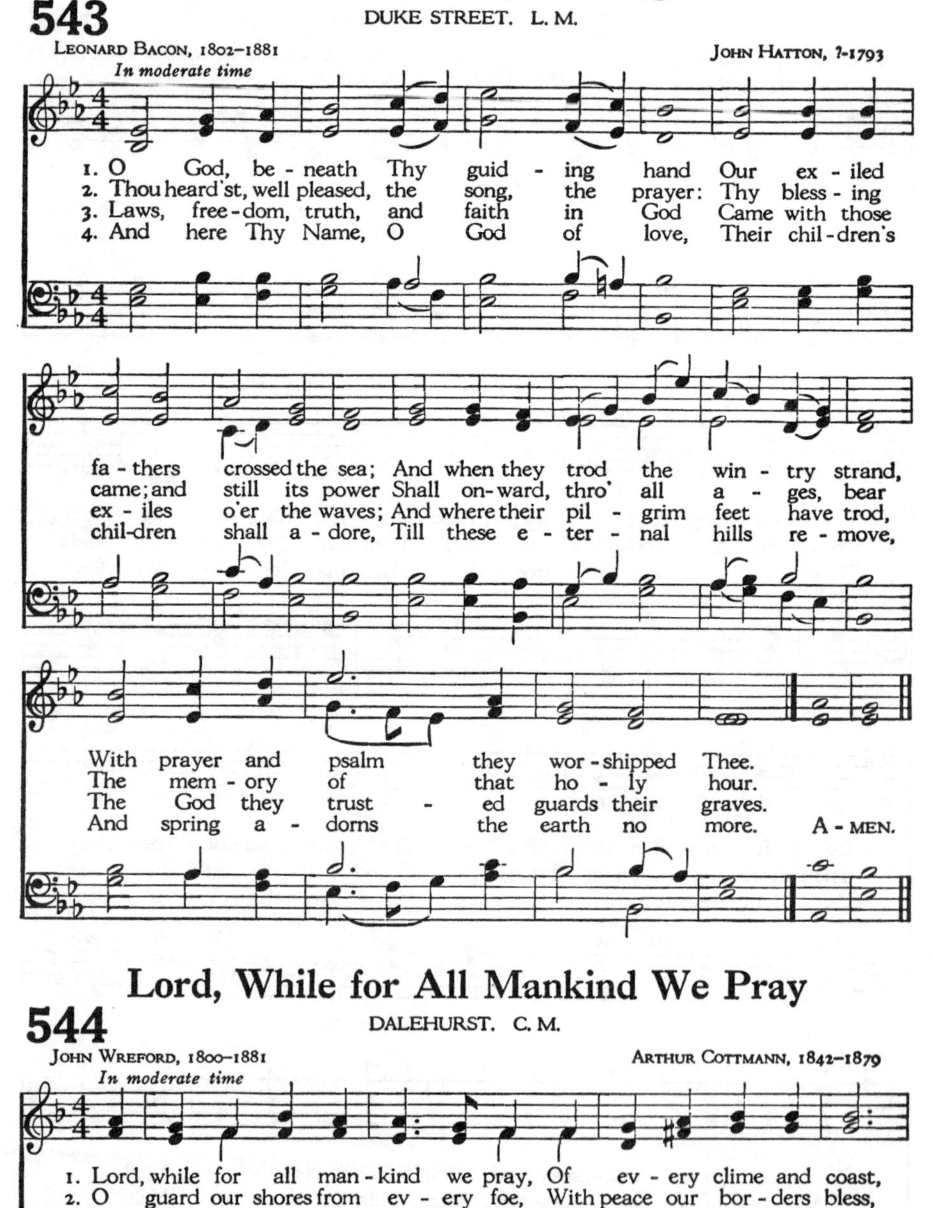
In moderate time
1. O God, be-neath Thy guid-ing hand Our ex-iled fa-thers crossed the sea; And when they trod the win-try strand, With prayer and psalm they wor-shipped Thee.
2. Thou heard'st, well pleased, the song, the prayer: Thy bless-ing came; and still its power Shall on-ward, thro' all a-ges, bear The mem-ory of that ho-ly hour.
3. Laws, free-dom, truth, and faith in God Came with those ex-iles o'er the waves; And where their pil-grim feet have trod, The God they trust-ed guards their graves.
4. And here Thy Name, O God of love, Their chil-dren's chil-dren shall a-dore, Till these e-ter-nal hills re-move, And spring a-dorns the earth no more. A-MEN.

Lord, While for All Mankind We Pray

544

DALEHURST. C. M.

JOHN WREFORD, 1800–1881 — ARTHUR COTTMANN, 1842–1879

In moderate time

1. Lord, while for all man-kind we pray, Of ev-ery clime and coast,
2. O guard our shores from ev-ery foe, With peace our bor-ders bless,
3. U-nite us in the sa-cred love Of knowl-edge, truth, and Thee;
4. Lord of the na-tions, thus to Thee Our coun-try we com-mend;

O hear us for our na - tive land, The land we love the most.
With pros-perous times our cit - ies crown, Our fields with plen-teous-ness.
And let our hills and val - leys shout The songs of lib - er - ty.
Be Thou her Ref - uge and her Trust, Her ev - er - last - ing Friend. A-MEN.

Judge Eternal, Throned in Splendor

ST. LEONARD (BACH). 8. 7. 8. 7. 8. 7.

545

HENRY SCOTT HOLLAND, 1847–1918

JOHANN CHRISTOPHER BACH, 1642–1703

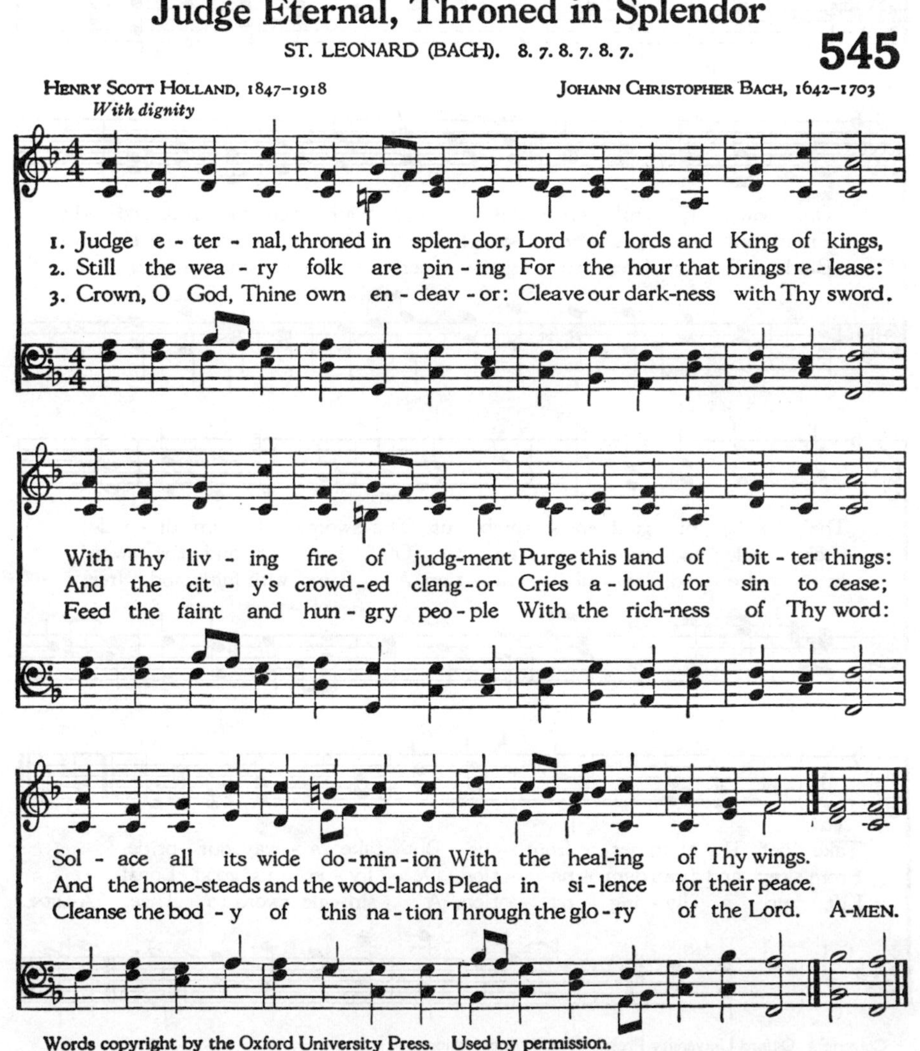
With dignity
1. Judge e - ter - nal, throned in splen - dor, Lord of lords and King of kings,
2. Still the wea - ry folk are pin - ing For the hour that brings re - lease:
3. Crown, O God, Thine own en - deav - or: Cleave our dark-ness with Thy sword.
With Thy liv - ing fire of judg-ment Purge this land of bit - ter things:
And the cit - y's crowd - ed clang - or Cries a - loud for sin to cease;
Feed the faint and hun - gry peo - ple With the rich-ness of Thy word:
Sol - ace all its wide do - min - ion With the heal-ing of Thy wings.
And the home-steads and the wood-lands Plead in si - lence for their peace.
Cleanse the bod - y of this na - tion Through the glo - ry of the Lord. A-MEN.

O God of Earth and Altar

546

LLANGLOFFAN. 7. 6. 7. 6. D.

GILBERT K. CHESTERTON, 1874–1936
With breadth and earnestness
Welsh hymn melody
D. EVANS' HYMNAU A THONAU, 1865
1. O God of earth and al - tar, Bow down and hear our cry;
2. From all that ter - ror teach - es, From lies of tongue and pen;
3. Tie in a liv - ing teth - er The priest and prince and thrall;
Our earth - ly rul - ers fal - ter, Our peo - ple drift and die;
From all the eas - y speech - es That com - fort cru - el men;
Bind all our lives to - geth - er, Smite us and save us all;
The walls of gold en - tomb us, The swords of scorn di - vide;
From sale and prof - a - na - tion Of hon - or and the sword;
In ire and ex - ul - ta - tion A - flame with faith, and free,
Take not Thy thun - der from us, But take a - way our pride.
From sleep and from dam - na - tion, De - liv - er us, good Lord!
Lift up a liv - ing na - tion, A sin - gle sword to Thee. A-MEN.

God Save America! New World of Glory

RUSSIAN HYMN. 11. 10. 11. 10.

547

WILLIAM G. BALLANTINE, 1848–1937
ALEXIS T. LWOFF, 1799–1870
With spirit
1. God save A - mer - i - ca! New world of glo - ry,
2. God save A - mer - i - ca! Here may all rac - es
3. God save A - mer - i - ca! Broth - er - hood ban - ish
4. God save A - mer - i - ca! Bear - ing the ol - ive,
5. God save A - mer - i - ca! 'Mid all her splen - dors,
New - born to free - dom and knowl - edge and power,
Min - gle to - geth - er as chil - dren of God,
Wail of the work - er and curse of the crushed;
Hers be the bless - ing the peace - mak - ers prove,
Save her from pride and from lux - u ry;
Lift - ing the towers of her light - ning - lit cit - ies
Found - ing an em - pire on broth - er - ly kind - ness,
Joy break in songs from her ju - bi - lant mil - lions,
Call - ing the na - tions to glad fed - er - a - tion,
Throne in her heart the un - seen and e - ter - nal;
Where the flood tides of hu - man - i - ty roar!
E - qual in lib - er - ty, made of one blood!
Hail - ing the day when all dis - cords are hush'd!
Lead - ing the world in the tri - umph of love!
Right be her might and the truth make her free! A-MEN.

548 My Country! Tis of Thee

AMERICA. 6. 6. 4. 6. 6. 6. 4.

SAMUEL F. SMITH, 1808–1895 HENRY CAREY, 1692–1743

1. My coun - try! 'tis of thee, Sweet land of lib - er - ty,
2. My na - tive coun - try, thee, Land of the no - ble, free,
3. Let mu - sic swell the breeze, And ring from all the trees
4. Our fa - thers' God! to Thee, Au - thor of lib - er - ty,
Of thee I sing: Land where my fa - thers died! Land of the
Thy name I love; I love thy rocks and rills, Thy woods and
Sweet free-dom's song: Let mor - tal tongues a - wake; Let all that
To Thee we sing: Long may our land be bright With free-dom's
pil - grims' pride! From ev - 'ry moun - tain side Let free-dom ring!
tem - pled hills: My heart with rap - ture thrills Like that a - bove.
breathe partake; Let rocks their si - lence break, The sound pro - long.
ho - ly light; Pro - tect us by Thy might, Great God, our King! A - MEN.

549 Two Empires by the Sea

1. Two empires by the sea,
   Two nations, great and free,
   One anthem raise.
   One race of ancient fame,
   One tongue, one faith, we claim,
   One God, whose glorious Name
   We love and praise.

2. What deeds our fathers wrought,
   What battles we have fought,
   Let fame record.
   Now, vengeful passion, cease;
   Come, victories of peace;
   Nor hate nor pride's caprice
   Unsheathe the sword.

3. Though deep the sea and wide
   'Twixt realm and realm, its tide
   Binds strand to strand.
   So be the gulf between
   Gray coasts and islands green
   With bonds of peace serene
   And friendship spanned.

4. Now may the God above
   Guard the dear lands we love,
   Both East and West;
   Let love more fervent glow,
   As peaceful ages go,
   And strength yet stronger grow,
   Blessing and blest. AMEN.

—George Huntington.

O Beautiful For Spacious Skies

MATERNA. C. M. D.

550

KATHARINE LEE BATES, 1859–1929 — SAMUEL A. WARD, 1847–1903

In moderate time
1. O beau - ti - ful for spa - cious skies, For am - ber waves of grain,
2. O beau - ti - ful for pil - grim feet, Whose stern, im-pas-sioned stress
3. O beau - ti - ful for he - roes proved In lib - er - at - ing strife,
4. O beau - ti - ful for pa - triot dream That sees, be - yond the years,
For pur - ple moun-tain maj - es - ties A - bove the fruit - ed plain!
A thor - ough-fare for free - dom beat A - cross the wil - der - ness!
Who more than self their coun - try loved, And mer - cy more than life!
Thine al - a - bas - ter cit - ies gleam, Un-dimmed by hu - man tears!
A - mer - i - ca! A - mer - i - ca! God shed His grace on thee,
A - mer - i - ca! A - mer - i - ca! God mend thine ev - ery flaw,
A - mer - i - ca! A - mer - i - ca! May God thy gold re - fine,
A - mer - i - ca! A - mer - i - ca! God shed His grace on thee,
And crown thy good with broth - er - hood From sea to shin - ing sea.
Con - firm thy soul in self - con - trol, Thy lib - er - ty in law.
Till all suc - cess be no - ble - ness, And ev - ery gain di - vine.
And crown thy good with broth - er - hood From sea to shin - ing sea. A - MEN.

God of Our Fathers, Whose Almighty Hand

551

NATIONAL HYMN. 10. 10. 10. 10.

Daniel C. Roberts, 1841–1907
George W. Warren, 1828–1902
With martial rhythm
Trumpets, before each stanza
1. God of our fa-thers, whose al-might-y hand
Leads forth in beau-ty all the star-ry band
Of shin-ing worlds in splen-dor through the skies,
Our grate-ful songs be-fore Thy throne a-rise.
2. Thy love di-vine hath led us in the past;
In this free land by Thee our lot is cast;
Be Thou our Rul-er, Guard-ian, Guide, and Stay,
Thy Word our law, Thy paths our cho-sen way.
3. From war's a-larms, from dead-ly pes-ti-lence,
Be Thy strong arm our ev-er sure de-fense;
Thy true re-li-gion in our hearts in-crease,
Thy boun-teous good-ness nour-ish us in peace.
4. Re-fresh Thy peo-ple on their toil-some way;
Lead us from night to nev-er-end-ing day;
Fill all our lives with love and grace di-vine,
And glo-ry, laud, and praise be ev-er Thine.
A-men.

To All the Nations, Lord

552

PAX ORBI. 6. 6. 6. 4. 6. 6. 6. 4.

THOMAS TIPLADY, 1882–
CLEO C. MILLIGAN
In moderate time
1. To all the na - tions, Lord, Thy bless - ing rich - ly give;
2. In right - eous - ness a - lone Can per - fect peace take root;
3. Yea, Lord, this truth we know; Yet strife and tu - mult rage;
And lead them to the truth By which men live;
The ar - mis - tice of might Bears not this fruit;
And might - y ar - mies still In war en - gage;
May knowl - edge of Thy ways Their steps sup - port and guide;
One fam - i - ly God made Of men be - neath the sun;
O give to us the will To live by right - eous deed;
And in Thy per - fect peace May they a - bide.
When love and law are one His will is done.
And melt in fires of love Self - will and greed! A - MEN.

Words from "Hymns for the Times." Used by permission of Thomas Tiplady. Music copyright by the Christian Board of Publication.

The Prince of Peace His Banner Spreads

553

WINSTED. C. M. D.

HARRY EMERSON FOSDICK, 1878–

Dutch melody
Arr. by JOHN N. BROWN

With martial rhythm; in unison

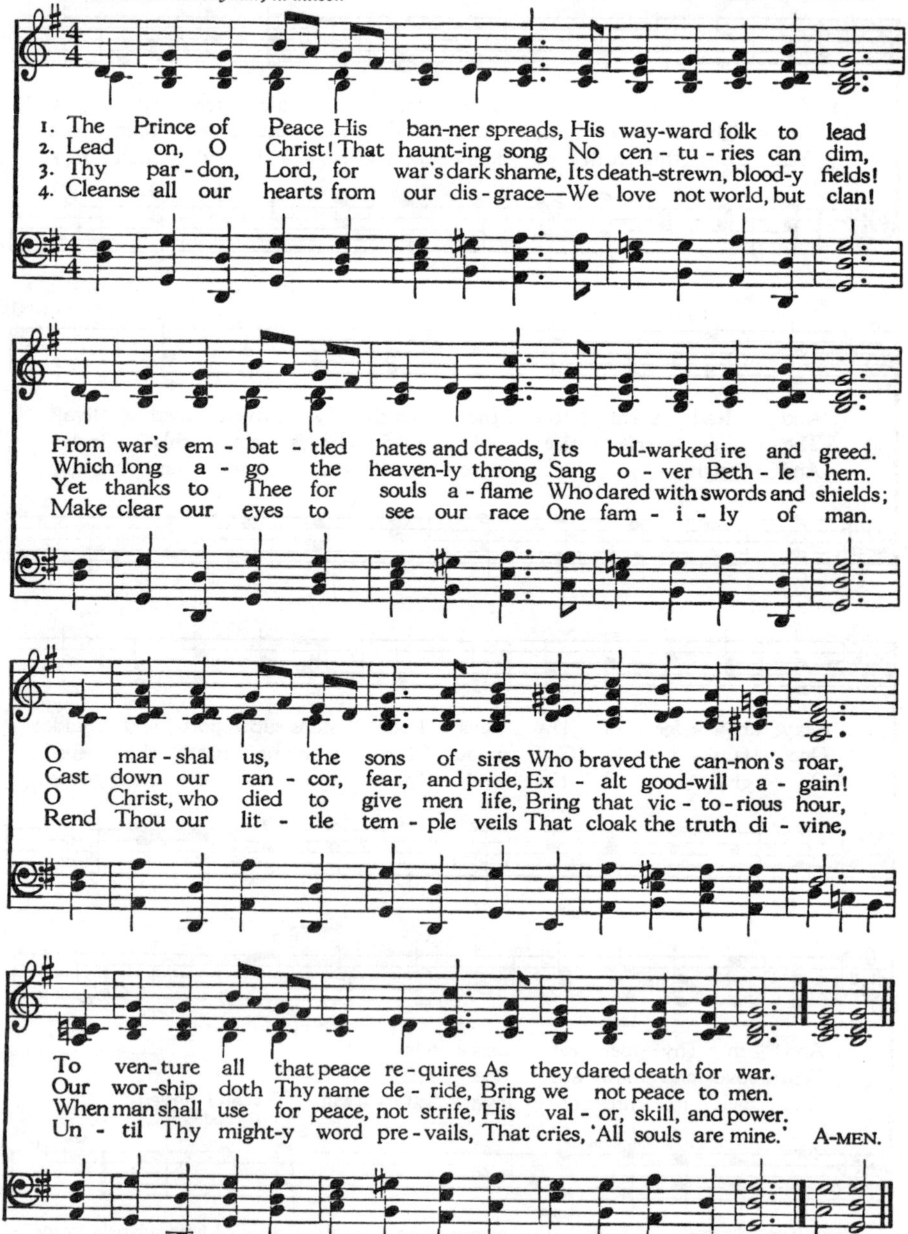

1. The Prince of Peace His ban-ner spreads, His way-ward folk to lead
2. Lead on, O Christ! That haunt-ing song No cen - tu - ries can dim,
3. Thy par - don, Lord, for war's dark shame, Its death-strewn, blood-y fields!
4. Cleanse all our hearts from our dis - grace—We love not world, but clan!

From war's em - bat - tled hates and dreads, Its bul-warked ire and greed.
Which long a - go the heaven-ly throng Sang o - ver Beth - le - hem.
Yet thanks to Thee for souls a - flame Who dared with swords and shields;
Make clear our eyes to see our race One fam - i - ly of man.

O mar - shal us, the sons of sires Who braved the can-non's roar,
Cast down our ran - cor, fear, and pride, Ex - alt good-will a - gain!
O Christ, who died to give men life, Bring that vic - to - rious hour,
Rend Thou our lit - tle tem - ple veils That cloak the truth di - vine,

To ven-ture all that peace re - quires As they dared death for war.
Our wor-ship doth Thy name de - ride, Bring we not peace to men.
When man shall use for peace, not strife, His val - or, skill, and power.
Un - til Thy might-y word pre - vails, That cries, 'All souls are mine.' A-MEN.

Thou God of All, Whose Spirit Moves

SERAPH (BETHLEHEM). C. M. D

JOHN HAYNES HOLMES, 1879-
GOTTFRIED W. FINK, 1783-1846
In moderate time
1. Thou God of all, whose spir - it moves From pole to si - lent pole;
2. One in the pa - tient com - pan - y Of those who heed Thy will,
3. One in the truth that makes men free, The faith that makes men brave;
Whose pur - pose binds the star - ry spheres In one stu - pend - ous whole;
And stead - fast - ly pur - sue the way Of Thy com - mand - ments still;
One in the love that suf - fers long To seek, and serve, and save;
Whose life, like light, is free - ly poured On all men 'neath the sun;
One in the ho - ly fel - low - ship Of those who chal - lenge wrong,
One in the vi - sion of Thy peace, The King - dom yet to be—
To Thee we lift our hearts, and pray That Thou wilt make us one.
And lift the spir - it's sword to shield The weak a - gainst the strong.
When Thou shalt be the God of all, And all be one in Thee. A-MEN.

Words used by permission of John Haynes Holmes.

Come! Peace of God, and Dwell Again on Earth

555

PAX. 10. 10. 10. 10.

MAY ROWLAND, 1870– LILY RENDLE, 1875–

Rather slowly

1. Come! Peace of God, and dwell a - gain on earth, Come, with the calm that
2. Break ev - ery wea - pon forged in fires of hate, Turn back the foes that
3. Bring self - ish lives from shad-ow-lands of loss In - to the ra - diance
4. Come! Bless - ed Peace, as when, in hush of eve, God's ben - e - dic - tion
hailed Thy Prin-ce's birth, Come, with the heal - ing of Thy gen - tle touch,
would as - sail Thy gate; Where fields of strife lie des - o - late and bare
of the Sav-iour's cross, Where, in that gift— so pre - cious, yet so lone—
falls on souls who grieve; As shines a star when wea - ry day de - parts,
Come, Peace of God, that this world needs so much.
Take Thy sweet flow'rs of peace and plant them there.
Life finds its broth - er - hood and love its throne.
Come! Peace of God, and rule with - in our hearts. A - MEN.

God of the Nations, Near and Far

556

ST. AGNES. C. M.

JOHN HAYNES HOLMES, 1879– JOHN B. DYKES, 1823–1876

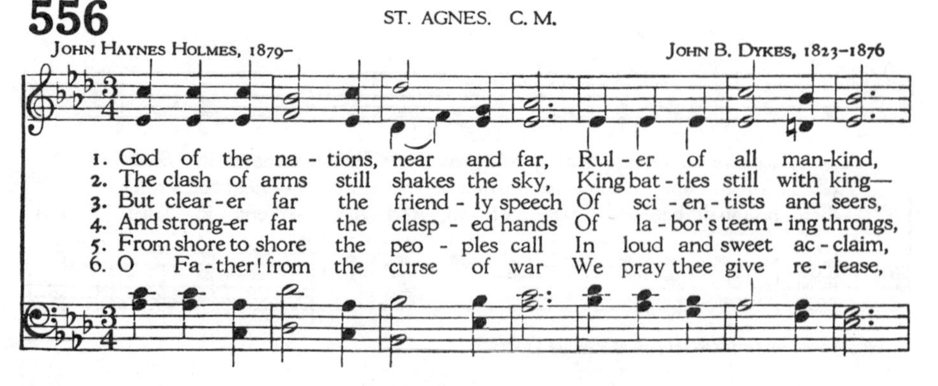
1. God of the na - tions, near and far, Rul - er of all man-kind,
2. The clash of arms still shakes the sky, King bat - tles still with king—
3. But clear - er far the friend - ly speech Of sci - en - tists and seers,
4. And strong-er far the clasp - ed hands Of la - bor's teem - ing throngs,
5. From shore to shore the peo - ples call In loud and sweet ac - claim,
6. O Fa - ther! from the curse of war We pray thee give re - lease,

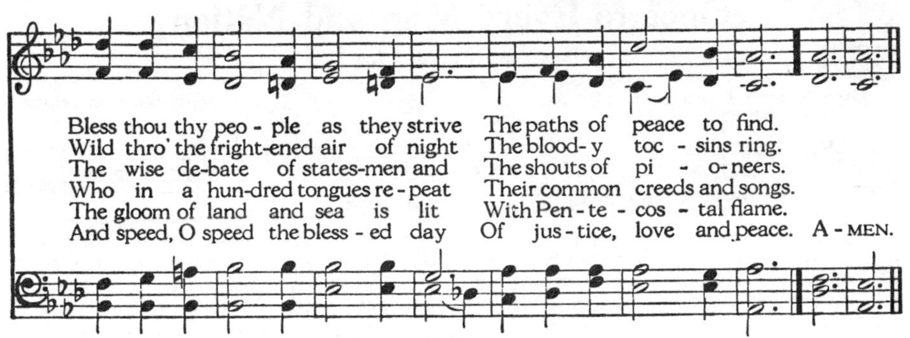
Bless thou thy peo - ple as they strive The paths of peace to find.
Wild thro' the fright-ened air of night The blood - y toc - sins ring.
The wise de-bate of states-men and The shouts of pi - o-neers.
Who in a hun-dred tongues re - peat Their common creeds and songs.
The gloom of land and sea is lit With Pen - te - cos - tal flame.
And speed, O speed the bless - ed day Of jus - tice, love and peace. A - MEN.

Used by permission of the author, John Haynes Holmes.

O God of Love! O King of Peace!

FEDERAL STREET. L. M.

557

HENRY W. BAKER, 1821–1877 — HENRY K. OLIVER, 1800–1885

In moderate time

1. O God of love! O King of peace! Make wars through-
2. Re - mem - ber, Lord, Thy works of old, The won - ders
3. Whom shall we trust but Thee, O Lord? Where rest but
4. Where saints and an - gels dwell a - bove, All hearts are
out the world to cease; The wrath of sin - ful
that our fa - thers told; Re - mem - ber not our
on Thy faith - ful word? None ev - er called on
knit in ho - ly love; O bind us in that
man re - strain; Give peace, O God, give peace a - gain.
sins' dark stain; Give peace, O God, give peace a - gain.
Thee in vain; Give peace, O God, give peace a - gain.
heav'n - ly chain; Give peace, O God, give peace a - gain. A-MEN.

Once to Every Man and Nation

558

TON-Y-BOTEL. 8. 7. 8. 7. D.

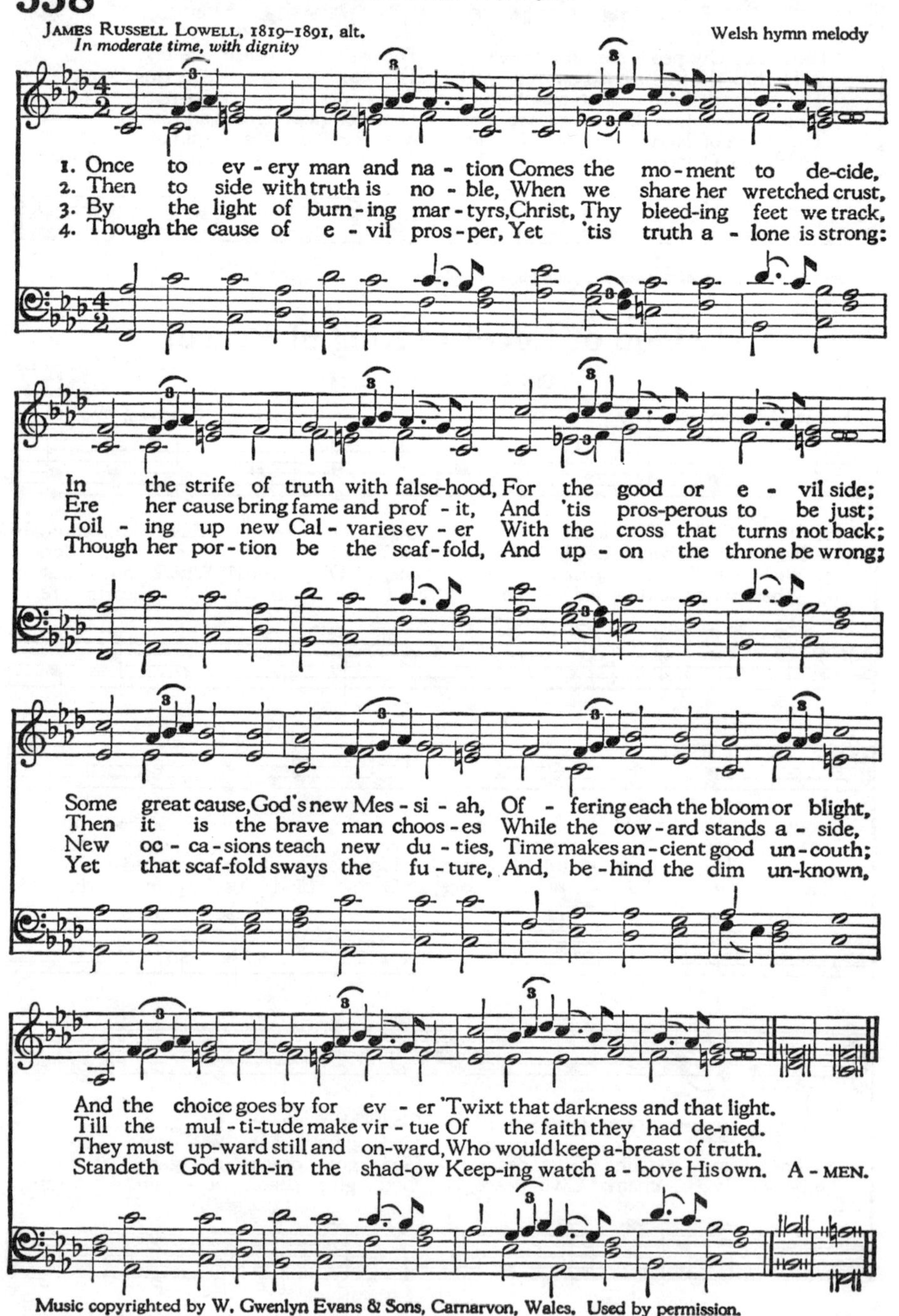
JAMES RUSSELL LOWELL, 1819–1891, alt.
Welsh hymn melody
In moderate time, with dignity
1. Once to ev - ery man and na - tion Comes the mo - ment to de-cide,
2. Then to side with truth is no - ble, When we share her wretched crust,
3. By the light of burn - ing mar - tyrs, Christ, Thy bleed-ing feet we track,
4. Though the cause of e - vil pros - per, Yet 'tis truth a - lone is strong:
In the strife of truth with false-hood, For the good or e - vil side;
Ere her cause bring fame and prof - it, And 'tis pros-perous to be just;
Toil - ing up new Cal - varies ev - er With the cross that turns not back;
Though her por - tion be the scaf - fold, And up - on the throne be wrong;
Some great cause, God's new Mes - si - ah, Of - fering each the bloom or blight,
Then it is the brave man choos - es While the cow - ard stands a - side,
New oc - ca - sions teach new du - ties, Time makes an - cient good un - couth;
Yet that scaf-fold sways the fu - ture, And, be - hind the dim un-known,
And the choice goes by for ev - er 'Twixt that darkness and that light.
Till the mul - ti - tude make vir - tue Of the faith they had de-nied.
They must up-ward still and on-ward, Who would keep a-breast of truth.
Standeth God with-in the shad-ow Keep-ing watch a - bove His own. A - MEN.

Music copyrighted by W. Gwenlyn Evans & Sons, Carnarvon, Wales. Used by permission.

The Son of God Goes Forth for Peace

ALL SAINTS. C. M. D.

559

ERNEST BOURNER ALLEN

HENRY S. CUTLER, 1824-1902

In moderate time, with martial rhythm
1. The Son of God goes forth for Peace, Our Fa-ther's love to show;
2. The Son of God goes forth for Peace, That men like broth-ers live,
3. The Son of God goes forth for Peace, Nor lands nor pow'r to gain;
4. Now let the world to Peace be won, And ev-'ry ha-tred slain;
5. We send our love to ev-'ry land—True neigh-bors would we be;
From war and woe He brings re-lease, O, who with Him will go?
And all de-sire the oth-er's good, And oth-er's sin for-give.
He seeks to serve, to love, to lift,—Who fol-lows in His train?
Let force and greed be o-ver-come And love su-preme re-main!
And pray God's Peace to reign in them, Wher-e'er their home-land be!
He strikes the fet-ters from the slave, Man's mind and heart makes free;
He turns our spears to prun-ing hooks, Our swords to ploughshares warm,
A glo-rious band, in ev-'ry age, In spite of scorn and pain,
Let jus-tice rule in all the earth, And mer-cy while we live,
O God, to us may grace be giv'n, Who bear the dear Christ's name,
And sends His mes-sen-gers to save O'er ev-'ry land and sea!
And war no more its death-blast brings, Nor men their broth-ers harm!
True sons of God, His peace have made; Who fol-lows in their train?
Lest we—for-giv-en much—for-get Our broth-er to for-give!
To live at peace with ev-'ry man, And thus our Christ ac-claim! A-MEN.

God of Our Fathers, Known of Old

560

LEST WE FORGET. 8. 8. 8. 8. 8. 8.

RUDYARD KIPLING, 1865–1936 *(First Tune)* GEORGE F. BLANCHARD, 1868–

With great breadth and dignity

1. God of our fa - thers, known of old, Lord of our far - flung
2. The tu - mult and the shout - ing dies; The cap - tains and the
3. Far - called our na - vies melt a - way, On dune and head - land
4. If drunk with sight of power, we loose Wild tongues that have not
5. For heath - en heart that puts her trust In reek - ing tube and

bat - tle line, Be - neath whose aw - ful hand we hold Do - min - ion
kings de - part; Still stands Thine an - cient sac - ri - fice, An hum - ble
sinks the fire; Lo, all our pomp of yes - ter - day Is one with
Thee in awe, Such boast - ing as the Gen - tiles use Or less - er
i - ron shard; All val - iant dust that builds on dust, And, guard - ing,

o - ver palm and pine: Lord God of hosts, be with us yet,
and a con - trite heart: Lord God of hosts, be with us yet,
Nin - e - veh and Tyre! Judge of the na - tions, spare us yet,
breeds with - out the law: Lord God of hosts, be with us yet,
calls not Thee to guard; For fran - tic boast and fool - ish word,

1–4. Lest we for - get, Lest we for - get.
5. Thy mer - cy on Thy peo - ple, Lord! A - MEN.

God of Our Fathers, Known of Old

RECESSIONAL. 8. 8. 8. 8. 8. 8.

561

RUDYARD KIPLING, 1865–1936 (*Second Tune*) JOHN H. GOWER, 1855–1922

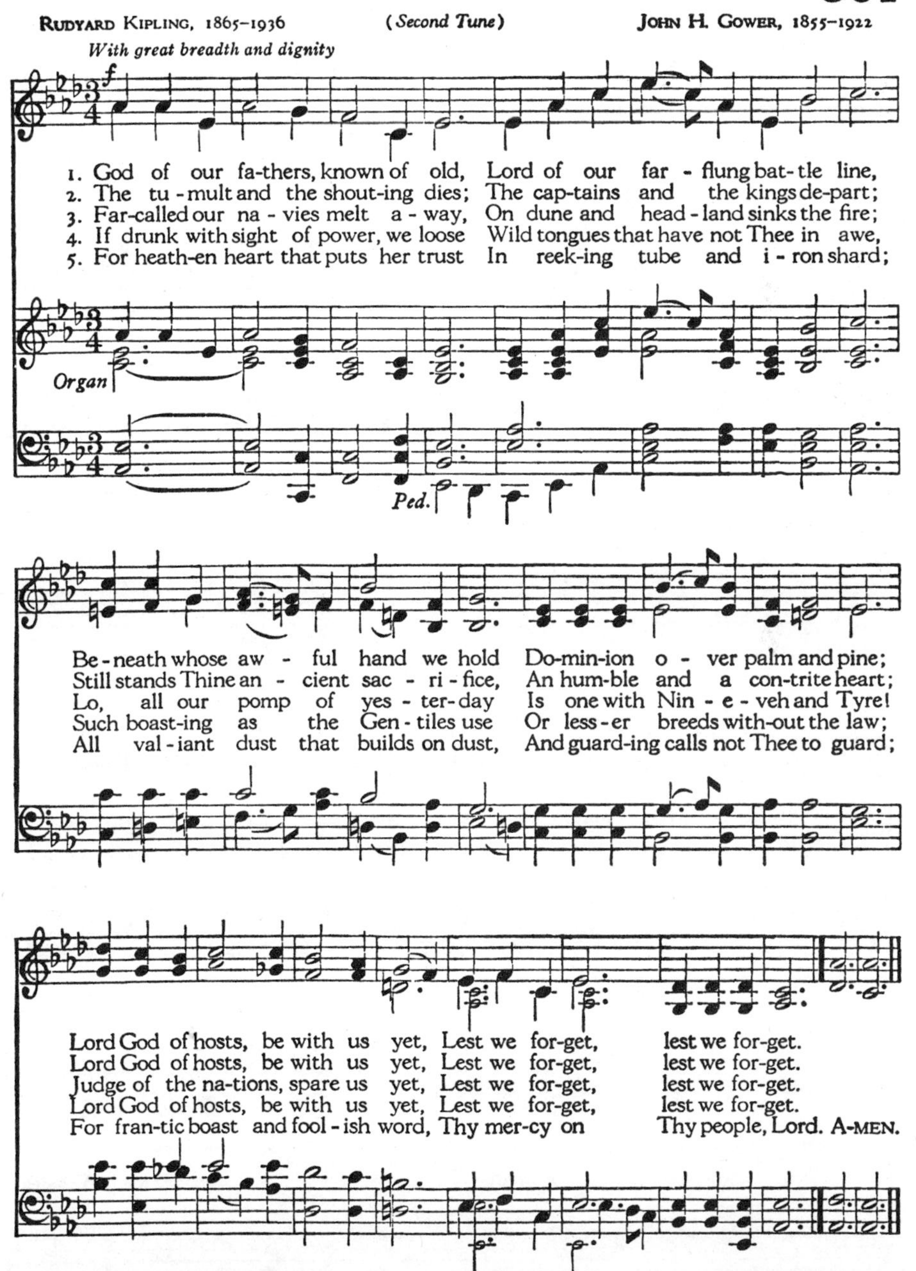
With great breadth and dignity
1. God of our fa-thers, known of old, Lord of our far - flung bat-tle line,
2. The tu-mult and the shout-ing dies; The cap-tains and the kings de-part;
3. Far-called our na - vies melt a - way, On dune and head - land sinks the fire;
4. If drunk with sight of power, we loose Wild tongues that have not Thee in awe,
5. For heath-en heart that puts her trust In reek-ing tube and i - ron shard;
Organ
Ped.
Be - neath whose aw - ful hand we hold Do-min-ion o - ver palm and pine;
Still stands Thine an - cient sac - ri - fice, An hum-ble and a con-trite heart;
Lo, all our pomp of yes - ter-day Is one with Nin - e - veh and Tyre!
Such boast-ing as the Gen - tiles use Or less - er breeds with-out the law;
All val - iant dust that builds on dust, And guard-ing calls not Thee to guard;
Lord God of hosts, be with us yet, Lest we for-get, lest we for-get.
Lord God of hosts, be with us yet, Lest we for-get, lest we for-get.
Judge of the na-tions, spare us yet, Lest we for-get, lest we for-get.
Lord God of hosts, be with us yet, Lest we for-get, lest we for-get.
For fran-tic boast and fool - ish word, Thy mer-cy on Thy people, Lord. A-MEN.

562 Thy Kingdom Come, O Lord

INVITATION. 6. 6. 6. 6. 6. 6. 6. 6.

FREDERICK L. HOSMER, 1840–1928
FREDERICK C. MAKER, 1844–1917
In moderate time
1. Thy king - dom come, O Lord, Wide - cir - cling as the sun;
2. Speed, speed the longed - for time Fore - told by rap - tured seers—
Ful - fill of old thy word, And make the na - tions one;—
The proph - e - cy sub - lime, The hope of all the years;—
One in the bond of peace, The serv - ice glad and free
Till rise at last, to span Its firm foun - da - tions broad,
Of truth and right - eous-ness, Of love and eq - ui - ty.
The com-mon-wealth of man, The cit - y of our God. A - MEN.

When Wilt Thou Save the People

COMMONWEALTH. 7. 6. 7. 6. 8. 8. 8. 5.

563

EBENEZER ELLIOTT, 1781–1849 JOSIAH BOOTH, 1852–1929

In moderate time, with earnestness
1. When wilt Thou save the peo - ple? O God of mer - cy, when?
2. Shall crime bring crime for - ev - er, Strength aid - ing still the strong?
3. When wilt Thou save the peo - ple? O God of mer - cy, when?
Not kings and lords, but na - tions, Not thrones and crowns, but men.
Is it Thy will, O Fa - ther, That man shall toil for wrong?
The peo - ple, Lord, the peo - ple, Not thrones and crowns, but men.
Flowers of Thy heart, O God, are they; Let them not pass, like weeds, a - way;
"No," say Thy moun-tains; "No," Thy skies; Man's cloud-ed sun shall bright-ly rise,
God save the peo - ple; Thine they are, Thy chil-dren, as Thine an - gels fair;
Their her - i - tage a sun - less day; God save the peo - ple.
And songs as - cend in-stead of sighs: God save the peo - ple.
From vice, op - pres - sion, and de - spair. God save the peo - ple. A - MEN.

Tune used by permission of Clifford Booth.

O Hear Them Marching, Marching

564

GREENLAND. 7. 6. 7. 6. D.

Marion Franklin Ham, 1867-

Arr. from J. Michael Haydn, 1737-1806
In B. Jacob's National Psalmody, 1819

With martial rhythm
1. O, hear them march-ing, march-ing, The le-gions of good will,
2. Through all the blood-stained a-ges Their num-bers have in-creased,
3. The men of war op-pose them, And seek to bar the way,
4. A might-y cap-tain leads them, The val-iant Prince of Peace;
The men of peace who seek not To bomb and maim and kill;
The spir-it strug-gling up-ward To o-ver-come the beast;
The powers of dark-ness striv-ing To thwart the com-ing day;
They shall pos-sess the fu-ture, And an-cient wrongs shall cease;
They march not to their con-quest With bat-tle-flags un-furled;
The meek who shall in-her-it And rule the war-ring earth,
But, led by un-seen for-ces, Their hosts are march-ing still,
O men of good will, march-ing To blood-less vic-to-ry,
But with their gen-tle spir-it They shall sub-due the world.
With pa-tient faith are bring-ing The new re-gime to birth.
To build for fu-ture a-ges The king-dom of good will.
We join your hosts in build-ing The king-dom that shall be. A-men.

God the All-Merciful! Earth Hath Forsaken

565

RUSSIAN HYMN. 11. 10. 11. 9.

HENRY F. CHORLEY, 1808–1872
JOHN ELLERTON, 1826–1893, alt.

ALEXIS LWOFF, 1799–1870

Majestically

1. God the All - mer - ci - ful! earth hath for - sak - en
2. God the All - right - eous One! man hath de - fied Thee;
3. God the All - pit - i - ful! is it not cry - ing—
4. God the All - wise! by the fire of Thy chas - tening
5. So shall Thy peo - ple, with thank - ful de - vo - tion,

Thy ways of bless - ed - ness, slight - ed Thy word;
Yet to e - ter - ni - ty stand - eth Thy word;
Blood of the guilt - less, like wa - ter out - poured?
Earth shall to free - dom and truth be re - stored;
Praise Him who saved them from per - il and sword,

Let not Thy wrath in its ter - rors a - wak - en;
False - hood and wrong shall not tar - ry be - side Thee;
Look on the an - guish, the sor - row, the sigh - ing;
Through the thick dark - ness Thy King - dom is has - tening;
Sing - ing in cho - rus from o - cean to o - cean

Give to us peace in our time, O Lord.
Give to us peace in our time, O Lord.
Give to us peace in our time, O Lord.
Thou wilt give peace in Thy time, O Lord.
Peace to the na - tions, and praise to the Lord. A - MEN.

Lead Us, O Father, in the Paths of Peace

566

OVERDALE. 10. 10. 10. 10.

William H. Burleigh, 1812–1871 — J. Rhosyd Williams, 1885–

In moderate time

1. Lead us, O Fa - ther, in the paths of peace;
2. Lead us, O Fa - ther, in the paths of truth:
3. Lead us, O Fa - ther, in the paths of right:
4. Lead us, O Fa - ther, to thy heav'n - ly rest,

With - out thy guid - ing hand we go a - stray,
Un - helped by thee, in er - ror's maze we grope,
Blind - ly we stum - ble when we walk a - lone,
How - ev - er rough and steep the path may be,

And doubts ap - pall, and sor - rows still in - crease;
While pas - sion stains and fol - ly dims our youth,
In - volved in shad - ows of a mor - al night;
Thro' joy or sor - row, as thou deem - est best,

Lead us thro Christ, the true and liv - ing Way.
And age comes on un-cheered by faith and hope.
On - ly with thee we jour - ney safe - ly on.
Un - til our lives are per - fect - ed in thee. A - men.

Music from the "Christian Hymnary Tune Book."

Turn Back, O Man, Forswear Thy Foolish Ways

OLD 124TH. 10. 10. 10. 10. 10.

567

CLIFFORD BAX, 1886–1932
GENEVAN PSALTER, 1551
May be sung in unison. With spirit, but broadly
1. Turn back, O man, for-swear thy fool-ish ways. Old now is earth, and none may count her days, Yet thou, her child, whose head is crowned with flame, Still wilt not hear thine in-ner God pro-claim— "Turn back, O man, for-swear thy fool-ish ways."
2. Earth might be fair and all men glad and wise. Age aft-er age their trag-ic em-pires rise, Built while they dream, and in that dream-ing weep: Would man but wake from out his haunt-ed sleep, Earth might be fair and all men glad and wise.
3. Earth shall be fair, and all her peo-ple one: Nor till that hour shall God's whole will be done. Now, ev-en now, once more from earth to sky, Peals forth in joy man's old, un-daunt-ed cry— "Earth shall be fair, and all her folk be one!" A-MEN.

Ten Thousand Times Ten Thousand

568

ALFORD. 7. 6. 8. 6. D.

HENRY ALFORD, 1810–1871

JOHN B. DYKES, 1823–1876

In moderate time, with exultation

1. Ten thou - sand times ten thou - sand In spar - kling rai - ment bright,
The ar - mies of the ran-somed saints Throng up the steeps of light:
'Tis fin - ished, all is fin - ished, Their fight with death and sin:
Fling o - pen wide the gold - en gates, And let the vic - tors in!

2. O then what rap - tured greet - ings On Ca - naan's hap - py shore,
What knit - ting sev - ered friend-ships up Where part-ings are no more!
Then eyes with joy shall spar - kle, That brimmed with tears of late;
Or - phans no long - er fa - ther -less, Nor wid - ows des - o - late.

3. What rush of al - le - lu - ias Fills all the earth and sky!
What ring - ing of a thou - sand harps Be - speaks the tri - umph nigh!
O day, for which cre - a - tion And all its tribes were made;
O joy, for all its for - mer woes A thou-sand-fold re - paid! A - MEN.

Jerusalem the Golden

EWING. 7. 6. 7. 6. D.
(*First Tune*)

569

BERNARD OF CLUNY, 12th century
Tr. by JOHN M. NEALE, 1818–1866

ALEXANDER EWING, 1830–1895

Jubilantly

1. Je - ru - sa - lem the gold - en, With milk and hon - ey blest!
2. They stand, those halls of Zi - on, All ju - bi - lant with song,
3. O sweet and bless - ed coun - try, The home of God's e - lect!

Be - neath thy con - tem - pla - tion Sink heart and voice op - pressed:
And bright with many an an - gel, And all the mar - tyr throng;
O sweet and bless - ed coun - try That ea - ger hearts ex - pect!

I know not, oh, I know not, What joys a - wait us there;
The Prince is ev - er in them, The day - light is se - rene;
Je - sus, in mer - cy bring us To that dear land of rest;

What ra - dian - cy of glo - ry, What light be - yond com-pare.
The pas - tures of the bless - ed Are decked in glo - rious sheen.
Who art, with God the Fa - ther, And Spir - it, ev - er blest. A-MEN.

Jerusalem the Golden

570

URBS BEATA. 7. 6. 7. 6. D. with Refrain

BERNARD OF CLUNY, 12th century
Tr. by JOHN M. NEALE, 1818–1866

(*Second Tune*)

GEORGE F. LE JEUNE, 1842–1904

Jubilantly

1. Je - ru - sa - lem the gold - en, With milk and hon - ey blest,
2. They stand, those halls of Zi - on, All ju - bi - lant with song,
3. O sweet and bless - ed coun - try, The home of God's e - lect!

Be - neath thy con - tem - pla - tion Sink heart and voice op - pressed;
And bright with many an an - gel, And all the mar - tyr throng;
O sweet and bless - ed coun - try, That ea - ger hearts ex - pect!

I know not, O I know not, What joys a - wait us there,
The Prince is ev - er in them; The day - light is se - rene;
Je - sus, in mer - cy bring us To that dear land of rest;

What ra - dian - cy of glo - ry, What light be - yond com - pare.
The pas - tures of the bless - ed Are decked in glo - rious sheen.
Who art, with God the Fa - ther, And spir - it ev - er blest.

Refrain
Je - ru - sa - lem, Je - ru - sa - lem,
Je - ru - sa - lem the gold - en, What joys a - wait us there,
What ra - dian - cy
What ra - dian - cy of glo - ry, What light be - yond com-pare. A-men.
Org.

I Know Not What the Future Hath

571

COOLING. C. M.

John G. Whittier, 1807–1892

Alonzo J. Abbey, 1825–1887

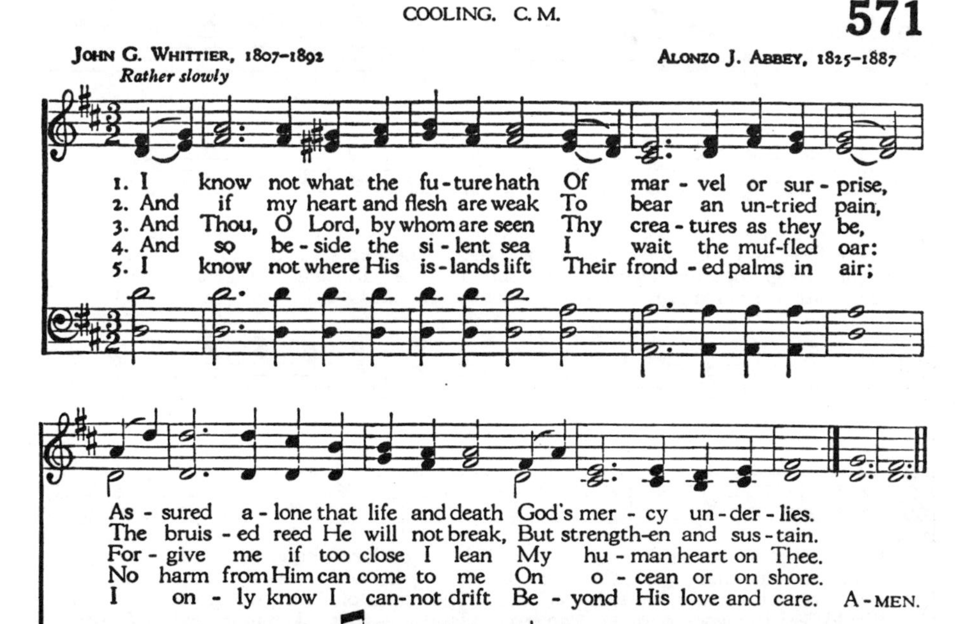
Rather slowly
1. I know not what the fu - ture hath Of mar - vel or sur - prise,
2. And if my heart and flesh are weak To bear an un-tried pain,
3. And Thou, O Lord, by whom are seen Thy crea - tures as they be,
4. And so be - side the si - lent sea I wait the muf-fled oar:
5. I know not where His is - lands lift Their frond - ed palms in air;
As - sured a - lone that life and death God's mer - cy un - der - lies.
The bruis - ed reed He will not break, But strength-en and sus - tain.
For - give me if too close I lean My hu - man heart on Thee.
No harm from Him can come to me On o - cean or on shore.
I on - ly know I can-not drift Be - yond His love and care. A - men.

O Mother Dear, Jerusalem

572

MATERNA. C. M. D.

Founded on "F. B. P." 16th century
Alt. by David Dickson
Samuel A. Ward, 1847-1903
In moderate time
1. O moth - er dear, Je - ru - sa - lem, When shall I come to thee?
2. No murk - y cloud o'er-shad - ows thee, Nor gloom, nor dark-some night;
3. Thy gar - dens and thy good - ly walks Con - tin - ual - ly are green,
4. Those trees for - ev - er-more bear fruit, And ev - er - more do spring;
When shall my sor - rows have an end? Thy joys when shall I see?
But eve - ry soul shines as the sun; For God him-self gives light.
Where grow such sweet and pleas - ant flowers As no-where else are seen.
There ev - er-more the an - gels are, And ev - er-more do sing.
O hap - py har - bor of the saints! O sweet and pleas-ant soil!
There lust and lu - cre can - not dwell, There en - vy bears no sway;
Right through the streets, with sil - ver sound; The liv - ing wa - ters flow;
Je - ru - sa - lem, my hap - py home, Would God I were in thee!
In thee no sor - row may be found, No grief, no care, no toil.
There is no hun - ger, heat, nor cold, But pleas-ure eve - ry way.
And on the banks, on eith - er side, The trees of life do grow.
Would God my woes were at an end, Thy joys that I might see!
A - MEN.

Rise, My Soul, and Stretch Thy Wings

AMSTERDAM. 7.6.7.6.7.7.7.6.

573

ROBERT SEAGRAVE, 1693-1759
JAMES NARES, 1715-1783
"THE FOUNDERY COLLECTION," 1742
With spirit
1. Rise, my soul, and stretch thy wings, Thy bet - ter por - tion trace;
2. Riv - ers to the o - cean run, Nor stay in all their course;
3. Cease, ye pil - grims, cease to mourn, Press on - ward to the prize;
Rise from tran - si - to - ry things Toward heaven, thy na - tive place:
Fire as - cend - ing seeks the sun; Both speed them to their source:
Soon our Sav - iour will re - turn, Tri - umph - ant in the skies:
Sun, and moon, and stars de - cay; Time shall soon this earth re - move;
So a soul that's born of God, Longs to view His glo - rious face,
Yet a sea - son, and you know Hap - py en - trance will be given,
Rise, my soul, and haste a - way To seats pre - pared a - bove.
For - ward tends to His a - bode, To rest in His em - brace.
All our sor - rows left be - low, And earth ex - changed for heaven. A - MEN.

Sunset and Evening Star

574

CROSSING THE BAR. Irregular

ALFRED TENNYSON, 1809–1892

JOSEPH BARNBY, 1838–1896

Rather slowly

Sun - set and eve - ning star, And one clear call for me! And may there be no moan-ing of the bar When I put out to sea, But such a tide as mov - ing seems a - sleep, Too full for sound and foam, When that which drew from out the bound-less deep Turns a - gain home.

home. Twi-

Twi - light and eve - ning bell, And aft - er that the dark!

- - - light and eve - ning bell,

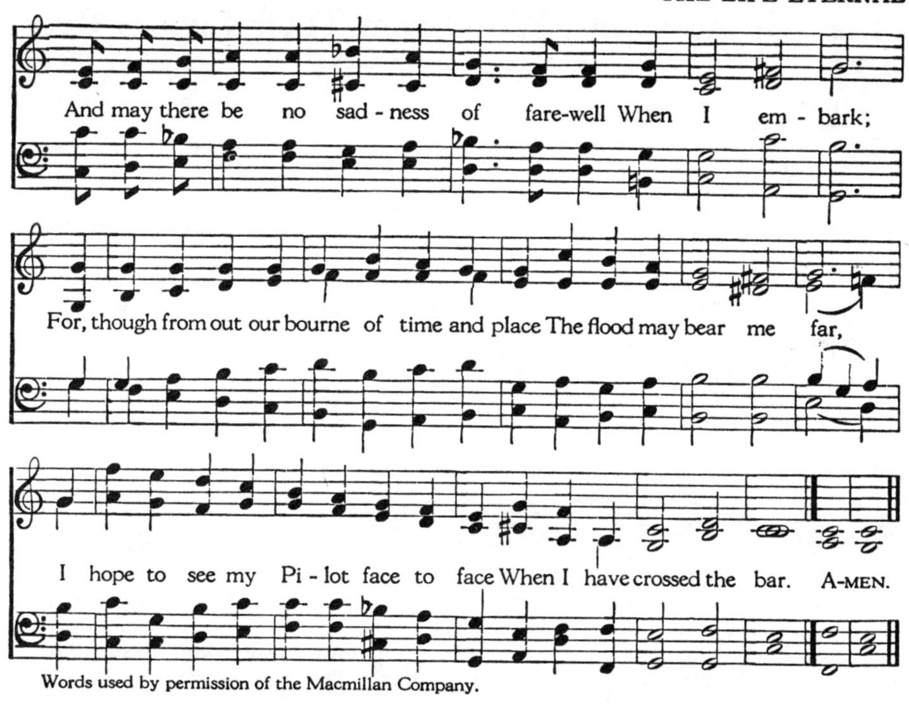
And may there be no sad - ness of fare-well When I em - bark;
For, though from out our bourne of time and place The flood may bear me far,
I hope to see my Pi - lot face to face When I have crossed the bar. A-MEN.

O Lord of Life Where'er They Be

PALESTRINA. 8. 8. 8. 4.

575

FREDERICK L. HOSMER, 1840–1928

GIOVANNI P. DA PALESTRINA, 1526–1594
Arr. by WILLIAM H. MONK, 1823–1889

In moderate time, with assurance

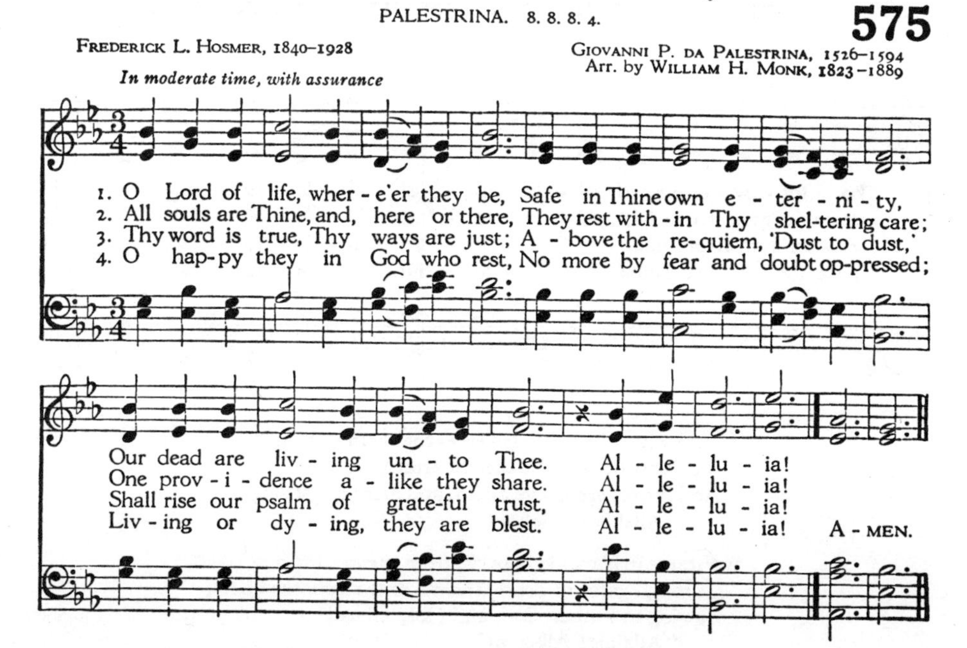
1. O Lord of life, wher - e'er they be, Safe in Thine own e - ter - ni - ty,
2. All souls are Thine, and, here or there, They rest with - in Thy shel-tering care;
3. Thy word is true, Thy ways are just; A - bove the re - quiem, 'Dust to dust,'
4. O hap - py they in God who rest, No more by fear and doubt op-pressed;
Our dead are liv - ing un - to Thee. Al - le - lu - ia!
One prov - i - dence a - like they share. Al - le - lu - ia!
Shall rise our psalm of grate-ful trust, Al - le - lu - ia!
Liv - ing or dy - ing, they are blest. Al - le - lu - ia! A - MEN.

For All the Saints, Who From Their Labors Rest

576
SARUM. 10. 10. 10. with Alleluias
(First Tune)
WILLIAM W. HOW, 1823–1897
JOSEPH BARNBY, 1838–1896
In moderate time
1. For all the saints, who from their la - bors rest, Who Thee by faith be - fore the world con - fessed, Thy Name, O Je - sus, be for - ev - er blessed, Al - le - lu - ia! Al - le - lu - ia!
2. Thou wast their Rock, their Fort-ress, and their Might; Thou, Lord, their Cap - tain in the well - fought fight; Thou, in the dark - ness drear, their one true Light. Al - le - lu - ia! Al - le - lu - ia!
3. O may Thy sol - diers, faith-ful, true, and bold, Fight as the saints who no - bly fought of old, And win with them the vic - tor's crown of gold. Al - le - lu - ia! Al - le - lu - ia!
4. O blest com - mun - ion, fel - low - ship di - vine! We fee - bly strug - gle, they in glo - ry shine; Yet all are one in Thee, for all are Thine. Al - le - lu - ia! Al - le - lu - ia!
A-MEN.

5 And when the strife is fierce, the warfare long,
Steals on the ear the distant triumph song,
And hearts are brave again, and arms are strong.
Alleluia! Alleluia!

6 From earth's wide bounds, from ocean's farthest coast,
Through gates of pearl streams in the countless host,
Singing to Father, Son, and Holy Ghost,
"Alleluia! Alleluia!"

For All the Saints, Who From Their Labors Rest

SINE NOMINE. 10. 10. 10. with Alleluias
(*Second Tune*)

577

WILLIAM W. HOW, 1823–1897

R. VAUGHAN WILLIAMS, 1872–

In unison, in moderate time

1. For all the saints who from their la - bors rest, Who Thee by faith be -
2. Thou wast their Rock, their For-tress, and their Might; Thou, Lord, their Cap-tain
3. O may Thy sol - diers, faith-ful, true, and bold, Fight as the saints who
4. O blest com-mun - ion, fel - low-ship di - vine! We fee - bly strug-gle,
5. And when the strife is fierce, the war-fare long, Steals on the ear the
6. From earth's wide bounds, from o-cean's far-thest coast, Through gates of pearl streams

fore the world con-fessed, Thy Name, O Je - sus, be for ev - er blest.
in the well-fought fight; Thou, in the dark - ness drear, their one true Light.
no - bly fought of old, And win with them the vic-tor's crown of gold.
they in glo - ry shine; Yet all are one in Thee, for all are Thine.
dis - tant tri - umph song, And hearts are brave a - gain, and arms are strong.
in the count-less host, Sing - ing to Fa - ther, Son, and Ho - ly Ghost,

Harmony

Al - le - lu - ia! Al - le - lu - ia! A-MEN.

Lead, Kindly Light, Amid th' Encircling Gloom

578 LUX BENIGNA. 10. 4. 10. 4. 10. 10.

JOHN HENRY NEWMAN, 1801-1890
JOHN B. DYKES, 1823-1876
In moderate time
1. Lead, kind-ly Light, a - mid th' en-cir-cling gloom, Lead Thou me on!
2. I was not ev - er thus, nor prayed that Thou Shouldst lead me on;
3. So long Thy power hath blest me, sure it still Will lead me on,
The night is dark, and I am far from home; Lead Thou me on!
I loved to choose and see my path; but now Lead Thou me on!
O'er moor and fen, o'er crag and tor - rent, till The night is gone,
Keep Thou my feet; I do not ask to see
I loved the gar - ish day, and, spite of fears,
And with the morn those an - gel fac - es smile;
The dis - tant scene — one step e - nough for me.
Pride ruled my will: re - mem-ber not past years.
Which I have loved long since, and lost a - while!
A - MEN.

It Singeth Low in Every Heart

ST. LEONARD (HILES). C. M. D.

579

John W. Chadwick, 1840–1904
Henry Hiles, 1826–1904
In moderate time
1. It sing-eth low in ev - ery heart, We hear it each and all,—
2. 'Tis hard to take the bur - den up, When these have laid it down;
3. More home-like seems the vast un-known, Since they have en - tered there;
A song of those who an - swer not, How - ev - er we may call.
They bright-ened all the joy of life, They soft-ened ev - ery frown.
To fol - low them were not so hard, Wher - ev - er they may fare.
They throng the si - lence of the breast, We see them as of yore,—
But oh, 'tis good to think of them, When we are trou-bled sore;
They can - not be where God is not, On an - y sea or shore;
The kind, the brave, the true, the sweet, Who walk with us no more.
Thanks be to God that such have been, Tho' they are here no more.
What-e'er be-tides, thy love a-bides, Our God, for ev - er-more.
A - MEN.

Sleep Thy Last Sleep

580

LAST SLEEP. 4. 6. 4. 6. D.

EDWARD A. DAYMAN, 1807–1890

JOSEPH BARNBY, 1838–1896

Rather slowly
1. Sleep thy last sleep, Free from care and sor - row;
2. Life's dream is past, All its sin, its sad - ness;
3. Though we may mourn Those in life the dear - est,
Rest, where none weep, Till th'e - ter - nal mor - row;
Bright - ly at last Dawns a day of glad - ness.
They shall re - turn, Christ, when Thou ap - pear - est.
Though dark waves roll O'er the si - lent riv - er,
Un - der the sod, Earth, re - ceive our treas - ure,
Soon shall Thy voice Com - fort those now weep - ing,
Thy faint - ing soul Je - sus can de - liv - er.
To rest in God, Wait - ing all His pleas - ure.
Bid - ding re - joice All in Je - sus sleep - ing.
A - MEN.

Sometimes a Light Surprises

BENTLEY. 7. 6. 7. 6. D.

581

WILLIAM COWPER, 1731–1800
JOHN HULLAH, 1812–1884
In moderate time
1. Some-times a light sur - pris - es The Chris - tian while he sings;
2. In ho - ly con - tem - pla - tion We sweet - ly then pur - sue
3. It can bring with it noth - ing But He will bear us through;
4. Though vine nor fig tree nei - ther Their wont - ed fruit shall bear,
It is the Lord, who ris - es With heal - ing in His wings:
The theme of God's sal - va - tion, And find it ev - er new;
Who gives the lil - ies cloth - ing Will clothe His peo - ple, too:
Though all the field should with - er, Nor flocks nor herds be there;
When com - forts are de - clin - ing, He grants the soul a - gain
Set free from pres - ent sor - row, We cheer - ful - ly can say,
Be - neath the spread-ing heav - ens No crea - ture but is fed;
Yet God the same a - bid - ing, His praise shall tune my voice,
A sea - son of clear shin - ing, To cheer it af - ter rain
Let the un-known to - mor - row Bring with it what it may.
And He who feeds the ra - vens Will give His chil - dren bread.
For while in Him con - fid - ing I can - not but re - joice.
A-MEN.

Hark, Hark, My Soul! Angelic Songs Are Swelling

582 PILGRIMS. 11. 10. 11. 10. with Refrain

FREDERICK W. FABER, 1814–1863 HENRY SMART 1812–1879

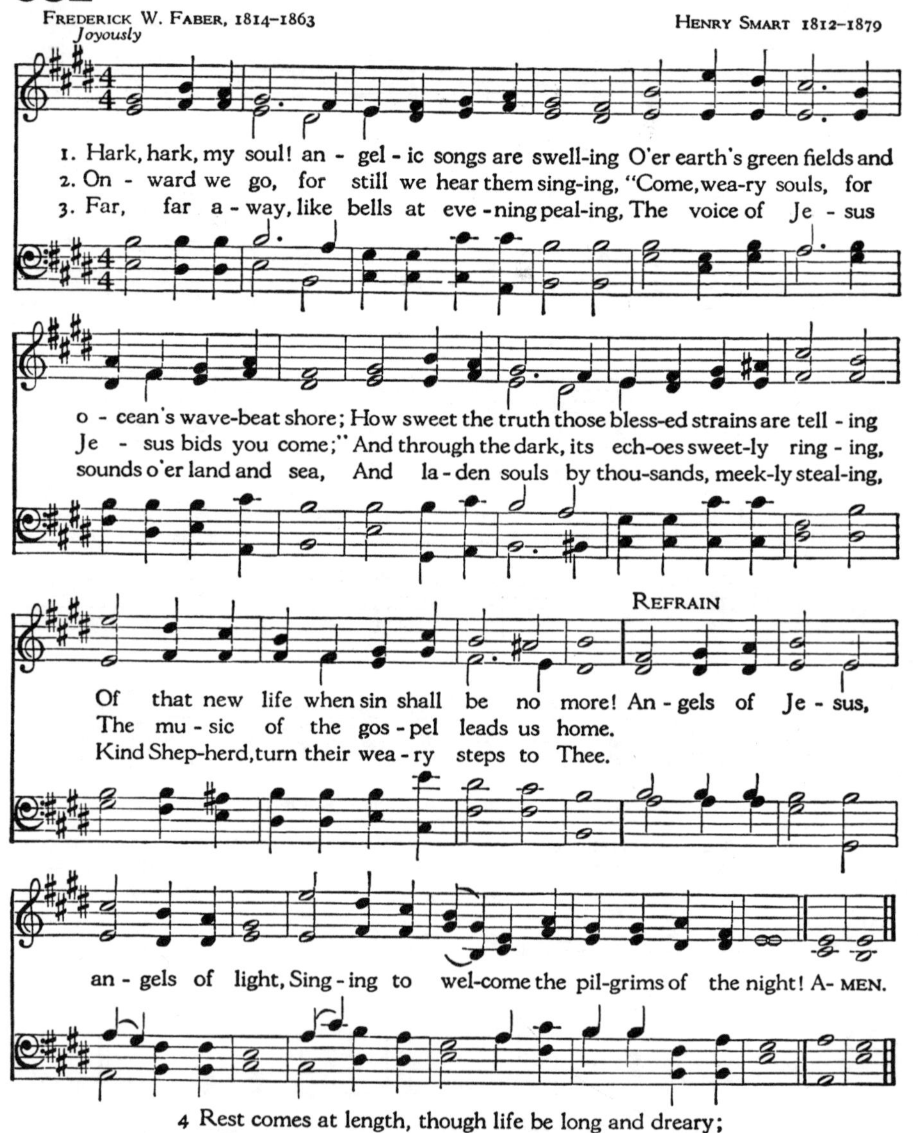
Joyously
1. Hark, hark, my soul! an - gel - ic songs are swell-ing O'er earth's green fields and
2. On - ward we go, for still we hear them sing-ing, "Come, wea-ry souls, for
3. Far, far a - way, like bells at eve - ning peal-ing, The voice of Je - sus
o - cean's wave-beat shore; How sweet the truth those bless-ed strains are tell - ing
Je - sus bids you come;" And through the dark, its ech-oes sweet-ly ring - ing,
sounds o'er land and sea, And la - den souls by thou-sands, meek-ly steal-ing,
Of that new life when sin shall be no more!
The mu - sic of the gos - pel leads us home.
Kind Shep-herd, turn their wea - ry steps to Thee.
REFRAIN
An - gels of Je - sus, an - gels of light, Sing - ing to wel-come the pil-grims of the night! A- MEN.

4 Rest comes at length, though life be long and dreary;
The day must dawn, and darksome night be past;
All journeys end in welcome to the weary,
And heaven, the heart's true home, will come at last.

5 Angels, sing on! your faithful watches keeping;
Sing us sweet fragments of the songs above;
Till morning's joy shall end the night of weeping,
And life's long shadows break in cloudless love.

God of Our Life, Through All the Circling Years

SANDON. 10. 4. 10. 4. 10. 10.

583

HUGH T. KERR, 1872–

CHARLES H. PURDAY, 1799–1885

In moderate time

1. God of our life, through all the cir-cling years, We trust in Thee;
In all the past, through all our hopes and fears, Thy hand we see.
With each new day, when morn-ing lifts the veil,
We own Thy mer-cies, Lord, which nev-er fail.

2. God of the past, our times are in Thy hand; With us a-bide.
Lead us by faith to hope's true Prom-ised Land; Be Thou our guide.
With Thee to bless, the dark-ness shines as light,
And faith's fair vi-sion chang-es in-to sight.

3. God of the com-ing years, through paths un-known We fol-low Thee;
When we are strong, Lord, leave us not a-lone; Our ref-uge be.
Be Thou for us in life our Dai-ly Bread,
Our heart's true Home when all our years have sped. A-MEN.

Standing at the Portal

584

ST. ALBAN. 6. 5. 6. 5. D. with Refrain

FRANCES R. HAVERGAL, 1836–1879

FRANZ JOSEPH HAYDN, 1732–1809

In moderate time, very rhythmically

1. Stand-ing at the por - tal Of the ope-ning year, Words of com-fort meet us, Hush-ing ev - 'ry fear; Spo-ken thro' the si - lence By our Fa-ther's voice, Ten - der, strong, and faithful, Mak-ing us re - joice.
2. "I, the Lord, am with thee, Be thou not a - fraid; I will help and strength-en, Be thou not dis-mayed: Yea, I will up - hold thee With my own right hand; Thou art called and chos - en In my sight to stand." On-ward, then, and fear not, Chil-dren of the day; For his word shall nev - er, Nev-er pass a -way.
3. For the year be - fore us, Oh, what rich sup-plies! For the poor and need - y Liv-ing streams shall rise; For the sad and sin - ful Shall his grace a - bound; For the faint and fee - ble Per-fect strength be found.
4. He will nev - er fail us, He will not for-sake; His e - ter - nal cov'-nant He will nev - er break. Rest-ing on his prom-ise, What have we to fear? God is all - suf - fi - cient For the com-ing year.

REFRAIN

On-ward, then, and fear not, Chil-dren of the day; For his word shall nev - er, Nev-er pass a -way. A-MEN.

O God, Our Help in Ages Past

ST. ANNE. C. M.
585
ISAAC WATTS, 1674–1748
WILLIAM CROFT, 1678–1727
With great dignity
1. O God, our help in a - ges past, Our hope for years to come,
2. Un - der the shad - ow of Thy throne Still may we dwell se - cure;
3. Be - fore the hills in or - der stood, Or earth re - ceived her frame,
4. A thou - sand a - ges, in Thy sight, Are like an eve - ning gone;
5. O God, our help in a - ges past, Our hope for years to come;
Our shel - ter from the storm - y blast, And our e - ter - nal home!
Suf - fi - cient is Thine arm a - lone, And our de - fense is sure.
From ev - er - last - ing Thou art God, To end - less years the same.
Short as the watch that ends the night, Be - fore the ris - ing sun.
Be Thou our guide while life shall last, And our e - ter - nal home! A - MEN.
Great God, We Sing That Mighty Hand
WAREHAM. L. M.
586
PHILIP DODDRIDGE, 1702–1751
WILLIAM KNAPP, 1698–1768
In moderate time
1. Great God, we sing that might-y hand By which sup - port - ed still we stand;
2. By day, by night, at home, a-broad, Still are we guard-ed by our God;
3. With grate-ful hearts the past we own; The fu - ture, all to us un-known,
4. In scenes ex-alt - ed or depressed, Thou art our Joy, and Thou our Rest;
The ope - ning year Thy mer-cy shows; That mer-cy crowns it till it close.
By His in - ces - sant bounty fed, By His un - err - ing coun - sel led.
We to Thy guardian care com-mit, And peaceful leave be - fore Thy feet.
Thy goodness all our hopes shall raise, A - dored thro' all our changing days. A-MEN.

587 Another Year Is Dawning

AURELIA. 7. 6. 7. 6. D.

Frances R. Havergal, 1836–1879
Samuel S. Wesley, 1810–1876
In moderate time
1. An - oth - er year is dawn - ing, Dear Fa - ther, let it be
2. An - oth - er year of mer - cies, Of faith - ful - ness and grace,
3. An - oth - er year of serv - ice, Of wit - ness for Thy love,
In work - ing or in wait - ing An - oth - er year with Thee;
An - oth - er year of glad - ness In the shin - ing of Thy face,
An - oth - er year of train - ing For ho - lier work a - bove.
An - oth - er year of prog - ress, An - oth - er year of praise,
An - oth - er year of lean - ing Up - on Thy lov - ing breast,
An - oth - er year is dawn - ing, Dear Fa - ther, let it be
An - oth - er year of prov - ing Thy pres-ence all the days;
An - oth - er year of trust - ing, Of qui - et, hap - py rest;
On earth, or else in heav - en, An - oth - er year for Thee.
A-men.

All Beautiful the March of Days

FOREST GREEN. C. M. D.

588

FRANCES W. WILE, 1878–

English traditional melody
Arr. by R. VAUGHAN WILLIAMS, 1872–

In moderate time, with spirit

1. All beau - ti - ful the march of days, As sea - sons come and go;
2. O'er white ex - pan - ses spark - ling pure The ra - diant morns un - fold;
3. O thou from whose un - fath - omed law The year in beau - ty flows,

The hand that shaped the rose hath wrought The crys - tal of the snow;
The sol - emn splen - dors of the night Burn bright-er thro' the cold;
Thy - self the vi - sion pass - ing by In crys - tal and in rose,

Hath sent the hoar - y frost of heav'n, The flow - ing wa - ters seal'd,
Life mounts in ev - 'ry throbb-ing vein, Love deep-ens round the hearth,
Day un - to day doth ut - ter speech, And night to night pro-claim,

And laid a si - lent love - li - ness On hill and wood and field.
And clear - er sounds the an - gel hymn, "Good will to men on earth."
In ev - er-chang - ing words of light, The won - ders of thy name. A-MEN.

Ring Out the Old, Ring in the New

589

WALTHAM. L. M.

ALFRED TENNYSON, 1809–1892 — JOHN B. CALKIN, 1827–1905

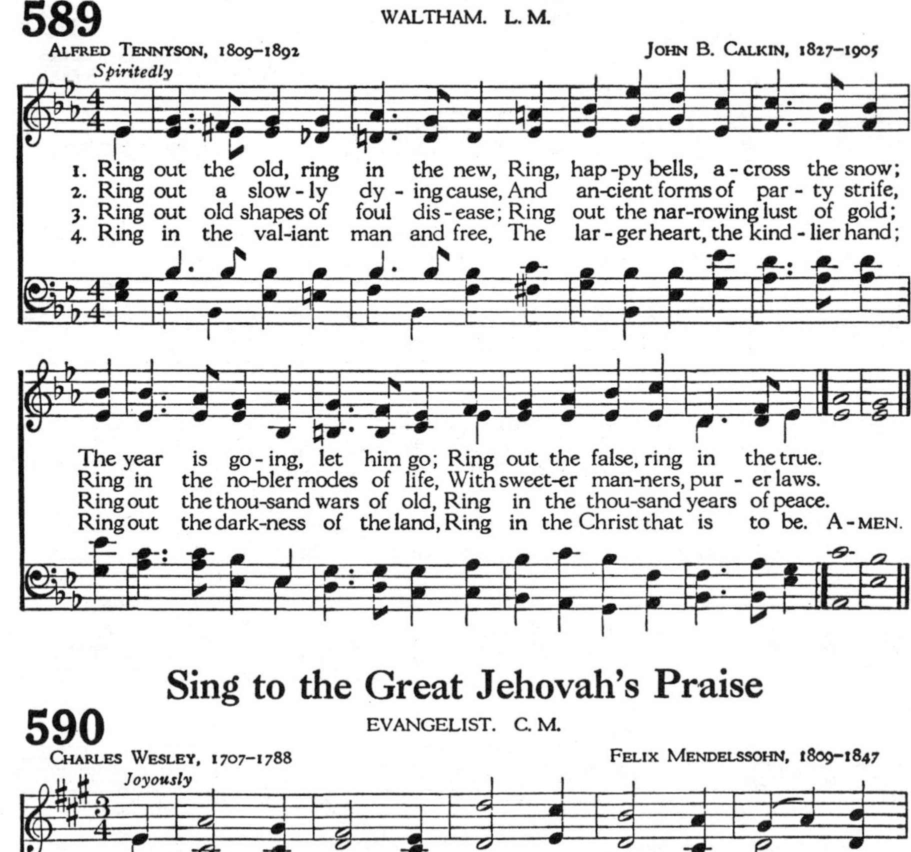
Spiritedly
1. Ring out the old, ring in the new, Ring, hap-py bells, a-cross the snow;
2. Ring out a slow-ly dy-ing cause, And an-cient forms of par-ty strife,
3. Ring out old shapes of foul dis-ease; Ring out the nar-rowing lust of gold;
4. Ring in the val-iant man and free, The lar-ger heart, the kind-lier hand;
The year is go-ing, let him go; Ring out the false, ring in the true.
Ring in the no-bler modes of life, With sweet-er man-ners, pur-er laws.
Ring out the thou-sand wars of old, Ring in the thou-sand years of peace.
Ring out the dark-ness of the land, Ring in the Christ that is to be. A-MEN.

Sing to the Great Jehovah's Praise

590

EVANGELIST. C. M.

CHARLES WESLEY, 1707–1788 — FELIX MENDELSSOHN, 1809–1847

Joyously
1. Sing to the great Je-ho-vah's praise! All praise to
2. His prov-i-dence hath brought us through An-oth-er
3. Fa-ther, Thy mer-cies past we own, And Thy con-
4. Our lips and lives shall glad-ly show The won-ders
Him be-longs; Who kind-ly length-ens out our
va-rious year; We all, with vows and an-thems
tin-ued care; To Thee pre-sent-ing, through Thy
of Thy love, While on in Je-sus' steps we

days, In - spires our choic - est songs.
new, Be - fore our God ap - pear.
Son, What - e'er we have or are.
go To see Thy face a - bove. A - MEN.

A Song of Spring Once More We Sing

ARABIA. 8. 6. 8. 6. 8. 6.

591

W. H. GROSER, 1834–1925

W. WILSON, 1833-

Joyfully
1. A song of spring once more we sing As win - ter flies a - way,
2. For once a - gain the prom-ise-strain Floats down from days of yore,
3. Thee, Lord, we praise for spring-tide days, And life's yet fair - er spring;
And changeful hours bring sun and showers To weave a crown for May;
That fruits of earth shall wake to birth, To bless the toil - er's store;
These gold - en hours, these opening powers, We in glad serv - ice bring,
With heart and voice we all re - joice On this re - turn-ing day.
Each an-nual round with bounties crowned, Till time shall be no more.
Thine own to be, from sin set free, Our Fa - ther. Saviour, King. A-MEN.

Words from "The Christian Hymnary."

When Spring Unlocks the Flowers

592

GOSTERWOOD. 7. 6. 7. 6. 8. 6. 8. 6.

Reginald Heber, 1783–1826

English traditional melody
Arr. by R. Vaughan Williams, 1872–

In moderate time, joyously
1. When spring un-locks the flow - ers, To paint the laugh-ing soil,
2. The birds that wake the morn - ing, And those that love the shade,
When sum-mer's balm-y show - ers Re-fresh the mow-er's toil,
The winds that sweep the moun - tain, Or lull the drow-sy glade,
When win - ter binds in frost-y chains The fal-low and the flood,
The sun that from his am-ber bower Re - joic-eth on his way,
In God the earth re - joic-eth still, And owns her Mak-er good.
The moon and stars their Mak-er s name In si - lent pomp dis-play. A-MEN.

Come, Ye Thankful People, Come

ST. GEORGE'S, WINDSOR. 7. 7. 7. 7. D.

593

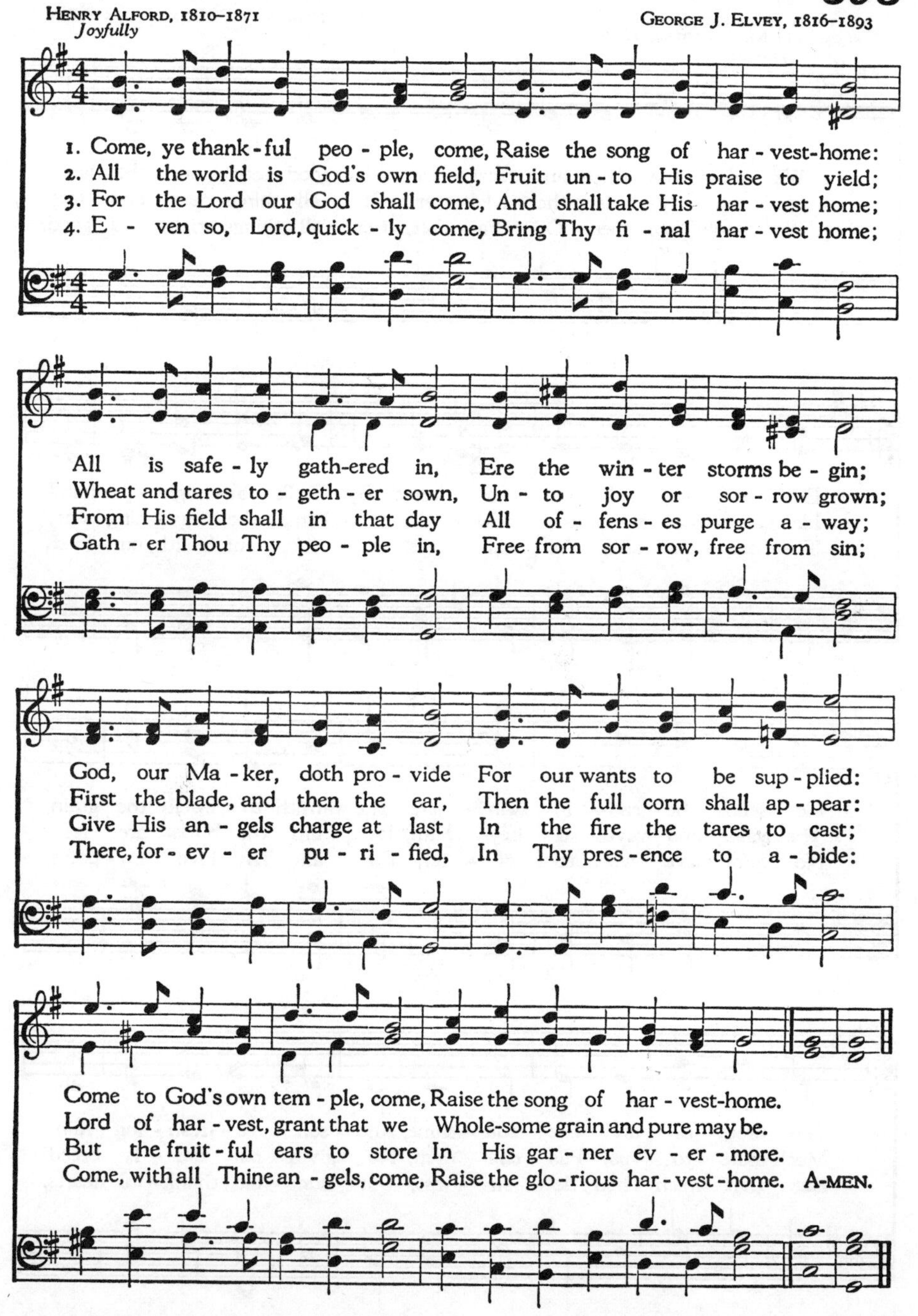
HENRY ALFORD, 1810–1871
GEORGE J. ELVEY, 1816–1893
Joyfully
1. Come, ye thank - ful peo - ple, come, Raise the song of har - vest-home:
2. All the world is God's own field, Fruit un - to His praise to yield;
3. For the Lord our God shall come, And shall take His har - vest home;
4. E - ven so, Lord, quick - ly come, Bring Thy fi - nal har - vest home;
All is safe - ly gath-ered in, Ere the win - ter storms be - gin;
Wheat and tares to - geth - er sown, Un - to joy or sor - row grown;
From His field shall in that day All of - fens - es purge a - way;
Gath - er Thou Thy peo - ple in, Free from sor - row, free from sin;
God, our Ma - ker, doth pro - vide For our wants to be sup - plied:
First the blade, and then the ear, Then the full corn shall ap - pear:
Give His an - gels charge at last In the fire the tares to cast;
There, for - ev - er pu - ri - fied, In Thy pres - ence to a - bide:
Come to God's own tem - ple, come, Raise the song of har - vest-home.
Lord of har - vest, grant that we Whole-some grain and pure may be.
But the fruit - ful ears to store In His gar - ner ev - er - more.
Come, with all Thine an - gels, come, Raise the glo - rious har - vest - home. A-MEN.

We Plow the Fields, and Scatter

594

WIR PFLÜGEN. 7. 6. 7. 6. D. with Refrain

MATTHIAS CLAUDIUS, 1740–1815
Tr. by JANE M. CAMPBELL, 1817–1878
JOHANN A. P. SCHULZ, 1747–1800
Spiritedly
1. We plow the fields, and scatter The good seed on the land,
2. He on - ly is the Mak - er Of all things near and far;
3. We thank Thee, then, O Fa - ther, For all things bright and good,
But it is fed and wa - tered By God's al - might - y hand;
He paints the way - side flow - er, He lights the eve - ning star;
The seed - time and the har - vest, Our life, our health, our food;
He sends the snow in win - ter, The warmth to swell the grain,
The winds and waves o - bey Him, By Him the birds are fed;
No gifts have we to of - fer, For all Thy love im - parts,
The breez - es and the sun - shine, And soft re - fresh - ing rain.
Much more to us, His chil - dren, He gives our dai - ly bread.
But that which Thou de - sir - est, Our hum - ble, thank - ful hearts.

Refrain
All good gifts a - round us Are sent from heaven a - bove;
Then thank the Lord, O thank the Lord For all His love. A-men.

Praise to God, Immortal Praise

PLEYEL'S HYMN. 7. 7. 7. 7.

595

Anna L. Barbauld, 1743–1825 Ignace Pleyel, 1757–1831

Joyfully

1. Praise to God, im-mor-tal praise, For the love that crowns our days!
2. All that Spring with boun-teous hand Scat-ters o'er the smil-ing land;
3. These to thee, my God, we owe, Source whence all our bless-ings flow;
4. Yet to thee my soul should raise Grate-ful vows and sol-emn praise,

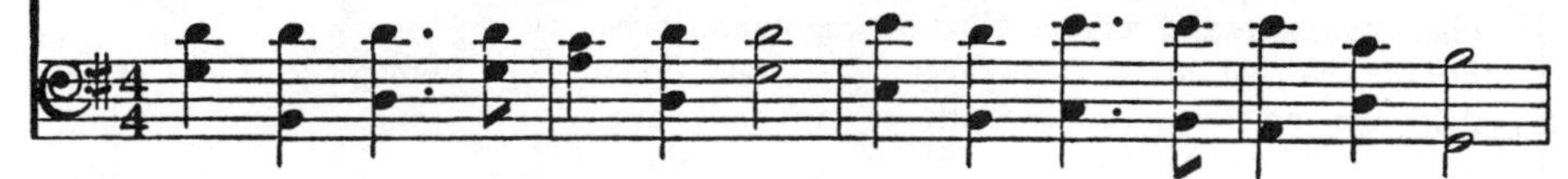

Boun-teous source of ev-'ry joy, Let thy praise our tongues em-ploy!
All that li-b'ral Au-tumn pours From her rich o'er-flow-ing stores,—
And for these my soul shall raise Grate-ful vows and sol-emn praise.
And, when ev-'ry bless-ing's flown, Love thee for thy-self a-lone. A-men.

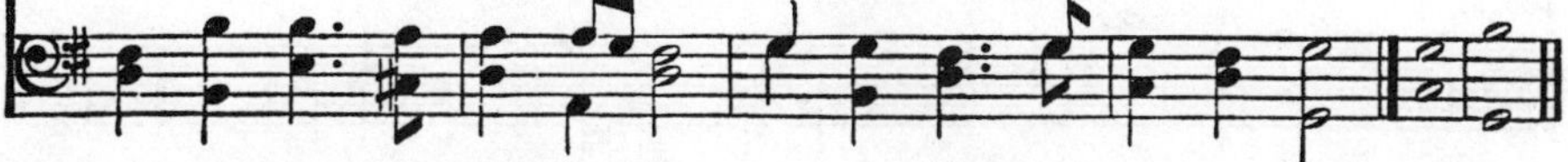

Earth Below Is Teeming

596

ST. ALBAN. 6. 5. 6. 5. D. with Refrain

JOHN S. B. MONSELL, 1811–1875 — FRANZ JOSEPH HAYDN, 1732–1809

In moderate time

1. Earth be - low is teem - ing, Heav'n is bright a - bove; Ev - ry brow is beam - ing
2. For the sun and show - ers, For the rain and dew, For the nurturing hours
3. Earth's broad harvest whit-ens In a bright-er sun Than the orb that light-ens

In the light of love; Ev - 'ry eye re - joi - ces, Ev - 'ry thought is praise;
Spring and sum-mer knew, For the gold-en au - tumn, And its pre-cious stores,
All we tread up - on; Send out la-b'rers, Fa - ther, Where fields rip'ning wave,

REFRAIN

Hap - py hearts and voi - ces Glad-den nights and days.
For the love that brought them Teeming to our doors. O al-might-y Giv - er!
All the na-tions gath - er, Gath - er in and save.

Boun-ti - ful and free, As the joy in har - vest, Joy we be-fore Thee. A - MEN.

Not Alone for Mighty Empire

AUSTRIAN HYMN. 8. 7. 8. 7. D.

597

WILLIAM P. MERRILL, 1867–

FRANZ JOSEPH HAYDN, 1732–1809

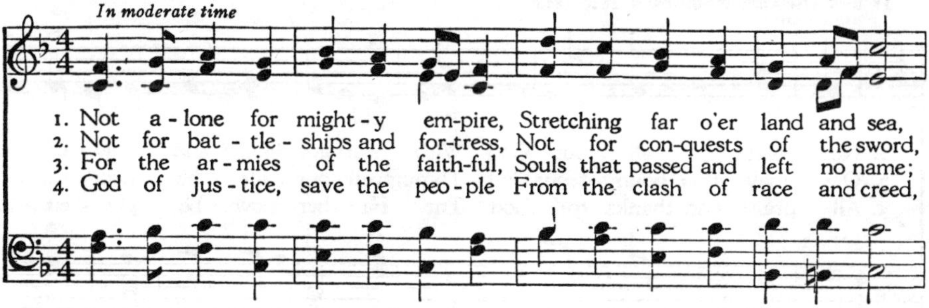

In moderate time

1. Not a - lone for might - y em-pire, Stretching far o'er land and sea,
2. Not for bat - tle - ships and for-tress, Not for con-quests of the sword,
3. For the ar - mies of the faith-ful, Souls that passed and left no name;
4. God of jus - tice, save the peo - ple From the clash of race and creed,

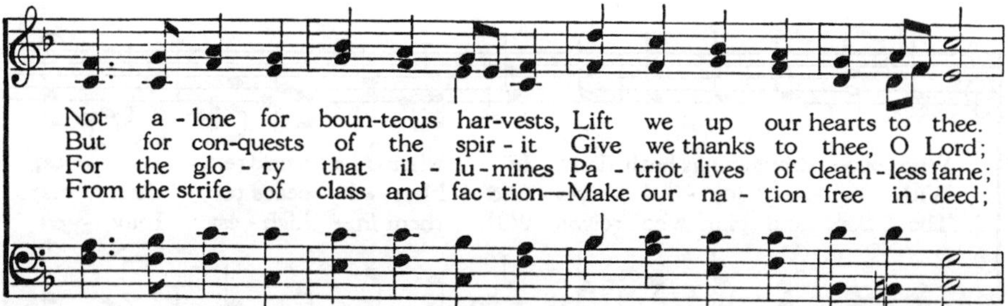

Not a - lone for boun-teous har-vests, Lift we up our hearts to thee.
But for con-quests of the spir - it Give we thanks to thee, O Lord;
For the glo - ry that il - lu - mines Pa - triot lives of death - less fame;
From the strife of class and fac - tion—Make our na - tion free in - deed;

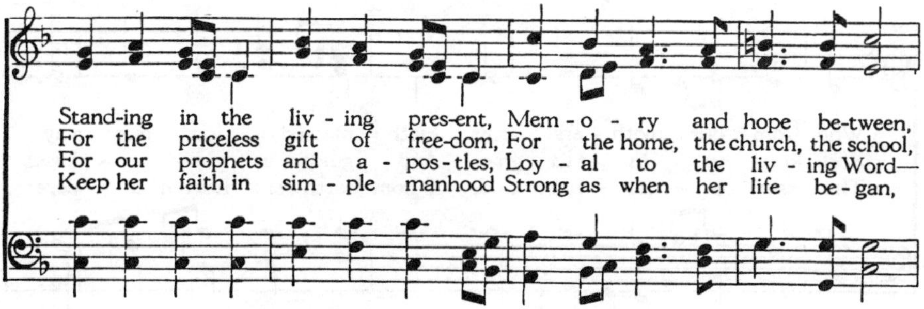

Stand-ing in the liv - ing pres-ent, Mem - o - ry and hope be-tween,
For the priceless gift of free-dom, For the home, the church, the school,
For our prophets and a - pos - tles, Loy - al to the liv - ing Word—
Keep her faith in sim - ple manhood Strong as when her life be - gan,

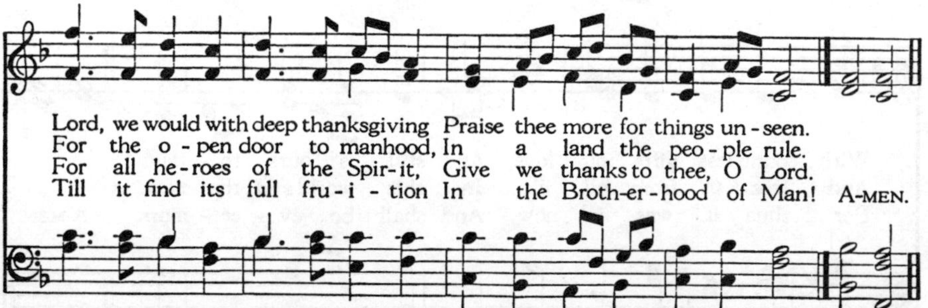

Lord, we would with deep thanksgiving Praise thee more for things un - seen.
For the o - pen door to manhood, In a land the peo - ple rule.
For all he - roes of the Spir - it, Give we thanks to thee, O Lord.
Till it find its full fru - i - tion In the Broth-er - hood of Man! A-MEN.

Now Thank We All Our God

598

NUN DANKET. 6. 7. 6. 7. 6. 6. 6. 6.

MARTIN RINKART, 1586-1649
Tr. by CATHERINE WINKWORTH, 1829-1878

JOHANN CRÜGER, 1598-1662

Majestically

1. Now thank we all our God With heart and hands and voic - es,
2. O may this boun - teous God, Through all our life be near us,
3. All praise and thanks to God The Fa - ther now be giv - en,

Who won - drous things hath done, In whom His world re - joic - es;
With ev - er joy - ful hearts And bless - ed peace to cheer us;
The Son, and Him who reigns With them in high - est heav - en,

Who, from our moth - ers' arms, Hath blessed us on our way
And keep us in His grace, And guide us when per - plexed,
The one e - ter - nal God, Whom earth and heaven a - dore;

With count-less gifts of love, And still is ours to - day.
And free us from all ills In this world and the next.
For thus it was, is now, And shall be ev - er - more. A-MEN.

Bless the Four Corners of This House

ABERGELE. C. M.

599

ARTHUR GUITERMAN, 1871– | JOHN A. LLOYD, 1815–1874

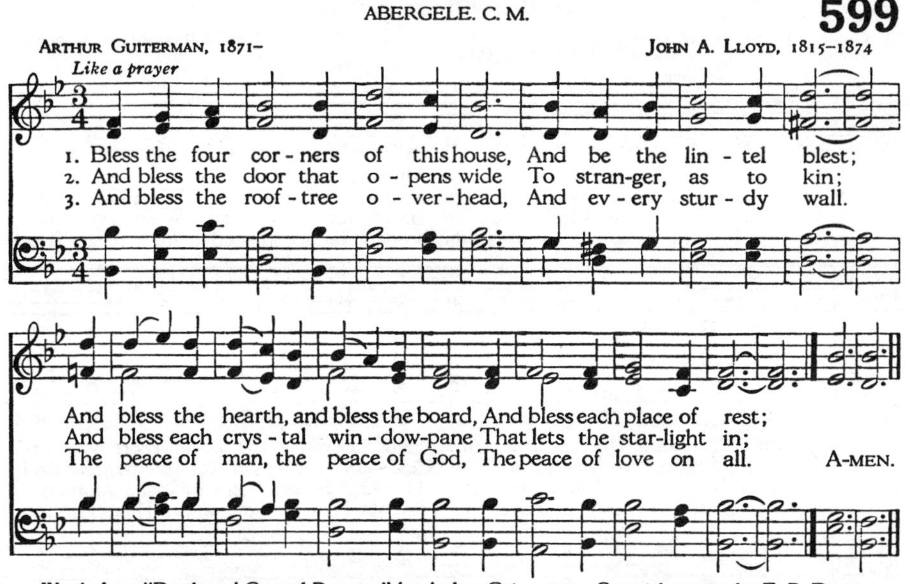
Like a prayer
1. Bless the four cor - ners of this house, And be the lin - tel blest;
2. And bless the door that o - pens wide To stran-ger, as to kin;
3. And bless the roof - tree o - ver - head, And ev - ery stur - dy wall.
And bless the hearth, and bless the board, And bless each place of rest;
And bless each crys - tal win - dow-pane That lets the star-light in;
The peace of man, the peace of God, The peace of love on all.
A-MEN.

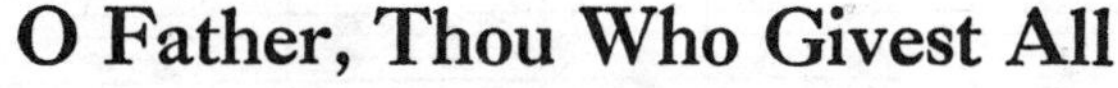

O Father, Thou Who Givest All

O JESU CHRIST, MEIN LEBENS LICHT. L. M.

600

JOHN HAYNES HOLMES, 1879– | ANONYMOUS, 1676, Arr.

In moderate time
1. O Fa-ther, thou who giv - est all The boun-ty of thy per - fect love,
2. We thank thee for the grace of home, For moth-er's love and fa - ther's care;
3. For eyes to see and ears to hear, For hands to serve and arms to lift,
4. For faith to con-quer doubt and fear, For love to an - swer ev - ery call,
We thank thee that up - on us fall Such ten - der bless-ings from a - bove.
For friends and teachers—all who come Our joys and hopes and fears to share.
For shoulders broad and strong to bear, For feet to run on er-rands swift,
For strength to do, and will to dare, We thank thee, O thou Lord of all.
A-MEN.

O Happy Home, Where Thou Art Loved the Dearest

601

ALVERSTROKE. 11. 10. 11. 10.

Carl J. P. Spitta, 1801–1859
Adapted from a tr. by Sarah B. Findlater, 1823–1907

Joseph Barnby, 1838–1896

In moderate time
1. O hap-py home, where Thou art loved the dear-est, Thou lov-ing Friend, and Sav-iour of our race, And where a-mong the guests there nev-er com-eth One who can hold such high and hon-ored place!
2. O hap-py home, where each one serves Thee, low-ly, What-ev-er his ap-point-ed work may be, Till ev-ery com-mon task seems great and ho-ly, When it is done, O Lord, as un-to Thee!
3. O hap-py home, where Thou art not for-got-ten When joy is o-ver-flow-ing, full, and free; O hap-py home, where ev-ery wound-ed spir-it Is brought, Phy-si-cian, Com-fort-er, to Thee—
4. Un-til at last, when earth's day's work is end-ed All meet Thee in the bless-ed home a-bove, From whence Thou cam-est, where Thou hast as-cend-ed, Thy ev-er-last-ing home of peace and love! A-MEN.
Thou Gracious God Whose Mercy Lends
602
ANGELUS. L. M.
Oliver W. Holmes, 1809–1894
Georg Joseph, 1657, in Heilige Seelenlust.
In moderate time
1. Thou gra-cious God whose mer-cy lends The light of home, the smile of friends;
2. Wilt Thou not hear us while we raise, In sweet ac-cord of sol-emn praise,
3. For all the bless-ings life has brought, For all its sorrowing hours have taught,
4. The noontide sun-shine of the past, These brief, bright moments fad-ing fast,
5. We thank Thee, Fa-ther; let Thy grace Our lov-ing cir-cle still em-brace,

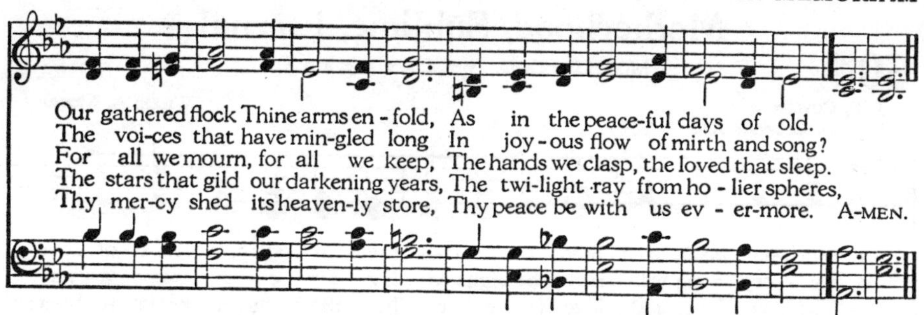
Our gathered flock Thine arms en - fold, As in the peace-ful days of old.
The voi-ces that have min-gled long In joy - ous flow of mirth and song?
For all we mourn, for all we keep, The hands we clasp, the loved that sleep.
The stars that gild our darkening years, The twi-light ray from ho - lier spheres,
Thy mer-cy shed its heaven-ly store, Thy peace be with us ev - er-more. A-MEN.

Now Praise We Great and Famous Men

DOMINUS REGIT ME. 8. 7. 8. 7.

603

WILLIAM G. TARRANT, 1853–1928

JOHN B. DYKES, 1823–1876

In moderate time
1. Now praise we great and fa - mous men, The fa - thers, named in sto - ry; And praise the Lord who now as then Re - veals in man His glo - ry.
2. Praise we the wise and brave and strong, Who graced their gen - er - a - tion; Who helped the right, and fought the wrong, And made our folk a na - tion.
3. Praise we the great of heart and mind, The sing - ers sweet - ly gift - ed, Whose mu - sic like a might - y wind The souls of men up - lift - ed.
4. Praise we the peace - ful men of skill Who build - ed homes of beau - ty, And, rich in art, made rich - er still The broth - er - hood of du - ty.
5. So praise we great and fa - mous men, The fa - thers, named in sto - ry; And praise the Lord who now as then Re - veals in man His glo - ry. A-MEN.

Motherhood, Sublime, Eternal

604

MOTHERHOOD. 8. 7. 4. 4. 7. 8. 7. 4. 4. 7.

J. S. Cutler — Willis A. Moore

In moderate time

1. Moth - er - hood, su - blime, e - ter - nal, Lives in God's great heart of Love;
2. Ev - ery wrong will sure be right-ed; Ev - ery e - vil swept a - way;
3. God is love, and love for - ev - er In the moth - er - heart is blest;
Ev - er holds us, Safe en- folds us, Un - der-neath, a - round, a - bove;
Truth up-spring-ing, Jus - tice bring-ing, Ush- ers in the bright-er day;
Lives the long - est, Lifts the strong-est, Far out-reach-ing all the rest;
Pa - tient, ten - der, kind, for - giv - ing, Tho' in de- vious paths we roam;
Moth - er calls her earth - ly chil-dren, Loves them, lifts them when they fall;
Not by might, and not by wis - dom Comes our lift - ing from the sod;
Gen - tly chides us, Ev - er guides us, And all - lov - ing, leads us home.
Striv - ing, call - ing, Faint-ing, fall - ing, Moth- er - love en - folds them all.
Love's pure glo - ry Tells the sto - ry In the Moth- er- heart of God. A - MEN.

O Thou, Whose Own Vast Temple Stands

DUNDEE. C. M.

605

WILLIAM CULLEN BRYANT, 1794–1878 — SCOTTISH PSALTER, 1615

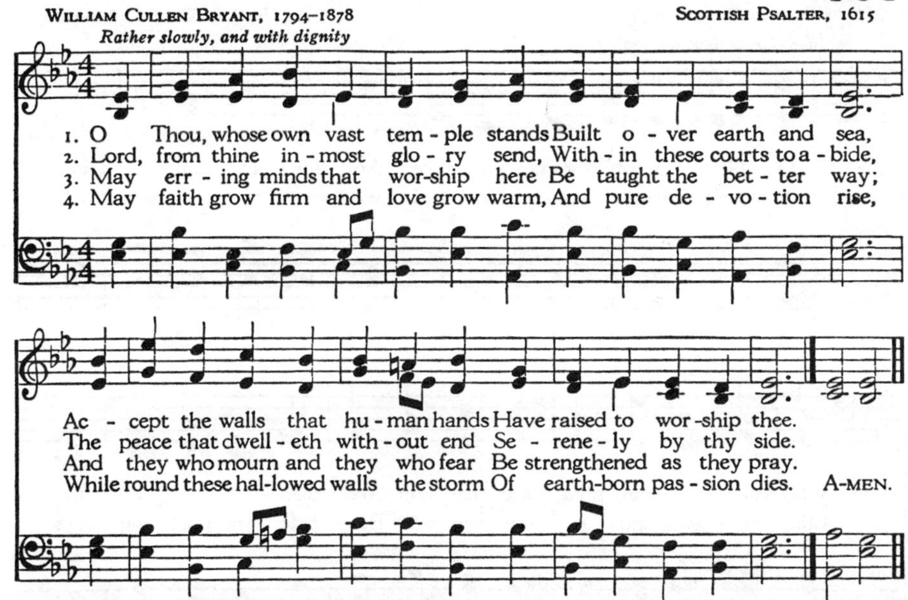
Rather slowly, and with dignity
1. O Thou, whose own vast tem - ple stands Built o - ver earth and sea,
2. Lord, from thine in - most glo - ry send, With - in these courts to a - bide,
3. May err - ing minds that wor-ship here Be taught the bet - ter way;
4. May faith grow firm and love grow warm, And pure de - vo - tion rise,
Ac - cept the walls that hu - man hands Have raised to wor - ship thee.
The peace that dwell - eth with - out end Se - rene - ly by thy side.
And they who mourn and they who fear Be strengthened as they pray.
While round these hal-lowed walls the storm Of earth-born pas - sion dies. A-MEN.

All Things Are Thine; No Gift Have We

GERMANY. L. M.

606

JOHN G. WHITTIER, 1807–1892 — Adapted from SACRED MELODIES, WILLIAM GARDINER, 1770–1853

In moderate time

1. All things are Thine; no gift have we, Lord of all gifts, to of - fer Thee,
2. Thy will was in the build-er's thought; Thy hand un-seen a - midst us wrought;
3. In weak-ness and in want we call On Thee for whom the heavens are small;
4. O Fa-ther, deign these walls to bless; Fill with Thy love their emp - ti - ness;

And hence with grate-ful hearts to - day Thine own be - fore Thy feet we lay.
Through mor-tal mo-tive, scheme and plan, Thy wise e - ter - nal pur - pose ran.
Thy glo - ry is Thy chil-dren's good, Thy joy Thy ten - der Fa - ther-hood.
And let their door a gate-way be To lead us from our-selves to Thee. A-MEN.

O God, in Whose Great Purpose

607

ALFORD. 7. 6. 8. 6. D.

JAMES GORDON GILKEY, 1899–

JOHN B. DYKES, 1823–1876

In moderate time, with spirit
1. O God, in whose great pur-pose An age is but a day,
2. A-gain with vi-sion kin-dled We sons of la-ter days
Who watch-est sun give place to sun And plan-ets burn a-way;
Lift ea-ger hands as here we wait Be-side the part-ing ways.
In Thee our fa-thers trust-ed, For Thee they dared the sea,
A-cross Thine earth we scat-ter To meet the tasks of men:
And Thou didst teach their fee-ble hands To shape a world for Thee.
O God of strength, be Thou to us Our fa-thers' God a-gain! A-men.

God of Our Youth, to Whom We Yield

LEST WE FORGET. 8. 8. 8. 8. 8. 8.

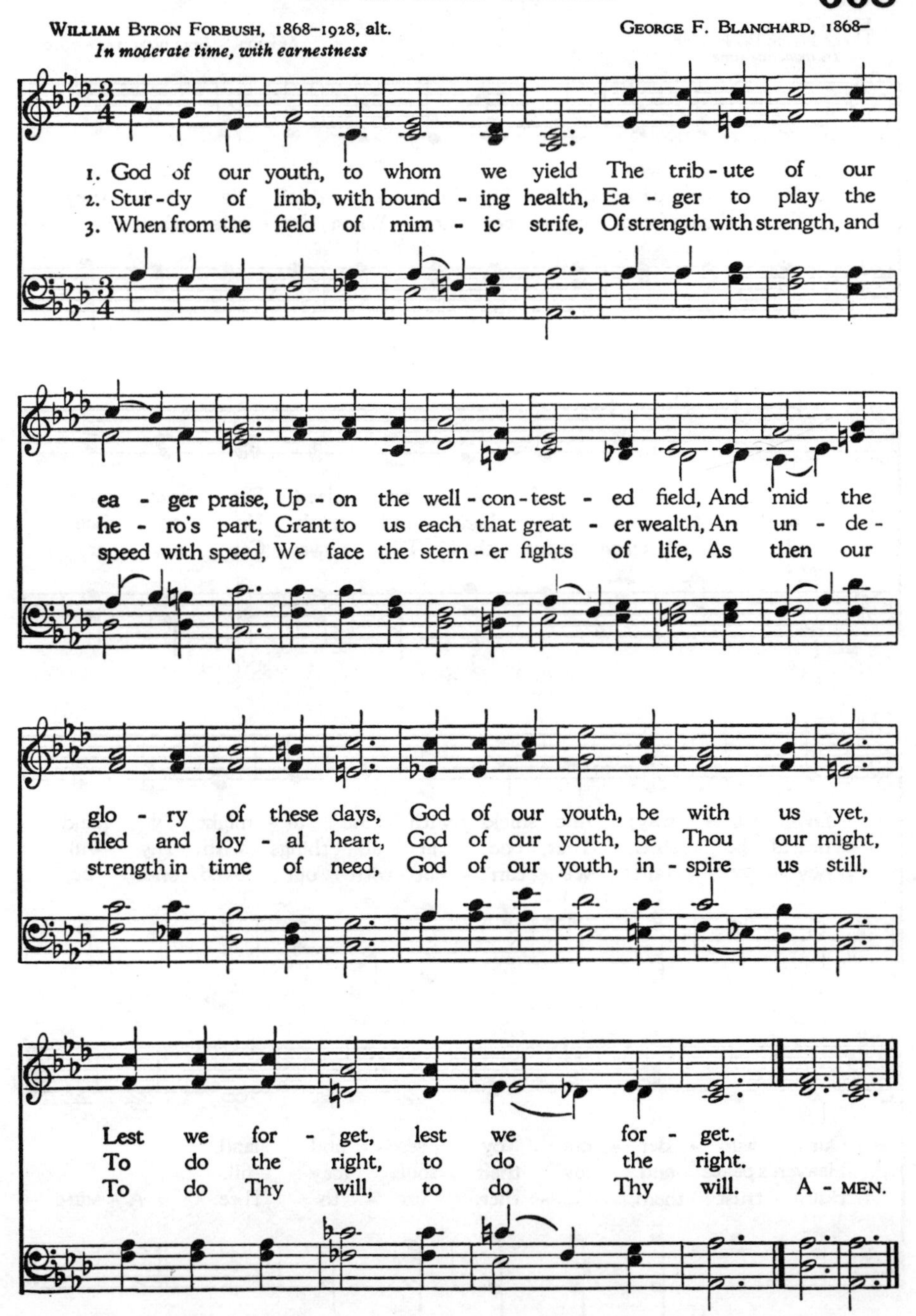
WILLIAM BYRON FORBUSH, 1868–1928, alt.
GEORGE F. BLANCHARD, 1868–
In moderate time, with earnestness
1. God of our youth, to whom we yield The trib - ute of our
2. Stur - dy of limb, with bound - ing health, Ea - ger to play the
3. When from the field of mim - ic strife, Of strength with strength, and
ea - ger praise, Up - on the well - con - test - ed field, And 'mid the
he - ro's part, Grant to us each that great - er wealth, An un - de -
speed with speed, We face the stern - er fights of life, As then our
glo - ry of these days, God of our youth, be with us yet,
filed and loy - al heart, God of our youth, be Thou our might,
strength in time of need, God of our youth, in - spire us still,
Lest we for - get, lest we for - get.
To do the right, to do the right.
To do Thy will, to do Thy will.
A - MEN.

Father, Who Art Alone

609

SAMUEL. 6. 6. 6. 6. 8. 8.

EDITH JONES
Home Hymn Book, 1885

ARTHUR S. SULLIVAN, 1842–1900

In moderate time

1. Fa - ther, who art a - lone Our help - er and our stay: O hear us! as we plead For loved ones far a - way; And shield with Thine al - might - y hand Our wan - der - ers by sea and land.
2. O com - pass with Thy love The dai - ly path they tread! And may Thy light and truth Up - on their hearts be shed; That, one in all things with Thy will, Heaven's peace and joy their souls may fill.
3. Guard them from ev - ery harm When dan - gers shall as - sail, And teach them that Thy power Can nev - er, nev - er fail; We can - not with our loved ones be, But trust them, Fa - ther, un - to Thee.
A - MEN.

Eternal Father, Strong to Save

MELITA. 8. 8. 8. 8. 8. 8.

610

William Whiting, 1825–1878
John B. Dykes, 1823–1876
In moderate time
1. E - ter - nal Fa - ther, strong to save, Whose arm hath bound the rest - less wave, Who bidd'st the might - y o - cean deep Its own ap - point - ed lim - its keep: O hear us when we cry to Thee For those in per - il on the sea.
2. O Christ, whose voice the wa - ters heard, And hushed their rag - ing at Thy word, Who walk - edst on the foam - ing deep, And calm a - mid the storm didst sleep: O hear us when we cry to Thee For those in per - il on the sea.
3. O Ho - ly Spir - it, who didst brood Up - on the wa - ters dark and rude, And bid their an - gry tu - mult cease, And give, for wild con - fu - sion, peace: O hear us when we cry to Thee For those in per - il on the sea.
4. O Trin - i - ty of love and power, Our breth - ren shield in dan - ger's hour; From rock and tem - pest, fire and foe, Pro - tect them where - so - e'er they go: Thus ev - er - more shall rise to Thee Glad hymns of praise from land and sea.
A - MEN.

611

OLD 100TH. L. M.

Thomas Ken, 1637–1711
From the Genevan Psalter
arr. by Louis Bourgeois, 1551
Praise God, from whom all bless-ings flow; Praise him, all crea-tures here be - low;
Praise him a - bove, ye heav'n-ly host; Praise Fa-ther, Son, and Ho - ly Ghost. A-men.
612
GLORIA PATRI
Edwin McNeill Poteat, 1892–
Glo - ry be to the Fa - ther, the Fa - ther and the Son and
to the Ho - ly Ghost; as it was in the be - gin - ning, is
now and ev - er shall be; world with - out end. A - men.

Used by permission of the composer, Edwin McNeill Poteat.

GLORIA PATRI

613
HENRY W. GREATOREX, 1851
From GREATOREX'S COLLECTION
Glo - ry be to the Fa-ther, and to the Son, and to the Ho - ly Ghost: As it
was in the be-gin-ning, is now, and ev-er shall be, world without end. A - MEN, A - MEN.
GLORIA PATRI
614
CHARLES MEINEKE, 1782–1850
Glo - ry be to the Fa-ther, and to the Son, and to the Ho - ly Ghost; As it
was in the be-gin-ning, is now and ev - er shall be, world with-out end. A-MEN, A -MEN.
SANCTUS
615
ALFRED R. GAUL, 1837–1913
Arr. from THE HOLY CITY.
3
Ho-ly, Ho - ly, Ho-ly Lord of Hosts: Ho-ly, Ho-ly, Ho-ly is the Lord of Hosts. A-MEN.

616

KARL P. HARRINGTON, 1861–

In unison or harmony

The Lord is in His ho-ly tem-ple; let all the earth keep si-lence be-fore Him.

617

CALVIN W. LAUFER, 1874–1938

The Lord is in His ho - ly tem - ple; let all the earth keep si - lence be - fore Him, keep si - lence be - fore Him.

618

PARKER C. PALMER

The Lord is in His ho - ly tem - ple; Let all the earth keep si - lence, keep si - lence be - fore Him. A - MEN.

619

EDWARD SHIPPEN BARNES, 1887–

O come, let us wor-ship and bow down; Let us kneel be-fore the Lord our Mak-er. A-MEN.

620
JOHN PORTER, 1877–
O worship the Lord in the beauty of holiness; Serve Him with gladness, all the earth. A-MEN.
621
EDWIN MCNEILL POTEAT, 1892–
O Thou Eternal and ever-present Spirit
Who art our Father
Grant Thy rich blessing Unto Thine unworthy servants
Who wait before Thee
That we may worship Thee
In spirit and in truth. A-MEN.
Used by permission of Edwin McNeill Poteat.
622
EDWIN MCNEILL POTEAT, 1892–
Ask, and it shall be given you; Seek, and ye shall find;
Knock, and it shall be opened unto you.
Used by permission of Edwin McNeill Poteat.

623 Bless the Lord, O My Soul

Minister: O all ye works of the Lord, bless ye the Lord; praise him and magnify him forever.

Choir:

IPPOLITOF-IVANOFF, 1859–

p
Bless the Lord, O . . . my soul, Bless-ed art Thou, O Lord.
p

Minister: O ye servants of the Lord, bless ye the Lord; praise him, and magnify him forever.

Choir:

mf
cresc.
f
Bless the Lord, O . . . my soul, and all that is with-in me bless His ho - ly name.

Minister: O ye holy and humble men of heart, bless ye the Lord; praise him, and magnify him forever.

Choir:

mf
p
rit.
pp
Bless the Lord, O . . . my soul, and all that is with-in me bless His ho - ly name.

Send Out Thy Light and Thy Truth

624

Minister: The Lord is my light and my salvation; whom shall I fear? The Lord is the strength of my life; of whom shall I be afraid? I will go unto the altar of God, unto God my exceeding joy.

Choir:

CHARLES F. GOUNOD, 1818–1893

Send out thy light and thy truth, let them lead me, and let them
bring me to thy ho - ly hill. Send out thy light and thy
truth, let them lead me, and let them bring me to thy
Slower
rit.
ho - ly hill. Send out thy light, O Lord, our God.

Our Father, Who Art in Heaven

625

Our Father who art in heaven, Hallowed be thy name,
Thy kingdom come. Thy will be done on earth, as it is in heaven.
Give us this day our daily bread.
And forgive us our debts, as we forgive our debtors.
And lead us not into temptation, but deliver us from evil:
For thine is the kingdom, and the power, and the glory, forever. A-MEN.

Our Father, who art in *heaven,* hal - low -ed be thy name.
Thy kingdom *come,*
Thy will be *done* in
earth, as it is in heaven. Give us this *day* our dai - ly bread,
And forgive us our *debts,* as we for - give our debt-ors;
And lead us not into
temptation, but de-
liv - er us from e - vil:
For thine is the *kingdom,* and
the power, and the *glory,* for
ev - er. A - MEN

626

Adam Geibel, 1855–1933
Bow down Thine ear, O Lord, and hear our prayer, Be mer - ci - ful, be
mer - ci - ful and hear...... us. ... A - men, A - men.
627
Thomas Moss
Hear our prayer, O Heaven - ly Fa - ther, And in - cline Thine
ear to us and grant us Thy peace. A - men.
628
Edna Bruner
Hear our pray'r, O Fa - ther, We be - seech Thee. A - men.

629

EDWIN MCNEILL POTEAT, 1892–

O - pen Thine eyes un - to the sup - pli - ca - tion of Thy

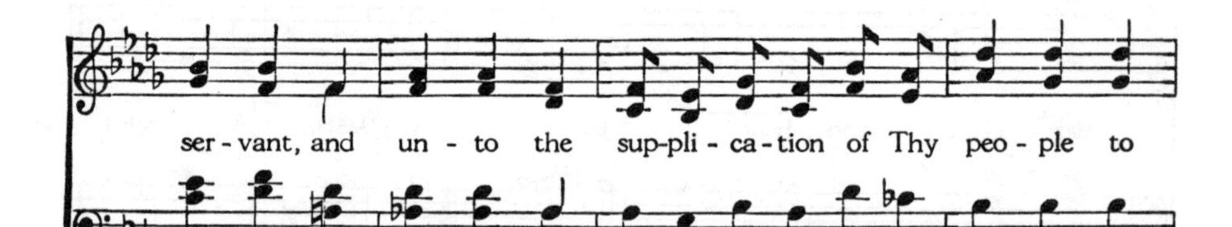
ser - vant, and un - to the sup - pli - ca - tion of Thy peo - ple to

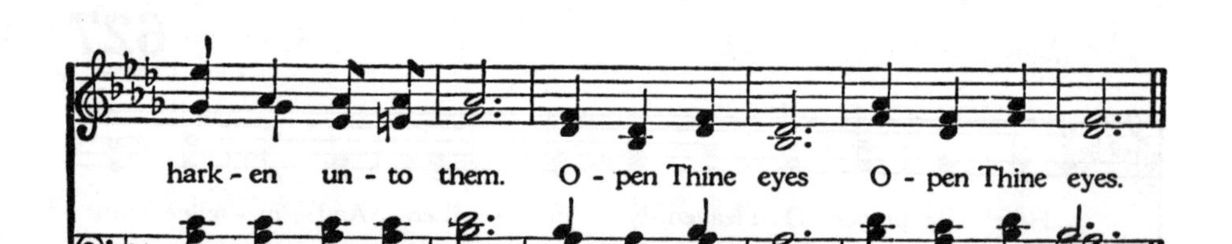
hark - en un - to them. O - pen Thine eyes O - pen Thine eyes.

630

GEORGE WHELPTON, 1847–1930

Hear our prayer, O Lord, Hear our prayer, O Lord;

In - cline Thine ear to us, And grant us Thy peace. A - MEN.

631

Edwin McNeill Poteat, 1892–

Give ear, O Shep-herd of Is - ra - el. Thou that lead-est Jo - seph
like a flock. Look down from heav'n and be - hold this vine, and the
stock which Thy right hand hath plant - ed. So shall we not go
back from Thee, Shep - herd of Is - ra - el.

632

Arr. from Felix Mendelssohn, 1809–1847

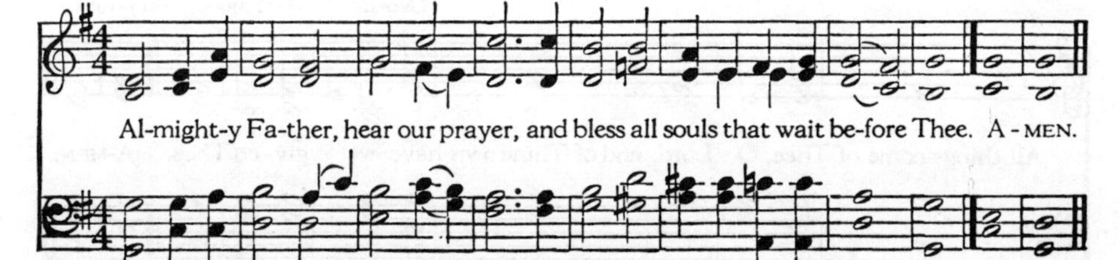
Al-might-y Fa-ther, hear our prayer, and bless all souls that wait be-fore Thee. A - men.

RESPONSE AFTER PRAYER

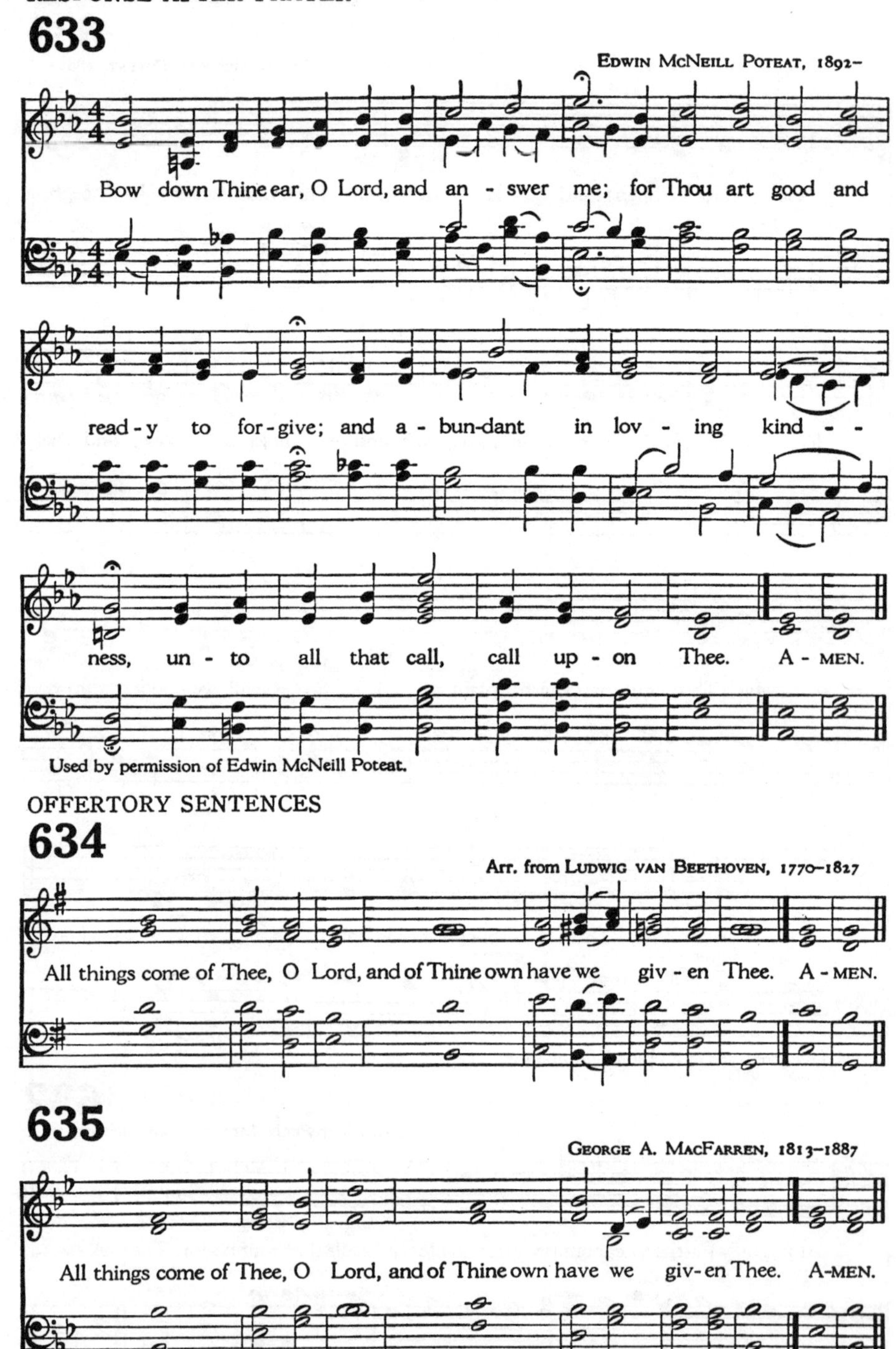
633
Edwin McNeill Poteat, 1892–
Bow down Thine ear, O Lord, and an - swer me; for Thou art good and
read - y to for - give; and a - bun - dant in lov - ing kind - -
ness, un - to all that call, call up - on Thee. A - men.
Used by permission of Edwin McNeill Poteat.
OFFERTORY SENTENCES
634
Arr. from Ludwig van Beethoven, 1770–1827
All things come of Thee, O Lord, and of Thine own have we giv - en Thee. A - men.
635
George A. MacFarren, 1813–1887
All things come of Thee, O Lord, and of Thine own have we giv - en Thee. A - men.

636

HERR JESU CHRIST. L. M.

John Greenleaf Whittier, 1807–1892

Pensum Sacrum, Gorlitz, 1648; arr. by Johann Sebastian Bach, 1685–1750

All things are Thine: no gift have we, Lord of all gifts, to of - fer Thee,
And hence with grate - ful hearts to - day, Thine own be - fore Thy feet we lay.
637
Bohemian Brethren, traditional
O dear - est Lord, Ac - cept to - day the gifts we bring, Our songs of praise,
The prayers we raise; And grant us, Lord, Thy bless - ing. A - men.
638
Let each man do according as he hath purposed in his heart; Not grudgingly, or of necessity: for God loveth a cheerful giver. A - men.

RESPONSES FOR CLOSING
639
HEBRON. L. M.
Joseph Hart, 1712–1768
Lowell Mason, 1792–1872
1. Dis-miss us with Thy bless-ing, Lord; Help us to feed up-on Thy word;
2. Tho' we are guilt-y, Thou art good; Cleanse all our sins in Je-sus' blood;
All that has been a-miss, for-give, And let Thy truth with-in us live.
Give ev-'ry burdened soul re-lease, And bid us all de-part in peace. A-men.
640
PLEYEL'S HYMN. 7. 7. 7. 7.
John Newton, 1725–1807
Ignace Pleyel, 1757–1831
1. Je-sus, hear our hum-ble pray'r; Ten-der Shep-herd of Thy sheep,
2. In Thy strength may we be strong; Sweet-en ev-'ry cross and pain;
Let Thy mer-cy and Thy care All our souls in safe-ty keep.
Give us, if Thou wilt, ere long Here to meet in peace a-gain. A-men.
641
Edna Bruner
Grant us Thy peace as we depart; May Thy love dwell in each heart Through ev'ry coming day. A-men.

RESPONSES FOR CLOSING
642
DUKE RESPONSE (BENEDICTION)
To be sung in unison only
EDWIN McNEILL POTEAT, 1892–
The Lord bless thee and keep thee; the Lord make His face to shine up-
on thee and be gra-cious un-to thee; The Lord lift up His
coun-te-nance up-on thee, and give thee peace. A - - - MEN.
Used by permission of Edwin McNeill Poteat.
EVANS RESPONSE
643
EDWIN McNEILL POTEAT, 1892–
May grace, mer-cy and peace, from God the Fa-ther, the Son and the Spir-it,
be and a-bide with you— Grace, mer-cy and peace— ev - er - more. A-MEN.
peace be up-on you
Used by permission of Edwin McNeill Poteat.
peace— now and ev-er-more.

644

EUCLID RESPONSE

EDWIN MCNEILL POTEAT, 1892–
Now Lord, let-test Thou Thy ser-vant de - part in peace, ac-cord-ing to Thy
word, ac-cord-ing to Thy word. For mine eyes have seen Thy sal-va-tion, which Thou
hast pre-pared be-fore the face of all peo-ple. A light to light-en the Gen-tiles,
and the glo - ry of Thy peo-ple Is - ra - el. Now Lord, let-test Thou Thy
ser - vant de - part in peace, de - part in peace. A - MEN.

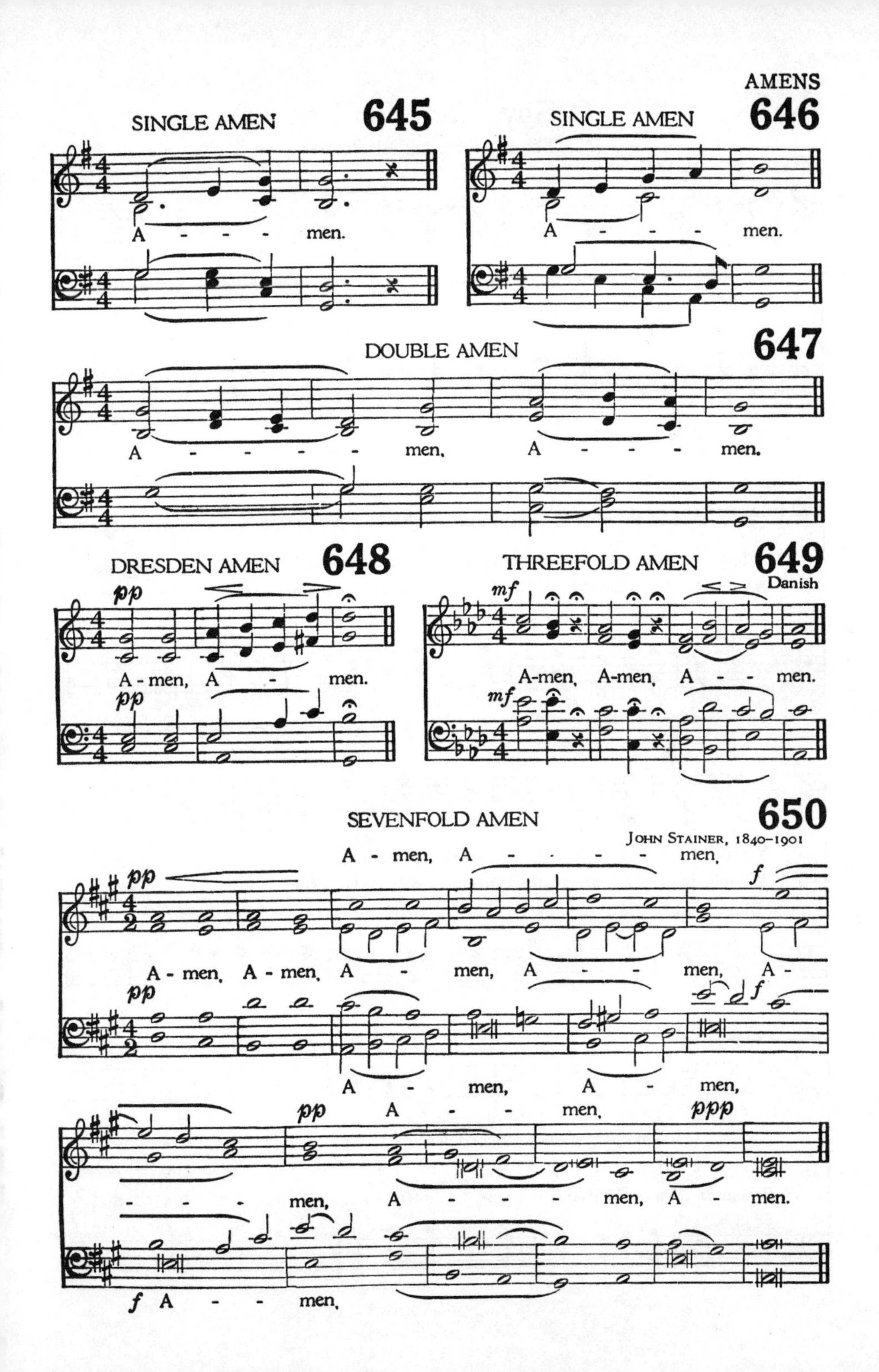

AMENS
SINGLE AMEN
645
A - - - men.
SINGLE AMEN
646
A - - - men.
DOUBLE AMEN
647
A - - - - - men. A - - - - men.
DRESDEN AMEN
648
pp
A-men, A - men.
pp
THREEFOLD AMEN
649
Danish
mf
A-men, A-men, A - - men.
mf
SEVENFOLD AMEN
650
JOHN STAINER, 1840–1901
A - men, A - - - - - men,
pp
f
A-men, A-men, A - men, A - - - men, A -
pp
f
A - men, A - men,
pp A - - - men,
ppp
- - - men, A - - - - - men, A - men.
f A - - men,

651 O Say, Can You See

The Star-Spangled Banner

Francis S. Key, 1814
John S. Smith, 1778
1. O say, can you see, by the dawn's ear - ly light,
2. On the shore dim - ly seen through the mists of the deep,
3. O thus be it ev - er when free - men shall stand
What so proud - ly we hailed at the twi - light's last gleam - ing,
Where the foe's haught-y host in dread si - lence re - pos - es,
Be - tween their loved homes and the war's des - o - la - tion;
Whose broad stripes and bright stars, through the per - il - ous fight,
What is that which the breeze, o'er the tow - er - ing steep
Blest with vic - tory and peace, may the Heaven - res - cued land
O'er the ram - parts we watched were so gal - lant - ly stream - ing?
As it fit - ful - ly blows, half con - ceals, half dis - clos - es?
Praise the Power that hath made and pre - served us a na - tion.

And the rock - ets' red glare, the bombs burst - ing in air,
Now it catch - es the gleam of the morn - ing's first beam,
Then con - quer we must, when our cause it is just,
Gave proof through the night that our flag was still there;
In full glo - ry re - flect - ed now shines on the stream;
And this be our mot - to, "In God is our trust;"
O say, does the Star - span - gled Ban - ner yet wave
'Tis the Star - span - gled Ban - ner— O long may it wave
And the Star - span - gled Ban - ner in tri - umph shall wave
O'er the land of the free and the home of the brave?
O'er the land of the free and the home of the brave.
O'er the land of the free and the home of the brave.

INDEXES

Topical Index

ACTIVITY AND ZEAL

NO.

Awake, my soul, stretch every nerve 369
Awake, awake to love and work 323
Christian, rise and act thy creed 518
Fight the good fight 376
I feel the winds of God today 301
Lead on, O King Eternal 363
Living for Jesus 304
March on, O soul, with strength 359
Marching with the heroes 322
My soul, be on thy guard 370
O Zion, haste 529
Onward, Christian Soldiers 482
Rise up, O men of God 374
Sowing in the morning, sowing seeds 416
Stand up, stand up for Jesus 371
The Son of God goes forth to war 358
Who is on the Lord's side 367

ADORATION

94 to 113, also
As the sun doth daily rise 114
At Thy feet, our God and Father 137
Come, my soul, thou must be waking 134
Come, Thou Almighty King 122
Come, we that love the Lord 119
Day is dying in the west 144
God Himself is with us 123
Immortal, invisible God only wise 159
Lord of all being throned afar 151
Lord, Thy glory fills the heaven 156
Lord, we come before Thee now 116
Mighty God, while angels bless Thee 160
Now thank we all our God 598
O could I speak the matchless worth 265
O God, the Rock of Ages 154
O Jesus, we adore Thee 234
Open now Thy gates of beauty 121
Praise to the living God 124
Saviour, blessed Saviour, listen 269
The heavens declare Thy glory 441
The spacious firmament on high 164
To God our hearts we lift 176
When morning gilds the skies 135

ADVENT

182-205, also
I know not how that Bethlehem Babe 206

ANNIVERSARIES

NO.

God of our life, through all the circling years 583
Joy because the circling year 447
Now praise we great and famous men 603
Now thank we all our God 598
O God, our help in ages past 585

ASCENSION AND REIGN OF CHRIST

(See Jesus Christ, The Everliving Christ)

ASPIRATION

317-323, also
Awake, my soul, stretch every nerve 369
Brightly gleams our banner 485
Come forth, ye men of every race 487
Creation's Lord, we give Thee thanks 492
Forward through the ages 498
God of our youth, to whom we yield 608
I sought His love in sun and stars 385
I sought the Lord, and afterward 403
I thank Thee, Lord, for strength of arm 499
Lord God of hosts, whose purpose 497
Lord of light, whose Name outshineth 504
More love to Thee 390
My Master was a worker 500
Nearer, my God, to Thee 329
O grant us light, that we may know 298
O Jesus, Prince of life and truth 505
O Master, let me walk with Thee 306, 307
Spirit of God, descend upon my heart 272
Take my life, and let it be 296
That cause can neither be lost 493
The light of God is falling 486
The voice of God is calling 490
We would be building 489

ASSURANCE

393-412, also
Children of the heavenly King 267
God of our life, through all the 583
In heavenly love abiding 384
In His love abiding 391
Jesus, still lead on 357
The King of love my shepherd is 169
The Lord is my shepherd 170
There's a wideness in God's mercy 172, 173

ATONEMENT

NO.

Art thou weary, art thou troubled 286
Beneath the cross of Jesus 235
Go to dark Gethsemane 227
I know not how that Bethlehem's Babe 206
In the cross of Christ I glory 237
Jesus, keep me near the cross 339
Just as I am without one plea 295
My faith looks up to Thee 355
My Master was so very poor 216
O come and mourn with me awhile 233
O sacred Head, now wounded 231
Rock of Ages, cleft for me 294
Saviour, Thy dying love 387
There is a green hill far away 230
When I survey the wondrous cross 228

BAPTISM

Beneath the cross of Jesus 235
Here, Saviour, we would come 450
Jesus, I my cross have taken 375
Must Jesus bear the cross alone 366
O God, Thy summons still is heard 449
O Jesus, I have promised 308
O Master, let me walk with Thee 306, 307
Spirit of God, descend upon my heart 272
Take my life, and let it be 296

BENEVOLENCE

All things are Thine; no gift have we 606
Christian, rise and act thy creed 518
I thank Thee, Lord, for strength 499
Master, no offering 303
Son of God, Eternal Saviour 502
Take my life, and let it be 296
Thy bounties, gracious Lord 421
We give Thee but Thine own 422
When thy heart with joy o'erflowing 508

BIBLE, THE

434-442, also
Break Thou the Bread of Life 461
How firm a foundation 406
I love to tell the story 532
We've a story to tell to the nations 530

TOPICAL INDEX

BROTHERHOOD

NO.

506-522, also
Blest be the dear, uniting love ---- 483
Blest be the tie that binds 476
Forgive, O Lord, our severing ways ---- 484
How sweet, how heavenly is the sight ---- 475
I bind my heart this tide-- 302
In Christ there is no East or West ---- 480
Not alone for mighty empire ---- 597
O Lord of Life, Thy Kingdom ---- 491
O Thou great Friend---- 347
O Thou not made with hands ---- 478
Rise, crowned with light, imperial Salem ---- 477
Rise up, O men of God--- 374
Son of God, Eternal Saviour ---- 502
Thou God of all, whose Spirit moves ---- 554
Walk in the light! so shalt thou know ---- 479
Where winds the road o'er hill and dale ---- 420

CALMNESS

Dear Lord and Father of mankind ---- 411
Father, in Thy mysterious presence ---- 345
From every stormy wind that blows ---- 394
God of the earth, the sky, the sea ---- 120
Immortal Love, forever full 254
Now, on land and sea descending ---- 141
O for a closer walk with God ---- 310
Take time to be holy ---- 346

CAROLS
(See Advent)

CHARITY
(See Love)

CHILDREN IN CHURCH
(See index—Hymns for use with Children)

CHRIST
(See Jesus Christ)

CHRISTIAN HOME
(See Home)

CHRISTIAN LIFE

The Call of Christ
277-287
Acceptance of Christ
288-299

Consecration and Service
300-316, also
In life's earnest morning-- 474
Jesus, keep me near the cross ---- 339

NO.

Must Jesus bear the cross alone ---- 366
My life, my love I give to Thee ---- 293
Take my life, and let it be 296
Aspiration and Vision
317-323, also
Brightly gleams our banner 485
O grant us light, that we may know ---- 298
O Jesus, Youth of Nazareth ---- 217

CHRISTIAN UNITY

475-484, also
City of God, how broad and far ---- 426
Glorious things of thee are spoken ---- 431
I love Thy Kingdom, Lord ---- 428, 429
Lord of our life, and God of our salvation ---- 430
May the grace of Christ--- 126
O Church of God, divided 433
O Church of God, our solitude ---- 432
One holy Church of God appears ---- 424
Son of God, Eternal Saviour ---- 502
The Church's one foundation ---- 423

CHRISTMAS
(See Advent)

CHURCH, THE

423-433, also
God of grace and God of glory ---- 378
O Spirit of the living God 273
Onward, Christian soldiers 482
Rise up, O men of God --- 374
The day Thou gavest, Lord, is ended ---- 140

CITY

Hail the glorious Golden City ---- 488
The fathers built this city- 503
The voice of God is calling 490
Where cross the crowded ways ---- 519

COMMUNION
(See Lord's Supper, The)

CONFESSION
(See Christian Life—Acceptance of Christ)

CONFIDENCE
(See Trust and Confidence)

CONFLICT

358-378, also
Jesus, Saviour, pilot me -- 409
Lord, as to Thy dear cross 326
Once to every man and nation ---- 558

CONSECRATION
(See Christian Life—Consecration and Service)

CONSOLATION

NO.

Come, ye disconsolate ---- 398
Give to the winds thy fears 402
I know not what the future hath ---- 571
It singeth low in every heart ---- 579
My Jesus, as Thou wilt -- 408
Sometimes a light surprises 581
There is no sorrow, Lord- 342
We would see Jesus, for the shadows ---- 400
What a Friend we have in Jesus ---- 331

CONTENTMENT

I sought the Lord, and afterward ---- 403
If thou but suffer God to guide ---- 404
In heavenly love abiding--- 384
In His love abiding ---- 391
My times are in Thy hand 395
O holy Saviour, Friend unseen ---- 350
Sometimes a light surprises 581
The King of Love my shepherd is ---- 169
The Lord is my shepherd-- 170

CONVERSION
(See Christian Life—Acceptance of Christ; Consecration)

COURAGE
(See Conflict)

A mighty fortress is our God ---- 155
How firm a foundation---- 406
When courage fails and faith burns ---- 356

CROSS, THE

Above the hills of time the cross ---- 236
Beneath the cross of Jesus 235
In the cross of Christ I glory ---- 237
Jesus, I my cross have taken ---- 375
Jesus, keep me near the cross ---- 339
Lord, as to Thy dear cross 326
Must Jesus bear the cross alone ---- 366
O come and mourn with me awhile ---- 233
O Jesus, we adore Thee -- 234
O Love that wilt not let me go ---- 388
O sacred Head, now wounded ---- 231
Saviour, Thy dying love--- 387
"Take up thy cross," the Saviour said ---- 285
There is a green hill far away ---- 230
When I survey the wondrous cross ---- 228

DEATH
(See Eternal Life)

TOPICAL INDEX

DECISION

NO.

(See Christian Life—Acceptance of Christ)

I am Thine, O Lord ---- 312
I bind my heart this tide 302
I feel the winds of God -- 301
In life's earnest morning-- 474
Jesus, I my cross have taken ---- 375
My life, my love I give to Thee ---- 293
Take my life, and let it be 296
Thy life was given for me 289

DEDICATION

Of Churches
All things are Thine ---- 606
O Thou whose own vast temple ---- 605
Rise, crowned with light -- 477
The Church's one foundation ---- 423

Of Homes
Bless the four corners of this house ---- 599
Thou gracious God whose mercy ---- 602

Of Resources
As with gladness men of old ---- 196
Lord, speak to me, that I may speak ---- 470
Saviour, Thy dying love--- 387
Son of God, Eternal Saviour ---- 502
Take my life, and let it be 296
We give Thee but Thine own ---- 422
When thy heart with joy o'erflowing ---- 508

Of Self
(See Christian Life—Consecration)

DISCIPLESHIP

(See Christian Life

Come, my soul, thou must be waking ---- 134
Faith of our fathers ---- 348
God of grace and God of glory ---- 378
He who would valiant be-- 364
Lord, speak to me, that I may speak ---- 470
March on, O soul ---- 359
O young and fearless prophet ---- 362

EASTER

(See Jesus Christ—Resurrection)

EDUCATION

(See School and College)

ETERNAL LIFE

568-582, also
Abide with me ---- 138
Jesus, still lead on ---- 357
Through the night of doubt and sorrow ---- 481

EVENING HYMNS

NO.

138-150

FAITH

347-357, also
He leadeth me: O blessed thought ---- 405
I know not how that Bethlehem's babe ---- 206

FAMILY, THE

For the beauty of the earth 167
O Father, Thou who givest all ---- 600
O God, whose love is over all ---- 175
O happy home, where Thou art loved ---- 601
The fathers built this city 503
Thou gracious God whose mercy lends ---- 602

FELLOWSHIP

(See Brotherhood)

Dear Lord and Father of mankind ---- 411
For the beauty of the earth ---- 167
I love Thy Kingdom, Lord ---- 428, 429
I thank Thee, Lord, for strength ---- 499
Lord God of Hosts, whose purpose ---- 497
O gracious Father of mankind ---- 338
We thank Thee, Lord, thy paths ---- 495

FORGIVENESS

Dear Lord and Father of mankind ---- 411
I heard the voice of Jesus say ---- 288
O gracious Father of mankind ---- 338
Saviour, blessed Saviour, listen ---- 269
Softly and tenderly Jesus is calling ---- 283

FRIENDSHIP

(See World Friendship)

FUTURE LIFE

(See Eternal Life)

GETHSEMANE

Go to dark Gethsemane -- 227
Into the woods my Master went ---- 225
Night with ebon pinion -- 226
'Tis midnight; and on Olive's brow ---- 232
Where the olive grove stood 229

GOD

Care
165-171, also
O worship the King ---- 94

Communion with
God speaks to us in bird and song ---- 180
Praise to the Living God-- 124
Still, still with Thee---- 136
Take time to be holy---- 346

Creator

NO.

160-164, also
Come, sound His praise--- 118
From all that dwell ---- 104
God, that madest earth and heaven ---- 143
Lord of all being, throned afar ---- 151
My God, I thank Thee, who hast made ---- 109
The heavens declare Thy glory ---- 441
This is my Father's world 171

Eternity of
Ancient of days ---- 99
Immortal, invisible, God only wise ---- 159
Lord, Thy glory fills the heaven ---- 156
Now thank we all our God 598
O God, the Rock of Ages— 154
Praise to the Living God-- 124
Praise the Lord, His glories show ---- 112
Praise the Lord, ye heavens 110
Praise to the Lord, the Almighty ---- 98
To Thee, my heart, Eternal King ---- 108

Faithfulness of
A mighty Fortress is our God ---- 155
Ancient of days ---- 99
Great is Thy faithfulness 165
O God, our help in ages past ---- 585
Praise, my soul, the King-- 259

Fatherhood of
Dear Lord and Father of mankind ---- 411
Eternal Father, strong to save ---- 610
Father Almighty, bless us-- 344
Father, in Thy mysterious presence ---- 345
Father of love and power-- 146
Father of mercies, in Thy Word ---- 440
Father, we praise Thee, now the night ---- 102
Hear us, our Father---- 336
How strong and sweet my Father's care ---- 168
Lead us, O Father, in the paths ---- 566
O Father, Thou who givest all ---- 600
O gracious Father of mankind ---- 338
Our Father, Thy dear Name doth show ---- 522
This is my Father's world- 171

Goodness of
As the sun doth daily rise 114
At Thy feet, our God and Father ---- 137
Ancient of Days ---- 99
God is love ---- 178
Great is Thy faithfulness-- 165
How strong and sweet my Father's care ---- 168
Joyful, joyful we adore Thee ---- 95
Now thank we all our God 598

TOPICAL INDEX

NO.

O God of Bethel 174
O God, whose love is over all 175
The King of love my shepherd is 169
The Lord is my shepherd.. 170
There's a wideness in God's mercy 172, 173

Justice of

Give to the winds thy fears 402
God moves in a mysterious way 162
God of our fathers, the strength 158
If thou but suffer God to guide thee 404
O God, in whom we live.. 179
O worship the King 94
There's a wideness in God's mercy 172, 173

Light of

Again, as evening's shadow falls 139
Be Thou my vision 321
Immortal, invisible God only wise 159
Light of Light, enlighten me 445
Light of the world, how long 320
Lord of all being 151
O God, Thy world is sweet 133
O Lord of life, Thy quickening voice 132
O Thou great Friend........ 347
Sun of my soul 150
Through the night of dark and sorrow 481

Love and Mercy of

172-181, also
Father, loving Father 325
God of our fathers, the strength 158
In His love, abiding 391
Love divine, all love excelling 379
O Love that will not let me go 388
Praise the Lord, His glories show 112
The King of love my shepherd is 169
The Lord is my shepherd.. 170
While Thee I seek........ 334

Majesty and Power

151-159, also
All my hope on God is founded 354
Come, Thou Almighty King 122
Glory be to God on high.. 100
God moves in a mysterious way 162
God of grace and God of glory 378
O worship the King 94
Praise to the Lord, the Almighty 98
With happy voices ringing 113

Presence of

Abide with me 138
Father, in Thy mysterious presence 345
God Himself is with us .. 123
Hear us, our Father 336

NO.

Jesus, where'er Thy people meet 115
Lead, kindly Light 578
O God, whose love is over all 175
Sometimes a light surprises 581
The Lord be with us 125
This is my Father's world. 171

Refuge

A mighty fortress is our God 155
Dear Father, loud the ocean rolls 330
How firm a foundation ... 406
In heavenly love abiding.. 384
In His love abiding 391
Mighty Rock, whose towering form 407
O God, our help in ages past 585
O God, the Rock of Ages.. 154
O Love Divine, that stooped 353

Will of

Go, labor on; spend and be spent 473
The Spirit of the Lord revealed 437

Wisdom

All my hope on God is founded 354
As the sun doth daily rise.. 114
Awake, my tongue, thy tribute bring 152
God is love 178
Immortal, invisible God only wise 159
O Word of God Incarnate 434

GOSPEL

(See Christian Life)

All the way my Saviour leads me 396
Christ for the world we sing 538
Fling out the banner 540
Heralds of Christ, who bear 533
I love to tell the story.... 532
I sought the Lord 403
I think when I read that sweet story 213
Jesus, I my cross have taken 375
Let the song go round the earth 531
No longer of Him be it said 305
O Christ, the Way, the Truth 410
O Zion, haste 529
Our faith is in the Christ.. 351
Saviour, more than life to me 397
Sing them over again to me 442
Sowing in the morning.... 416
Tell me the old, old story . 438
Tell me the stories of Jesus 214
The morning light is breaking 524
"Thy kingdom come," on bended knee 539
We have heard a joyful sound 537
We've a story to tell 530
When the Lord of love was here 215

GRACE

NO.

Begin, my tongue, some heavenly theme 153
Blest be the dear, uniting love 483
Come, Thou Fount of every blessing 111
"Come unto me, ye weary" 277
Glorious things of Thee are spoken 431
God of grace and God of glory 378
I hear the Saviour say.... 284
Jesus, Lover of my soul... .... 414, 415
The Son of God goes forth to war 358
There's a wideness in God's mercy 172, 173
Thou whose Almighty Word 536

GRATITUDE

(See Special Days—Thanksgiving)

GRIEF

(See Consolation)

GUIDANCE

All the way my Saviour leads me 396
Be Thou my vision 321
Father of love and power.. 146
Guide me, O Thou great Jehovah 393
He leadeth me: O blessed thought 405
Holy Spirit, faithful Guide 276
If thou but suffer God to guide 404
Jesus, Saviour, pilot me ... 409
Jesus, still lead on 357
Lead, kindly Light 578
Lead on, O King Eternal . 363
Lead us, O Father, in the paths 566
Lord, for tomorrow and its needs 327
March on, O soul 359
My times are in Thy hand 395
O Christ, the Way, the Truth 410
O God, whose love is over all 175
Saviour, like a shepherd lead us 401
The King of love my shepherd is 169

HEAVEN

Father, we praise Thee.... 102
Hark! hark! my soul 582
Jerusalem the golden... 569, 570
O Mother dear, Jerusalem . 572
Praise, my soul, the King of 259
Ten thousand times ten thousand 568

HOLINESS

Gracious Spirit, dwell with me 270
Spirit of God, descend upon my heart 272
Take time to be holy 346
Worship the Lord in the beauty 106

TOPICAL INDEX

HOLY SCRIPTURES

NO.

(See Bible, The)

HOLY SPIRIT

270-276, also
Praise to the Living God — 124
The Spirit of the Lord revealed — 437

HOME

599-602, also
In homes where pride and splendor — 501
In life's earnest morning — 474
O God, whose love is over all — 175
The fathers built this city — 503

HOPE

All my hope on God is founded — 354
In heavenly love abiding — 384
In His love abiding — 391
O God, in whom we live — 179
O God, our help in ages past — 585
O Master, let me walk with Thee — 306, 307
While Thee I seek, protecting power — 334

HUMILITY

According to Thy gracious word — 456
God of our fathers, known of old — 560, 561
Have Thine own way, Lord — 324
I would be true — 361
Lord, we come before Thee now — 116
O Master, let me walk with Thee — 306, 307
The Spirit of the Lord revealed — 437

IMMORTALITY

(See Eternal Life)

INNER LIFE

Be Thou my vision — 321
Dear Lord and Father of mankind — 411
Dear Master, in whose life I see — 318
Gracious Spirit, dwell with me — 270
I need Thee every hour — 341
I sought the Lord — 403
Jesus, I live to Thee — 314
Jesus, Lover of my soul — 414, 415
Jesus, the very thought of Thee — 392
Jesus, these eyes have never seen — 352
Jesus, Thou joy of loving hearts — 419
No longer of Him be it said — 305
O for a closer walk with God — 310
Spirit of God, descend upon my heart — 272
Still, still with Thee — 136
We would see Jesus, for the shadows — 400

INTERCESSION

NO.

(See Prayer)

INTERNATIONAL GOOD WILL

(See Peace—World Peace; also, Brotherhood)

INVITATION

(See Christian Life—The Call of Christ)

JESUS CHRIST

Birth and Infancy

(See Advent)

The Cross

(See Cross, The)

Decision for

(See Christian Life—Acceptance of Christ)

The Everliving Christ

249-258

Life and Ministry

207-220

Our Light

Brightest and best of the sons — 202
Brightly beams our Father's mercy — 313
Fairest Lord Jesus — 261
God of the strong, God of the weak — 311
Jesus, Thou joy of loving hearts — 419
Lamp of our feet — 436
Lead, kindly light — 578
Light of light, enlighten me — 445
Light of the world, how long — 320
Light of the world, we hail Thee — 208
Lord of light, whose Name — 504
No longer of Him be it said — 305
O Christ the Way, the Truth — 410
O grant us light — 298
O Love that wilt not let me go — 388
O Thou great Friend — 347
Sometimes a light surprises — 581
Through the night of doubt — 481
Walk in the light — 479

Our Saviour

All the way my Saviour leads me — 396
Jesus Saviour, pilot me — 409
Majestic sweetness sits enthroned — 381
Saviour, like a shepherd — 401
Saviour, more than life to me — 397
Son of God, Eternal Saviour — 502
Sun of my soul — 150
"Take up thy cross" — 285
Thou, Lord of Life, our saving — 309
Thy life was given for me — 289

Resurrection

238-248

Suffering and Death

NO.

(See Cross, The)

All glory, laud and honor — 221
From Bethany, the Master — 222
Go to dark Gethsemane — 227
Into the woods my Master went — 225
Night, with ebon pinion — 226
Ride on! ride on in majesty — 223
'Tis midnight; and on Olive's brow — 232
Where the olive grove stood darkly — 229

JOY

All my heart this night rejoices — 186
Come, my soul, thou must be waking — 134
Come, ye faithful, raise the strain — 242
Fairest Lord Jesus — 261
Joy because the circling year — 447
Joy to the world! the Lord is come — 190
Joyful, joyful we adore Thee — 95
Let us with a gladsome mind — 181
Light of Light, enlighten me — 445
My God, I thank Thee who hast made — 109
On our way rejoicing — 417
Rejoice, the Lord is King — 260
Rejoice, ye pure in heart — 418
The day of resurrection — 247
This is the day of light — 446
We have heard a joyful sound — 537
When morning gilds the skies — 135
When thy heart with joy o'erflowing — 508
With happy voices ringing — 113

KINGDOM OF GOD

A mighty fortress is our God — 155
An endless line of splendor — 534
Come forth, ye men of every race — 487
Creation's Lord, we give Thee thanks — 492
Forward through the ages — 498
God of grace and God of glory — 378
God the All-merciful — 565
Heralds of Christ, who bear — 533
I love Thy Kingdom, Lord — 428, 429
Jesus shall reign where'er the sun — 527
Lead on, O King Eternal — 363
Lord God of Hosts, whose purpose — 497
Lord of light, whose Name — 504
No longer of Him be it said — 305
O blessed Son of God — 520
O hear them marching, marching — 564
O Lord of life, Thy Kingdom — 491
O Zion, haste — 529
Of one blood hath God created — 510

NO.
Remember all the people 528
Rise up, O men of God 374
The day Thou gavest, Lord 140
The light of God is falling 486
Thou God of all, whose Spirit 554
Thy Kingdom come, O Lord 562
"Thy Kingdom come," on bended knee 539
We would be building 489
We've a story to tell 530
Where cross the crowded ways 519
Whom oceans part, O Lord, unite 525

LIFE

Break Thou the Bread of Life 461
"Come unto me, ye weary" 277
Come, ye disconsolate 398
Dear Master, in whose life 318
Go forth to life O child 319
Jesus Saviour, pilot me 409
Just as I am, Thine own to be 297
Life is good, for God contrives it 248
Life of ages, richly poured 177
Lord of our life 430
My life, my love I give 293
My times are in Thy hand 395
O Christ, the Way, the Truth 410
O Jesus, Youth of Nazareth 217
O Lord of life, Thy kingdom 491
O Lord of life, Thy quickening voice 132
O Lord of life, where'er they be 575
Saviour, more than life to me 397
Take my life, and let it be 296
Thou, Lord of life, our saving health 309
Thy life was given for me 289
Unbar the door 287

LORD'S DAY

443-448

(See Worship)

LORD'S SUPPER, THE

A holy air is breathing round 467
A parting hymn we sing 469
According to Thy gracious word 456
Beneath the forms of outward rite 459
Blest feast of love divine 457
Bread of the world 453
Break Thou the Bread of Life 461
For the bread, which Thou hast broken 463
From the table now retiring 468
Here at Thy table, Lord 451
Here at Thy table, Lord, we meet 455
Here, O my Lord, I see Thee 458
In memory of the Saviour's love 462
Lord, at Thy table we behold 464

NO.
Lord of our highest love 466
O Christ, Thou gift of love 454
O God, unseen, yet ever near 452
Shepherd of souls, refresh and bless 465
While in sweet communion 460

LOVE

Awake, awake to love and work 323
Blest be the dear, uniting love 483
Blest be the tie that binds 476
Blest feast of love divine 457
Come we that love the Lord 119
Dear Father, loud the ocean rolls 330
Father, loving Father 325
Father of love and power 146
God is love 178
I love Thy kingdom, Lord 428, 429
I sought His love in sun and stars 385
Immortal Love, forever full 254
In heavenly love abiding 384
In His love abiding 391
In memory of the Saviour's love 462
I've found a Friend 290
Jesus, my Lord, my Life, my All 383
Jesus, the very thought of Thee 392
Jesus, Thy boundless love to me 380
Life of ages, richly poured 177
Love divine, all love excelling 379
Love is kind and suffers long 386
Majestic sweetness sits enthroned 381
More love to Thee, O Christ 390
My Jesus, I love Thee 382
My life, my love I give to Thee 293
O God of love, O King of peace 557
O God, whose love is over all 175
O Love divine, that stooped 353
O Love that wilt not let me go 388
Saviour, teach me day by day 389
Saviour, Thy dying love 387
Strong Son of God, immortal love 349
When the Lord of love was here 215

LOYALTY

"Are ye able?" said the Master 360
Faith of our fathers 348
Forward through the ages 498
God send us men, whose aim 377
He who would valiant be 364
I would be true 361
I've found a Friend 290
Lead on, O King Eternal 363
Lord God of Hosts, whose purpose 497

NO.
March on, O Soul, with strength 359
Marching with the heroes 322
My Master was a worker 500
O Jesus, I have promised 308
O Jesus, Master, when today 517
Once to every man and nation 558
Stand up, stand up for Jesus 371
The Son of God goes forth to war 358
This is my Father's world 171
Who is on the Lord's side 367

MINISTRY

470-474, also
God send us men, whose aim 377
I love to tell the story 532
Life of ages, richly poured 177
O master, let me walk with Thee 306, 307
Take my life, and let it be 296
We've a story to tell 530

MISSIONS

523-541, also
Come forth, ye men of every race 487
Forward through the ages 498
Hail the glorious Golden City 488
In Christ there is no East or West 480
Lord God of Hosts, whose purpose 497
Lord of Light, whose name 504
O Jesus, Prince of life and truth 505
The voice of God is calling 490
Thy kingdom come, O Lord 562
Where cross the crowded ways 519

NATIONAL
(See Patriotism)

NATIVITY (See Advent)

NATURE

All beautiful the march of days 588
All creatures of our God 157
Awake, my tongue 152
Day is dying in the west 144
Fairest Lord Jesus 261
For the beauty of the earth 167
God of the earth, the sky, the sea 120
God speaks to us in bird and song 180
God who touchest earth with beauty 315
Immortal, invisible God only wise 159
Joyful, joyful we adore Thee 95
Let the whole creation cry 103
Lord of all being, throned afar 151
Men and children everywhere 96
My God, I thank Thee who hast made 109
O God, whose love is over all 175
O God, whose smile is in the sky 163

TOPICAL INDEX

NO.

O worship the king 94
The heavens declare Thy glory 441
The spacious firmament on high 164
This is my Father's world 171
To Thee, my heart, eternal King 108
We plow the fields and scatter 594

NEW YEAR

583-590, also
All hail the pageant of the years 516

OBEDIENCE

Christian, rise and act thy creed 518
Come, my soul, thou must be waking 134
How gentle God's commands 399
I heard the voice of Jesus say 288
I would be true 361
Jesus calls us, o'er the tumult 281
Not in dumb resignation 368
Saviour, teach me day by day 389
The voice of God is calling 490
Walk in the light 479
Who is on the Lord's side 367
Worship the Lord in the beauty 106

PATIENCE

Creation's Lord, we give Thee thanks 492
Give to the winds thy fears 402
Go, labor on; spend and be spent 473
O come and mourn with me awhile 233
O Master, let me walk with Thee 306, 307
Spirit of God, descend upon my heart 272

PATRIOTISM

Patriotism

542-551, also
God of our fathers, known of old 560, 561
Lead on, O King Eternal 363
Not alone for mighty empire 597
O God of truth, whose living word 365
O God, our help in ages past 585
O say, can you see 651

PEACE

Inner Peace

Dear Father, loud the ocean rolls 330
Dear Lord and Father of mankind 411
Father of love and power 146
I do not ask, O Lord, that life 340
Jesus, kneel beside me 328
Lord, as to Thy dear cross 326
Lord, at this closing hour 131

NO.

Lord of our life, and God of our salvation 430
Saviour, again to Thy dear Name 128
Send down Thy truth 271
The Lord be with us 125
The shadows of the evening 142
What a Friend we have in Jesus 331

World Peace

All hail the pageant of the years 516
Come, Peace of God 555
God of our fathers, the strength 158
God of the nations, near and far 556
God, the All-merciful 565
It came upon the midnight clear 191
Lead us, O Father, in the paths 566
Let there be light, Lord God 513
O Church of God, divided 433
O God of love; O King of peace 557
O hear them marching, marching 564
Of one blood hath God created 510
Son of God, Eternal Saviour 502
The Prince of Peace His banner 553
The Son of God goes forth for peace 559
Thy kingdom come, O Lord 562
To all the nations, Lord 552

PENITENCE

Come to the Saviour now 278
Dear God, our Father, at Thy knee 291
Draw Thou my soul, O Christ 299
Father, in Thy mysterious presence 345
In the hour of trial 333
Just as I am without one plea 295
"Lift up your hearts" 372
Lord, as to Thy dear cross 326
My life, my love I give to Thee 293
Rock of Ages, cleft for me 294

PENTECOST

Holy Spirit, Truth divine 274
Joy because the circling year 447
O Spirit of the Living God 273
Spirit of God, descend upon my heart 272

PERSEVERANCE

A charge to keep I have 373
Awake, my soul, stretch every nerve 369
Faith of our fathers 348
Fight the good fight 376
He who would valiant be 364
Master, no offering 303
My soul, be on thy guard 370
O Jesus, I have promised 308
Onward, Christian Soldiers 482

PRAISE

NO.

(See Adoration)

PRAYER

324-346, also
Again, as evening's shadow 139
Dear Lord and Father of mankind 411
Dear Master, in whose life I see 318
Draw Thou my soul, O Christ 299
Eternal Father, strong to save 610
Jesus, still lead on 357
Jesus, where'er thy people meet 115
"Lift up your hearts" 372
O God, Thy world is sweet with prayer 133
Softly now the light of day 145

PROCESSIONAL HYMNS

All glory, laud, and honor 221
Ancient of Days 99
At Thy feet, our God and Father 137
Brightly gleams our banner 485
Come, ye faithful, raise the 242
Come, ye thankful people, come 593
Crown Him with many crowns 250
For the beauty of the earth 167
Forward through the ages 498
Glorious things of Thee are spoken 431
God of grace and God of glory 378
God of our fathers, whose almighty hand 551
Holy, holy, holy is the Lord 97
Holy, holy, holy, Lord God 107
How firm a foundation 406
Jerusalem the golden 569, 570
Lead on, O King Eternal 363
O come, all ye faithful 205
O hear them marching, marching 564
O Zion, haste 529
On our way rejoicing 417
Onward, Christian soldiers 482
Praise the Lord, His glories show 112
Saviour, blessed Saviour, listen 269
Stand up, stand up for Jesus 371
Standing at the portal 584
Ten thousand times ten thousand 568
The Church's one foundation 423
The day of resurrection 247
The Prince of Peace His banner 553
The Son of God goes forth for peace 559
The Son of God goes forth to war 358
Through the night of doubt 481
"Welcome, happy morning" 246
When morning gilds the skies 135
With happy voices ringing 113

TOPICAL INDEX

PROVIDENCE

NO.

Give to the winds thy fears 402
God moves in a mysterious way 162
How gentle God's commands 399
If thou but suffer God to guide 404
Mighty God, while angels bless Thee 160
There's a wideness in God's mercy 172, 173

PSALMS

O God, our help in ages past 585
Praise, my soul, the King of heaven 259
Praise the Lord, His glories show 112
The King of love my shepherd is 169
The Lord is my shepherd 170
Unto the hills do I lift up 166

RECESSIONAL HYMNS

All glory, laud, and honor 221
Forward through the ages 498
From ocean unto ocean 541
God of grace and God of glory 378
Hark, hark my soul 582
Heralds of Christ, who bear 533
Jerusalem the golden 569, 570
Lead, on, O King Eternal 363
Lord of light, whose Name 504
March on, O soul, with strength 359
Marching with the heroes 322
My Master was a worker 500
O Zion, haste 529
On our way rejoicing 417
Stand up, stand up for Jesus 371
Ten thousand times ten thousand 568
The Church's one foundation 423
The Prince of Peace His banner 553
The Son of God goes forth for peace 559
Through the night of doubt 481
We are living, we are dwelling 494

REDEMPTION

(See Salvation)

REPENTANCE

(See Penitence)

REST

Again, as evening's shadow 139
Art thou weary, art thou troubled 286
Come to Jesus, ye who labor 282
Come unto me, ye weary 277
Day is dying in the west 144
Dear Lord and Father of mankind 411
God, that madest earth and heaven 143
I heard the voice of Jesus say 288

NO.

Lead us, O Father, in the paths 566
Love divine, all love excelling 379
O day of rest and gladness 443
O God whose smile is in the sky 163
Safely through another week 448
This is the day of light 446

RESURRECTION OF CHRIST

(See Jesus Christ—Resurrection)

SALVATION

Hail to the Lord's Anointed 257
I love to tell the story 532
Light of the world, we hail Thee 208
Lord of our life, and God of our salvation 430
Love divine, all love excelling 379
Mighty God, while angels bless Thee 160
O Love that wilt not let me go 388
Rock of Ages, cleft for me 294
The voice of God is calling 490
There is a green hill far away 230
Unto the hills do I lift up 166
"Welcome, happy morning" 246

SCHOOL AND COLLEGE

Come, my soul, thou must be waking 134
Go forth to life, O child 319
God of our youth 608
In life's earnest morning 474
O God, in whose great purpose 607
O Son of Man, our Hero 220
O young and fearless Prophet 362
The wise may bring their learning 316

SCRIPTURES

(See Bible, The)

SERVICE

(See Social Service)

SIN

Brightly beams our Father's mercy 313
Come to Jesus, ye who labor 282
Dear God, our Father, at Thy knee 291
Father of love and power 146
I hear the Saviour say 284
Jesus is tenderly calling thee 280
O God, whose smile is in the sky 163
Purer in heart, O God 343
Rock of Ages, cleft for me 294
Softly and tenderly Jesus is calling 283
There is no sorrow, Lord 342
Unbar the door 287
What a Friend we have in Jesus 331

SOCIAL SERVICE

NO.

486-507, also
Christian, rise and act thy creed 518
Master, no offering 303
O blessed Son of God 520
O Jesus, Master, when today 517
O Master Workman of the race 210
O young and fearless Prophet 362
Where cross the crowded ways 519

SORROW

(See Consolation)

SOWING AND REAPING

Come, ye thankful people, come 593
God of the strong 311
Praise to God, immortal praise 595
Sowing in the morning 416
We plow the fields, and scatter 594

SPECIAL DAYS

Advent

(See Advent)

Children's Day

Fairest Lord Jesus 261
Father, loving Father 325
I think when I read 213
Marching with the heroes 322
Tell me the stories of Jesus 214
The wise may bring their learning 316
With happy voices ringing 113

Christmas

(See Advent)

Easter

(See Jesus Christ—Resurrection)

Good Friday

Above the hills of time 236
Beneath the cross of Jesus 235
In the cross of Christ I glory 237
O come and mourn with me awhile 233
O Jesus, we adore Thee 234
O sacred Head, now wounded 231
There is a green hill far away 230
When I survey the wondrous cross 228

Independence Day

(See Patriotism)

Labor Day

I thank Thee, Lord, for strength 499
My Master was a worker 500
O Master Workman of the race 210
They who tread the path of labour 496

INDEX OF AUTHORS AND SOURCES OF HYMNS

NO.

Memorial Day
Faith of our fathers 348
For all the saints 576, 577
Life of ages, richly poured 177
March on, O soul, with strength 359
Now praise we great and famous men 603
O God, our help in ages past 585

Mother's Day
Motherhood, sublime, eternal 604
O Father, Thou who givest all 600

New Year
(See New Year)

Palm Sunday
All glory, laud, and honor 221
From Bethany, the Master 222
Lift up your heads, ye mighty 224
Ride on! ride on in majesty 223

Pentecost
(See Pentecost; also, Christian Unity)

Thanksgiving
593-598, also
My God, I thank Thee who hast made 109
O God, beneath Thy guiding hand 543
We gather together to seek 117

SPIRIT
(See Holy Spirit)

STEWARDSHIP
Awake, awake to love and work 323
Master, no offering 303
Son of God, Eternal Saviour 502
Take my life and let it be 296
Thy bounties, gracious Lord 421
We give Thee but Thine own 422

SURRENDER
(See Decision)

TEMPTATION
Dear Father, loud the ocean rolls 330
Fight the good fight 376
I need Thee every hour 341
In the hour of trial 333
Jesus, Saviour, pilot me 409
Jesus, still lead on 357
My soul be on thy guard 370
O Jesus, I have promised 308
What a Friend we have in Jesus 331

THANKSGIVING
(See Special Days—Thanksgiving)

TRAVEL
Eternal Father, strong to save 610
Father, who art alone 609

TRIALS
All the way my Saviour leads me 396
How firm a foundation 406
If thou but suffer God to guide 404
In the hour of trial 333
Jesus, Saviour, pilot me 409
'Tis the blessed hour of prayer 332
What a Friend we have in Jesus 331

TRUST AND CONFIDENCE
393-411, also
A mighty fortress is our God 155
Blessed assurance, Jesus is mine 412
God moves in a mysterious way 162
God of our life, through all 583
I know not what the future hath 571
In heavenly love abiding 384
In His love abiding 391
Jesus, Lover of my soul 414, 415
My faith looks up to Thee 355
Nearer, my God, to Thee 329
O Master, let me walk with Thee 306, 307
O worship the King 94
Our faith is in the Christ 351
While Thee I seek, protecting 334

TRUTH
A mighty fortress is our God 155
Break Thou the Bread of Life 461
Father of mercies 440
From all that dwell 104
Gracious Spirit, dwell with me 270
Holy Spirit, Truth divine 274
Lead us, O Father, in the paths 566
Lord of our life, and God 430
O Christ, the Way, the Truth 410
O Church of God, divided 433
O God of truth 365
O grant us light 298
O Jesus, Youth of Nazareth 217
O Spirit of the living God 273
O Thou great Friend to all 347
O Word of God Incarnate 434
Send down Thy Truth, O God 271
The heavens declare Thy glory 441
There is a Book that all 435
When courage fails, and faith 356
Worship the Lord in the beauty 106

VESPERS
(See Evening Hymns)

WATCHFULNESS
A charge to keep I have 373
Go, labor on; spend and be spent 473
I would be true 361
My soul, be on thy guard 370

WORD OF GOD
(See Bible, The)

WORLD FRIENDSHIP
At length there dawns the glorious day 511
Come forth, ye men of every race 487
Creation's Lord, we give Thee thanks 492
Eternal God, whose power 535
Eternal Ruler of the ceaseless round 506
In Christ there is no East or West 480
Let there be light 513
Lord of Light, whose Name 504
My country is the world 514
Of one blood hath God created 510
Our Father, Thy dear Name 522
These things shall be 507
Thou God of all, whose Spirit 554
Thy kingdom come, O Lord 562
To all the nations, Lord 552
Turn back, O man 567

WORSHIP
(See Adoration)

Closing
125-131

Evening
138-150

Morning
132-137, also
Holy, holy, holy, Lord God 107

Opening
114-124

The Lord's Day
(See Lord's Day)

YOUTH
"Are ye able," said the Master 360
Go forth to life, O child 319
God of our youth, to whom 608
I would be true 361
Just as I am, Thine own to be 297
Now in the days of youth 300
O Jesus, Prince of life and truth 505
O Jesus, Youth of Nazareth 217
O Son of Man, our Hero 220
Shepherd of eager youth 266
We would be building 489
When courage fails 356
Whom oceans part, O Lord 525

Index of Authors and Sources of Hymns

HYMN

Aaberg, J. A. ---------- 493
Adams, Jessie (1863-) ---------- 301
Adams, Sarah Flower (1805-1848) ---------- 329
Addison, Joseph (1672-1719) ---------- 164
Adler, Felix (1851-1936) ---------- 488
Alexander, Cecil Frances (1818-1895) 230, 281
Alexander, James Waddell (1804-1859) ---------- 231
Alford, Henry (1810-1871) ----------568, 593
Allen, Ernest Bourner ---------- 559
Anonymous----117, 122, 168, 187, 197, 244, 316, 321, 336, 382, 403, 450, 452, 505, 514
Anonymous Latin Hymn ---------- ----------182, 193, 194, 205, 238, 419, 447
Anonymous German 17th Century ---------- 261

Babcock, Maltbie Davenport (1858-1901) -- 171
Bacon, Leonard (1802-1881) ---------- 543
Baker, Henry Williams (1821-1877) -- 169, 557
Baker, Theodore ---------- 117, 194
Ballantine, William Gay (1848-1937) ---- 547
Barbauld, Anna Letitia (1743-1825) ---------- 595
Baring-Gould, Sabine (1834-1924) - 149, 481, 482
Barton, Bernard D. (1784-1849) ---------- 436, 479
Bates, Katharine Lee (1859-1929) ---- 291, 550
Bax, Clifford (1886-1932) ---------- 567
Ben Judah, Daniel (14th century) ---------- 124
Benson, Louis F. (1855-1930) ---------- 463, 486
Bernard of Clairvaux (1091-1153) ---- 231, 392
Bernard of Cluny (c. 1145) ---------- 569, 570
Berwick Hymnal (1886) ---------- 344
Bethune, George W. (1805-1862) ---------- 218
Bickersteth, Edward Henry (1825-1906) -- 154
Blanchard, Ferdinand Quincy (1876-) ---- 217
Blaisdell, James Arnold (1867-1957) ---------- 459
Bliss, Philip P. (1838-1876) ---------- 313, 442
Bode, John Earnest (1816-1874) ---------- 308
Bonar, Horatius (1808-1889)--288, 317, 458, 473
"Book of Praise for Children, The" (1881) 316
Borthwick, Jane (1813-1897) ---------- 408
Bowring, John (1792-1872) ---------- 178, 183, 237
Bridges, Matthew (1800-1894) ---------- 250
Briggs, George W. (1875-) ---------- 437
Brooke, Stopford Augustus (1832-1916) 103, 215
Brooks, Phillips (1835-1893) ---------- 184
Brown, Jessie H. (Mrs. John Pounds) (1861-1921) ---------- 255
Bryant, William Cullen (1794-1878) ---------- 605
Buckoll, Henry J. (1803-1871) ---------- 134
Bunyan, John (1628-1688) ---------- 364
Burleigh, William Henry (1812-1871) ---- 566
Burns, James Drummond (1823-1864) ---------- 137
Burton, Henry (1840-1930) ---------- 249
Butler, Henry Montagu (1833-1918) ---------- 372
Byrne, Mary Elizabeth ---------- 321

Campbell, Alexander (1788-1866) ---------- 450
Campbell, Jane Montgomery (1817-1878) -- 594
Campbell, John (1845-1914) ---------- 166
Canitz, Friedrich R. L. von (1654-1699 -- 134
Caswall, Edward (1814-1878) ---------- 135, 392
Cennick, John (1718-1755) ---------- 267
Chadwick, John White (1840-1904) -- 506, 579
Chesterton, Gilbert K. (1874-1936) ---------- 546
Chisholm, Thomas O. (1866-) ---------- 165, 304
Chorley, Henry Fothergill (1808-1872) -- 565
"Christian Hymn Book" (Alexander Campbell's) (1872) ---------- 450
Clark, Thomas Curtis (1877-1953) --- 351, 385
Claudius, Matthias (1740-1815) ---------- 594
Clement of Alexandria (c. 220) ---------- 266
Clephane, Elizabeth C. (1830-1869) ---------- 235
Coffin, Henry Sloane (1877-1954) ---------- 182

HYMN

Collins, Henry (1827-1919) ---------- 383
Copenhaver, Laura Scherer (1868-1940) -- 533
Coster, George Thomas (1835-1912) ---------- 359
Cotterill, Thomas (1779-1823) ---------- 462
Cowper, William (1731-1800) 115, 162, 310, 581
Coxe, Arthur Cleveland (1818-1896) - 427, 494
Crain, Harry L. ---------- 520
Crewdson, Jane (1809-1863) ---------- 342
Croly, George (1780-1860) ---------- 272
Crosby, Fanny Jane (1823-1915) ---------- - 97, 280, 312, 332, 339, 396, 397, 407, 412, 413
Cross, Allen Eastman (1864-1943) ---------- 328
Cutler, J. S. ---------- 604

Davis, Ozora Stearns (1866-1931) ---- 511, 521
Davis, Robert (1881-1949) ---------- 499
Davison, Anna L. ---------- 343
Dawson, William J. (1854-1928) ---------- 212
Dayman, Edward Arthur (1807-1890) ---- 580
Dearmer, Percy (1867-1936) ---- 102, 248, 528
Deitz, Purd E. ---------- 489
Denny, Edward (1796-1889) ---------- 219, 457, 460
Dexter, Henry Martyn (1821-1890) ---------- 266
Dickson, David (1583-1663) ---------- 572
Dix, William Chatterton (1837-1898) ---------- ---------- 196, 200, 277
Doane, George Washington (1799-1859) 145, 540
Doane, William Crosswell (1832-1913) -- 99
Doddridge, Philip (1702-1751) 174, 369, 399, 586
Draper, William H. (1855-1933) ---- 157, 195
Duffield, George, Jr. (1818-1888) ---------- 371
Dwight, Timothy (1752-1817) ---------- 428, 429

East, James ---------- 203
Edgar, Mary S. ---------- 315
Ellerton, John (1826-1893) ---------- ---------- 125, 128, 140, 246, 446, 447, 565
Elliott, Charlotte (1789-1871) ---------- 295, 350
Elliott, Ebenezer (1781-1849) ---------- 563
Elliott, Emily Elizabeth Steele (1836-1897) ---------- 292
Everest, Charles W. (1814-1877) ---------- 285
"Exeter Collection" ---------- 108

"F. B. P." 16th Century ---------- 572
Faber, Frederick William (1814-1863) ---- ---------- 172, 173, 233, 348, 582
Farrington, Harry Webb (1880-1931) ---- 206
Fawcett, John (1740-1817) ---------- 127, 476
Findlater, Sarah B. (1823-1907) ---------- 601
Fitch, Eleazor T. ---------- 131
Fletcher, Frank (1870-1954) ---------- 220
Forbush, William Byron (1868-1928) ---- 608
Fortunatus, Venantius (530-609) ---------- 246
Fosdick, Harry Emerson (1878-) ---- 378, 553
Foster, Frederick W. (1760-1835) ---------- 123
"Foundling Hospital Collection" (1796) - 110

Garrison, Winfred Ernest (1874-) ---------- 158
Gerhardt, Paul (1607-1676) - 186, 231, 380, 402
Gilder, Richard W. (1844-1909) ---------- 311
Gilkey, James Gordon (1889-) ---------- 607
Gillman, Frederick J. (1866-1949) ---------- 377
Gilmore, Joseph Henry (1834-1918) ---------- 405
Gladden, Washington (1836-1918) ---- 306, 307
Gower, Jean Milne (Mrs. John) (1867-)--- ---------- 325, 330
Grant, Robert (1785-1838) ---------- 94
Gregory the Great (540-604) ---------- 102
Groser, W. H. (1834-1925) ---------- 591
Guiterman, Arthur (1871-1943) ---------- 599
Gurney, A. T. (1820-1887) ---------- 240
Gurney, John H. (1802-1862) ---------- 326

INDEX OF AUTHORS AND SOURCES OF HYMNS

HYMN

Hall, Elvina M. (1818-?) 284
Ham, Marion Franklin (1867-1956) 222, 433, 491, 564
Hammond, William (1719-1783) 116
Hankey, Katherine (1834-1911) 438, 532
Harbaugh, Henry (1817-1867) 314
Harlow, S. Ralph (1885-) 362
Harmer, Charles H. (1865-) 454
Hart, Joseph (1712-1768) 639
Hastings, Thomas (1784-1872) 398, 523
Havergal, Frances Ridley (1836-1879) 289, 296, 367, 470, 584, 587
Hawks, Annie Sherwood (1835-1918) 341
Hay, John (1838-1905) 368
Hayward, Thomas (J. Dobell's Collection) (1806) 444
Hearn, Marianne (1834-1909) 297
Heath, George (1750-1822) 370
Heber, Reginald (1783-1826) 107, 143, 202, 358, 453, 592
Hedge, Frederick H. (1805-1890) 155
Herbert, Petrus (?-1571) 147
Holland, Henry Scott (1847-1918) 545
Holmes, John Haynes (1879-) 163, 175, 490, 516, 554, 556, 600
Holmes, Oliver Wendell (1809-1894) 151, 353, 602
Home Hymn Book (1885) 609
Hopkins, John Henry (1820-1891) 204
Hopper, Edward (1818-1888) 409
Hort, Fenton J. A. (1828-1892) 447
Hosmer, Frederick Lucian (1840-1928) 143, 356, 498, 539, 542, 562, 575
How, William Walsham (1823-1897) 243, 279, 422, 434, 576, 577
Hoyle, R. Birch 244
Hoyt, May P. 451
Hudson, R. E. 293
Hughes, Thomas (1823-1896) 365
Hull, Eleanor 321
Hunter, John (1848-1917) 318
Huntington, George 549
Hutton, Frances A. (1811-1877) 333
Hyde, William DeWitt (1858-1903) 492

Ingemann, Bernhardt S. (1789-1862) 481
Isaacs, A. S. (1851-1920) 512

Jameson, Love H. (1811-1892) 226
John of Damascus (c. 750) 242, 247
Johnson, J. (1849-1926) 180
Johnson, Samuel (1822-1882) 177, 345, 426
Jones, Edith 609

"K" in John Rippon's "Selection" (1787) (Keith, George) 406
Keble, John (1792-1866) 150, 435
Kelly, Thomas (1769-1854) 256, 268
Ken, Thomas (1637-1711) 148, 611
Kerr, Hugh Thompson (1872-1950) 583
Key, Francis S. (1814) 651
Kilmer, Joyce (1886-1918) 305
Kipling, Rudyard (1865-1936) 560, 561
Knapp, Shepherd (1873-1946) 497

Lanier, Sidney (1842-1881) 225
Larcom, Lucy (1826-1893) 133, 299
Lathbury, Mary Artemisia (1841-1913) 144, 461
Laufer, Calvin Weiss (1874-1938) 495
Lee, Harry 216
Leeson, Jane E. (1807-1882) 389
Lewis, Howell Elvet (1860-1953) 504, 525
Lindsay, Vachel (1879-1930) 534
Livermore, Abiel Abbott (1811-1892) 467
Lloyd, William F. (1791-1853) 395
Logan, John (1748-1788) 174
Longfellow, Samuel (1819-1892) 120, 139, 141, 179, 274, 275, 309, 319, 424
Longstaff, W. D. (1822-1894) 346

HYMN

Lowell, James Russell (1819-1891) 558
Lowenstern, Matthaus A. von (1594-1648) 430
Lowry, Somerset Corry (1855-1932) 502
Luke, Jemima (1813-1906) 213
Luther, Martin (1483-1546) 155, 199
Lynch, Thomas Toke (1818-1871) 270
Lyte, Henry Francis (1793-1847) 112, 138, 259, 375

MacDonald, George (1824-1905) 132
MacKellar, Thomas (1812-?) 439
Mant, Richard (1776-1848) 156
Marlatt, Earl (1892-) 360
Marriott, John (1780-1825) 536
Mathams, Walter J. (1853-1932) 300
Mather, Howard, E. 420
Matheson, George (1842-1906) 388
Medley, Samuel (1738-1799) 265
Merrill, William Pierson (1867-1954) 374, 597
Miller, John (d. 1810) 123
Milman, Henry Hart (1791-1868) 223
Milton, John (1608-1674) 181
Mohr, Joseph (1792-1848) 188
Moment, John J. 96
Monsell, John Samuel Bewley (1811-1875) 106, 208, 376, 417, 596
Montgomery, James (1771-1854) 170, 192, 227, 257, 333, 335, 456, 465
Moore, Thomas (1779-1852) 398
Murray, Robert (1832-1910) 541

Neale, John Mason (1818-1866) 182, 193, 221, 241, 242, 247, 286, 569, 570
Neander, Joachim (1650-1680) 98, 354
Needham, John (d. 1787) 152
Nelson, Horatio Earl (1823-1913) 114
Neumark, Georg (1621-1681) 404
Newhall, Charles S. (1842-1935) 517
Newman, John Henry (1801-1890) 578
Newton, John (1725-1807) 126, 264, 431, 448, 640
Niedermeyer, Mabel (1899-) 425
North, Frank Mason (1850-1935) 519

"O. B. C." 114
Oakeley, Frederick (1802-1880) 205
Oakley, Ebenezer Sherman (1865-1935) 474
Osler, Edward (1798-1863) 110
Ostergaard, Christian 493
Owens, Priscilla J. (1829-1907) 537
Oxenham, John (d. 1941) 287, 480

Palgrave, Francis Turner (1824-1897) 478
Palmer, Ray (1808-1887) 352, 355, 419
Park, John Edgar (1879-1956) 209
Parker, Edwin Pond (1836-1925) 282, 303
Parker, Theodore (1810-1860) 347
Parker, William H. (1845-1929) 214
Partridge, Sybil F. (Sister Mary Xavier) 326
Perronet, Edward (1726-1792) 252, 253
Phelps, Sylvanus D. (1816-1895) 387
Pierpoint, Folliot Sanford (1835-1917) 167
Plumptre, Edward Hayes (1821-1891) 418
Pollard, Adelaide A. (1860-1934) 324
Pope, Alexander (1688-1744) 477
Poteat, Edwin McNeill (1892-1955) 320
Pott, Francis (1832-1909) 101, 238
Potter, Thomas J. (1827-1873) 485
Prentiss, Elizabeth P. (1818-1878) 390
Procter, Adelaide Anne (1825-1864) 109, 142, 340
Pusey, Philip (1799-1855) 430

Radford, Benjamin J. (1838-1933) 501
Rankin, Jeremiah E. (1828-1904) 129
Rawson, George (1807-1889) 146
Reed, Andrew (1787-1862) 275
Richards, Charles H. (1839-1925) 522
Rinkart, Martin (1586-1649) 598

INDEX OF AUTHORS AND SOURCES OF HYMNS

HYMN

Rippon, John (1751-1836) ---------- 252, 253
Roberts, Daniel Crane (1841-1907) ---------- 551
Robins, Henry B. ---------- 161, 510
Robinson, Robert (1735-1790) ---------- 111, 160
Rowe, John (1764-1833) ---------- 468
Rowland, May (1870-) ---------- 555
Russell, Arthur T. (1806-1874) ---------- 234
Russell, Francis Albert Rollo (1849-1914) 518

St. Francis of Assisi (1182-1226) ---------- 157
Sangster, Margaret E. (1838-1912) ---------- 526
Schloerb, Rolland W. (1893-1958) ---------- 432, 449
Schmolck, Benjamin (1672-1737) -- 121, 408, 445
Scott, Elizabeth ---------- 421
"Scottish Paraphrases" (1781) ---------- 174
Scriven, Joseph (1820-1886) ---------- 331
Seagrave, Robert (1693-1759) ---------- 573
Sears, Edmund H. (1810-1876) ---------- 191, 201
Shaw, Knowles (1834-1878) ---------- 416
Shepherd, Thomas (1665-1739) ---------- 366
Shurtleff, Ernest Warburton (1862-1917) -- 363
Sill, Edward R. (1841-1887) ---------- 271
Small, James G. (1817-1888) ---------- 290
Smith, Jay Holmes ---------- 487
Smith, Samuel Francis (1808-1895) ---- 524, 548
Smith, Walter Chalmers (1824-1908) ---------- 159
Spitta, Carl J. P. (1801-1859) ---------- 601
Squier, George L. ---------- 410
Stanley, Arthur Penrhyn (1815-1881) ---------- 251
Steele, Anne (1716-1778) ---------- 440
Stennett, Joseph (1663-1713) ---------- 464
Stennett, Samuel (1728-1795) ---------- 381, 455
Sterne, Colin (Henry Ernest Nichol) (1862-1828) ---------- 530
Stock, Sarah G. (1838-1898) ---------- 531
Stocking, Jay Thomas (1870-1936) ---------- 210
Stone, Samuel John (1839-1900) ---------- 423
Stowe, Harriet Beecher (1812-1896) ---------- 136
Stowell, Hugh (1799-1865) ---------- 394
Studdert-Kennedy, Geoffrey Anketell (1883-1929) ---------- 323
Swain, Joseph (1761-1796) ---------- 475
Swinburne, Algernon C. (1837-1909) ---------- 509
Symonds, John Addington (1840-1893) ---------- 507

Tappan, William B. (1794-1849) ---------- 232
Tarrant, William George (1853-1928) ---------- 113, 322, 500, 503, 603
Tate, Nahum (1652-1715) ---------- 185
Tennyson, Alfred (1809-1892) ---------- 349, 574, 589
Tersteegen, Gerhard (1697-1769) ---------- 123

HYMN

Theodulph of Orleans (d. 821) ---------- 221
Thompson, Will L. (1847-1909) ---------- 283
Thomson, Mary Ann (1834-1923) ---------- 529
Thring, Godfrey (1823-1903) ---------- 127, 250, 269
Thrupp, Dorothy A. (1779-1847) ---------- 401
Tickle, G. Y. (1819-1888) ---------- 466
Tillett, Wilbur Fiske (1854-1936) ---------- 211
Tiplady, Thomas (1882-) ---------- 130, 176, 229, 236, 471, 552
Toplady, Augustus Montague (1740-1778) -- 294
Tuittiett, Lawrence (1825-1897) ---------- 298
Tweedy, Henry Hallam (1868-1953) ---------- 273, 338, 535

Van Dyke, Henry (1852-1933) ---------- 95, 496
Vories, William Merrell (1880-) ---------- 513

Walford, William W. ---------- 337
Walter, Howard Arnold (1883-1918) ---------- 361
Waring, Anna Laetitia (1820-1910) ---------- 384
Warner, Anna B. (1820-1915) ---------- 400
Watt, Lauchlan MacLean (1867-) ---------- 302
Watts, Isaac (1674-1748) ---------- 104, 105, 118, 119, 153, 190, 207, 228, 441, 527, 585
Weissel, George (1590-1635) ---------- 224
Wells, Marcus M. (1815-1895) ---------- 276
Wengel, Paul (1892-) ---------- 263, 391
Wesley, Charles (1707-1788) ---------- 189, 239, 245, 258, 260, 262, 373, 379, 414, 415, 483, 590
Wesley, John (1703-1791) ---------- 380, 402
Whitefield, George (1714-1770) ---------- 189
Whiting, William (1825-1878) ---------- 610
Whittaker, Robert ---------- 514
Whittier, John Greenleaf (1807-1892) ---------- 254, 411, 484, 515, 571, 606, 636
Wigner, John M. (1844-?) ---------- 278
Wile, Frances Whitmarsh (1878-1939) ---------- 588
Williams, Helen M. (1762-1827) ---------- 334
Williams, Theodore C. (1855-1915) ---------- 100, 508
Williams, William (1717-1791) ---------- 393
Winkworth, Catherine (1829-1878) ---------- 98, 121, 147, 186, 224, 404, 445, 598
Wolcott, Samuel (1813-1886) ---------- 538
Wolfe, Aaron R. (1831-1902) ---------- 469
Wordsworth, Christopher (1807-1885) -- 386, 443
Wortman, Denis (1835-1932) ---------- 472
Wreford, John R. (1800-1881) ---------- 544

"Yattendon Hymnal" ---------- 354
"Yigdal, The" ---------- 124

Zinzendorf, Nicolaus L. von (1700-1760) --- 357

Index of Composers, Arrangers aud Sources of Tunes

NUMBER

ABBEY, ALONZO J. (1825-1887) 571
ALLEN, GEORGE NELSON (1812-1877) 366
AMERICAN MELODY 406
ANCIENT PLAINSONG (13th century) 182
ANONYMOUS 600
ARNE, THOMAS A. (1710-1778) 435
ATKINSON, FREDERICK COOK (1841-1897) 272

BACH, JOHANN CHRISTOPHER (1642-1703) 545
BACH, JOHANN SEBASTIAN (1685-1750) 231, 636
BAKER, HENRY (1835-1910) 353, 419, 473
BAKER, HENRY WILLIAMS (1821-1877) 286
BAMBRIDGE, WILLIAM SAMUEL (1842-1923) 137, 481
BARING-GOULD, SABINE (1834-1924) 328
BARKER, CYRIL 195
BARNBY, JOSEPH (1838-1896) 135, 149, 220, 243, 291, 297, 305, 383, 430, 574, 576, 580, 601
BARNES, EDWARD SHIPPEN (1887-) 171, 619
BEETHOVEN, LUDWIG VAN (1770-1827) 95, 634
BERRIDGE, ARTHUR (1855-?) 385
BLANCHARD, GEORGE F. (1868-) 560, 608
BLANCHARD, WILLIAM G. (1905-) 311
BLISS, PHILIP P. (1838-1876) 289, 313, 442
BOHEMIAN BRETHREN'S "GESANGBUCH" (1566) 484
BOHEMIAN BRETHREN, TRADITIONAL 637
BOOTH, JOSIAH (1852-1929) 563
BORNSCHEIN, FRANZ C. (1879-) 287
BORTNIANSKY, DIMITRI S. (1752-1825) 141
BOURGEOIS, LOUIS (c. 1500-1561) 104, 611
BRADBURY, WILLIAM B. (1816-1868) 97, 213, 232, 295, 337, 401, 405, 475
BROWN, JOHN N. 553
BRUNER, EDNA (MRS. B. H.) 628, 641
BULLINGER, ETHELBERT W. (1837-1913) 282, 508
"BUNDES LIEDER" (Neander) (1680) 123
BUNNETT, EDWARD (1834-1923) 146, 266
BURNAP, UZZIAH C. (1834-1900) 210, 445

CALKIN, JOHN BAPTISTE (1827-1905) 241, 368, 426, 540, 589
"CANTICA LAUDIS" (1850) (Mason and Webb) 422, 520
"CANTUS DIVERSI" (1751) (J. F. Wade) 205
CAREY, HENRY (1692-1743) 548
CARTER, EDMUND S. (1845-?) 178
CHALLINOR, FREDERIC A. (1866-1952) 214
"CHORALE UNSER HERRSCHER" 121, 354
"CHRISTMAS CAROLS" (W. Sandys') (1833) 197
CONANT, GRACE WILBUR 302
CONKEY, ITHAMAR (1815-1867) 237
CONVERSE, CHARLES C. (1832-1918) 331
COTTMAN, ARTHUR (1842-1879) 219, 544
COURTEVILLE, RAPHAEL (d. 1772) 424
CROFT, WILLIAM (1678-1727) 258, 427, 585
CRUEGER, JOHANN (1598-1662) 176, 275, 598
CUMMINGS, WILLIAM HAYMAN (1831-1918) 189
CUTLER, HENRY STEPHEN (1824-1902) 358, 511, 559

DARWALL, JOHN (1731-1789) 260
DARWALL, LEICESTER (1813-?) 357
"DAY'S PSALTER" (1563) 437
DICKINSON, CHARLES J. (1822-1883) 463
DOANE, WILLIAM H. (1831-1915) 312, 332, 339, 390, 397, 438
DOUGLAS, WINFRED (1867-1944) 364
DUNBAR, C. R. 293
DUTCH TRADITIONAL MELODY 502, 533
DYER, SAMUEL (1785-1835) 120, 319
DYKES JOHN BACCHUS (1823-1876) 107, 169, 201, 223, 233, 288, 334, 362, 392, 410, 417, 456, 465, 485, 536, 556, 568, 578, 584, 603, 607, 610

NUMBER

EBELING, JOHANN GEORG (1620-1676) 186
ELLIOTT, JAMES W. (1833-1915) 222
ELVEY, GEORGE J. (1816-1893) 250, 300, 349, 402, 593
EMERSON, LUTHER O. (1820-1916) 143
EMMELAR 172
ENGLISH MELODY 200, 257, 301, 316, 447, 588, 592
"ESSAY ON THE CHURCH PLAIN CHANT" (1782) 259
"ESTE'S PSALTER" (1592) 478
EVANS, D., "HYMNAU A THONAU" (1865) 546
EVANS, DAVID (1874-1948) 321
EWING, ALEXANDER (1830-1895) 569

FILITZ, FRIEDRICH (1804-1876) 386
FILLMORE, JAMES H. (1849-1941) 255, 343
FINK, GOTTFRIED W. (1783-1846) 505, 554
FISCHER, WILLIAM G. (1835-1912) 532
FLEMMING, FRIEDRICH F. (1778-1813) 147, 344, 350
FOSTER, M. B. (1851-1922) 215
"FOUNDERY COLLECTION, THE" (1742) 573
FRENCH-ENGLISH CAROL 187

GARDINER, WILLIAM (1770-1853) 108, 125, 420, 452, 459, 519, 606
GAUL, ALFRED ROBERT (1837-1913) 615
GEIBEL, ADAM (1855-1933) 626
"GEISTLICHE KIRCHENGESÄNGE" (1623) 157
"GENEVAN PSALTER" (1551) 104, 160, 372, 491, 567, 611
GERMAN MELODY 120, 193
"GESANGBUCH DER HERZOGL" (WIRTEMBERGISCHEN KATHOLISCHEN HOFKAPELLE) (1784) 522, 528
GIARDINI, FELICE DE (1716-1796) 122, 538
GLAESER, CARL G. (1784-1829) 262
GORDON, ADONIRAM J. (1836-1895) 382
GOSS, JOHN (1800-1880) 359, 367
GOTTSCHALK, LOUIS MOREAU (1829-1869) 274
GOULD, JOHN EDGAR (1822-1875) 409
GOUNOD, CHARLES F. (1818-1893) 270, 624
GOWER, JEAN MILNE (1867-) 325
GOWER, JOHN HENRY (1855-1922) 330, 561
GRAPE, JOHN T. (1833-) 284
GREATOREX, HENRY WELLINGTON, "COLLECTION" (1851) 153, 479, 613
GREEK FOLK SONG 213
GRUBER, FRANZ (1787-1863) 188

HANDEL, GEORGE FREDERICK (1685-1759) 185, 190, 244, 245, 369, 457
HARDING, JOHN P. (1850-1911) 202
HARMER, CHARLES H. (1865-) 454
HARPER, EARL ENYEART (1895-) 206
HARRINGTON, KARL POMEROY (1861-1953) 198, 616
HASSLER, HANS LEO (1564-1612) 231
HASTINGS, THOMAS (1784-1872) 294, 381, 393, 394
HATTON, JOHN (d. 1793) 152, 527, 543
HAVERGAL, WILLIAM H. (1793-1870) 466
HAWEIS, THOMAS (1733-1820) 539
HAYDN, FRANZ JOSEPH (1732-1809) 94, 134, 164, 417, 431, 485, 487, 488, 584, 596, 597
HAYDN, JOHANN MICHAEL (1737-1806) 462, 486, 564
HEBREW MELODY 124
"HEILIGE SEELENLUST" (Georg Joseph) (1657) 602
HEMY, HENRY F. (1818-1888) 348, 380
HEWS, GEORGE (1806-1873) 470
HILES, HENRY (1826-1904) 142, 273, 338, 579
"HIRSCHBERG GESANGBUCH" (1741) 499, 516
HODGES, JOHN S. B. (1830-1915) 453
HOLBROOK, JOSEPH P. (1822-1888) 154, 408
HOLDEN, OLIVER (1765-1844) 252

INDEX OF COMPOSERS, ARRANGERS AND SOURCES OF TUNES

NUMBER

Hopkins, Edward J. (1818-1901) 128, 460
Hopkins, John H. (1820-1891) 204
Houseley, H. 175
Howard, Alonzo Potter (1838-1902) 203
Hughes, John (1873-1932) 256
Hullah, John (1812-1884) 581
Husband, Edward (1843-1908) 279

Ippolitof-Ivanoff (1859-1935) 623
Irish melody 236, 321, 326

Jackson, Robert (1842-1914) 450
Jackson, Thomas (c. 1715-1781) 132
Jeffery, J. Albert (1854-1929) 99
Jones, Darius Elliott (1815-1881) 126
Jones, J. D. (1827-1879) 100
Joseph, Georg (17th century) 602
Jude, William Herbert (1852-1892) 281

"Katholisches Gesangbuch" (1774) 150, 318
Kingsley, George (1811-1884) 395, 421
Kirkpatrick, William J. (1838-1921) 537
Knak, Gustave 263
Knapp, Mrs. Joseph F. (1839-1908) 412
Knapp, William (1698-1768) 285, 351, 525, 586
Knecht, Justin Heinrich (1752-1817) 103, 279
Kocher, Conrad (1786-1872) 167, 196
Koenig, Johann B. (1691-1750) 466
Koschat, Thomas (1845-1914) 170
Kremser, Edward (1838-1914) 117

Lane, Spencer (1843-1903) 333
Langran, James (1835-1909) 347
Laufer, Calvin Weiss (1874-1938) 212, 403, 495, 617
LeJeune, George F. (1842-1904) 570
Lloyd, John A. (1815-1874) 599
Lockwood, Charlotte Mathewson 96
Longacre, L. B. 514
Lowden, C. Harold (1883-) 304, 315
Lowry, Robert (1826-1899) 341, 387, 396
Luther, Martin (1483-1546) 155
Lutkin, Peter Christian (1858-1931) 225
Lwoff, Alexis Theodore (1799-1870) 477, 547, 565
"Lyra Davidica" (1708) 239

Macfarren, George A. (1813-1887) 635
Main, Hubert P. (1839-1926) 375
Maker, Frederick Charles (1844-1927) 109, 218, 235, 278, 336, 377, 411, 509, 562
Malan, Henri Abraham Caesar (1787-1864) 116, 296
Mann, Arthur H. (1850-1929) 308
Marsh, Simeon B. (1798-1875) 414
Mason, Harry S. (1881-) 360
Mason, Lowell (1792-1872) 115, 131, 183, 228, 262, 265, 268, 310, 329, 335, 345, 355, 370, 373, 399, 439, 441, 443, 448, 464, 467, 469, 476, 523, 541, 639
Matthews, Timothy R. (1826-1910) 211, 292, 306, 501
Meineke, Charles (1782-1850) 614
Mendelssohn-Bartholdy, Felix Jacob Ludwig (1809-1847) 136, 189, 384, 400, 458, 500, 590, 632
Messiter, Arthur Henry (1831-1916) 418
"Méthode du plain-chant" (La Feillée) (1808) 102
Miller, Edward (1735-1807) 492
Milligan, Cleo Cannon (Mrs. Roy H.)* 552
Minor, George A. 416
Monk, William Henry (1823-1889) 138, 238, 575
Moore, Willis A. 604
Moravian Hymnal 510
Morley, Thomas (1845-1891) 269, 474
Morson, W. C. T. 515
Moss, Thomas 627
"Motetts or Antiphons" (S. Webbe) (1792) 496

Mountain, James (1843-1933) 229
Mozart, Wolfgang Amadeus (1756-1791) 265, 375, 376, 513
Mueller, Carl 199
Murray, J. R. 168
"Musikalisches Handbuch" (1690) 471

Naegeli, Johann Hans Georg (1768-1836) 310, 335, 399, 467, 476
Nares, James (1715-1783) 573
"National Psalmody" (B. Jacob's) (1819) 486, 564
Neander, Joachim (1650-1680) 121, 123, 354
Netherlands folk song (1625) 117
Neumark, Georg (1621-1681) 404
"Neuvermehrtes Meiningisches Gesangbuch" (1693) 434, 545
Nichol, Henry Ernest (1862-1928) 530

O'Kane, Tullius C. (1830-?) 407
Oliver, Henry K. (1800-1885) 207, 557

Palestrina, Giovanni P. da (1526-1594) 238, 575
Palmer, Horatio Richmond (1834-1907) 327
Palmer, Parker C. 618
"Parish Choir, The" (1850) 114, 181, 518
Parker, Edwin P. (1836-1925) 303
Parry, Joseph (1841-1903) 415
Peace, Albert L. (1844-1912) 340, 388
Peek, Joseph Yates 361
Peery, Rob Roy (1900-) 130
"Pensum Sacrum" (Gorlitz) (1648) 636
Petrie's "Collection" 326
Pleyel, Ignace Joseph (1757-1831) 267, 309, 595, 640
Plymouth "Collection" (1855) 504
Porter, John (1877-) 620
Poteat, Edwin McNeill (1892-1955) 320, 612, 621, 622, 629, 631, 633, 642, 643, 644
Powell, Joseph P. 226
Praetorius, Michael (1571-1621) 194
"Praxis Pietatis Melica" (1668) 98, 158, 275
"Psalmodia Evangelica" (T. Williams') (1789) 224, 425, 507
Purday, Charles Henry (1799-1885) 166, 583

Räder, I. I. 391
Redhead, Richard (1820-1901) 227
Redner, Louis H. (1831-1908) 184
Reimann, Johann Balthazar 516
Reinagle, Alexander R. (1799-1877) 264, 356, 480
Reissiger, Carl G. (1798-1859) 179
Rendle, Lily (1875-) 555
Runyan, William M. (1870-) 165

"Sacred Harp" (Mason) (1843) 428
"Sacred Melodies" (William Gardiner) (1815) 108, 125, 420, 452, 459, 519, 606
Sanderson, Wilfrid 317
Sandys, W., "Christmas Carols" (1833) 197
"Schlesische Volkslieder" (1842) 261
Schneider, Friedrich (1786-1853) 444
Scholefield, Clement C. (1839-1904) 140
Schulthes, William A. F. (1816-1879) 436
Schulz, Johann A. P. (1747-1800) 594
Schumann, Robert (1810-1856) 133, 139, 298
Scott-Gatty, Alfred (1847-1918) 497
"Scottish Psalter" (1615) 162, 174, 605
"Scottish Psalter" (1635) 342
Sheppard, Franklin L. (1852-1930) 171
Sherwin, William Fiske (1826-1888) 106, 144, 451, 461
Shrubsole, William (1760-1806) 253
Sibelius, Jean (1865-1957) 161, 432, 489
Sicilian melody 127
Smart, Henry (1813-1879) 192, 247, 363, 378, 534, 582
Smith, Henry Percy (1825-1898) 307

INDEX OF COMPOSERS, ARRANGERS AND SOURCES OF TUNES

Smith, Isaac (1735-1800) ---- 118
Smith, John S. (1778) ---- 651
Southgate, Thomas B. (1814-1868) ---- 217
Stainer, John (1840-1901) ---- 650
Stebbins, George C. (1846-1945) ---- 230, 280, 290, 324, 346
Storer, Henry J. (1860-1935) ---- 503
"Stralsund Gesangbuch" (1665) ---- 98, 158
Strattner, George C. (1650-1705) ---- 177
"Students' Hymnal, A" (University of Wales, 1923) ---- 180
Sullivan, Arthur Seymour (1842-1900) ---- 101, 240, 242, 246, 299, 482, 498, 609

Tallis, Thomas (c. 1520-1585) ---- 148
Taylor, Virgil Corydon (1817-1891) ---- 151
Teschner, Melchior (d. c. 1615) ---- 221
Thompson, Will L. (1847-1909) ---- 283
Tomer, William G. (1833-1896) ---- 129
Tourjee, Lizzie S. (1858-1913) ---- 173
Tours, Berthold (1838-1897) ---- 113, 433
Traditional melodies
- American ---- 406
- Bohemian Bretheren ---- 637
- Danish ---- 493
- Dutch ---- 117, 502, 553
- English 200, 216, 257, 301, 316, 447, 588, 592
- French-English ---- 187
- German ---- 120, 193, 319, 323
- Greek ---- 213
- Hebrew ---- 96, 124
- Irish ---- 236, 321, 326
- Sicilian ---- 127
- Welsh ---- 100, 143, 248, 494

Trembath, Henry G. (1844-1908) ---- 322
Tuckerman, Samuel P. (1819-1890) ---- 517
Turner, Herbert B. (1852-1927) ---- 209

Vail, Silas J. (1818-1884) ---- 413
Vincent, Charles John, Jr, (1852-) ---- 531
Vulpius, Melchior (c. 1560-1616) ---- 365

Wade, James C. (1847-?) ---- 483
Wade's (John F.) "Cantus Diversi" (1751) 205
Wainwright, John (1723-1768) ---- 506
Walch, James (1837-1901) ---- 352, 440, 529
Wallace, William Vincent (1814-1865) ---- 254, 449, 521
Walter, William H. (1825-1893) ---- 374
Walton, James G. (1821-1905) ---- 348, 380
Ward, Samuel Augustus (1847-1903) ---- 535, 550, 572
Warren, George W. (1828-1902) ---- 533, 551
Watson, Lawrence White (1860-1927) 208, 542
Webb, George James (1803-1887) ---- 371, 524
Webbe, Samuel (1740-1816) ---- 259, 398, 496
Weber, Carl Maria von (1786-1826) ---- 145, 389, 408
Wells, Marcus M. ---- 276
Welsh hymn melody ---- 159, 234, 256, 277, 490, 546, 558
Welsh traditional melody -- 100, 143, 248, 494
Wesley, Samuel S. (1810-1876) ---- 423, 587
Whelpton, George (1847-1930) ---- 630
Willcox, John H. (1827-1875) ---- 100, 156
Williams, Aaron (1731-1776) - 105, 119, 271, 429
Williams, J. Rhosyd (1885-) ---- 566
"Williams' Psalmsody" (1770) 105, 119, 271, 429
Williams, Ralph Vaughn (1872-1958) ---- 216, 316, 577, 588, 592
Williams, Robert (c. 1781-1821) ---- 112, 251
Williams, Thomas, "Psalmodia Evangelica" (1789) ---- 224, 425, 507
Willis, Richard S. (1819-1900) ---- 191, 261
Wilson, Hugh (1766-1824) ---- 163, 455
Wilson, W. (1833-?) ---- 591
Woodbury, Isaac B. (1819-1858) ---- 314, 468
Woodman, Johnathan Call (1813-1894) --- 446
Wostenholm, Maurice L. (1887-) ---- 249
Wyeth, John (1770-1858) ---- 111

Zeuner, Charles Heinrich Christopher (1797-1857) ---- 512, 526
Zundell, John (1815-1882) ---- 379

Metrical Index of Tunes

HYMN

S. M.

Boylston 131, 373, 469
Dennis 399, 476
Ferguson 395, 421
Festal Song 374
Franconia 466
Laban 370
Lake Enon 314
St. Thomas 105, 119, 271, 429
Schumann 422, 520
Silver Street 118
State Street 446
Thatcher 457
Trentham 450

S. M. D.

Bealoth 428
Diademata 250, 300, 402
Terra Patris 171

S. M. with Refrain

Marion 418

C. M.

Abergele 599
Antioch 190
Arlington 435
Avon (Martyrdom) 163, 455
Azmon 262
Beatitudo 334, 410, 456
Belmont 125, 452, 459
Bradford 245
Brown 475
Chesterfield 539
Chimes 464
Christmas 185, 369
Cooling 571
Coronation 252
Dalehurst 219, 544
Dundee 162, 174, 605
Evangelist 590
Gräfenberg 275
Green Hill 230
Holy Cross 483
Hummel 512
Jackson 132
Lambeth 436
Maitland 366
Manoah 153, 479
Memory 454
Miles' Lane 253
Naomi 310, 335, 467
Nox Praecessit 426
Ortonville (with Repeat) 381
Paraclete 218
St. Agnes 201, 392, 465, 556
St. Anne 427, 585
St. Columba (Irish) 326
St. James 424
St. Peter 264, 356, 480
Salzburg 462
Sawley 352, 440
Serenity 254, 449, 521
Shirleyn 206
Vulpius 365
Wigtown 342

C. M. D.

All Saints 358, 511, 559
Amesbury 210
Carol 191

HYMN

Denver 175
Ellacombe 522
Forest Green 316, 588
Kingsfold 301
Materna 535, 550, 572
St. Leonard (Hiles) 142, 273, 338, 579
Seraph (Bethlehem) 505, 554
Vox Dilecti 288
Winsted 553

L. M.

Angelus 602
Beloit 179
Brookfield 217
Canonbury 133, 139, 298
Duke Street 152, 527, 543
Federal Street 207, 557
Germany 108, 420, 519, 606
Godwin 311
Hamburg 228
Hebron 115, 639
Herongate 216
Herr Jesu Christ 636
Hesperus (Quebec) 353, 419, 473
Holley 470
Humility 517
Hursley 150, 318
Louvan 151
Maryton 307
Melrose 377
Mendon 120, 319
Missionary Chant 526
Mozart (Zelotes 376, 513
O Jesu Christ, Mein Lebens Licht 600
Old 100th 104, 611
Olive's Brow 232
Quebec (Hesperus) 353, 419, 473
Quest 320
Retreat 394
Rockingham, Old 492
St. Crispin 349
St. Cross 233
St. Drostane 223
St. Polycarp 309
Saxby 306
Sheltering Wing 305
Stirewalt 130
Tallis' Canon 148
Truro 224, 425, 507
Uxbridge 441
Waltham 241, 540, 589
Wareham 285, 351, 525, 586
Winchester, New 471
Woodworth 295
Zelotes (Mozart) 376, 513

L. M. D.

Creation 164
Walford 337

L. M. with Refrain

He Leadeth Me 405

4.6.4.6.D.

Last Sleep 580

HYMN

5.4.5.4.D.

Adelaide 324

5.5.6.5.6.5.6.5. with Refrain

Judas Maccabeus 244

5.5.8.8.5.5.

St. Hubert 357

5.6.8.5.5.8.

Crusader's Hymn 261

6.4.6.4.D.

Bread of Life 451, 461

6.4.6.4. with Refrain

I Need Thee 341

6.4.6.4.6.6.4.4.

Love's Offering 303
More Love to Thee 390
Purer in Heart 343

6.4.6.4.6.6.6.4.

Bethany 329
St. Edmund 299
Something for Jesus 387

6.5.6.5.

Eudoxia 328
Livermore 325
Merrial 149

6.5.6.5.D.

David 269
Holiness 346
Lonely Midnight 203
Morley 474
Penitence 333

6.5.6.5.D. with Refrain

Rosmore 322
St. Alban 417, 485, 584, 596
St. Gertrude 482, 498

6.5.6.5. 12 L

Armageddon 367

6.5.6.5.6.6.6.5.

St. Dunstan's 364

6.5.6.5.7.6.6.5.

Sorrows 226

6.6.4.6.6.6.4.

America 548, 549
Fiat Lux 536
Italian Hymn (Trinity) 122, 538
Kirby Bedon 146, 266
New America 514
Olivet 355

6.6.6.4.6.6.6.4.

Pax Orbi 552

6.6.6.6.D.

Invitation 278, 562
Jewett 408

6.6.6.6.6.5.

St. Germans 509

6.6.6.6.6.6.

Laudes Domini 135
Old 120th 478

6.6.6.6.8.6.8.6.

Kenosis 289

6.6.6.6.8.8.

Arthur's Seat 359
Darwall's 148th 260
Mansfield 243
Samuel 609

6.6.6.6.8.8.8.

Lischer 444

6.6.6.6.12.12.

Christmas Song 198

METRICAL INDEX OF TUNES

HYMN

6.6.7.7. with Refrain

All to Christ I Owe 284

6.6.8.4.D.

Leoni (Yigdal) 124

6.6.8.D. 3.3.6.6.

Arnsberg 123

6.6.12.12.12.

Prince of Peace, The 195

6.7.6.7.6.6.6.6.

Nun Danket 176, 598

6.7.7.7.6.7.7.7.

Fealty 302

7.4.7.4.D.

Gwalchmai 100

7.5.7.5.7.7.

Silksworth 531

7.6.7.6. with Refrain

Near the Cross 339

7.6.7.6.D.

Angel's Story 308
Aurelia 423, 587
Bentley 581
Chenles 211, 501
Day of Rest 222
Ellacombe 528
Ewing 569
Greenland 486, 564
Lancashire 247, 363, 534
Llangloffan 546
Meirionydd 234, 277, 490
Mendebras 443
Miriam 154
Missionary Hymn 541
Münich 434
Passion Chorale 231
Rotterdam 433
St. Hilda 279
St. Kevin 242
St. Theodulph 221
Salve Domine 208, 542
Seasons 384, 500
Sheffield 257
Tours 113
Webb 371, 524

7.6.7.6.D. with Refrain

Hankey 532
Old, Old Story 438
Urbs Beata 570
Wir Pflügen 594

7.6.7.6.7.7.7.6.

Amsterdam 573
Jesus Saves 537

7.6.7.6.8.6.8.6.

Gosterwood 592

7.6.7.6.8.8.8.5.

Commonwealth 563

7.6.8.6.D.

Alford 568, 607
Patmos 503
Savoy Chapel 368

7.6.8.6.8.6.8.6.

St. Christopher 235

HYMN

7.7.5.7.7.5.

Salvator 215

7.7.7.5.

Capetown 386

7.7.7.7. with Alleluias

Easter Hymn (Worgan) 239
Llanfair 112, 251
Song of Praise 447

7.7.7.7.

Innocents 114, 181, 518
Last Hope (Mercy) 274
O How Lovely 263
Pleyel's Hymn 267, 595, 640
Posen 177
Seymour 145, 389
Vienna 103

7.7.7.7. with Refrain

Angels We Have Heard 187
Mighty Rock 407

7.7.7.7.D.

Aberystwyth 415
Faithful Guide 276
Martyn 414
Sabbath 448
St. George's, Windsor 593
Watchman 183

7.7.7.7.D. with Refrain

Mendelssohn 189

7.7.7.7.4. with Refrain

Chautauqua 144

7.7.7.7.5.7. with Refrain

Rock of Ages 96

7.7.7.7.7.

Hendon 116, 296

7.7.7.7.7.7.

Dix 167, 196
Lux Prima 270
Pilot 409
Redhead No. 76 (Ajalon) 227
Toplady 294

7.8.7.8.7.7.

Hinchman 445

7.9.7.9. with Refrain

Every Day and Hour 397

8.3.3.6.D.

Ebeling (Bonn) 186

8.4.7.8.4.7.

Haydn 134

8.4.8.4.5.4.5.4.

Stories of Jesus 214

8.4.8.4.8.4.

Wentworth 109

8.4.8.4.D.

Petition 330
Vincent 327

8.4.8.4.8.8

O Jesu 499

8.4.8.4.8.8.8.4.

Ar Hyd Y Nos 143

8.5.8.3.

Bullinger 282, 508
Stephanos 286

HYMN

8.5.8.5.

Geneva 315

8.5.8.5.D.

Jesus, Saviour, Blessed Centre 229

8.5.8.5.8.4.3.

Angel Voices 101

8.6.8.6.6.6. with Refrain

Wonderful Words 442

8.6.8.6.6.6.8.8.6

Old 137th 437

8.6.8.6.7.6.8.6

St. Louis 184

8.6.8.6.8.6.

Arabia 591
Sheltered Dale 323

8.6.8.6.8.8.

Harvard 385
O Jesu 516

8.6.8.8.6.

Whittier (Rest) 411

8.7.4.4.7.8.7.4.4.7.

Motherhood 604

8.7.8.4.8.4.

Star of Peace 439

8.7.8.7.

Agape 463
Carter 178
Dominus Regit Me 169, 603
Dorrnance 468
Galilee 281
Knowsley 460
Rathbun 237
Stockwell 126
Wellesley 173

8.7.8.7. with Refrain

Close to Thee 413
Greensleeves 200
Lower Lights 313

8.7.8.7.D.

All the Way (with Repeat) 396
Austrian Hymn 431, 488, 597
Autumn 160
Beecher 379
Bithynia (Tantum Ergo) 160
Blaenhafren 494
Bradbury 401
Ellesdie 375
Erie 331
Faben 110, 156
Friend 290
Hymn to Joy 95
In Babilone 502
Mt. Holyoke 249
Nettleton 111
Pleading Saviour 504
Richards 172
St. Asaph 137, 481
Ton-Y-Botel 558

8.7.8.7.4.7.4.7.

Zion 393

METRICAL INDEX OF TUNES

HYMN

8.7.8.7.6.6.6.6.7.
Ein' Feste Burg 155

8.7.8.7.6.7.
Neander 354

8.7.8.7.7.5.7.5. with Refrain
Resurrexit 240

8.7.8.7.7.7.
Neander 121

8.7.8.7.7.7. with Alleluias
Harwell 268

8.7.8.7.8.6.8.7.
Vesper Hymn 141

8.7.8.7.8.7.
Cwm Rhondda 256
Dulce Carmen 259
Regent Square 192, 378
St. Leonard (Bach) 545
Sicilian Mariners 127

8.7.8.7.8.8.7.7.
Zürich 510

8.7.8.7.8.8.8.7.
Trefaenan 248

8.7.11.8.7.11.
Stockwell, New 212

8.8.4.4.8.8. with Alleluias
Lasst Uns Erfreuen 157

8.8.6.D. with Repeat
Ariel 265

8.8.8.
O Mensch Sieh 484

8.8.8.4.
Eudora 168
Palestrina (with Alleluias) 238, 575

8.8.8.6.
Childhood 180
Flemming 350
Just as I Am 297

8.8.8.6. with Refrain
I'll Live for Him 293
Kings of Orient 204

8.8.8.8.6.
St. Margaret 388

8.8.8.8.8.8.
Lest We Forget 560, 608
Melita 610
Recessional 561
St. Catherine 348, 380
St. Chrysostom 383
Veni Emmanuel 182

9.8.8.9 with Refrain
Farewell 129

9.8.9.8
Eucharistic Hymn 453
St. Clement 140

9.8.9.8. with Refrain
Pounds 255

HYMN

9.8.9.8.8.8.
Neumark 404

9.9.10.10.
Ostergaard 493

9.10.9.D. with Refrain
Sabaoth 97

9.10.9.9. with Refrain
Assurance 412

10.4.10.4
Submission 340

10.4.10.4.10.10.
Lux Benigna 578
Sandon 166, 583

10.7.10.7. with Refrain
Draw Me Nearer 312

10.8.8.7.7. with Refrain
Message 530

10.8.10.7. with Refrain
Stebbins 280

10.10.10. with Alleluias
Sarum 576
Sine Nomine 577

10.10.10.6.
Kerr 403

10.10.10.10.
Conisborough 317
Consolation 458
Ellers 128
Eventide 138
Field 495
Langran 347
Morecambe 272
National Hymn 533, 551
Old 124th 372
Overdale 566
Pax 555
Pax Veritatis 287
Russian Hymn 477
Slane 321
Toulon 472, 491

10.10.10.10. with Refrain
Living for Jesus 304

10.10.10.10.10.
Old 124th 567

10.10.10.10.10.10.
Finlandia 489
Yorkshire 506

10.10.11.11.
Hanover 258
Lyons 94

11.7.11.7. with Refrain
Softly and Tenderly 283

11.10.11.9.
Russian Hymn 565

11.10.11.10.
Acadia 515
Alverstroke 601
Ancient of Days 99

HYMN

Consolation 136, 400
Consolator 398
Curfew 336
Cushman 209
Henley 345
Morning Star 202
O Perfect Love 291
Peek 361
Russian Hymn 547
Welwyn 497
Wesley 523
Windsor 220

11.10.11.10. with Refrain
Faithfulness 165
Pilgrims 582
Tidings 529

11.10.11.10.11.9.
Finlandia 432

11.10.11.10.11.10.
Finlandia 161

11.10.11.10.D.
Londonderry 236

11.11.11.5.
Christe Sanctorum 102
Cloisters 430
Flemming 147, 344

11.11.11.11.
Foundation 406
Gordon 382
Joanna 159
Mueller 199
Poland (Koschat) 170

11.11.11.11. with Refrain
Fortunatus 246

11.12.12.10.
Nicaea 107

12.10.12.10.
Monsell 106

12.11.12.11. with Refrain
Bringing in the Sheaves 416

13.12.13.13. with Refrain
Doane 332

13.13.13.13.
Blairgowrie (Dykes) 362

14.14.4.7.8.
Lobe den Herren 98, 158

Irregular
Adeste Fideles (with Refrain) 205
Beacon Hill 360
Creation 487
Crossing the Bar 574
In Dulci Jubilo 193
In His Love Abiding 391
Kremser 117
Lanier 225
Margaret 292
Praetorius 194
Stille Nacht 188
Sweet Story 213
The First Noel (with Refrain) 197

Alphabetical Index of Tunes

HYMN

Abergele 599
Aberystwyth 415
Acadia 515
Adelaide 324
Adeste Fideles 205
Agapè 463
Ajalon (Redhead No. 76) 227
Alford 568, 607
All Saints 358, 511, 559
All the Way 396
All to Christ I Owe 284
Alverstroke 601
America 548, 549
Amesbury 210
Amsterdam 573
Ancient of Days 99
Angel Voices 101
Angel's Story 308
Angels We Have Heard 187
Angelus 602
Antioch 190
Ar Hyd Y Nos 143
Arabia 591
Ariel 265
Arlington 435
Armageddon 367
Arnsberg 123
Arthur's Seat 359
Assurance 412
Aurelia 423, 587
Austrian Hymn 431, 488, 597
Autumn 160
Avon (Martyrdom) 163, 455
Azmon 262

Beacon Hill 360
Bealoth 428
Beatitudo 334, 410, 456
Beecher 379
Belmont 125, 452, 459
Beloit 179
Bentley 581
Bethany 329
Bethlehem (Seraph) 505, 554
Bithynia (Tantum Ergo) 496
Blaenhafren 494
Blairgowrie (Dykes) 362
Bonn (Ebeling) 186
Boylston 131, 373, 469
Bradbury 401
Bradford 245
Bread of Life 451, 461
Bringing in the Sheaves 416
Brookfield 217
Brown 475
Bullinger 282, 508

Canonbury 133, 139, 298
Capetown 386
Carol 191
Carter 178
Chautauqua 144
Chenies 211, 501
Chesterfield 539
Childhood 180
Chimes 464
Christe Sanctorum 102
Christmas 185, 369
Christmas Song 198
Cloisters 430
Close to Thee 413
Commonwealth 563
Conisborough 317

HYMN

Consolation 136, 400, 458
Consolator 398
Cooling 571
Coronation 252
Creation 164, 487
Crossing the Bar 574
Crusader's Hymn 261
Curfew 336
Cushman 209
Cwm Rhondda 256

Dalehurst 219, 544
Darwall's 148th 260
David 269
Day of Rest 222
Dennis 399, 476
Denver 175
Diademata 250, 300, 402
Dix 167, 196
Doane 332
Dominus Regit Me 169, 603
Dorrnance 468
Draw Me Nearer 312
Duke Street 152, 527, 543
Dulce Carmen 259
Dundee 162, 174, 605

Easter Hymn (Worgan) 239
Ebeling (Bonn) 186
Ebenezer 558
Ein' Feste Burg 155
Ellacombe 522, 528
Ellers 128
Ellesdie 375
Erie 331
Eucharistic Hymn 453
Eudora 168
Eudoxia 328
Evangelist 590
Eventide 138
Every Day and Hour 397
Ewing 569

Faben 110, 156
Faithful Guide 276
Faithfulness 165
Farewell 129
Fealty 302
Federal Street 207, 557
Ferguson 395, 421
Festal Song 374
Fiat Lux 536
Field 495
Finlandia 161, 432, 489
First Noel, The 197
Flemming 147, 344, 350
Forest Green 316, 588
Fortunatus 246
Foundation 406
Franconia 466
Friend 290

Galilee 281
Geneva 315
Germany 108, 420, 519, 606
Godwin 311
Gordon 382
Gosterwood 592
Gräfenberg 275
Green Hill 230
Greenland 486, 564
Greensleeves 200
Gwalchmai 100

HYMN

Hamburg 228
Hankey 532
Hanover 258
Harvard 385
Harwell 268
Haydn 134
He Leadeth Me 405
Hebron 115, 639
Hendon 116, 296
Henley 345
Herongate 216
Herr Jesu Christ 636
Hesperus (Quebec) 353, 419, 473
Hinchman 445
Holiness 346
Holley 470
Holy Cross 483
Humility 517
Hummel 512
Hursley 150, 318
Hymn to Joy 95

I Need Thee 341
I'll Live for Him 293
In Babilone 502
In Dulci Jublio 193
In His Love Abiding 391
Innocents 114, 181, 518
Invitation 278, 562
Italian Hymn (Trinity) 122, 538

Jackson 132
Jesus Saves 132
Jesus Saviour, Blessed Centre 229
Jewett 408
Joanna 159
Judas Maccabeus 244
Just As I Am 297

Kenosis 289
Kerr 403
Kings of Orient 204
Kingsfold 301
Kirby Bedon 146, 266
Knowsley 460
Koschat (Poland) 170
Kremser 117

Laban 370
Lake Enon 314
Lambeth 436
Lancashire 247, 363, 534
Langran 347
Lanier 225
Lasst Uns Erfreuen 157
Last Hope (Mercy) 274
Last Sleep 580
Laudes Domini 135
Leoni (Yigdal) 124
Lest We Forget 560, 608
Lischer 444
Livermore 325
Living for Jesus 304
Llanfair 112, 251
Llangloffan 546
Lobe den Herren 98, 158
Londonderry 236
Lonely Midnight 203
Louvan 151

ALPHABETICAL INDEX OF TUNES

HYMN

Love's Offering 303
Lower Lights 313
Lux Benigna 578
Lux Prima 270
Lyons 94

Maitland 366
Manoah 153, 479
Mansfield 243
Margaret 292
Marion 418
Martyn 414
Martyrdom (Avon) 163, 455
Maryton 307
Materna 535, 550, 572
Meirionydd 234, 277, 490
Melita 610
Melrose 377
Memory 454
Mendebras 443
Mendelssohn 189
Mendon 120, 319
Mercy (Last Hope) 274
Merrial 149
Message 530
Mighty Rock 407
Miles' Lane 253
Miriam 154
Missionary Chant 526
Missionary Hymn 541
Monsell 106
More Love to Thee 390
Morecambe 272
Morley 474
Morning Star 202
Motherhood 604
Mozart (Zelotes) 376, 513
Mt. Holyoke 249
Mueller 199
Münich 434

Naomi 310, 335, 467
National Hymn 533, 551
Neander 121, 354
Near the Cross 339
Nettleton 111
Neumark 404
New America 514
Nicaea 107
Nox Praecessit 426
Nun Danket 176, 598

O How Lovely 263
O Jesu 499, 516
O Jesu Christ, Mein Lebens Licht 600
O Mensch Sieh 484
O Perfect Love 291
Old 100th 104, 611
Old 120th 478
Old 124th 372, 567
Old 137th 437
Old, Old Story 438
Olive's Brow 232
Olivet 355
Ortonville 381
Ostergaard 493
Overdale 566

Palestrina 238, 575
Paraclete 218
Passion Chorale 231
Patmos 503
Pax 555
Pax Orbi 552
Pax Veritatis 287

HYMN

Peek 361
Penitence 333
Petition 330
Pilgrims 582
Pilot 409
Pleading Saviour 504
Pleyel's Hymn 267, 595, 640
Poland (Koschat) 170
Posen 177
Pounds 255
Praetorius 194
Prince of Peace, The 195
Purer in Heart 343

Quebec (Hesperus) 353, 419, 473
Quest 320

Rathbun 237
Recessional 561
Redhead No. 76 (Ajalon) 227
Regent Square 192, 378
Rest (Whittier) 411
Resurrexit 240
Retreat 394
Richards 172
Rock of Ages 96
Rockingham, Old 492
Rosmore 322
Rotterdam 433
Russian Hymn 477, 547, 565

Sabaoth 97
Sabbath 448
St. Agnes 201, 392, 465, 556
St. Alban 417, 485, 584, 596
St. Anne 427, 585
St. Asaph 137, 481
St. Catherine 348, 380
St. Christopher 235
St. Chrysostom 383
St. Clement 140
St. Columba (Irish) 326
St. Crispin 349
St. Cross 233
St. Drostane 223
St. Dunstan's 364
St. Edmund 299
St. George's, Windsor 593
St. Germans 509
St. Gertrude 482, 498
St. Hilda 279
St. Hubert 357
St. James 424
St. Kevin 242
St. Leonard (Bach) 545
St. Leonard (Hiles) 142, 273, 338, 579
St. Louis 184
St. Margaret 388
St. Peter 264, 356, 480
St. Polycarp 309
St. Theodulph 221
St. Thomas 105, 119, 271, 429
Salvator 215
Salve Domine 208, 542
Salzburg 462
Samuel 609
Sandon 166, 583
Sarum 576
Savoy Chapel 368
Sawley 352, 440
Saxby 306
Schumann 422, 520
Seasons 384, 500
Seraph (Bethlehem) 505, 554

HYMN

Serenity 254, 449, 521
Seymour 145, 389
Sheffield 257
Sheltered Dale 323
Sheltering Wing 305
Shirleyn 206
Sicilian Mariners 127
Silksworth 531
Silver Street 118
Sine Nomine 577
Slane 321
Softly and Tenderly 283
Something for Jesus 387
Song of Praise 447
Sorrows 226
Star of Peace 439
Star-Spangled Banner 651
State Street 446
Stebbins 280
Stephanos 286
Stille Nacht 188
Stirewalt 130
Stockwell 126
Stockwell, New 212
Stories of Jesus 214
Submission 340
Sweet Story 213

Tallis' Canon 148
Tantum Erge (Bithynia) 496
Terra Patris 171
Thatcher 457
Tidings 529
Toplady 294
Toulon 472, 491
Tours 113
Trefaenan 248
Trentham 450
Trinity (Italian Hymn) 122, 538
Truro 224, 425, 507

Urbs Beata 570
Uxbridge 441

Veni Emmanuel 182
Vesper Hymn 141
Vienna 103
Vincent 327
Vox Dilecti 288
Vulpius 365

Walford 337
Waltham 241, 540, 589
Wareham 285, 351, 525, 586
Watchman 183
Webb 371, 524
Wellesley 173
Welwyn 497
Wentworth 109
Wesley 523
Whittier (Rest) 411
Wigtown 342
Winchester, New 471
Windsor 220
Winsted 553
Wir Pflügen 594
Wonderful Words 442
Woodworth 295
Worgan (Eastern Hymn) 239

Yigdal (Leoni) 124
Yorkshire 506

Zelotes (Mozart) 376, 513
Zion 393
Zürich 510

Index of First Lines of Responses

NUMBER

Doxology and Glorias

Glory be to the Father and to the Son ---------- 612, 613, 614
Praise God from whom all blessings flow ---------- 611

Opening Sentences—Introits

Ask, and it shall be given you---- 622
Bless the Lord, O my soul---------- 623
Holy, holy, holy Lord of Hosts (Sanctus) ---------- 615
O come, let us worship and bow down ---------- 619
O Thou Eternal and Ever-present Spirit ---------- 621
O worship the Lord in the beauty of holiness ---------- 620
Send out Thy light and Thy truth-- 624
The Lord is in His holy temple---- 616, 617, 618

Prayer Responses

Almighty Father, hear our prayer--- 632
Bow down Thine ear, O Lord- 626, 633
Give ear, O Shepherd of Israel---- 631
Hear our prayer, O Father---------- 628
Hear our prayer, O heavenly Father 627
Hear our prayer, O Lord---------- 630

NUMBER

Open Thine eyes unto the supplication of Thy servant---------- 629
Our Father who art in heaven (The Lord's prayer) ---------- 625

Offertory Sentences

All things are Thine: no gift have we ---------- 636
All things come of Thee, O Lord 634, 635
Let each man do according as he has purposed ---------- 638
O dearest Lord, accept today the gifts we bring ---------- 637

Benedictions

Dismiss us with Thy blessing, Lord- 639
Grant us Thy peace as we depart-- 641
Jesus, hear our humble prayer----- 640
May grace, mercy and peace-------- 643
Now, Lord lettest Thou Thy servant depart in peace---------- 644
The Lord bless thee and keep thee-- 642

Amens

Double ---------- 647
Dresden ---------- 648
Sevenfold ---------- 650
Single ---------- 645, 646
Threefold ---------- 649

Index of Hymns for Use With Children

(9 to 12 years of age)

NUMBER

*All beautiful the march of days---- 588
*All creatures of our God and King-- 157
*All glory, laud, and honor ---------- 221
As with gladness men of old------- 196
Away in a manger------------------ 199

Book of grace and Book of glory-- 439

*Christ the Lord is risen today----- 239
*Come, Thou almighty King--------- 122
*Come, ye thankful people, come (Stanza 1) --------------------- 593

*Fairest Lord Jesus----------------- 261
Faith of our fathers--------------- 348
Father, loving Father -------------- 325
*Fling out the banner (Stanzas 1 & 4) ------------------------------ 540
*For the beauty of the earth--------- 167
*Forward through the ages---------- 498

God of the earth, the sky, the sea--- 120
God speaks to us in bird and song-- 180
God that madest earth and heaven-- 143
God who touchest earth with beauty 315

*Hark! the herald angels sing-------- 189
*Holy, holy, holy! Lord God Almighty ----------------------------- 107
How strong and sweet my Father's care ------------------------------ 168
Hush, all ye sounds of war---------- 195

*I love Thy kingdom, Lord ------428, 429
I love to tell the story-------------- 532
I think when I read that sweet story of old ------------------------- 213
I would be true-------------------- 361
In Christ there is no East or West- 480
It came upon the midnight clear--- 191

Jesus shall reign where'er the sun-- 527
*Joy to the world! the Lord is come 190
*Joyful, joyful we adore Thee-------- 95
Just as I am, Thine own to be---- 297

*Lead on, O King Eternal---------- 363
Lord of all being, throned afar----- 151
Lord, Thy glory fills the heaven---- 156
Lord, while for all mankind we pray 544

*Marching with the heroes---------- 322
*Men and children everywhere------ 96
My country is the world----------- 514
My country, tis of thee------------ 548

NUMBER

My God, I thank Thee, who hast made ----------------------------- 109
My Master was a worker----------- 500

*Now in the days of youth---------- 300
Now praise we great and famous men ------------------------------ 603
Now thank we all our God--------- 598
Now the day is over--------------- 149

*O beautiful for spacious skies------ 550
*O come, all ye faithful------------ 205
O Father, Thou who givest all----- 600
O God, beneath Thy guiding hand-- 543
O God, our help in ages past------ 585
O happy home, where Thou art loved the dearest (Stanzas 1, 2, 3) 601
O little town of Bethlehem---------- 184
O Master workman of the race---- 210
*O worship the King, all-glorious above -------------------------- 94
*O Zion, haste-------------------- 529
Our Church proclaims God's love and care ----------------------- 425

*Praise to God, immortal praise----- 595
Rejoice, ye pure in heart----------- 418
Remember all the people---------- 528

Saviour, teach me day by day------- 389
Silent night, holy night------------ 188

Tell me the stories of Jesus-------- 214
That cause can neither be lost nor stayed -------------------------- 493
*The Church's one foundation ------ 423
The fathers built this city--------- 503
*The wise may bring their learning-- 316
There's a song in the air----------- 198
*This is my Father's world--------- 171
To all the nations, Lord----------- 552

We give Thee but Thine own------ 422
We plow the fields and scatter----- 594
We three kings of Orient are------ 204
*We've a story to tell to the nations 530
*When morning gilds the skies------ 135
When spring unlocks the flowers--- 592
While shepherds watched their flocks by night ------------------------ 185
*Wise men seeking Jesus------------ 203
*With happy voices ringing--------- 113

*Suitable for Processionals.

Index of First Lines of Hymns

NUMBER

A charge to keep I have ---- 373
A holy air is breathing round ---- 467
A mighty fortress is our God ---- 155
A noble life, a simple faith ---- 512
A parting hymn we sing ---- 469
A song of spring once more we sing ---- 591
Abide with me, fast falls the eventide ---- 138
Above the hills of time the cross is gleaming ---- 236
According to Thy gracious word ---- 456
Again, as evening's shadow falls ---- 139
All beautiful the march of days ---- 588
All creatures of our God and King ---- 157
All glory, laud and honor ---- 221
All hail the pageant of the years ---- 516
All hail the power of Jesus' Name 252, 253
All my heart this night rejoices ---- 186
All my hope on God is founded ---- 354
All praise to Thee, my God, this night ---- 148
All the toil and sorrow done ---- 251
All the way my Saviour leads me ---- 396
All things are Thine; no gift have we ---- 606
An endless line of splendor ---- 534
Ancient of Days, who sittest throned 99
Angel voices, ever singing ---- 101
Angels from the realms of glory ---- 192
Angels we have heard on high ---- 187
Another year is dawning ---- 587
"Are ye able?" said the Master ---- 360
Art thou weary? Art thou troubled? 286
As the sun doth daily rise ---- 114
As with gladness men of old ---- 196
At length there dawns the glorious day ---- 511
At Thy feet, our God and Father ---- 137
Awake, awake to love and work ---- 323
Awake, my soul, stretch every nerve ---- 369
Awake, my tongue, thy tribute bring 152
Away in a manger, no crib for a bed ---- 199

Be Thou my vision, O Lord of my heart ---- 321
Begin, my tongue, some heavenly theme ---- 153
Beneath the cross of Jesus ---- 235
Beneath the forms of outward rite ---- 459
Bless the four corners of this house ---- 599
Blessed assurance, Jesus is mine ---- 412
Blest be the dear, uniting love ---- 483
Blest be the tie that binds ---- 476

NUMBER

Blest feast of love divine ---- 457
Book of grace and Book of glory ---- 439
Bread of the world, in mercy broken 453
Break Thou the bread of life ---- 461
Brightest and best of the sons of the morning ---- 202
Brightly beams our Father's mercy ---- 313
Brightly gleams our banner ---- 485

Calm on the listening ear of night ---- 201
Children of the heavenly King ---- 267
Christ for the world we sing ---- 538
Christ is risen, Christ is risen ---- 240
Christ the Lord is risen today ---- 239
Christian, rise and act thy creed ---- 518
City of God, how broad and far ---- 426
Come forth, ye men of every race and nation ---- 487
Come, my soul, thou must be waking 134
Come, Peace of God, and dwell again on earth ---- 555
Come, sound His praise abroad ---- 118
Come, Thou almighty King ---- 122
Come, Thou Fount of every blessing 111
Come to Jesus, ye who labor ---- 282
Come to the Saviour now ---- 278
"Come unto me, ye weary" ---- 277
Come, we that love the Lord ---- 119
Come, ye disconsolate, where'er ye languish ---- 398
Come, ye faithful, raise the strain ---- 242
Come, ye thankful people, come ---- 593
Creation's Lord, we give Thee thanks 492
Crown Him with many crowns ---- 250

Day is dying in the west ---- 144
Dear Father, loud the ocean rolls ---- 330
Dear God, our Father, at Thy knee confessing ---- 291
Dear Lord and Father of mankind ---- 411
Dear Master, in whose life I see ---- 318
Draw Thou my soul, O Christ ---- 299

Earth below is teeming ---- 596
Eternal Father, strong to save ---- 610
Eternal God, whose power upholds ---- 535
Eternal Ruler of the ceaseless round 506
Eternal Spirit, evermore creating ---- 161

Fairest Lord Jesus ---- 261
Faith of our fathers, living still ---- 348
Father Almighty, bless us with Thy blessing ---- 344

INDEX OF FIRST LINES OF HYMNS

NUMBER

Father, in Thy mysterious Presence kneeling ---- 345
Father, loving Father ---- 325
Father of love and power---- 146
Father of mercies, in Thy Word---- 440
Father, we praise Thee, now the night is over ---- 102
Father, who art alone---- 609
Fight the good fight with all thy might ---- 376
Fling out the banner, let it float---- 540
For all the saints who from their labors rest ----576, 577
For the beauty of the earth---- 167
For the bread, which Thou hast broken ---- 463
Forgive, O Lord, our severing ways 484
Forward through the ages---- 498
From all that dwell below the skies-- 104
From Bethany, the Master---- 222
From every stormy wind that blows-- 394
From ocean unto ocean---- 541
From the table now retiring---- 468
Give to the winds thy fears---- 402
Glorious things of thee are spoken-- 431
Glory be to God on high---- 100
Go forth to life, O child of earth---- 319
Go, labor on, spend and be spent---- 473
Go to dark Gethsemane---- 227
God be with you till we meet again- 129
God Himself is with us---- 123
God is love; His mercy brightens--- 178
God moves in a mysterious way---- 162
God of grace and God of glory---- 378
God of our fathers, known of old 560, 561
God of our fathers, the strength of our people and nation---- 158
God of our fathers, whose almighty hand ---- 551
God of our life, through all the circling years ---- 583
God of our youth, to whom we yield 608
God of the earth, the sky, the sea-- 120
God of the nations, near and far---- 556
God of the prophets! bless the phophets' sons ---- 472
God of the strong, God of the weak- 311
God save America ---- 547
God send us men, whose aim 'twill be 377
God speaks to us in bird and song-- 180
God that madest earth and heaven-- 143
God, the all-merciful, earth hath forsaken ---- 565
God, who touchest earth with beauty- 315
Good Christian men, rejoice---- 193
Gracious Spirit, dwell with me---- 270

NUMBER

Great God, we sing that mighty hand 586
Great is Thy faithfulness ---- 165
Great Master, touch us ---- 317
Guide me, O Thou great Jehovah--- 393

Hail the glorious Golden City---- 488
Hail to the brightness of Zion's glad morning ---- 523
Hail to the Lord's Anointed---- 257
Hark, hark, my soul! angelic songs are swelling ---- 582
Hark! ten thousand harps and voices 268
Hark! the herald angels sing ---- 189
Have Thine own way, Lord ---- 324
He leadeth me: O blessed thought -- 405
He who would valiant be ---- 364
Hear us, our Father ---- 336
Heralds of Christ, who bear the King's commands ---- 533
Here at Thy table, Lord ---- 451
Here at Thy table, Lord, we meet --- 455
Here, O my Lord, I see Thee face to face ---- 458
Here, Saviour, we would come ---- 450
Holy, holy, holy is the Lord ---- 97
Holy, holy, holy, Lord God Almighty 107
Holy Spirit, faithful Guide ---- 276
Holy Spirit, Truth divine ---- 274
How firm a foundation, ye saints of the Lord ---- 406
How gentle God's commands ---- 399
How strong and sweet my Father's care ---- 168
How sweet, how heavenly is the sight 475
How sweet the Name of Jesus sounds 264
Hush, all ye sounds of war ---- 195

I am Thine, O Lord, I have heard Thy voice ---- 312
I bind my heart this tide ---- 302
I do not ask, O Lord, that life may be 340
I feel the winds of God today ---- 301
I hear the Saviour say ---- 284
I heard the voice of Jesus say ---- 288
I know not how that Bethlehem's babe 206
I know not what the future hath ---- 571
I know that my Redeemer lives ---- 245
I know that my Redeemer liveth ---- 255
I love Thy kingdom, Lord ---- 428, 429
I love to tell the story ---- 532
I need Thee every hour ---- 341
I sought His love in sun and stars---- 385

INDEX OF FIRST LINES OF HYMNS

NUMBER

I sought the Lord, and afterward I knew ---------------------------- 403
I thank Thee, Lord, for strength of arm ------------------------------- 499
I think when I read that sweet story of old ---------------------------- 213
I would be true, for there are those who trust me -------------------- 361
If thou but suffer God to guide thee - 404
Immortal, invisible, God only wise -- 159
Immortal Love, forever full -------- 254
In Christ there is no East or West -- 480
In heavenly love abiding ------------ 384
In His love abiding ----------------- 391
In homes where pride and splendor - 501
In life's earnest morning ------------ 474
In memory of the Saviour's love ---- 462
In the cross of Christ I glory ------ 237
In the hour of trial ----------------- 333
Into the woods my Master went ---- 225
It came upon the midnight clear ---- 191
It singeth low in every heart -------- 579
I've found a Friend, O such a Friend 290

Jerusalem the golden ----------- 569, 570
Jesus calls us, o'er the tumult ------- 281
Jesus, I live to Thee -----------------314
Jesus, I my cross have taken -------375
Jesus is tenderly calling thee home -- 280
Jesus, keep me near the cross ------- 339
Jesus, kneel beside me -------------- 328
Jesus, Lover of my soul -------- 414, 415
Jesus, my Lord, my Life, my All --- 383
Jesus, Saviour, pilot me ------------ 409
Jesus shall reign where'er the sun ---- 527
Jesus, still lead on ------------------ 357
Jesus, the very thought of Thee----- 392
Jesus, these eyes have never seen --- 352
Jesus, Thou joy of loving hearts ---- 419
Jesus, Thy boundless love to me ---- 380
Jesus, where'er Thy people meet ---- 115
Joy because the circling year -------- 447
Joy to the world! the Lord is come -- 190
Joyful, joyful we adore Thee ------- 95
Judge eternal, throned in splendor -- 545
Just as I am, Thine own to be ------ 297
Just as I am, without one plea ------ 295

Lamp of our feet, whereby we trace - 436
Lead, kindly Light, amid the encircling gloom ---------------------- 578
Lead on, O King Eternal ----------- 363
Lead us, O Father, in the paths of peace ------------------------------ 566
Let the song go round the earth ---- 531
Let the whole creation cry ---------- 103

NUMBER

Let there be light, Lord God of Hosts 513
Let us with a gladsome mind ------ 181
Life is good, for God contrives it ---- 248
Life of ages, richly poured ---------- 177
Lift up your heads, ye mighty gates -- 224
"Lift up your hearts" -------------- 372
Lift up, lift up your voices now ----- 241
Light of Light, enlighten me -------- 445
Light of the world, how long the quest 320
Light of the world, we hail Thee ---- 208
Living for Jesus a life that is true -- 304
Lo, how a Rose e'er blooming ------ 194
Look, ye saints, the sight is glorious - 256
Lord, as to Thy dear cross we flee -- 326
Lord, at this closing hour ---------- 131
Lord, at Thy table we behold ------- 464
Lord, dismiss us with Thy blessing -- 127
Lord, for tomorrow and its needs --- 327
Lord God of Hosts, whose purpose never swerving -------------------- 497
Lord of all being, throned afar ------ 151
Lord of light, whose Name outshineth 504
Lord of our highest love ------------ 466
Lord of our life, and God of our salvation ----------------------------- 430
Lord, speak to me that I may speak -- 470
Lord, Thy glory fills the heaven ----- 156
Lord, we come before Thee now ---- 116
Lord, while for all mankind we pray - 544
Love divine, all love excelling ------ 379
Love is kind and suffers long ------- 386

Majestic sweetness sits enthroned --- 381
March on, O soul, with strength ---- 359
Marching with the heroes ---------- 322
Master, no offering ---------------- 303
May the grace of Christ our Saviour - 126
Men and children everywhere ------ 96
Mighty God, while angels bless Thee - 160
Mighty Rock, whose towering form -- 407
More love to Thee, O Christ ------- 390
Motherhood, sublime, eternal -------- 604
Must Jesus bear the cross alone ----- 366
My country is the world ------------ 514
My country! 'tis of thee ------------ 548
My dear Redeemer and my Lord ---- 207
My faith looks up to Thee ---------- 355
My God, I thank Thee, who hast made 109
My Jesus, as Thou wilt ------------- 408
My Jesus, I love Thee -------------- 382
My life, my love, I give to Thee ---- 293
My Master was a worker ---------- 500
My Master was so very poor -------- 216

INDEX OF FIRST LINES OF HYMNS

NUMBER

My soul, be on thy guard ---------- 370
My times are in Thy hand ---------- 395

Nearer, my God, to Thee ------------ 329
Night, with ebon pinion ------------- 226
No longer of Him be it said -------- 305
Not alone for mighty empire -------- 597
Not in dumb resignation ------------ 368
Now God be with us, for the night is closing ---------------------------- 147
Now in the days of youth ---------- 300
Now, on land and sea descending ---- 141
Now praise we great and famous men 603
Now thank we all our God ---------- 598
Now the day is over ---------------- 149

O beautiful for spacious skies ----------550
O beautiful, my country ------------ 542
O bless the Lord, my soul ---------- 105
O blessed Son of God -------------- 520
O brother man, fold to thy heart thy brother -------------------------- 515
O Christ, forget not them who stand 526
O Christ, the Way, the Truth, the Life 410
O Christ, Thou Gift of Love Divine - 454
O Church of God, divided ---------- 433
O Church of God, our solitude forsaking --------------------------- 432
O come, all ye faithful, joyful and triumphant ---------------------- 205
O come and mourn with me awhile - 233
O come, O come, Emmanuel -------- 182
O could I speak the matchless worth - 265
O day of rest and gladness ---------- 443
O Father, Thou who givest all ------ 600
O for a closer walk with God ------- 310
O for a thousand tongues to sing ---- 262
O God, beneath Thy guiding hand -- 543
O God, in whom we live and move -- 179
O God, in whose great purpose ------ 607
O God of Bethel, by whose hand ---- 174
O God of earth and altar ----------- 546
O God of love! O King of peace ---- 557
O God of truth, whose living Word -- 365
O God, our help in ages past ------ 585
O God, the Rock af Ages ----------- 154
O God, Thy summons still is heard -- 449
O God, Thy world is sweet with prayer ---------------------------- 133
O God, unseen, yet ever near -------- 452
O God, whose love is over all ------ 175
O God, whose smile is in the sky ---- 163
O gracious Father of mankind ------ 338
O grant us light, that we may know -- 298
O happy home, where Thou art loved the dearest ------------------------ 601

NUMBER

O hear them marching, marching ---- 564
O holy Saviour, Friend unseen ------ 350
O how lovely, O how sweet --------- 263
O Jesus, I have promised ----------- 308
O Jesus, Master, when today -------- 517
O Jesus, Prince of life and truth ---- 505
O Jesus, Thou art standing ---------- 279
O Jesus, we adore Thee ------------ 234
O Jesus, when I think of Thee------- 218
O Jesus, youth of Nazareth -------- 217
O little town of Bethlehem ---------- 184
O Lord of life, Thy kingdom is at hand ------------------------------ 491
O Lord of Life, Thy quickening voice 132
O Lord of life, where'er they be ---- 575
O Love divine, that stooped to share - 353
O Love that wilt not let me go ----- 388
O Master, let me walk with Thee 306, 307
O Master workman of the race ----- 210
O men of God, go forth to win ---- 471
O mother dear, Jerusalem ---------- 572
O sacred Head, now wounded ------ 231
O say, can you see ----------------- 651
O Son of God incarnate ------------ 211
O Son of Man, our Hero strong and tender ----------------------------- 220
O Spirit of the Living God -------- 273
O Thou great Friend to all the sons of men --------------------------- 347
O Thou not made with hands ------- 478
O Thou whose own vast temple ---- 605
O where are kings and empires now - 427
O Word of God Incarnate ---------- 434
O worship the king, all-glorious above 94
O young and fearless Prophet ------ 362
O Zion, haste, Thy mission high fulfilling ----------------------------- 529
Of one blood hath God created ------ 510
On our way rejoicing -------------- 417
On wings of living light ------------ 243
Once to every man and nation ------ 558
One holy Church of God appears ---- 424
Onward, Christian soldiers ---------- 482
Open now Thy gates of beauty ------ 121
Our Church proclaims God's love and care ------------------------------ 425
Our faith is in the Christ who walks 351
Our Father, Thy dear Name doth show ----------------------------- 522

Praise, my soul, the King of heaven 259
Praise the Lord, His glories show --- 112
Praise the Lord, ye heavens adore Him ------------------------------ 110

INDEX OF FIRST LINES OF HYMNS

NUMBER

Praise to God, immortal praise ------ 595
Praise to the Living God ------------ 124
Praise to the Lord, the Almighty ---- 98
Prayer is the soul's sincere desire --- 335
Purer in heart, O God -------------- 343

Rejoice, the Lord is King ---------- 260
Rejoice, ye pure in heart ------------ 418
Remember all the people ------------ 528
Ride on, ride on in majesty ---------- 223
Ring out the old, ring in the new ---- 589
Rise, crowned with light, imperial Salem, rise ---------------------- 477
Rise, my soul, and stretch thy wings 573
Rise up, O men of God ------------- 374
Rock of Ages, cleft for me ---------- 294

Safely through another week -------- 448
Saviour, again to Thy dear Name we raise ------------------------------ 128
Saviour, blessed Saviour, listen while we sing -------------------------- 269
Saviour, like a shepherd lead us ---- 401
Saviour, more than life to me ------ 397
Saviour, teach me day by day ------- 389
Saviour, Thy dying love ------------ 387
Send down Thy truth, O God ------- 271
Shepherd of eager youth ------------ 266
Shepherd of souls, refresh and bless - 465
Silent night, holy night ------------ 188
Sing them over again to me -------- 442
Sing to the great Jehovah's praise -- 590
Sleep thy last sleep ---------------- 580
Softly and tenderly Jesus is calling -- 283
Softly now the light of day ---------- 145
Sometimes a light surprises -------- 581
Son of God, Eternal Saviour -------- 502
Sowing in the morning, sowing seeds of kindness ----------------------- 416
Spirit divine, attend our prayer ------ 275
Spirit of God, descend upon my heart 272
Stand up, stand up for Jesus -------- 371
Standing at the portal -------------- 584
Still, still with Thee --------------- 136
Strong Son of God, immortal love --- 349
Sun of my soul, Thou Saviour dear -- 150
Sunset and evening star ------------ 574
Sweet hour of prayer, sweet hour of prayer ---------------------------- 337

Take my life, and let it be ---------- 296
Take time to be holy --------------- 346
"Take up thy cross," the Saviour said 285
Tell me the old, old story ----------- 438
Tell me the stories of Jesus -------- 214
Ten thousand times ten thousand ---- 568

NUMBER

That cause can neither be lost nor stayed ---------------------------- 493
The Church's one foundation -------- 423
The day of resurrection ------------ 247
The day Thou gavest, Lord, is ended 140
The fathers built this city ---------- 503
The first Noel, the angel did say ---- 197
The heavens declare Thy glory, Lord 441
The King of love my Shepherd is ---- 169
The light of God is falling ---------- 486
The Lord be with us as each day ---- 125
The Lord is my Shepherd ---------- 170
The morning light is breaking ------ 524
The Prince of Peace His banner spreads --------------------------- 553
The shadows of the evening hours-- 142
The Son of God goes forth for peace 559
The Son of God goes forth to war -- 358
The spacious firmament on high ----- 164
The spirit of the Lord revealed ------ 437
The strife is o'er: the battle done ---- 238
The voice of God is calling --------- 490
The wise may bring their learning -- 316
There is a Book that all may read -- 435
There is a green hill far away ------- 230
There is no sorrow, Lord, too light - 342
There's a light upon the mountains -- 249
There's a song in the air ----------- 198
There's a wideness in God's mercy ---------------------------- 172, 173
These things shall be: a loftier race - 507
They who tread the path of labor --- 496
Thine is the glory ----------------- 244
This is my Father's world ---------- 171
This is the day of light ------------ 446
Thou didst leave Thy throne and Thy kingly crown ---------------------- 292
Thou God of all, whose spirit moves 554
Thou gracious God whose mercy lends 602
Thou Lord of life, our saving health - 309
Thou my everlasting portion -------- 413
Thou, whose almighty word -------- 536
Through the night of doubt and sorrow --------------------------- 481
Thy bounties, gracious Lord -------- 421
Thy kingdom come, O Lord -------- 562
"Thy kingdom come," on bended knee 539
Thy life was given for me ---------- 289
'Tis midnight; and on Olive's brow -- 232
'Tis the blessed hour of prayer ------ 332
To all the nations, Lord ------------ 552
To God our hearts we lift ---------- 176
To Thee, my heart, eternal King ---- 108
Turn back, O man, forswear thy foolish ways ----------------------- 567
Two empires by the sea ------------ 549

INDEX OF FIRST LINES OF HYMNS

NUMBER

Unbar the door, and let the Lord Christ in ---- 287
Unto the hills around do I lift up ---- 166

Walk in the light! so shalt thou know 479
Watchman, tell us of the night ---- 183
We are living, we are dwelling ---- 494
We bear the strain of earthly care ---- 521
We gather together to ask the Lord's blessing ---- 117
We give Thee but Thine own ---- 422
We have heard a joyful sound ---- 537
We leave Thy house but leave not Thee ---- 130
We mix from many lands ---- 509
We plow the fields and scatter ---- 594
We thank Thee, Lord, Thy paths of service lead ---- 495
We three kings of Orient are ---- 204
We would be building ---- 489
We would see Jesus, for the shadows lengthen ---- 400
We would see Jesus; lo! His star is shining ---- 209
Welcome, delightful morn ---- 444
"Welcome, happy morning!" age to age shall say ---- 246
We've a story to tell to the nations ---- 530
What a Friend we have in Jesus ---- 331

NUMBER

What Child is this, who, laid to rest - 200
What grace, O Lord, and beauty shone ---- 219
When courage fails and faith burns low ---- 356
When I survey the wondrous cross ---- 228
When morning gilds the skies ---- 135
When spring unlocks the flowers ---- 592
When the golden evening gathered ---- 212
When the Lord of love was here ---- 215
When thy heart with joy o'erflowing - 508
When wilt thou save the people ---- 563
Where cross the crowded ways of life 519
Where the olive grove stood darkly ---- 229
Where winds the road o'er hill and dale ---- 420
While in sweet communion feeding ---- 460
While shepherds watched their flocks by night ---- 185
While Thee I seek, protecting Power 334
Who is on the Lord's side? ---- 367
Whom oceans part, O Lord, unite ---- 525
Wise men seeking Jesus ---- 203
With happy voices ringing ---- 113
Worship the Lord in the beauty of holiness ---- 106

Ye servants of God, your Master proclaim ---- 258